# Biology
## Bio 122 Cells and Genetics

Custom Edition for Drexel University

Taken from:

*Campbell Biology In Focus* by Lisa A. Urry, Michael L. Cain,
Steven A. Wasserman, Peter V. Minorsky, Robert B. Jackson, and Jane B. Reece

*Campbell Biology*, Tenth Edition by Jane B. Reece, Lisa A. Urry, Michael L. Cain,
Steven A. Wasserman, Peter V. Minorsky, and Robert B. Jackson

Cover Art: Courtesy of Photodisc/Getty Images.

Taken from:

*Campbell Biology In Focus*
by Lisa A. Urry, Michael L. Cain, Steven A. Wasserman, Peter V. Minorsky, Robert B. Jackson, and Jane B. Reece
Copyright © 2014 by Pearson Education, Inc.
New York, New York 10013

*Campbell Biology*, Tenth Edition
by Jane B. Reece, Lisa A. Urry, Michael L. Cain, Steven A. Wasserman, Peter V. Minorsky, and Robert B. Jackson
Copyright © 2014, 2011, 2008 by Pearson Education, Inc.
New York, New York 10013

This special edition published in cooperation with Pearson Learning Solutions.

All trademarks, service marks, registered trademarks, and registered service marks are the property of their respective owners and are used herein for identification purposes only.  .

Pearson Learning Solutions, 330 Hudson Street, New York, New York 10013
A Pearson Education Company
www.pearsoned.com

Printed in the United States of America

1 2 3 4 5 6 7 8 9 10 V0UD 19 18 17 16 15

000200010272008904

ML

ISBN 10: 1-323-26357-8
ISBN 13: 978-1-323-26357-0

# Preface

The short-toed snake eagle (*Circaetus gallicus*) that gazes from the cover of this book has an eye much like our own, yet evolutionary forces have honed its ability to spot a snake from a quarter mile up in the air. The eagle's keen eye is a metaphor for our goal in writing this text: to focus with high intensity on the core concepts that biology majors need to master in the introductory biology course. The current explosion of biological information, while exhilarating in its scope, poses a significant challenge—how best to teach a subject that is constantly expanding its own boundaries. In particular, instructors have become increasingly concerned that their students are overwhelmed by a growing volume of detail and are losing sight of the important ideas in biology.

In response to this challenge, groups of biologists have initiated efforts to refine and in some cases redesign the introductory biology course, summarizing their findings in reports that include *Bio 2010: Transforming Undergraduate Education for Future Research Biologists*[1] and *Vision and Change in Undergraduate Biology Education*.[2] Clear recommendations emerging from these initiatives are to focus course material and instruction on key ideas while transforming the classroom through active learning and scientific inquiry. Many instructors have embraced such approaches and changed how they teach. Cutting back on the amount of detail they present, they focus on core biological concepts, explore select examples, and engage in a rich variety of active learning exercises. We were inspired by the ongoing changes in biology education to develop this text, *CAMPBELL BIOLOGY IN FOCUS*. Based on the best-selling *CAMPBELL BIOLOGY*, this new, shorter textbook provides undergraduate biology majors and their instructors with a more focused exploration of the key questions, approaches, and ideas of modern biology.

## Our Guiding Principles

Our objective in creating *CAMPBELL BIOLOGY IN FOCUS* was to produce a shorter text by streamlining selected material, while emphasizing conceptual understanding and maintaining clarity, proper pacing, and rigor. Here, briefly, are the four guiding principles for our approach.

### Focus on Core Concepts and Skills

We developed this text to help students master the fundamental content and scientific skills they need as college biology majors. In structuring the text, we were guided by discussions with many biology professors, analysis of hundreds of syllabi, study of the debates in the literature of scientific pedagogy, and our experience as instructors at a range of institutions. The result is a **briefer book for biology majors** that is designed to inform, engage, and inspire.

### Evolution as the Foundation of Biology

Evolution is the central theme of all biology, and it is the core theme of this text, as exemplified by the various ways that evolution is integrated into the text:

- Every chapter explicitly addresses the topic of evolution through an **Evolution section** that leads students to consider the material in the context of natural selection and adaptation.
- Each Chapter Review includes a **Focus on Evolution Question** that asks students to think critically about how an aspect of the chapter relates to evolution.
- Evolution is the unifying idea of **Chapter 1**, *Introduction: Evolution and the Foundations of Biology*, which outlines five key themes that students will encounter throughout the text and introduces the process of scientific inquiry.
- Following the in-depth coverage of evolutionary mechanisms in Unit 3, evolution also provides the storyline for the **novel approach to presenting biological diversity** in Unit 4, The Evolutionary History of Life. Focusing on landmark events in the history of life, the text highlights how

---

[1] The National Research Council of the National Academies, 2003

[2] The American Association for the Advancement of Science, supported by the National Science Foundation, the National Institutes of Health, and Howard Hughes Medical Institute, 2009

key adaptations arose within groups of organisms and how evolutionary events led to the diversity of life on Earth today.

## Engaging Students in Scientific Thinking

Helping students learn to "think like a scientist" is a nearly universal goal of introductory biology courses. Students need to understand how to formulate and test hypotheses, design experiments, and interpret data. Scientific thinking and data interpretation skills top lists of learning outcomes and foundational skills desired for students entering higher-level courses. CAMPBELL BIOLOGY IN FOCUS meets this need in several ways:

- **Scientific Skills Exercises** in every chapter use real data to build skills in graphing, interpreting data, designing experiments, and working with math—skills essential for students to succeed in biology. These exercises can also be assigned and automatically graded in MasteringBiology.
- **Scientific Inquiry Questions** in the end-of-chapter material give students further practice in scientific thinking.
- **Inquiry Figures** and **Research Method Figures** reveal *how* we know *what* we know and model the process of scientific inquiry.

## Outstanding Pedagogy

Since the publication of the first edition in 1987, CAMPBELL BIOLOGY has been praised for its clear and engaging narrative, superior pedagogy, and innovative use of art to promote student learning. These hallmark values are also at the core of CAMPBELL BIOLOGY IN FOCUS:

- In each chapter, a framework of carefully selected **Key Concepts** helps students distinguish the "forest" from the "trees."
- Questions throughout the text catalyze learning by encouraging students to **actively engage with and synthesize key material**:
  - To counter students' tendencies to compartmentalize information, **Make Connections Questions** ask students to connect what they are learning in a particular chapter to material covered in other chapters or units.
  - **Figure Legend Questions** foster student interaction with the figures.
  - Tiered **Concept Check Questions** test comprehension, require application, and prompt synthesis.
  - **Draw It Exercises** encourage students to test their understanding of biology through drawing.
  - **Summary of Key Concepts Questions** make reading the summary an active learning experience.

Our overall aim is to help students see biology as a whole, with each chapter adding to the network of knowledge they are building. To support this goal further, each unit in CAMPBELL

BIOLOGY IN FOCUS opens with a **visual preview** that tells the story of the chapters' contents, showing how the material in the unit fits into a larger context.

## Organization of the Text

CAMPBELL BIOLOGY IN FOCUS is organized into an introductory chapter and seven units that cover thoughtfully paced core concepts. In the course of streamlining this material, we have worked diligently to maintain the finely tuned coverage of fundamental concepts found in CAMPBELL BIOLOGY. As we developed this alternative text, we carefully considered each chapter of CAMPBELL BIOLOGY. Based on surveys and discussions with instructors and analyses of hundreds of syllabi and reviews, we made informed choices about how to design each chapter of CAMPBELL BIOLOGY IN FOCUS to meet the needs of instructors and students. In some chapters, we retained most of the material; in other chapters, we pruned material; and in still others, we completely reconfigured the material. We summarize the highlights here.

### Chapter 1: Introduction: Evolution and the Foundations of Biology

Chapter 1 introduces the **five biological themes** woven throughout this text: the core theme of **Evolution**, together with **Organization**, **Information**, **Energy and Matter**, and **Interactions**. Chapter 1 also explores the process of scientific inquiry through a case study describing experiments on the evolution of coat color in the beach mouse. The chapter concludes with a discussion of the importance of diversity within the scientific community.

### MasteringBiology®

MasteringBiology is the most widely used online assessment and tutorial program for biology, providing an extensive library of homework assignments that are graded automatically. Self-paced tutorials provide individualized coaching with specific hints and feedback on the most difficult topics in the course. For example:

- The **Scientific Skills Exercises** from the text can be assigned and automatically graded in MasteringBiology.
- **Make Connections Tutorials** help students connect what they are learning in one chapter with material they have learned in another chapter.
- **Data Analysis Tutorials** allow students to analyze real data from online databases.
- **BioFlix® Tutorials** use 3-D movie-quality animations to help students master tough topics.

In addition, Reading Quiz questions, Student Misconception questions, and approximately 3,000 Test Bank questions are available for assignment.

MasteringBiology and the text work together to provide an unparalleled learning experience.

* * *

Our overall goal in developing this text was to assist instructors and students in their exploration of biology by emphasizing essential content and skills while maintaining rigor. Although this first edition is now completed, we recognize that *CAMPBELL BIOLOGY IN FOCUS*, like its subject, will evolve. As its authors, we are eager to hear your thoughts, questions, comments, and suggestions for improvement. We are counting on you—our teaching colleagues and all students using this book—to provide us with this feedback, and we encourage you to contact us directly by e-mail:

Lisa Urry (Chapter 1): lurry@mills.edu

Michael Cain (Chapter): mcain@bowdoin.edu

Peter Minorsky: pminorsky@mercy.edu

Steven Wasserman (Chapter 1): stevenw@ucsd.edu

Rob Jackson: jackson@duke.edu

Jane Reece: janereece@cal.berkeley.edu

The author team's contributions reflect their biological expertise as researchers and their teaching sensibilities gained from years of experience as instructors at diverse institutions. They are also experienced textbook authors, having written CAMPBELL BIOLOGY in addition to CAMPBELL BIOLOGY IN FOCUS.

## Lisa A. Urry

Lisa Urry (Chapter 1) is Professor of Biology and Chair of the Biology Department at Mills College in Oakland, California, and a Visiting Scholar at the University of California, Berkeley. After graduating from Tufts University with a double major in biology and French, Lisa completed her Ph.D. in molecular and developmental biology at Massachusetts Institute of Technology (MIT) in the MIT/Woods Hole Oceanographic Institution Joint Program. She has published a number of research papers, most of them focused on gene expression during embryonic and larval development in sea urchins. Lisa has taught a variety of courses, from introductory biology to developmental biology and senior seminar. As a part of her mission to increase understanding of evolution, Lisa also teaches a nonmajors course called Evolution for Future Presidents and is on the Teacher Advisory Board for the Understanding Evolution website developed by the University of California Museum of Paleontology. Lisa is also deeply committed to promoting opportunities for women and underrepresented minorities in science.

## Michael L. Cain

Michael Cain (Chapter 1) is an ecologist and evolutionary biologist who is now writing full-time. Michael earned a joint degree in biology and math at Bowdoin College, an M.Sc. from Brown University, and a Ph.D. in ecology and evolutionary biology from Cornell University. As a faculty member at New Mexico State University and Rose-Hulman Institute of Technology, he taught a wide range of courses, including introductory biology, ecology, evolution, botany, and conservation biology. Michael is the author of dozens of scientific papers on topics that include foraging behavior in insects and plants, long-distance seed dispersal, and speciation in crickets. In addition to his work on CAMPBELL BIOLOGY IN FOCUS, Michael is also the lead author of an ecology textbook.

## Steven A. Wasserman

Steve Wasserman (Chapter 1) is Professor of Biology at the University of California, San Diego (UCSD). He earned his A.B. in biology from Harvard University and his Ph.D. in biological sciences from MIT. Through his research on regulatory pathway mechanisms in the fruit fly *Drosophila*, Steve has contributed to the fields of developmental biology, reproduction, and immunity. As a faculty member at the University of Texas Southwestern Medical Center and UCSD, he has taught genetics, development, and physiology to undergraduate, graduate, and medical students. He currently focuses on teaching introductory biology. He has also served as the research mentor for more than a dozen doctoral students and more than 50 aspiring scientists at the undergraduate and high school levels. Steve has been the recipient of distinguished scholar awards from both the Markey Charitable Trust and the David and Lucille Packard Foundation. In 2007, he received UCSD's Distinguished Teaching Award for undergraduate teaching.

## Peter V. Minorsky

Peter Minorsky is Professor of Biology at Mercy College in New York, where he teaches introductory biology, evolution, ecology, and botany. He received his A.B. in biology from Vassar College and his Ph.D. in plant physiology from Cornell University. He is also the science writer for the journal *Plant Physiology*. After a postdoctoral fellowship at the University of Wisconsin at Madison, Peter taught at Kenyon College, Union College, Western Connecticut State University, and Vassar College. His research interests concern how plants sense environmental change. Peter received the 2008 Award for Teaching Excellence at Mercy College.

## Robert B. Jackson

Rob Jackson is Professor of Biology and Nicholas Chair of Environmental Sciences at Duke University. Rob holds a B.S. in chemical engineering from Rice University, as well as M.S. degrees in ecology and statistics and a Ph.D. in ecology from Utah State University. Rob directed Duke's Program in Ecology for many years and just finished a term as the Vice President of Science for the Ecological Society of America. Rob has received numerous awards, including a Presidential Early Career Award in Science and Engineering from the National Science Foundation. He also enjoys popular writing, having published a trade book about the environment, *The Earth Remains Forever*, and two books of poetry for children, *Animal Mischief* and *Weekend Mischief*.

## Jane B. Reece

The head of the author team for recent editions of *CAMPBELL BIOLOGY*, Jane Reece was Neil Campbell's longtime collaborator. Earlier, Jane taught biology at Middlesex County College and Queensborough Community College. She holds an A.B. in biology from Harvard University, an M.S. in microbiology from Rutgers University, and a Ph.D. in bacteriology from the University of California, Berkeley. Jane's research as a doctoral student and postdoctoral fellow focused on genetic recombination in bacteria. Besides her work on the Campbell textbooks for biology majors, she has been an author of *Campbell Biology: Concepts & Connections*, *Campbell Essential Biology*, and *The World of the Cell*.

## Neil A. Campbell

Neil Campbell (1946–2004) combined the investigative nature of a research scientist with the soul of an experienced and caring teacher. He earned his M.A. in zoology from the University of California, Los Angeles, and his Ph.D. in plant biology from the University of California, Riverside, where he received the Distinguished Alumnus Award in 2001. Neil published numerous research articles on desert and coastal plants and how the sensitive plant (*Mimosa*) and other legumes move their leaves. His 30 years of teaching in diverse environments included introductory biology courses at Cornell University, Pomona College, and San Bernardino Valley College, where he received the college's first Outstanding Professor Award in 1986. Neil was a visiting scholar in the Department of Botany and Plant Sciences at the University of California, Riverside.

# Focus on Scientific Skills

## Practice Scientific Skills

**Scientific Skills Exercises** in every chapter use real data to build key skills needed for biology, including data analysis, graphing, experimental design, and math skills.

Selected Scientific Skills Exercises include:

- Making a Line Graph and Calculating a Slope
- Interpreting Histograms
- Using the Chi-Square ($\chi^2$) Test
- Analyzing DNA Deletion Experiments
- Making and Testing Predictions
- Interpreting Data in a Phylogenetic Tree
- Using the Hardy-Weinberg Equation to Interpret Data and Make Predictions
- Understanding Experimental Design and Interpreting Data
- Interpreting Data Values Expressed in Scientific Notation
- Designing an Experiment Using Genetic Mutants
- Interpreting a Graph with Log Scales
- Using the Logistic Equation to Model Population Growth

---

**Scientific Skills Exercise**

### Interpreting a Scatter Plot with a Regression Line

**How Does the Carbonate Ion Concentration of Seawater Affect the Calcification Rate of a Coral Reef?** Scientists predict that acidification of the ocean due to higher levels of atmospheric $CO_2$ will lower the concentration of dissolved carbonate ions, which living corals use to build calcium carbonate reef structures. In this exercise, you will analyze data from a controlled experiment that examined the effect of carbonate ion concentration ($[CO_3^{2-}]$) on calcium carbonate deposition, a process called calcification.

**How the Experiment Was Done** The Biosphere 2 aquarium in Arizona contains a large coral reef system that behaves like a natural reef. For several years, a group of researchers measured the rate of calcification by the reef organisms and examined how the calcification rate changed with differing amounts of dissolved carbonate ions in the seawater.

**Data from the Experiment** The black data points in the graph below form a scatter plot. The red line, known as a linear regression line, is the best-fitting straight line for these points. These data are from one set of experiments, in which the pH, temperature, and calcium ion concentration of the seawater were held constant.

**Interpret the Data**
1. When presented with a graph of experimental data, the first step in analysis is to determine what each axis represents. (a) In words,

explain what is being shown on the x-axis. Be sure to include the units. (b) What is being shown on the y-axis (including units)? (c) Which variable is the independent variable—the variable that was *manipulated* by the researchers? (d) Which variable is the dependent variable—the variable that responded to or depended on the treatment, which was *measured* by the researchers? (For additional information about graphs, see the Scientific Skills Review in Appendix F and in the Study Area in MasteringBiology.)

2. Based on the data shown in the graph, describe in words the relationship between carbonate ion concentration and calcification rate.

3. (a) If the seawater carbonate ion concentration is 270 µmol/kg, what is the approximate rate of calcification, and approximately how many days would it take 1 square meter of reef to accumulate 30 mmol of calcium carbonate ($CaCO_3$)? To determine the rate of calcification, draw a vertical line up from the x-axis at the value of 270 µmol/kg until it intersects the red line. Then draw a horizontal line from the intersection over to the y-axis to see what the calcification rate is at that carbonate ion concentration. (b) If the seawater carbonate ion concentration is 250 µmol/kg, what is the approximate rate of calcification, and approximately how many days would it take 1 square meter of reef to accumulate 30 mmol of calcium carbonate? (c) If carbonate ion concentration decreases, how does the calcification rate change, and how does that affect the time it takes coral to grow?

4. (a) Referring to the equations in Figure 2.24, determine which step of the process is measured in this experiment. (b) Do the results of this experiment support the hypothesis that increased atmospheric $[CO_2]$ will slow the growth of coral reefs? Why or why not?

Data from C. Langdon et al., Effect of calcium carbonate saturation state on the calcification rate of an experimental coral reef, *Global Biogeochemical Cycles* 14:639–654 (2000).

A version of this Scientific Skills Exercise can be assigned in MasteringBiology.

---

## MasteringBiology®
**www.masteringbiology.com**

**Scientific Skills Exercises** from the text have assignable versions in MasteringBiology.

**Interpreting Data Tutorials** coach students on how to read and interpret data and graphs.

# Engage in Scientific Thinking

## Analyzing Polypeptide Sequence Data

**Are Rhesus Monkeys or Gibbons More Closely Related to Humans?** As discussed in Concept 3.6, DNA and polypeptide sequences from closely related species are more similar to each other than are sequences from more distantly related species. In this exercise, you will look at amino acid sequence data for the β polypeptide chain of hemoglobin, often called β-globin. You will then interpret the data to hypothesize whether the monkey or the gibbon is more closely related to humans.

**How Such Experiments Are Done** Researchers can isolate the polypeptide of interest from an organism and then determine the amino acid sequence. More frequently, the DNA of the relevant gene is sequenced, and the amino acid sequence of the polypeptide is deduced from the DNA sequence of its gene.

**Data from the Experiments** In the data below, the letters give the sequence of the 146 amino acids in β-globin from humans, rhesus monkeys, and gibbons. Because a complete sequence would not fit on one line here, the sequences are broken into three segments. Note that the sequences for the three different species are aligned so that you can compare them easily. For example, you can see that for all three species, the first amino acid is V (valine; see Figure 3.17) and the 146th amino acid is H (histidine).

**Interpret the Data**

1. Scan along the monkey and gibbon sequences, letter by letter, circling any amino acids that do not match the human sequence. (a) How many amino acids differ between the monkey and the human sequences? (b) Between the gibbon and human?
2. For each nonhuman species, what percent of its amino acids are identical to the human sequence of β-globin?
3. Based on these data alone, state a hypothesis for which of these two species is more closely related to humans. What is your reasoning?
4. What other evidence could you use to support your hypothesis?

Data from Human: http://www.ncbi.nlm.nih.gov/protein/AAA21113.1; rhesus monkey: http://www.ncbi.nlm.nih.gov/protein/122634; gibbon: http://www.ncbi.nlm.nih.gov/protein/122616

A version of this Scientific Skills Exercise can be assigned in MasteringBiology.

| Species | Alignment of Amino Acid Sequences of β-globin |
|---------|-----------------------------------------------|
| Human   | 1 VHLTPEEKSA VTALWGKVNV DEVGGEALGR LLVVYPWTQR FFESFGDLST PDAVMGNPKV |
| Monkey  | 1 VHLTPEEKNA VTTLWGKVNV DEVGGEALGR LLLVVYPWTQR FFESFGDLSS PDAVMGNPKV |
| Gibbon  | 1 VHLTPEEKSA VTALWGKVNV DEVGGEALGR LLVVYPWTQR FFESFGDLST PDAVMGNPKV |
| | |
| Human   | 61 KAHGKKVLGA FSDGLAHLDN LKGTFATLSE LHCDKLHVDP ENFRLLGNVL VCVLAHHFGK |
| Monkey  | 61 KAHGKKVLGA FSDGLNHLDN LKGTFAQLSE LHCDKLHVDP ENFKLLGNVL VCVLAHHFGK |
| Gibbon  | 61 KAHGKKVLGA FSDGLAHLDN LKGTFAQLSE LHCDKLHVDP ENFRLLGNVL VCVLAHHFGK |
| | |
| Human   | 121 EFTPPVQAAY QKVVAGVANA LAHKYH |
| Monkey  | 121 EFTPQVQAAY QKVVAGVANA LAHKYH |
| Gibbon  | 121 EFTPQVQAAY QKVVAGVANA LAHKYH |

▼ **Inquiry Figures** reveal "how we know what we know" by highlighting how researchers designed an experiment, interpreted their results, and drew conclusions.

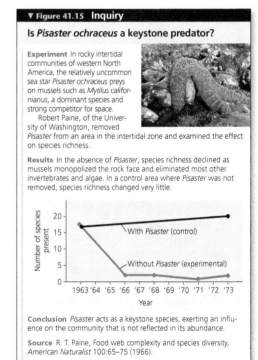

▼ **Figure 41.15** Inquiry

### Is *Pisaster ochraceus* a keystone predator?

**Experiment** In rocky intertidal communities of western North America, the relatively uncommon sea star *Pisaster ochraceus* preys on mussels such as *Mytilus californianus*, a dominant species and strong competitor for space.
Robert Paine, of the University of Washington, removed *Pisaster* from an area in the intertidal zone and examined the effect on species richness.

**Results** In the absence of *Pisaster*, species richness declined as mussels monopolized the rock face and eliminated most other invertebrates and algae. In a control area where *Pisaster* was not removed, species richness changed very little.

**Conclusion** *Pisaster* acts as a keystone species, exerting an influence on the community that is not reflected in its abundance.

**Source** R. T. Paine, Food web complexity and species diversity, *American Naturalist* 100:65–75 (1966).

**WHAT IF?** Suppose that an invasive fungus killed most individuals of *Mytilus* at these sites. Predict how species richness would be affected if *Pisaster* were then removed.

After exploring the featured experiment, ▶ students test their analytical skills by answering the **What If? question**.

**Experimental Inquiry Tutorials**, based on some of biology's most influential experiments, give students practice analyzing experimental design and data and help students understand how to reach conclusions based on collected data. Topics include:

- What Can You Learn About the Process of Science from Investigating a Cricket's Chirp?
- Which Wavelengths of Light Drive Photosynthesis?
- Does DNA Replication Follow the Conservative, Semiconservative, or Dispersive Model?
- Did Natural Selection of Ground Finches Occur When the Environment Changed?
- What Factors Influence the Loss of Nutrients from a Forest Ecosystem?

# Synthesize and Assess

## Make Connections Across Biology

By relating the content of a chapter to material presented earlier in the course, **Make Connections questions** help students develop a deeper understanding of biological principles.

**CONCEPT CHECK 28.3**
1. Contrast primary growth in roots and shoots.
2. **WHAT IF?** If a plant species has vertically oriented leaves, would you expect its mesophyll to be divided into spongy and palisade layers? Explain.
3. **MAKE CONNECTIONS** How are root hairs and microvilli analogous structures? (See Figure 4.7 and the discussion of analogy in Concept 20.2.)

**MAKE CONNECTIONS** *Review the idea of energy coupling (see Concept 6.3). Then use that idea to explain why heat is produced in the absorption of nutrients, in cellular respiration, and in the synthesis of large biological molecules.*

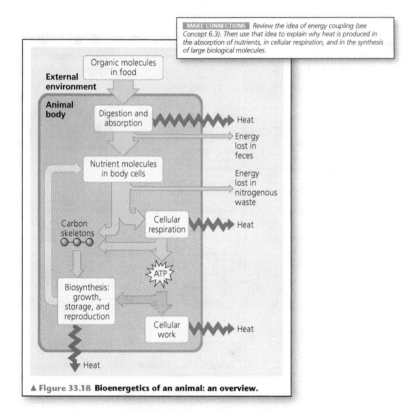

▲ **Figure 33.18 Bioenergetics of an animal: an overview.**

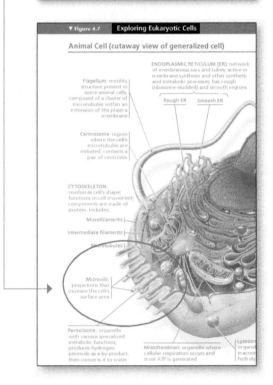

▼ Figure 4.7 **Exploring Eukaryotic Cells**

## MasteringBiology®
www.masteringbiology.com

**Make Connections Tutorials** help students connect biological concepts across chapters in an interactive way.

## Focus on Evolution

Every chapter has a section explicitly relating the chapter content to **evolution**, the fundamental theme of biology. Each section is highlighted by an Evolution banner.

**The Evolutionary Origins of Mitochondria and Chloroplasts**

**EVOLUTION** Mitochondria and chloroplasts display similarities with bacteria that led to the **endosymbiont theory**, illustrated in Figure 4.16. This theory states that an early ancestor of eukaryotic cells engulfed an oxygen-using nonphotosynthetic prokaryotic cell. Eventually, the engulfed cell formed a relationship with the host cell in which it was enclosed, becoming an *endosymbiont* (a cell living within another cell). Indeed, over the course of evolution, the host cell and its endosymbiont...

# Review and Test Understanding

**Chapter Reviews** help students master the chapter content by focusing on the main points and offering opportunities to practice for exams.

**Summary of Key Concepts questions** check students' understanding of a key idea from each concept.

**Scientific Inquiry questions** ask students to practice scientific thinking by developing hypotheses, designing experiments, and analyzing real research data.

## 32 Chapter Review

### SUMMARY OF KEY CONCEPTS

**CONCEPT** 32.1

**Feedback control maintains the internal environment in many animals (pp. 642–647)**

- Animal bodies are based on a hierarchy of cells, **tissues**, **organs**, and **organ systems**. **Epithelial tissue** forms active interfaces on external and internal surfaces; **connective tissue** binds and supports other tissues; **muscle tissue** contracts, moving body parts; and **nervous tissue** transmits nerve impulses throughout the body.
- Animals *regulate* certain internal variables while allowing other internal variables to *conform* to external changes. **Homeostasis** is the maintenance of a steady state despite internal and external changes.

[Figure: Homeostasis cycle — Homeostasis, Response/effector, Stimulus: Change in internal variable, Control center, Sensor/receptor]

- An animal maintains its internal temperature within a tolerable range by **thermoregulation**. **Endotherms** are warmed mostly by heat generated by metabolism. **Ectotherms** get most of their heat from external sources. The **hypothalamus** acts as the thermostat in mammalian regulation of body temperature.

? *Given that humans thermoregulate, explain why your skin is cooler than your body core.*

**CONCEPT** 32.2

**Endocrine signals trigger homeostatic mechanisms in target tissues (pp. 648–653)**

- In communicating between different locations in the body, the **endocrine system** broadcasts signaling molecules called

**hormones** everywhere via the bloodstream. Only certain cells are responsive to each hormone. The **nervous system** uses dedicated cellular circuits involving electrical and chemical signals to send information to specific locations. Hormone pathways may be regulated by **negative feedback**, which damps the stimulus, or **positive feedback**, which amplifies the stimulus and drives the response to completion.

? *Why would a water-soluble hormone likely have no effect if injected directly into the cytosol of a target cell?*

**CONCEPT** 32.3

**A shared system mediates osmoregulation and excretion in many animals (pp. 653–658)**

- When blood **osmolarity** rises, the posterior pituitary releases **antidiuretic hormone (ADH)**, which increases permeability to water in collecting ducts by increasing the number of water channels. When blood pressure or blood volume in the afferent arteriole drops, the **juxtaglomerular apparatus (JGA)** releases renin. **Angiotensin II**, formed in response to renin, constricts arterioles and triggers release of the hormone **aldosterone**, raising blood pressure. This **renin-angiotensin-aldosterone system (RAAS)** has functions that overlap with those of ADH.

? *How do cortical nephrons and juxtamedullary nephrons differ in reabsorbing nutrients and concentrating urine?*

### TEST YOUR UNDERSTANDING

**Level 1: Knowledge/Comprehension**

1. The body tissue that consists largely of material located outside of cells is
   a. epithelial tissue.
   b. connective tissue.
   c. skeletal muscle.
   d. smooth muscle.
   e. nervous tissue.

2. Which of the following would increase the rate of heat exchange between an animal and its environment?
   a. feathers or fur
   b. vasoconstriction
   c. wind blowing across the body surface
   d. countercurrent heat exchanger
   e. blubber or fat layer

3. Which process in the nephron is *least* selective?
   a. filtration
   b. reabsorption
   c. active transport
   d. secretion
   e. salt pumping by the loop of Henle

**Level 2: Application/Analysis**

4. Homeostasis typically relies on negative feedback because positive feedback
   a. requires a response but not a stimulus.
   b. drives processes to completion rather than to a balance point.
   c. acts within, but not beyond, a normal range.
   d. can decrease but not increase a variable.
   e. involves one location rather than several across the body.

5. Which of the following is an accurate statement about thermoregulation?
   a. Endotherms are regulators and ectotherms are conformers.
   b. Endotherms maintain a constant body temperature and ectotherms do not.
   c. Endotherms are warm-blooded and ectotherms are cold-blooded.
   d. Endotherms and ectotherms differ in their primary source of heat for thermoregulation.
   e. Endothermy has a lower energy cost than ectothermy.

6. Natural selection should favor the highest proportion of juxtamedullary nephrons in which of the following species?
   a. a river otter
   b. a mouse species living in a tropical rain forest
   c. a mouse species living in a temperate broadleaf forest
   d. a mouse species living in a desert
   e. a beaver

7. African lungfish, which are often found in small stagnant pools of fresh water, produce urea as a nitrogenous waste. What is the advantage of this adaptation?
   a. Urea takes less energy to synthesize than ammonia.
   b. Small stagnant pools do not provide enough water to dilute the toxic ammonia.
   c. The highly toxic urea makes the pool uninhabitable to potential competitors.
   d. Urea forms an insoluble precipitate.
   e. Urea makes lungfish tissue hypoosmotic to the pool.

**Level 3: Synthesis/Evaluation**

8. **DRAW IT** Draw a model of the control circuit(s) required for driving an automobile at a fairly constant speed over a hilly road. Indicate each feature that represents a sensor, stimulus, or response.

9. **SCIENTIFIC INQUIRY**
   You are exploring kidney function in kangaroo rats. You measure urine volume and osmolarity, as well as the amount of chloride ions (Cl⁻) and urea in the urine. If the water source provided to the animals were switched from tap water to a 2% NaCl solution, what change in urine osmolarity would you expect? How would you determine if this change was more likely due to a change in the excretion of Cl⁻ or urea?

10. **FOCUS ON EVOLUTION**
    Merriam's kangaroo rats (*Dipodomys merriami*) live in North American habitats ranging from moist, cool woodlands to hot deserts. Assuming that natural selection has resulted in differences in water conservation between *D. merriami* populations, propose a hypothesis concerning the relative rates of evaporative water loss by populations that live in moist versus dry environments. Using a humidity sensor to detect evaporative water loss by kangaroo rats, how could you test your hypothesis?

11. **FOCUS ON ORGANIZATION**
    In a short essay (100–150 words), compare how membrane structures in the loop of Henle and collecting duct of the mammalian kidney enable water to be recovered from filtrate in the process of osmoregulation.

*For selected answers, see Appendix A.*

**MasteringBiology®**

Students Go to **www.masteringbiology.com** for assignments, the eText, and the Study Area with practice tests, animations, and

**Summary figures** present key information in a visual way.

**Test Your Understanding questions** are organized into three levels based on Bloom's Taxonomy.

**Focus on a Theme questions** give students practice writing a short essay that connects the chapter's content to the five bookwide themes introduced in Chapter 1: **Evolution, Organization, Information, Energy and Matter,** and **Interactions.**

## MasteringBiology®
### www.masteringbiology.com

**Student Misconception Questions** provide assignable quizzes for each chapter to assess and remediate common student misconceptions.

# Visualize Biology

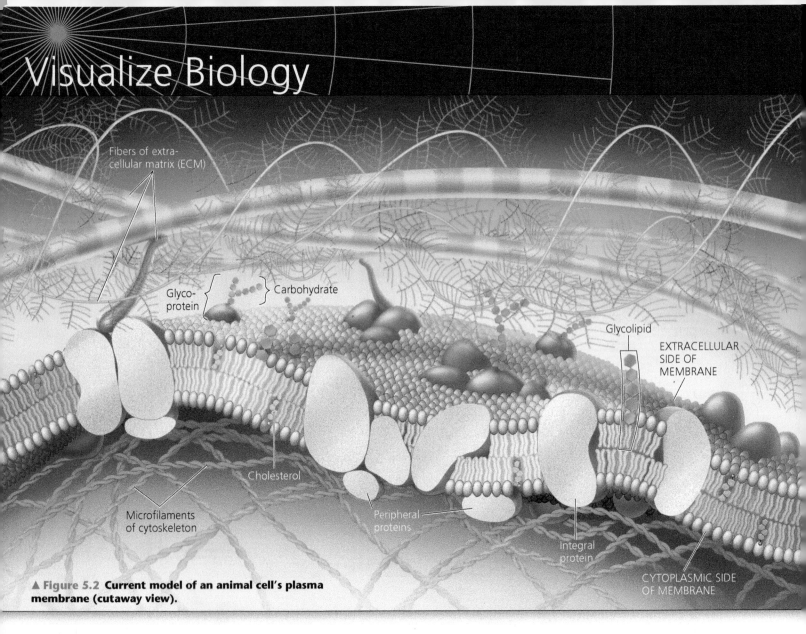

Fibers of extra-cellular matrix (ECM)

Glyco-protein

Carbohydrate

Glycolipid

EXTRACELLULAR SIDE OF MEMBRANE

Cholesterol

Microfilaments of cytoskeleton

Peripheral proteins

Integral protein

CYTOPLASMIC SIDE OF MEMBRANE

▲ **Figure 5.2 Current model of an animal cell's plasma membrane (cutaway view).**

▲ Selected figures are rendered in a **3-D style** to help students visualize biological structures.

## MasteringBiology®
www.masteringbiology.com

Many **Tutorials** and **Activities** integrate art from the textbook, providing a unified learning experience.

▼ Figure 33.14 **Dentition and diet.**

**Carnivore**

Carnivores, such as members of the dog and cat families, generally have large, pointed incisors and canines that can be used to kill prey and rip or cut away pieces of flesh. The jagged premolars and molars crush and shred food.

**Herbivore**

Herbivores, such as horses and deer, usually have premolars and molars with broad, ridged surfaces that grind tough plant material. The incisors and canines are generally modified for biting off pieces of vegetation. In some herbivores, canines are absent.

**Omnivore**

As omnivores, humans are adapted to eating both plants and meat. Adults have 32 teeth. From front to back along either side of the mouth are four bladelike incisors for biting, a pair of pointed canines for tearing, four premolars for grinding, and six molars for crushing (see inset, top view).

**Key**  Incisors   Canines   Premolars   Molars

◄ **Visual Organizers** highlight the main parts of a figure, helping students see the key categories at a glance.

### ▼ Figure 4.27    Exploring Cell Junctions in Animal Tissues

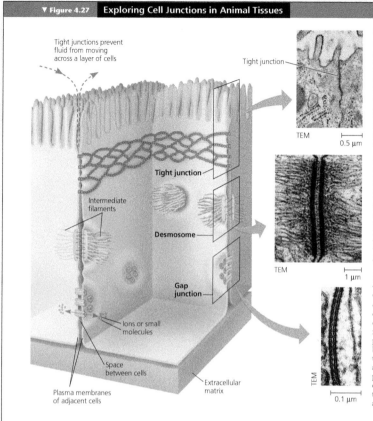

Tight junctions prevent fluid from moving across a layer of cells

Intermediate filaments

Tight junction

Desmosome

Gap junction

Ions or small molecules

Space between cells

Plasma membranes of adjacent cells

Extracellular matrix

#### Tight Junctions

Tight junction

TEM    0.5 μm

At **tight junctions**, the plasma membranes of neighboring cells are very tightly pressed against each other, bound together by specific proteins (purple). Forming continuous seals around the cells, tight junctions prevent leakage of extracellular fluid across a layer of epithelial cells. For example, tight junctions between skin cells make us watertight by preventing leakage between cells in our sweat glands.

#### Desmosomes

TEM    1 μm

**Desmosomes** (also called anchoring junctions) function like rivets, fastening cells together into strong sheets. Intermediate filaments made of sturdy keratin proteins anchor desmosomes in the cytoplasm. Desmosomes attach muscle cells to each other in a muscle. Some "muscle tears" involve the rupture of desmosomes.

#### Gap Junctions

TEM    0.1 μm

**Gap junctions** (also called communicating junctions) provide cytoplasmic channels from one cell to an adjacent cell and in this way are similar in their function to the plasmodesmata in plants. Gap junctions consist of membrane proteins that surround a pore through which ions, sugars, amino acids, and other small molecules may pass. Gap junctions are necessary for communication between cells in many types of tissues, such as heart muscle, and in animal embryos.

◀ By integrating text, art, and photos, **Exploring Figures** help students access information efficiently.

---

## MasteringBiology®
www.masteringbiology.com

**BioFlix**

**BioFlix® 3-D Animations** help students visualize biology with movie-quality animations that can be presented in class, reviewed by students on their own in the Study Area, and assigned in MasteringBiology. **BioFlix Tutorials** use the animations as a jumping-off point for coaching exercises on tough topics in MasteringBiology. Tutorials and animations include:

- A Tour of the Animal Cell
- A Tour of the Plant Cell
- Membrane Transport
- Cellular Respiration
- Photosynthesis
- Mitosis
- Meiosis
- DNA Replication
- Protein Synthesis
- Mechanisms of Evolution

- Water Transport in Plants
- Homeostasis: Regulating Blood Sugar
- Gas Exchange
- How Neurons Work
- How Synapses Work
- Muscle Contraction
- Population Ecology
- The Carbon Cycle

# MasteringBiology®

**MasteringBiology®** is the most effective and widely used online science tutorial, homework, and assessment system available.

www.masteringbiology.com

## Personalized Coaching and Feedback

Assign self-paced **MasteringBiology tutorials** that provide individualized coaching with specific hints and feedback on the toughest topics in the course.

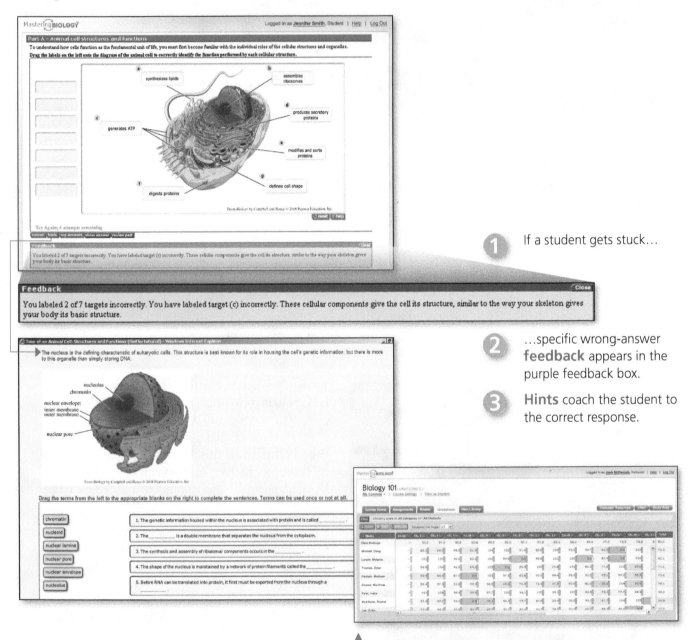

**1** If a student gets stuck…

**2** …specific wrong-answer **feedback** appears in the purple feedback box.

**3** **Hints** coach the student to the correct response.

▲ The MasteringBiology **gradebook** provides instructors with quick results and easy-to-interpret insights into student performance. Every assignment is **automatically graded** and shades of red highlight vulnerable students and challenging assignments.

# Students can use the Study Area on their own or in a study group.

## BioFlix

**BioFlix 3-D Animations** explore the most difficult biology topics, reinforced with tutorials, quizzes, and more.

The **Study Area** also includes:

- Scientific Skills Review
- Cumulative Test
- MP3 Tutor Sessions
- Videos
- Activities
- Investigations
- Lab Media
- Audio Glossary
- Word Roots
- Key Terms
- Flashcards
- Art

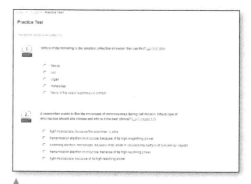

**Practice Tests** help students assess their understanding of each chapter, providing feedback for right and wrong answers.

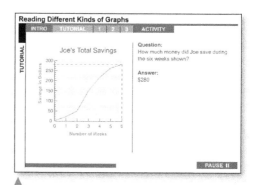

**Get Ready for Biology** helps students get up to speed for their course by covering study skills, basic math review, terminology, biology basics, chemistry, and cell biology.

---

# Access *Campbell BIOLOGY IN FOCUS* Online

◄ The Pearson **eText** gives students access to the text whenever and wherever they can access the Internet. The eText can be viewed on PCs, Macs, and tablets, including iPad and Android. The eText includes powerful interactive and customization functions:

- Write notes
- Highlight text
- Bookmark pages
- Zoom
- Click hyperlinked words to view definitions
- Search
- Link to media activities and quizzes

Instructors can even write notes for the class and highlight important material using a tool that works like an electronic pen on a whiteboard.

# Supplements

## For Instructors

### Instructor's Resource DVD Package
978-0-321-83322-8 • 0-321-83322-8

Assets for each chapter include:

- Editable figures (art and photos) and tables from the text in PowerPoint®
- Prepared PowerPoint Lecture Presentations for each chapter, with lecture notes, editable figures, tables, and links to animations and videos
- JPEG Images, including labeled and unlabeled art, photos from the text, and extra photos
- Clicker Questions in PowerPoint
- 250+ Instructor Animations and Videos, including BioFlix® 3-D Animations and *ABC News* Videos
- Test Bank questions in TestGen® software and Microsoft® Word
- Digital Transparencies
- Quick Reference Guide

**BioFlix® Animations** invigorate classroom lectures with 3-minute "movie-quality" 3-D graphics.
▼

**Customizable PowerPoints** provide a jumpstart for each lecture.
▼

**Clicker Questions** can be used to stimulate effective classroom discussions (for use with or without clickers).
▼

**All of the art and photos** from the book are provided with customizable labels.
▼

---

### Test Bank
978-0-321-83153-8 • 0-321-83153-5

The Test Bank is available as part of the Instructor's Resource DVD Package or separately.

### Course Management Systems

Content is available in Blackboard. Also, **MasteringBiology New Design** offers the usual Mastering features plus:

- Blackboard integration with single sign-on
- Temporary access (grace period)
- Discussion boards
- Email
- Chat and class live (synchronous whiteboard presentation)
- Submissions (dropbox)

### Instructor Resources Area in MasteringBiology

This area includes:

- Figures and Tables in PowerPoint®
- PowerPoint Lecture Presentations
- JPEG Images
- Clicker Questions
- Animations
- Videos
- Test Bank Files
- Digital Transparencies
- Quick Reference Guide
- Instructor Guides for Supplements
- Rubric and Tips for Grading Short-Answer Essays
- Suggested Answers for Essay Questions
- Lab Media

# For Students

### Study Guide
by Martha R. Taylor, Cornell University
978-0-321-86499-4 • 0-321-86499-9

This study guide helps students extract key ideas from the text-book and organize their knowledge of biology. Exercises include concept maps, chapter summaries, word roots, chapter tests, and a variety of interactive questions in various formats.

### Inquiry in Action: Interpreting Scientific Papers, Second Edition*
by Ruth Buskirk, University of Texas at Austin, and Christopher M. Gillen, Kenyon College
978-0-321-68336-6 • 0-321-68336-6

Nine research papers are summarized in Inquiry Figures. Each complete original research paper is also reprinted and accompanied by questions that help students analyze the paper.

### Practicing Biology: A Student Workbook, Fourth Edition*
by Jean Heitz and Cynthia Giffen, University of Wisconsin, Madison
978-0-321-68328-1 • 0-321-68328-5

This workbook offers a variety of activities to suit different learning styles. Activities such as modeling and mapping allow students to visualize and understand biological processes. Other activities focus on basic skills, such as reading and drawing graphs.

### Biological Inquiry: A Workbook of Investigative Cases, Third Edition*
by Margaret Waterman, Southeast Missouri State University, and Ethel Stanley, BioQUEST Curriculum Consortium and Beloit College
978-0-321-68320-5 • 0-321-68320-X

This workbook offers ten investigative cases. A link to a student website is in the Study Area in MasteringBiology.

### Study Card
978-0-321-68322-9 • 0-321-68322-6

This quick-reference card provides an overview of the entire field of biology and helps students see the connections between topics.

### Spanish Glossary
by Laura P. Zanello, University of California, Riverside
978-0-321-68321-2 • 0-321-68321-8

This resource provides definitions in Spanish for all the glossary terms.

### Into the Jungle: Great Adventures in the Search for Evolution
by Sean B. Carroll, University of Wisconsin, Madison
978-0-321-55671-4 • 0-321-55671-2

These nine short tales vividly depict key discoveries in evolutionary biology and the excitement of the scientific process. Online resources available at www.aw-bc.com/carroll.

* An Instructor Guide is available for download in the Instructor Resources Area at www.masteringbiology.com.

### Get Ready for Biology
by Lori K. Garrett, Parkland College
978-0-321-50057-1 • 0-321-50057-1

This engaging workbook helps students brush up on important math and study skills and get up to speed on biological terminology and the basics of chemistry and cell biology. Also available online through MasteringBiology.

### A Short Guide to Writing About Biology, Seventh Edition
by Jan A. Pechenik, Tufts University
978-0-321-66838-7 • 0-321-66838-3

This best-selling writing guide teaches students to think as biologists and to express ideas clearly and concisely through their writing.

### An Introduction to Chemistry for Biology Students, Ninth Edition
by George I. Sackheim, University of Illinois, Chicago
978-0-8053-9571-6 • 0-8053-9571-7

This text/workbook helps students review and master all the basic facts, concepts, and terminology of chemistry that they need for their life science course.

# For Lab

### Investigating Biology Laboratory Manual, Seventh Edition
by Judith Giles Morgan, Emory University, and M. Eloise Brown Carter, Oxford College of Emory University
978-0-321-66821-9 • 0-321-66821-9

The Seventh Edition emphasizes connections to recurring themes in biology, including structure and function, unity and diversity, and the overarching theme of evolution.

### Annotated Instructor Edition for Investigating Biology Laboratory Manual, Seventh Edition
by Judith Giles Morgan, Emory University, and M. Eloise Brown Carter, Oxford College of Emory University
978-0-321-67668-9 • 0-321-67668-8

### Preparation Guide for Investigating Biology Laboratory Manual, Seventh Edition
by Judith Giles Morgan, Emory University, and M. Eloise Brown Carter, Oxford College of Emory University
978-0-321-67669-6 • 0-321-67669-6

### Symbiosis: The Pearson Custom Library for the Biological Sciences
www.pearsonlearningsolutions.com/custom-library/symbiosis
Professors can create a custom lab manual.

### MasteringBiology® Virtual Biology Labs
www.masteringbiology.com

This online environment promotes critical thinking skills using virtual experiments and explorations that may be difficult to perform in a wet lab environment due to time, cost, or safety concerns. Designed to supplement or substitute for existing wet labs, this product offers students unique learning experiences and critical thinking exercises in the areas of microscopy, molecular biology, genetics, ecology, and systematics.

# Featured Figures

*The Inquiry Figure, original research paper, and a worksheet to guide you through the paper are provided in *Inquiry in Action: Interpreting Scientific Papers*, Second Edition.

†A related Experimental Inquiry Tutorial can be assigned in MasteringBiology.

# Scientific Skills Exercises

MB · Each Scientific Skills Exercise is also available as an automatically graded Tutorial in MasteringBiology.

# Acknowledgments

The authors wish to express their gratitude to the global community of instructors, researchers, students, and publishing professionals who have contributed to the first edition of **CAMPBELL BIOLOGY IN FOCUS**.

As authors of this text, we are mindful of the daunting challenge of keeping up to date in all areas of our rapidly expanding subject. We are grateful to the many scientists who helped shape this text by discussing their research fields with us, answering specific questions in their areas of expertise, and sharing their ideas about biology education. We are especially grateful to the following, listed alphabetically: Monika Abedin, John Archibald, Daniel Boyce, Nick Butterfield, Jean DeSaix, Eileen Gregory, Hopi Hoekstra, Fred Holtzclaw, Theresa Holtzclaw, Azarias Karamanlidis, Patrick Keeling, David Lamb, Teri Liegler, Thomas Montavon, Joe Montoya, Kevin Peterson, Michael Pollock, Susannah Porter, Andrew Roger, Andrew Schaffner, Tom Schneider, Alastair Simpson, Doug Soltis, Pamela Soltis, and George Watts. In addition, the biologists listed on pages xxiii–xxiv provided detailed reviews, helping us ensure the text's scientific accuracy and improve its pedagogical effectiveness. We thank Marty Taylor, author of the Study Guide, for her many contributions to the accuracy, clarity, and consistency of the text; and we thank Carolyn Wetzel, Ruth Buskirk, Joan Sharp, Jennifer Yeh, and Charlene D'Avanzo for their contributions to the Scientific Skills Exercises.

Thanks also to the other professors and students, from all over the world, who contacted the authors directly with useful suggestions. We alone bear the responsibility for any errors that remain, but the dedication of our consultants, reviewers, and other correspondents makes us confident in the accuracy and effectiveness of this text.

The value of **CAMPBELL BIOLOGY IN FOCUS** as a learning tool is greatly enhanced by the supplementary materials that have been created for instructors and students. We recognize that the dedicated authors of these materials are essentially writing mini (and not so mini) books. We appreciate the hard work and creativity of all the authors listed, with their creations, on page xix. We are also grateful to Kathleen Fitzpatrick and Nicole Tunbridge (PowerPoint® Lecture Presentations) and Fleur Ferro, Brad Stith, and Loraine Washburn (Clicker Questions).

MasteringBiology® and the electronic media for this text are invaluable teaching and learning aids. We thank the hardworking, industrious instructors who worked on the revised and new media: Willy Cushwa, Tom Kennedy, Michael Pollock, and Heather Wilson-Ashworth. We are also grateful to the many other people—biology instructors, editors, and production experts—who are listed in the credits for these and other elements of the electronic media that accompany the text.

**CAMPBELL BIOLOGY IN FOCUS** results from an unusually strong synergy between a team of scientists and a team of publishing professionals. Our editorial team at Pearson Science again demonstrated unmatched talents, commitment, and pedagogical insights. Our Senior Acquisitions Editor, Josh Frost, brought publishing savvy, intelligence, and a much appreciated level head to leading the whole team. The clarity and effectiveness of every page owe much to our extraordinary Supervising Editors Pat Burner and Beth Winickoff, who worked with a top-notch team of Developmental Editors in Matt Lee and Mary Ann Murray. Our unsurpassed Senior Editorial Manager Ginnie Simione Jutson, Executive Director of Development Deborah Gale, Assistant Editor Katherine Harrison-Adcock, and Editor-in-Chief Beth Wilbur were indispensable in moving the project in the right direction. We also want to thank Robin Heyden for organizing the annual Biology Leadership Conferences and keeping us in touch with the world of AP Biology.

You would not have this beautiful text if not for the work of the production team: Director of Production Erin Gregg; Managing Editor Michael Early; Assistant Managing Editor Shannon Tozier; Senior Photo Editor Donna Kalal; Photo Researcher Maureen Spuhler; Copy Editor Janet Greenblatt; Proofreader Joanna Dinsmore; Permissions Editor Sue Ewing; Permissions Project Manager Joe Croscup; Permissions Manager Tim Nicholls; Senior Project Editor Emily Bush, Paging Specialists Jodi Gaherty and Donna Healy, and the rest of the staff at S4Carlisle; Art Production Manager Kristina Seymour, Developmental Artist Andrew Recher, and the rest of the staff at Precision Graphics; Design Manager Marilyn Perry; Text Designer Gary Hespenheide; Cover Designer Yvo Riezebos; and Manufacturing Buyer Michael Penne. We also thank those who worked on the text's supplements: Susan Berge, Brady Golden, Jane Brundage, David Chavez, Kris Langan, Pete Shanks, and John Hammett. And for creating the wonderful package of electronic media that accompanies the text, we are grateful to Tania Mlawer (Director of Content Development for MasteringBiology), Sarah Jensen, Jonathan Ballard, Brienn Buchanan, Katie Foley, and Caroline Ross, as well as Director of Media Development Lauren Fogel and Director of Media Strategy Stacy Treco.

For their important roles in marketing the text and media, we thank Christy Lesko, Lauren Harp, Scott Dustan, Chris Hess, Lillian Carr, Jane Campbell, and Jessica Perry. For their market development support, we thank Brooke Suchomel, Michelle Cadden, and Cassandra Cummings. We are grateful to Paul Corey, President of Pearson Science, for his enthusiasm, encouragement, and support.

The Pearson sales team, which represents **CAMPBELL BIOLOGY IN FOCUS** on campus, is an essential link to the users of the text. They tell us what you like and don't like about the text, communicate the features of the text, and provide prompt service. We thank them for their hard work and professionalism. For representing our text to our international audience, we thank our sales and marketing partners throughout the world. They are all strong allies in biology education.

Finally, we wish to thank our families and friends for their encouragement and patience throughout this long project. Our special thanks to Lily, Ross, Lily-too, and Alex (L.A.U.); Debra and Hannah (M.L.C.); Harry, Elga, Aaron, Sophie, Noah, and Gabriele (S.A.W.); Natalie (P.V.M.); Sally, Robert, David, and Will (R.B.J.); and Paul, Dan, Maria, Armelle, and Sean (J.B.R.). And, as always, thanks to Rochelle, Allison, Jason, McKay, and Gus.

Lisa A. Urry, Michael L. Cain, Steve A. Wasserman, Peter V. Minorsky, Robert B. Jackson, and Jane B. Reece

# Reviewers

Ann Aguanno, *Marymount Manhattan College*
Marc Albrecht, *University of Nebraska*
John Alcock, *Arizona State University*
Eric Alcorn, *Acadia University*
Rodney Allrich, *Purdue University*
John Archibald, *Dalhousie University*
Terry Austin, *Temple College*
Brian Bagatto, *University of Akron*
Virginia Baker, *Chipola College*
Teri Balser, *University of Wisconsin, Madison*
Bonnie Baxter, *Westminster College*
Marilee Benore, *University of Michigan, Dearborn*
Catherine Black, *Idaho State University*
William Blaker, *Furman University*
Edward Blumenthal, *Marquette University*
David Bos, *Purdue University*
Scott Bowling, *Auburn University*
Beverly Brown, *Nazareth College*
Beth Burch, *Huntington University*
Warren Burggren, *University of North Texas*
Dale Burnside, *Lenoir-Rhyne University*
Ragan Callaway, *The University of Montana*
Kenneth M. Cameron, *University of Wisconsin, Madison*
Patrick Canary, *Northland Pioneer College*
Cheryl Keller Capone, *Pennsylvania State University*
Mickael Cariveau, *Mount Olive College*
Karen I. Champ, *Central Florida Community College*
David Champlin, *University of Southern Maine*
Brad Chandler, *Palo Alto College*
Wei-Jen Chang, *Hamilton College*
Jung Choi, *Georgia Institute of Technology*
Steve Christenson, *Brigham Young University, Idaho*
Reggie Cobb, *Nashville Community College*
James T. Colbert, *Iowa State University*
Sean Coleman, *University of the Ozarks*
William Cushwa, *Clark College*
Deborah Dardis, *Southeastern Louisiana University*
Shannon Datwyler, *California State University, Sacramento*
Melissa Deadmond, *Truckee Meadows Community College*
Eugene Delay, *University of Vermont*
Daniel DerVartanian, *University of Georgia*
Jean DeSaix, *University of North Carolina, Chapel Hill*
Janet De Souza-Hart, *Massachusetts College of Pharmacy & Health Sciences*
Jason Douglas, *Angelina College*
Kathryn A. Durham, *Lorain Community College*
Anna Edlund, *Lafayette College*
Curt Elderkin, *College of New Jersey*
Mary Ellard-Ivey, *Pacific Lutheran University*
Kurt Elliott, *Northwest Vista College*
George Ellmore, *Tufts University*
Rob Erdman, *Florida Gulf Coast College*
Dale Erskine, *Lebanon Valley College*
Robert C. Evans, *Rutgers University, Camden*
Sam Fan, *Bradley University*
Paul Farnsworth, *University of New Mexico*
Myriam Alhadeff Feldman, *Cascadia Community College*
Teresa Fischer, *Indian River Community College*
David Fitch, *New York University*
T. Fleming, *Bradley University*
Robert Fowler, *San Jose State University*
Robert Franklin, *College of Charleston*
Art Fredeen, *University of Northern British Columbia*
Kim Fredericks, *Viterbo University*
Matt Friedman, *University of Chicago*
Cynthia M. Galloway, *Texas A&M University, Kingsville*

Kristen Genet, *Anoka Ramsey Community College*
Phil Gibson, *University of Oklahoma*
Eric Gillock, *Fort Hayes State University*
Simon Gilroy, *University of Wisconsin, Madison*
Edwin Ginés-Candelaria, *Miami Dade College*
Jim Goetze, *Laredo Community College*
Lynda Goff, *University of California, Santa Cruz*
Roy Golsteyn, *University of Lethbridge*
Barbara E. Goodman, *University of South Dakota*
Eileen Gregory, *Rollins College*
Bradley Griggs, *Piedmont Technical College*
David Grise, *Texas A&M University, Corpus Christi*
Edward Gruberg, *Temple University*
Karen Guzman, *Campbell University*
Carla Haas, *Pennsylvania State University*
Pryce "Pete" Haddix, *Auburn University*
Heather Hallen-Adams, *University of Nebraska, Lincoln*
Monica Hall-Woods, *St. Charles Community College*
Bill Hamilton, *Washington & Lee University*
Devney Hamilton, *Stanford University (student)*
Matthew B. Hamilton, *Georgetown University*
Dennis Haney, *Furman University*
Jean Hardwick, *Ithaca College*
Luke Harmon, *University of Idaho*
Jeanne M. Harris, *University of Vermont*
Stephanie Harvey, *Georgia Southwestern State University*
Bernard Hauser, *University of Florida*
Chris Haynes, *Shelton State Community College*
Andreas Hejnol, *Sars International Centre for Marine Molecular Biology*
Albert Herrera, *University of Southern California*
Chris Hess, *Butler University*
Kendra Hill, *San Diego State University*
Jason Hodin, *Stanford University*
Laura Houston, *Northeast Lakeview College*
Sara Huang, *Los Angeles Valley College*
Catherine Hurlbut, *Florida State College, Jacksonville*
Diane Husic, *Moravian College*
Thomas Jacobs, *University of Illinois*
Kathy Jacobson, *Grinnell College*
Mark Jaffe, *Nova Southeastern University*
Emmanuelle Javaux, *University of Liege, Belgium*
Douglas Jensen, *Converse College*
Lance Johnson, *Midland Lutheran College*
Roishene Johnson, *Bossier Parish Community College*
Cheryl Jorcyk, *Boise State University*
Caroline Kane, *University of California, Berkeley*
The-Hui Kao, *Pennsylvania State University*
Nicholas Kapp, *Skyline College*
Jennifer Katcher, *Pima Community College*
Judy Kaufman, *Monroe Community College*
Eric G. Keeling, *Cary Institute of Ecosystem Studies*
Chris Kennedy, *Simon Fraser University*
Hillar Klandorf, *West Virginia University*
Mark Knauss, *Georgia Highlands College*
Charles Knight, *California Polytechnic State University*
Roger Koeppe, *University of Arkansas*
Peter Kourtev, *Central Michigan University*
Jacob Krans, *Western New England University*
Eliot Krause, *Seton Hall University*
Steven Kristoff, *Ivy Tech Community College*
William Kroll, *Loyola University*
Barb Kuemerle, *Case Western Reserve University*
Rukmani Kuppuswami, *Laredo Community College*
Lee Kurtz, *Georgia Gwinnett College*
Michael P. Labare, *United States Military Academy, West Point*
Ellen Lamb, *University of North Carolina, Greensboro*

*(Continued)*

William Lamberts, *College of St. Benedict and St. John's University*
Tali D. Lee, *University of Wisconsin, Eau Claire*
Hugh Lefcort, *Gonzaga University*
Alcinda Lewis, *University of Colorado, Boulder*
Jani Lewis, *State University of New York*
Graeme Lindbeck, *Valencia Community College*
Hannah Lui, *University of California, Irvine*
Nancy Magill, *Indiana University*
Cindy Malone, *California State University, Northridge*
Mark Maloney, *University of South Mississippi*
Julia Marrs, *Barnard College (student)*
Kathleen Marrs, *Indiana University-Purdue University, Indianapolis*
Mike Mayfield, *Ball State University*
Kamau Mbuthia, *Bowling Green State University*
Tanya McGhee, *Craven Community College*
Darcy Medica, *Pennsylvania State University*
Susan Meiers, *Western Illinois University*
Mike Meighan, *University of California, Berkeley*
Jan Mikesell, *Gettysburg College*
Alex Mills, *University of Windsor*
Sarah Milton, *Florida Atlantic University*
Eli Minkoff, *Bates College*
Subhash Minocha, *University of New Hampshire*
Ivona Mladenovic, *Simon Fraser University*
Linda Moore, *Georgia Military College*
Courtney Murren, *College of Charleston*
Karen Neal, *Reynolds University*
Ross Nehm, *Ohio State University*
Kimberlyn Nelson, *Pennsylvania State University*
Jacalyn Newman, *University of Pittsburgh*
Kathleen Nolta, *University of Michigan*
Gretchen North, *Occidental College*
Margaret Olney, *St. Martin's University*
Aharon Oren, *The Hebrew University*
Rebecca Orr, *Spring Creek College*
Henry R. Owen, *Eastern Illinois University*
Matt Palmtag, *Florida Gulf Coast University*
Stephanie Pandolfi, *Michigan State University*
Nathalie Pardigon, *Institut Pasteur*
Cindy Paszkowski, *University of Alberta*
Andrew Pease, *Stevenson University*
Nancy Pelaez, *Purdue University*
Irene Perry, *University of Texas of the Permian Basin*
Roger Persell, *Hunter College*
Eric Peters, *Chicago State University*
Larry Peterson, *University of Guelph*
Mark Pilgrim, *College of Coastal Georgia*
Vera M. Piper, *Shenandoah University*
Deb Pires, *University of California, Los Angeles*
Crima Pogge, *City College of San Francisco*
Michael Pollock, *Mount Royal University*
Roberta Pollock, *Occidental College*
Therese M. Poole, *Georgia State University*
Angela R. Porta, *Kean University*
Jason Porter, *University of the Sciences, Philadelphia*
Robert Powell, *Avila University*
Elena Pravosudova, *University of Nevada, Reno*
Eileen Preston, *Tarrant Community College Northwest*
Terrell Pritts, *University of Arkansas, Little Rock*
Pushpa Ramakrishna, *Chandler-Gilbert Community College*
David Randall, *City University Hong Kong*
Monica Ranes-Goldberg, *University of California, Berkeley*
Robert S. Rawding, *Gannon University*
Robert Reavis, *Glendale Community College*
Sarah Richart, *Azusa Pacific University*

Todd Rimkus, *Marymount University*
John Rinehart, *Eastern Oregon University*
Kenneth Robinson, *Purdue University*
Deb Roess, *Colorado State University*
Heather Roffey, *Marianopolis College*
Suzanne Rogers, *Seton Hill University*
Patricia Rugaber, *College of Coastal Georgia*
Scott Russell, *University of Oklahoma*
Glenn-Peter Saetre, *University of Oslo*
Sanga Saha, *Harold Washington College*
Kathleen Sandman, *Ohio State University*
Louis Santiago, *University of California, Riverside*
Tom Sawicki, *Spartanburg Community College*
Andrew Schaffner, *California Polytechnic State University, San Luis Obispo*
Thomas W. Schoener, *University of California, Davis*
Patricia Schulte, *University of British Columbia*
Brenda Schumpert, *Valencia Community College*
David Schwartz, *Houston Community College*
Duane Sears, *University of California, Santa Barbara*
Brent Selinger, *University of Lethbridge*
Alison M. Shakarian, *Salve Regina University*
Joan Sharp, *Simon Fraser University*
Robin L. Sherman, *Nova Southeastern University*
Eric Shows, *Jones County Junior College*
Sedonia Sipes, *Southern Illinois University, Carbondale*
John Skillman, *California State University, San Bernardino*
Doug Soltis, *University of Florida, Gainesville*
Joel Stafstrom, *Northern Illinois University*
Alam Stam, *Capital University*
Judy Stone, *Colby College*
Cynthia Surmacz, *Bloomsburg University*
David Tam, *University of North Texas*
Yves Tan, *Cabrillo College*
Emily Taylor, *California Polytechnic State University*
Marty Taylor, *Cornell University*
Franklyn Tan Te, *Miami Dade College*
Kent Thomas, *Wichita State University*
Mike Toliver, *Eureka College*
Saba Valadkhan, *Center for RNA Molecular Biology*
Sarah VanVickle-Chavez, *Washington University, St. Louis*
William Velhagen, *New York University*
Amy Volmer, *Swarthmore College*
Janice Voltzow, *University of Scranton*
Margaret Voss, *Penn State Erie*
Charles Wade, *C.S. Mott Community College*
Claire Walczak, *Indiana University*
Jerry Waldvogel, *Clemson University*
Robert Lee Wallace, *Ripon College*
James Wandersee, *Louisiana State University*
Fred Wasserman, *Boston University*
James Wee, *Loyola University*
John Weishampel, *University of Central Florida*
Susan Whittemore, *Keene State College*
Murray Wiegand, *University of Winnipeg*
Kimberly Williams, *Kansas State University*
Janet Wolkenstein, *Hudson Valley Community College*
Grace Wyngaard, *James Madison University*
Shuhai Xiao, *Virginia Polytechnic Institute*
Paul Yancey, *Whitman College*
Anne D. Yoder, *Duke University*
Ed Zalisko, *Blackburn College*
Nina Zanetti, *Siena College*
Sam Zeveloff, *Weber State University*
Theresa Zucchero, *Methodist University*

# Brief Contents

# Detailed Contents

**8**

## Cell Communication  154

**9**

## The Cell Cycle  176

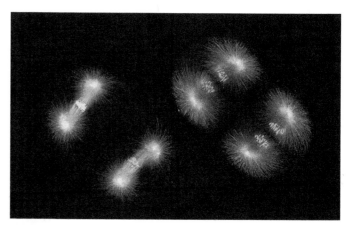

**10**

## Meiosis and Sexual Life Cycles  196

## 15 Viruses 300

Chapters 1-3, 5-6, and 11-15, taken from:
*Campbell Biology In Focus*
by Lisa A. Urry, Michael L. Cain, Steven A. Wasserman, Peter V. Minorsky, Robert B. Jackson, and Jane B. Reece

Chapters 4, and 7-10, taken from:
*Campbell Biology*, Tenth Edition
by Jane B. Reece, Lisa A. Urry, Michael L. Cain, Steven A. Wasserman, Peter V. Minorsky, and Robert B. Jackson

# Introduction: Evolution and the Foundations of Biology

**Figure 1.1** What can this beach mouse teach us about biology?

**OVERVIEW**

## Inquiring About Life

The brilliant white sand dunes and sparse clumps of beach grass along the Florida seashore afford little cover for the beach mice that live there. However, a beach mouse's light, dappled fur acts as camouflage, allowing the mouse to blend into its surroundings (**Figure 1.1**). Although mice of the same species (oldfield mice, *Peromyscus polionotus*) also inhabit nearby inland areas, the inland mice are much darker in color, matching the darker soil and vegetation where they live (**Figure 1.2**). This close match of each mouse to its environment is vital for survival, since hawks, herons, and other sharp-eyed predators periodically scan the landscape for food. How has the color of each mouse come to be so well matched, or *adapted*, to the local background?

An organism's adaptations to its environment, such as camouflage that helps protect it from predators, are the result of **evolution**, the process of change that has transformed life from its beginnings to the astounding array of organisms today. Evolution is the fundamental principle of biology and the core theme of this book.

Although biologists know a great deal about life on Earth, many mysteries remain. The question of how the mice's coats have come to match the colors of their habitats is just one example. Posing questions about the living world and seeking answers through scientific inquiry are the central activities of **biology**, the scientific study of life. Biologists' questions can be ambitious. They may ask how a single tiny cell becomes a tree or a dog, how the human mind works, or how the different forms of life in a forest interact. When questions occur to you as you observe the living world, you are already thinking like a biologist.

How do biologists make sense of life's diversity and complexity? This opening chapter sets up a framework for answering this question. The first part of the chapter provides a panoramic view of the biological "landscape," organized around a set of unifying themes. We'll then focus on biology's core theme, evolution. Finally, we'll examine the process of scientific inquiry—how scientists ask and attempt to answer questions about the natural world.

**Figure 1.2 An "inland" oldfield mouse (*Peromyscus polionotus*).** This mouse has a much darker back, side, and face than mice of the same species that inhabit sand dunes.

# Studying the diverse forms of life reveals common themes

Biology is a subject of enormous scope, and exciting new biological discoveries are being made every day. How can you organize and make sense of all the information you'll encounter as you study biology? Focusing on a few big ideas—ways of thinking about life that will still hold true decades from now—will help. Here, we'll describe five unifying themes to serve as touchstones as you proceed through this book.

## Theme: New Properties Emerge at Successive Levels of Biological Organization

**ORGANIZATION** The study of life extends from the microscopic scale of the molecules and cells that make up organisms to the global scale of the entire living planet. As biologists, we can divide this enormous range into different levels of biological organization.

Imagine zooming in from space to take a closer and closer look at life on Earth. It is spring in Ontario, Canada, and our destination is a local forest, where we will eventually narrow our focus down to the molecules that make up a maple leaf. **Figure 1.3** narrates this journey into life, as the numbers guide

---

**▼ Figure 1.3** **Exploring Levels of Biological Organization**

### ◀ 1 The Biosphere

Even from space, we can see signs of Earth's life—in the green mosaic of the forests, for example. We can also see the scale of the entire biosphere, which consists of all life on Earth and all the places where life exists: most regions of land, most bodies of water, the atmosphere to an altitude of several kilometers, and even sediments far below the ocean floor.

### ◀ 2 Ecosystems

Our first scale change brings us to a North American forest with many deciduous trees (trees that lose their leaves and grow new ones each year). A deciduous forest is an example of an ecosystem, as are grasslands, deserts, and coral reefs. An ecosystem consists of all the living things in a particular area, along with all the nonliving components of the environment with which life interacts, such as soil, water, atmospheric gases, and light.

### ▶ 3 Communities

The array of organisms inhabiting a particular ecosystem is called a biological community. The community in our forest ecosystem includes many kinds of trees and other plants, various animals, mushrooms and other fungi, and enormous numbers of diverse microorganisms, which are living forms, such as bacteria, that are too small to see without a microscope. Each of these forms of life is called a *species*.

### ▶ 4 Populations

A population consists of all the individuals of a species living within the bounds of a specified area. For example, our forest includes a population of sugar maple trees and a population of white-tailed deer. A community is therefore the set of populations that inhabit a particular area.

### ▲ 5 Organisms

Individual living things are called organisms. Each of the maple trees and other plants in the forest is an organism, and so is each deer, frog, beetle, and other forest animals. The soil teems with microorganisms such as bacteria.

you through photographs illustrating the hierarchy of biological organization.

Zooming in at ever-finer resolution illustrates the principle of *reductionism*—the approach of reducing complex systems to simpler components that are more manageable to study. Reductionism is a powerful strategy in biology. For example, by studying the molecular structure of DNA that had been extracted from cells, James Watson and Francis Crick inferred the chemical basis of biological inheritance. However, although it has propelled many major discoveries, reductionism provides a necessarily incomplete view of life on Earth, as we'll discuss next.

### Emergent Properties

Let's reexamine Figure 1.3, beginning this time at the molecular level and then zooming out. Viewed this way, we see that at each level, novel properties emerge that are absent from the preceding one. These **emergent properties** are due to the arrangement and interactions of parts as complexity increases. For example, although photosynthesis occurs in an intact chloroplast, it will not take place in a disorganized test-tube mixture of chlorophyll and other chloroplast molecules. The coordinated processes of photosynthesis require a specific organization of these molecules in the chloroplast. Isolated components of living systems, acting as the objects of study in

## ▼ 6 Organs and Organ Systems

The structural hierarchy of life continues to unfold as we explore the architecture of more complex organisms. A maple leaf is an example of an organ, a body part that carries out a particular function in the body. Stems and roots are the other major organs of plants. The organs of complex animals and plants are organized into organ systems, each a team of organs that cooperate in a larger function. Organs consist of multiple tissues.

## ◄ 7 Tissues

To see the tissues of a leaf requires a microscope. Each tissue is a group of cells that work together, performing a specialized function. The leaf shown here has been cut on an angle. The honeycombed tissue in the interior of the leaf (left side of photo) is the main location of photosynthesis, the process that converts light energy to the chemical energy of sugar. The jigsaw puzzle–like "skin" on the surface of the leaf is a tissue called epidermis (right side of photo). The pores through the epidermis allow entry of the gas $CO_2$, a raw material for sugar production.

50 μm

Cell    10 μm

## ▶ 10 Molecules

Our last scale change drops us into a chloroplast for a view of life at the molecular level. A molecule is a chemical structure consisting of two or more units called atoms, represented as balls in this computer graphic of a chlorophyll molecule. Chlorophyll is the pigment molecule that makes a maple leaf green, and it absorbs sunlight during photosynthesis. Within each chloroplast, millions of chlorophyll molecules are organized into systems that convert light energy to the chemical energy of food.

Atoms

Chlorophyll molecule

## ▲ 8 Cells

The cell is life's fundamental unit of structure and function. Some organisms are single cells, while others are multicellular. A single cell performs all the functions of life, while a multicellular organism has a division of labor among specialized cells. Here we see a magnified view of cells in a leaf tissue. One cell is about 40 micrometers (μm) across— about 500 of them would reach across a small coin. As tiny as these cells are, you can see that each contains numerous green structures called chloroplasts, which are responsible for photosynthesis.

## ▶ 9 Organelles

Chloroplasts are examples of organelles, the various functional components present in cells. This image, taken by a powerful microscope, shows a single chloroplast.

Chloroplast

1 μm

a reductionist approach to biology, typically lack some of the properties that emerge at higher levels of organization.

Emergent properties are not unique to life. A box of bicycle parts won't transport you anywhere, but if they are arranged in a certain way, you can pedal to your chosen destination. Compared to such nonliving examples, however, the unrivaled complexity of biological systems makes the emergent properties of life especially challenging to study.

To fully explore emergent properties, biologists today complement reductionism with **systems biology**, the exploration of a biological system by analyzing the interactions among its parts. A single leaf cell can be considered a system, as can a frog, an ant colony, or a desert ecosystem. By examining and modeling the dynamic behavior of an integrated network of components, systems biology enables us to pose new kinds of questions. For example, how does a drug that lowers blood pressure affect the functioning of organs throughout the body? At a larger scale, how does a gradual increase in atmospheric carbon dioxide alter ecosystems and the entire biosphere? Systems biology can be used to study life at all levels.

### Structure and Function

At each level of the biological hierarchy, we find a correlation of structure and function. Consider the leaf in Figure 1.3: Its thin, flat shape maximizes the capture of sunlight by chloroplasts. More generally, analyzing a biological structure gives us clues about what it does and how it works. Conversely, knowing the function of something provides insight into its structure and organization. Many examples from the animal kingdom show a correlation between structure and function, including the hummingbird **(Figure 1.4)**. The hummingbird's anatomy allows the wings to rotate at the shoulder, so hummingbirds have the ability, unique among birds, to fly backward or hover in place. Hovering, the birds can extend their long slender beaks into flowers and feed on nectar. The

elegant match of form and function in the structures of life is explained by natural selection, as we'll explore shortly.

### The Cell: An Organism's Basic Unit of Structure and Function

In life's structural hierarchy, the cell is the smallest unit of organization that can perform all required activities. In fact, the activities of organisms are all based on the activities of cells. For instance, the movement of your eyes as you read this sentence results from the activities of muscle and nerve cells. Even a process that occurs on a global scale, such as the recycling of carbon atoms, is the cumulative product of cellular functions, including the photosynthetic activity of chloroplasts in leaf cells.

All cells share certain characteristics. For instance, every cell is enclosed by a membrane that regulates the passage of materials between the cell and its surroundings. Nevertheless, we recognize two main forms of cells: prokaryotic and eukaryotic. The cells of two groups of single-celled microorganisms—bacteria (singular, *bacterium*) and archaea (singular, *archaean*)—are prokaryotic. All other forms of life, including plants and animals, are composed of eukaryotic cells.

A **eukaryotic cell** contains membrane-enclosed organelles **(Figure 1.5)**. Some organelles, such as the DNA-containing nucleus, are found in the cells of all eukaryotes; other organelles are specific to particular cell types. For example, the chloroplast in Figure 1.3 is an organelle found only in eukaryotic cells that carry out photosynthesis. In contrast to eukaryotic cells, a **prokaryotic cell** lacks a nucleus or other membrane-enclosed organelles. Furthermore, prokaryotic cells are generally smaller than eukaryotic cells, as shown in Figure 1.5.

▲ **Figure 1.4 Form fits function in a hummingbird's body.** The unusual bone structure of a hummingbird's wing allows the bird to rotate its wings in all directions, enabling it to fly backward and to hover while it feeds.

? *What other examples of form fitting function do you observe in this photograph?*

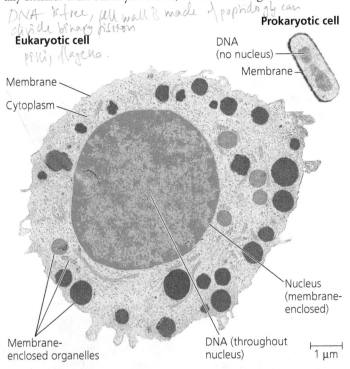

▲ **Figure 1.5 Contrasting eukaryotic and prokaryotic cells in size and complexity.**

## Theme: Life's Processes Involve the Expression and Transmission of Genetic Information

Within cells, structures called chromosomes contain genetic material in the form of **DNA (deoxyribonucleic acid)**. In cells that are preparing to divide, the chromosomes may be made visible using a dye that appears blue when bound to the DNA (**Figure 1.6**).

▲ Figure 1.6 **A lung cell from a newt divides into two smaller cells that will grow and divide again.**

### DNA Structure and Function

Each time a cell divides, the DNA is first *replicated*, or copied, and each of the two cellular offspring inherits a complete set of chromosomes, identical to that of the parent cell. Each chromosome contains one very long DNA molecule with hundreds or thousands of **genes**, each a stretch of DNA arranged along the chromosome. Transmitted from parents to offspring, genes are the units of inheritance. They encode the information necessary to build all of the molecules synthesized within a cell, which in turn establish that cell's identity and function. Each of us began as a single cell stocked with DNA inherited from our parents. The replication of that DNA during each round of cell division transmitted copies of the DNA to what eventually became the trillions of cells of the human body. As the cells grew and divided, the genetic information encoded by the DNA directed our development (**Figure 1.7**).

The molecular structure of DNA accounts for its ability to store information. A DNA molecule is made up of two long chains, called strands, arranged in a double helix. Each chain is made up of four kinds of chemical building blocks called nucleotides, abbreviated A, T, C, and G (**Figure 1.8**). The way DNA encodes information is analogous to how we arrange the letters of the alphabet into words and phrases with specific meanings. The word *rat*, for example, evokes a rodent; the words *tar* and *art*, which contain the same letters, mean very different things. We can think of nucleotides as a four-letter alphabet. Specific sequences of these four nucleotides encode the information in genes.

DNA provides the blueprints for making proteins, which are the major players in building and maintaining the cell and

▲ Figure 1.7 **Inherited DNA directs development of an organism.**

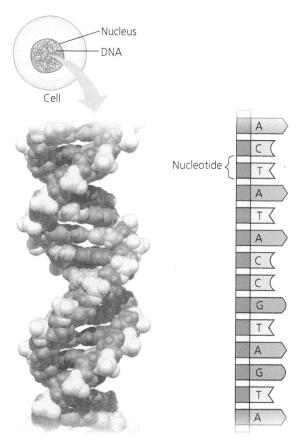

**(a) DNA double helix.** This model shows each atom in a segment of DNA. Made up of two long chains of building blocks called nucleotides, a DNA molecule takes the three-dimensional form of a double helix.

**(b) Single strand of DNA.** These geometric shapes and letters are simple symbols for the nucleotides in a small section of one chain of a DNA molecule. Genetic information is encoded in specific sequences of the four types of nucleotides. (Their names are abbreviated A, T, C, and G.)

▲ Figure 1.8 **DNA: The genetic material.**

carrying out its activities. For instance, a particular bacterial gene may specify a certain enzyme protein required to assemble the cell membrane, while a human gene may denote an antibody protein that helps fight off infection.

Genes control protein production indirectly, using a related molecule called RNA as an intermediary. The sequence of nucleotides along a gene is transcribed into RNA, which is then translated into a specific protein with a unique shape and function. This entire process, by which the information in a gene directs the manufacture of a cellular product, is called **gene expression**.

In translating genes into proteins, all forms of life employ essentially the same genetic code: A particular sequence of nucleotides says the same thing in one organism as it does in another. Differences between organisms reflect differences between their nucleotide sequences rather than between their genetic codes.

Not all RNA molecules in the cell are translated into protein; some RNAs carry out other important tasks. For example, we have known for decades that some types of RNA are actually components of the cellular machinery that manufactures proteins. Recently, scientists have discovered whole new classes of RNA that play other roles in the cell, such as regulating the functioning of protein-coding genes. All these RNAs are specified by genes, and the production of these RNAs is also referred to as gene expression. By carrying the instructions for making proteins and RNAs and by replicating with each cell division, DNA ensures faithful inheritance of genetic information from generation to generation.

### Genomics: Large-Scale Analysis of DNA Sequences

The entire "library" of genetic instructions that an organism inherits is called its **genome**. A typical human cell has two similar sets of chromosomes, and each set has approximately 3 billion nucleotide pairs of DNA. If the one-letter abbreviations for the nucleotides of one strand in a set were written in letters the size of those you are now reading, the genetic text would fill about 800 introductory biology textbooks.

Since the early 1990s, the pace at which researchers can determine the sequence of a genome has accelerated at an almost unbelievable rate, enabled by a revolution in technology. The entire sequence of nucleotides in the human genome is now known, along with the genome sequences of many other organisms, including other animals and numerous plants, fungi, bacteria, and archaea. To make sense of the deluge of data from genome-sequencing projects and the growing catalog of known gene functions, scientists are applying a systems biology approach at

the cellular and molecular levels. Rather than investigating a single gene at a time, researchers study whole sets of genes in one or more species—an approach called **genomics**.

Three important research developments have made the genomic approach possible. One is "high-throughput" technology, tools that can analyze biological materials very rapidly. The second major development is **bioinformatics**, the use of computational tools to store, organize, and analyze the huge volume of data that results from high-throughput methods. The third key development is the formation of interdisciplinary research teams—melting pots of diverse specialists that may include computer scientists, mathematicians, engineers, chemists, physicists, and, of course, biologists from a variety of fields. Researchers in such teams aim to learn how the activities of all the proteins and non-translated RNAs encoded by the DNA are coordinated in cells and in whole organisms.

### Theme: Life Requires the Transfer and Transformation of Energy and Matter

**ENERGY AND MATTER** Moving, growing, reproducing, and the various cellular activities of life are work, and work requires energy. Input of energy, primarily from the sun, and transformation of energy from one form to another make life possible **(Figure 1.9)**. Chlorophyll molecules within plants' leaves convert the energy of sunlight to the chemical energy of food, the sugars produced during photosynthesis (see Figure 1.3). The chemical energy in sugar is then passed along by plants and other photosynthetic organisms (producers) to consumers. Consumers are organisms, such as animals, that feed on producers and other consumers.

▲ Figure 1.9 **Energy flow and chemical cycling.** There is a one-way flow of energy in an ecosystem: During photosynthesis, plants convert energy from sunlight to chemical energy (stored in sugars), which is used by plants and other organisms to do work and is eventually lost from the ecosystem as heat. In contrast, chemicals cycle between organisms and the physical environment.

When an organism uses chemical energy to perform work, some of that energy is converted to thermal energy and is dissipated to the surroundings as heat. As a result, energy flows *through* an ecosystem, usually entering as light and exiting as heat. In contrast, chemical elements are recycled *within* an ecosystem (see Figure 1.9). Chemicals that a plant absorbs from the air or soil may be incorporated into the plant's body, then passed to an animal that eats the plant. Eventually, these chemicals will be returned to the environment by decomposers, such as bacteria and fungi, that break down waste products, organic debris, and the bodies of dead organisms. The chemicals are then available to be taken up by plants again, thereby completing the cycle.

## Theme: Organisms Interact with Other Organisms and the Physical Environment

**INTERACTIONS** Turn again to Figure 1.3, this time focusing on the ecosystem, including the forest and its surroundings. Each organism interacts continuously with physical factors in its environment. The leaves of a tree, for example, absorb light from the sun, take in carbon dioxide from the air, and release oxygen to the air. The environment is also affected by the organisms living there. For example, a plant takes up water and minerals from the soil through its roots, and its roots break up rocks, thereby contributing to the formation of soil. On a global scale, plants and other photosynthetic organisms have generated all the oxygen in the atmosphere.

A tree also interacts with other organisms, such as soil microorganisms associated with its roots, insects that live in the tree, and animals that eat its leaves and fruit. Such interactions between organisms include those that are mutually beneficial **(Figure 1.10)**; those in which one species benefits and the other is harmed (as when a lion kills and eats a zebra); and those in which both species are harmed (as when two plants compete for a soil resource that is in short supply). As we'll see, interactions between organisms not only affect the participants; they also affect how populations evolve over time.

▼ **Figure 1.10 An interaction between species that benefits both participants.** These surgeonfish feed on small organisms living on the sea turtle's skin. The sea turtle benefits from the removal of parasites, and the surgeonfish gain a meal and protection from enemies.

## Evolution, the Core Theme of Biology

Having considered four of the unifying themes that run through this text, let's now turn to biology's core theme—evolution. Evolution makes sense of everything we know about living organisms. Life has been evolving on Earth for billions of years, resulting in a vast diversity of past and present organisms. But along with the diversity are many shared features. For example, while sea horses, jackrabbits, hummingbirds, crocodiles, and giraffes all look very different, their skeletons are basically similar. The scientific explanation for this unity and diversity—as well as for the adaptation of organisms to their environments—is evolution: the idea that the organisms living on Earth today are the modified descendants of common ancestors. In other words, we can explain traits shared by two organisms with the idea that they have descended from a common ancestor, and we can account for differences with the idea that heritable changes have occurred along the way. Many kinds of evidence support the occurrence of evolution and the theory that describes how it takes place. In the next section, we'll consider the fundamental concept of evolution in greater detail.

**CONCEPT CHECK 1.1**

1. For each biological level in Figure 1.3, write a sentence that includes components from the previous (lower) level of biological organization; for example: "A community consists of populations of the various species inhabiting a certain area."
2. Identify the theme or themes exemplified by (a) the sharp spines of a porcupine, (b) the cloning of a plant from a single cell, and (c) a hummingbird using sugar to power its flight.
3. **WHAT IF?** For each theme discussed in this section, give an example not mentioned in the text.

For suggested answers, see Appendix A.

**CONCEPT** 1.2

# The Core Theme: Evolution accounts for the unity and diversity of life

**EVOLUTION** Diversity is a hallmark of life. To date, biologists have identified and named about 1.8 million species of organisms, and estimates of the number of living species range from about 10 million to over 100 million. The remarkably diverse forms of life on this planet arose by evolutionary processes. Before exploring the core theme of evolution further, let's first consider how biologists make sense of the great variety of life-forms on this planet.

## Classifying the Diversity of Life: The Three Domains of Life

Humans have a tendency to group diverse items according to their similarities and relationships to each other. Following this inclination, biologists have long used careful comparisons of form and function to classify life-forms into a hierarchy of increasingly inclusive groups. Consider, for example, the species known as the American black bear (*Ursus americanus*). Black bears belong to the same genus (*Ursus*) as the brown bear species and the polar bear species. Bringing together several similar genera forms a family, which in turn is a component of an order and then a class. For the black bear, this means being grouped with panda bears, raccoons, and others in the family Ursidae, with wolves in the order Carnivora, and with dolphins in the class Mammalia. These animals can be classified into still broader groupings: the phylum Chordata and the kingdom Animalia.

In the last few decades, new methods of assessing species relationships, especially comparisons of DNA sequences, have led to a reevaluation of the larger groupings. Although the reevaluation is ongoing, there is consensus among biologists that the kingdoms of life, whatever their number, can be further grouped into three so-called domains: Bacteria, Archaea, and Eukarya (Figure 1.11).

As you read earlier, the organisms making up two of the three domains—**Bacteria** and **Archaea**—are prokaryotic. All the eukaryotes (organisms with eukaryotic cells) are grouped in domain **Eukarya**. This domain includes three kingdoms of multicellular eukaryotes: Plantae, Fungi, and Animalia. These three kingdoms are distinguished partly by their modes of nutrition. Plants produce their own sugars and other food molecules by photosynthesis; fungi absorb dissolved nutrients from their surroundings; and animals obtain food by eating and digesting other organisms. Animalia is, of course, our own kingdom.

### Unity in the Diversity of Life

As diverse as life is, it also displays remarkable unity. Earlier we mentioned both the similar skeletons of different vertebrate

---

▼ Figure 1.11 **The three domains of life.**

**(a) Domain Bacteria**

**Bacteria** are the most diverse and widespread prokaryotes and are now classified into multiple kingdoms. Each rod-shaped structure in this photo is a bacterial cell.

**(b) Domain Archaea**

Some of the prokaryotes known as **archaea** live in Earth's extreme environments, such as salty lakes and boiling hot springs. Domain Archaea includes multiple kingdoms. Each round structure in this photo is an archaeal cell.

**(c) Domain Eukarya**

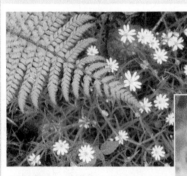

▲ **Kingdom Plantae** consists of terrestrial multicellular eukaryotes (land plants) that carry out photosynthesis, the conversion of light energy to the chemical energy in food.

▶ **Kingdom Fungi** is defined in part by the nutritional mode of its members (such as this mushroom), which absorb nutrients from outside their bodies.

◀ **Kingdom Animalia** consists of multicellular eukaryotes that ingest other organisms.

▶ **Protists** are mostly unicellular eukaryotes and some relatively simple multicellular relatives. Pictured here is an assortment of protists inhabiting pond water. Scientists are currently debating how to classify protists in a way that accurately reflects their evolutionary relationships.

animals and the universal genetic language of DNA (the genetic code). In fact, similarities between organisms are evident at all levels of the biological hierarchy.

How can we account for life's dual nature of unity and diversity? The process of evolution, explained next, illuminates both the similarities and differences in the world of life and introduces another dimension of biology: the passage of time.

## Charles Darwin and the Theory of Natural Selection

The history of life, as documented by fossils and other evidence, is the saga of a changing Earth billions of years old, inhabited by an evolving cast of living forms (**Figure 1.12**). This view of life came into sharp focus in November 1859, when Charles Robert Darwin published one of the most influential books ever written, *On the Origin of Species by Means of Natural Selection* (**Figure 1.13**).

▶ **Figure 1.12 Digging into the past.** Paleontologists carefully excavate the hind leg of a long-necked dinosaur (*Rapetosaurus krausei*) from rocks in Madagascar.

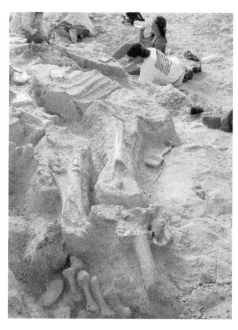

▶ **Figure 1.13 Charles Darwin in 1840.** His revolutionary book *The Origin of Species* was published in 1859.

*The Origin of Species* articulated two main points. The first was that species have arisen from a succession of ancestors that differed from them. Darwin called this process "descent with modification." It was an insightful phrase, as it captured the duality of life's unity and diversity—unity in the kinship among species that descended from common ancestors, diversity in the modifications that evolved as species branched from their common ancestors (**Figure 1.14**). Darwin's second main point was his proposal that "natural selection" is a mechanism for descent with modification.

Darwin developed his theory of natural selection from observations that by themselves were not revolutionary. Others had described the pieces of the puzzle, but Darwin saw how they fit together. He started with the following three observations from nature: First, individuals in a population vary in their traits, many of which seem to be heritable, passed on from parents to offspring. Second, a population can produce far more offspring than can survive to produce offspring of their own. Competition is thus inevitable. Third, species generally are suited to their environments—in other words, they are adapted to their environments. For instance, various birds that feed on hard seeds tend to have especially strong beaks.

Darwin inferred that individuals with inherited traits that are better suited to the local environment are more likely to survive and reproduce than are less well-suited individuals. As a result, over many generations, a higher and higher proportion of individuals in a population will have the advantageous traits. Darwin called this mechanism of evolutionary

▲ **Figure 1.14 Unity and diversity among birds.** These three birds are variations on a common body plan. For example, each has feathers, a beak, and wings, but these features are highly specialized for the birds' diverse lifestyles.

① Population with varied inherited traits

② Elimination of individuals with certain traits

③ Reproduction of survivors

④ Increasing frequency of traits that enhance survival and reproductive success

▲ **Figure 1.15 Natural selection.** This imaginary beetle population has colonized a locale where the soil has been blackened by a recent brush fire. Initially, the population varies extensively in the inherited coloration of the individuals, from very light gray to charcoal. For birds that prey on the beetles, it is easiest to spot the lighter ones.

adaptation **natural selection** because the natural environment "selects" for the propagation of certain traits among naturally occurring variant traits in the population **(Figure 1.15)**.

## The Tree of Life

For another example of unity and diversity, consider the human arm. Your forelimb has the same bones, joints, nerves, and blood vessels found in other limbs as diverse as the foreleg of a horse, the flipper of a whale, and the wing of a bat. Indeed, all mammalian forelimbs are anatomical variations of a common architecture. According to the Darwinian concept of descent with modification, the shared anatomy of mammalian limbs reflects inheritance of the limb structure from a common ancestor—the "prototype" mammal from which all other mammals descended. The diversity of mammalian forelimbs results from modification by natural selection operating over millions of years in different environmental contexts.

Darwin proposed that natural selection, by its cumulative effects over time, could cause an ancestral species to give rise to two or more descendant species. This could occur, for example, if one population of organisms fragmented into several subpopulations isolated in different environments. In these separate arenas of natural selection, a species could gradually radiate into multiple species as the geographically isolated populations adapted over many generations to different environmental conditions.

The "family tree" of six finch species in **Figure 1.16** illustrates a famous example of this process of radiation.

Darwin collected specimens of these birds during his 1835 visit to the remote Galápagos Islands, 900 kilometers (km) off the Pacific coast of South America. The Galápagos finches are believed to have descended from an ancestral finch species that reached the archipelago from South America or the Caribbean. Over time, the Galápagos finches diversified from their ancestor as they adapted to different food sources on the various islands. Years after Darwin collected the finches, researchers began to sort out their evolutionary relationships, first from anatomical and geographic data and more recently using DNA sequence comparisons.

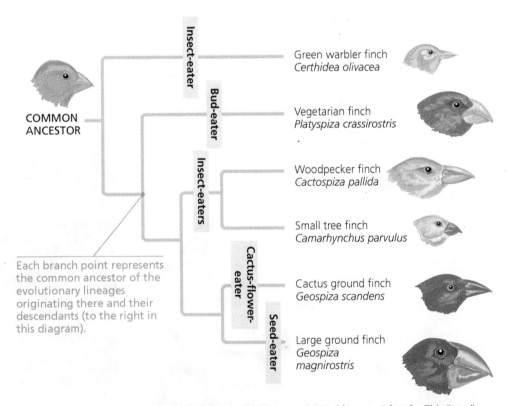

Each branch point represents the common ancestor of the evolutionary lineages originating there and their descendants (to the right in this diagram).

▲ **Figure 1.16 Descent with modification: finches on the Galápagos Islands.** This "tree" diagram illustrates a current model for the evolutionary relationships among some of the finches on the Galápagos. Note the different beaks, which are adapted to food sources on the different islands.

Biologists' diagrams of such evolutionary relationships generally take treelike forms, though the trees are often turned sideways as in Figure 1.16. Tree diagrams make sense: Just as an individual has a genealogy that can be diagrammed as a family tree, each species is one twig of a branching tree of life extending back in time through ancestral species more and more remote. Species that are very similar, such as the Galápagos finches, share a relatively recent common ancestor. But through an ancestor that lived much farther back in time, finches are related to sparrows, hawks, penguins, and all other birds. And birds, mammals, and all other vertebrates share a common ancestor even more ancient. Trace life back far enough, and we reach the early prokaryotes that inhabited Earth 3.5 billion years ago. We can recognize their vestiges in our own cells—in the universal genetic code, for example. Indeed, all of life is connected through its long evolutionary history.

### CONCEPT CHECK 1.2

1. How is a mailing address analogous to biology's hierarchical classification system?
2. Explain why "editing" is an appropriate metaphor for how natural selection acts on a population's heritable variation.
3. **WHAT IF?** Recent evidence indicates that fungi and animals are more closely related to each other than either of these kingdoms is to plants. Draw a simple branching pattern that symbolizes the proposed relationship between these three kingdoms of multicellular eukaryotes.

For suggested answers, see Appendix A.

---

**CONCEPT** 1.3

# Biological inquiry entails forming and testing hypotheses based on observations of nature

The word *science* is derived from a Latin verb meaning "to know." **Science** is a way of knowing—an approach to understanding the natural world. It developed out of our human curiosity about ourselves, other life-forms, our planet, and the universe. Striving to make sense of our experiences seems to be one of our basic urges.

At the heart of science is **inquiry**, a search for information and explanations of natural phenomena. There is no formula for successful scientific inquiry, no single scientific method that researchers must rigidly follow. As in all quests, science includes elements of challenge, adventure, and luck, along with careful planning, reasoning, creativity, patience, and the persistence to overcome setbacks. Such diverse elements of inquiry make science far less structured than most people realize. That said, it is possible to distill certain characteristics that help to distinguish science from other ways of describing and explaining nature.

Scientists use a process of inquiry that includes making observations, forming logical hypotheses, and testing them. The process is necessarily repetitive: In testing a hypothesis, our observations may lead to conclusions that inspire revision of the original hypothesis or formation of a new one, thus leading to further testing. In this way, scientists circle closer and closer to their best estimation of the laws governing nature.

## Making Observations

In the course of their work, scientists describe natural structures and processes as accurately as possible through careful observation and analysis of data. Observation is the use of the senses to gather information either directly or indirectly, such as with the help of microscopes or other tools that extend our senses. Recorded observations are called **data**. Put another way, data are items of information on which scientific inquiry is based.

The term *data* implies numbers to many people. But some data are *qualitative*, often in the form of recorded descriptions. For example, British primate researcher Jane Goodall spent decades recording her observations of chimpanzee behavior during field research in a Tanzanian jungle **(Figure 1.17)**. She also documented her observations with photographs and movies. Along with these qualitative data, Goodall also gathered and recorded volumes of *quantitative* data, a type of information generally expressed as numerical measurements and often organized into tables or graphs.

Collecting and analyzing observations can lead to important conclusions based on a type of logic called **inductive reasoning**. Through induction, we derive generalizations from a large number of specific observations. The generalization "All

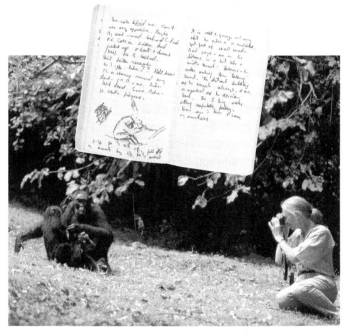

▲ **Figure 1.17 Jane Goodall collecting qualitative data on chimpanzee behavior.** Goodall recorded her observations in field notebooks, often with sketches of the animals' behavior.

organisms are made of cells" was based on two centuries of microscopic observations made by biologists examining cells in diverse biological specimens. Careful observations and data analyses, along with the generalizations reached by induction, are fundamental to our understanding of nature.

## Forming and Testing Hypotheses

Our innate curiosity often stimulates us to pose questions about the natural basis for the phenomena we observe in the world. What *caused* the diversification of finches on the Galápagos Islands? What *explains* the variation in coat color among mice of a single species, such as the beach and inland mice pictured in Figures 1.1 and 1.2? In science, answering such questions usually involves proposing and testing hypothetical explanations—that is, hypotheses.

In science, a **hypothesis** is a tentative answer to a well-framed question; it is an explanation on trial. The hypothesis is usually a rational accounting for a set of observations, based on the available data and guided by inductive reasoning. A scientific hypothesis leads to predictions that can be tested by making additional observations or by performing experiments.

We all use hypotheses in solving everyday problems. Let's say, for example, that your flashlight fails during a camp-out. That's an observation. The question is obvious: Why doesn't the flashlight work? Two reasonable hypotheses based on your experience are that (1) the batteries in the flashlight are dead or (2) the bulb is burnt out. Each of these alternative hypotheses leads to predictions you can test with experiments. For example, the dead-battery hypothesis predicts that replacing the batteries will fix the problem. Figuring things out in this way by trial and error is a hypothesis-based approach.

### Deductive Reasoning

A type of logic called deduction is also built into the use of hypotheses in science. While induction entails reasoning from a set of specific observations to reach a general conclusion, **deductive reasoning** involves logic that flows in the opposite direction, from the general to the specific. From general premises, we extrapolate to the specific results we should expect if the premises are true. In the scientific process, deductions usually take the form of predictions of results that will be found if a particular hypothesis (premise) is correct. We then test the hypothesis by carrying out experiments or observations to see whether or not the results are as predicted. This deductive testing takes the form of "*If . . . then*" logic. In the case of the flashlight example: *If* the dead-battery hypothesis is correct, *then* the flashlight should work when you replace the batteries with new ones.

The flashlight inquiry demonstrates two other key points about the use of hypotheses in science. First, the initial observations may give rise to multiple hypotheses. The ideal is to design experiments to test all these candidate explanations. For instance, another of the many possible alternative hypotheses to explain our dead flashlight is that *both* the batteries *and*

the bulb are bad, and you could design an experiment to test this. Second, we can never *prove* that a hypothesis is true. The dead-battery hypothesis stands out as the most likely explanation, but testing supports that hypothesis *not* by proving that it is correct, but rather by not eliminating it through falsification (proving it false). Replacing the batteries might have fixed the flashlight, but perhaps the endpiece had simply not been screwed on tight enough in the first place. No amount of experimental testing can prove a hypothesis beyond a shadow of doubt, because it is impossible to test *all* alternative hypotheses. A hypothesis gains credibility by surviving multiple attempts to falsify it while alternative hypotheses are eliminated (falsified) by testing.

### Questions That Can and Cannot Be Addressed by Science

Scientific inquiry is a powerful way to learn about nature, but there are limitations to the kinds of questions it can answer. A scientific hypothesis must be falsifiable; there must be some observation or experiment that could reveal if such an idea is actually *not* true. The hypothesis that dead batteries are the sole cause of the broken flashlight could be falsified by replacing the old batteries with new ones and finding that the flashlight still doesn't work.

Not all hypotheses meet the criteria of science: You wouldn't be able to falsify the hypothesis that invisible campground ghosts are fooling with your flashlight! Because science requires natural explanations for natural phenomena, it can neither support nor falsify hypotheses that angels, ghosts, or spirits, whether benevolent or evil, cause storms, rainbows, illnesses, and cures. Such supernatural explanations are simply outside the bounds of science, as are religious matters, which are issues of personal faith.

### A Case Study in Scientific Inquiry: Investigating Coat Coloration in Mouse Populations

Now that we have highlighted the key features of scientific inquiry—making observations and forming and testing hypotheses—you should be able to recognize these features in a case study of actual scientific research.

The story begins with a set of observations and inductive generalizations. Color patterns of animals vary widely in nature, sometimes even between members of the same species. What accounts for such variation? As you may recall, the two mice depicted at the beginning of this chapter are members of the same species (*Peromyscus polionotus*), but they reside in very different habitats. Beach mice live along the ocean on white sand dunes, whereas "inland" mice live on darker, loamy soil away from the shore (**Figure 1.18**). Even a brief glance at the photographs in Figure 1.18 reveals a striking match of mouse coloration to environment. The natural predators of these mice, including hawks, owls, foxes, and coyotes, are all visual hunters

► **Figure 1.18 Different coloration in two beach and inland populations of *Peromyscus polionotus*.**

◄ Beach mice living on sparsely vegetated sand dunes along the coast have light tan, dappled coats that allow them to blend into their surroundings (camouflage).

► Members of the same species living about 30 km inland are darker in color, camouflaging them against the dark ground of their habitat.

(they use their eyes to look for prey). It was logical, therefore, for Francis Bertody Sumner, a naturalist studying populations of these mice in the 1920s, to hypothesize that their color patterns had evolved as adaptations that camouflage the mice in their native environments, protecting them from predation.

As obvious as the camouflage hypothesis may seem, it still required testing. In 2010, biologist Hopi Hoekstra of Harvard University and a group of her students headed to Florida to test the prediction that mice with coloration that did not match their habitat would be preyed on more heavily than the native, well-matched mice. **Figure 1.19** summarizes this field experiment, introducing a format we will use throughout the book to walk through other examples of biological inquiry.

The researchers built hundreds of silicone models of mice and spray-painted them to resemble either beach or inland mice, so that the models differed only in their color patterns. The researchers placed equal numbers of these model mice randomly in both habitats and left them overnight. The mouse models resembling the native

---

**▼ Figure 1.19  Inquiry**

## Does camouflage affect predation rates on two populations of mice?

**Experiment**  Hopi Hoekstra and colleagues tested the hypothesis that coloration of beach and inland popluations of oldfield mice (*Peromyscus polionotus*) provides camouflage that protects them from predation in their respective habitats. The researchers made mouse models with either light or dark color patterns that matched those of the beach and inland mice, then placed models with both patterns in each of the habitats. The next morning, they counted damaged or missing mice.

**Results**  The researchers calculated the proportion of attacked mice that were camouflaged or non-camouflaged for each habitat. In both cases, the mice whose pattern did not match their surroundings suffered a much higher predation rate than did the camouflaged mice.

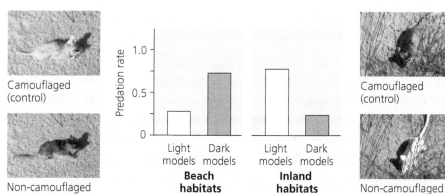

**Conclusion**  The results do not falsify the researchers' prediction that mouse models with camouflage coloration would be preyed on less often than non-camouflaged mouse models. Thus, the experiment supports the camouflage hypothesis.

**Source**  S. N. Vignieri, J. G. Larson, and H. E. Hoekstra, The selective advantage of crypsis in mice, *Evolution* 64:2153–2158 (2010).

**WHAT IF?**   If you found a habitat with reddish, iron-rich soil, what would you predict with respect to the coat color of resident mice? What prediction would you make about the predation rate on beach mice and inland mice if you placed them in this new habitat?

mice in the habitat were the *control* group (for instance, light-colored beach mice in the dune habitat), while the mice with the non-native coloration were the *experimental* group (for example, the darker mainland mice in the dunes). The following morning, the team counted and recorded signs of predation events, which ranged from bites and gouge marks on some models to the outright disappearance of others. Judging by the shape of the predator's bites and the tracks surrounding the experimental sites, the predators appeared to be split fairly evenly between mammals (such as foxes and coyotes) and birds (such as owls, herons, and hawks).

For each environment, the researchers then calculated the fraction of predation events that targeted camouflaged mice. The results were clear-cut: Camouflaged mice showed much lower predation rates than those lacking camouflage in both the dune habitat (where light mice were less vulnerable) and the mainland habitat (where dark mice were less vulnerable). The data thus fit the key prediction of the camouflage hypothesis.

### Experimental Controls

The mouse camouflage experiment described in Figure 1.19 is an example of a **controlled experiment**, one that is designed to compare an experimental group (the non-camouflaged mice, in this case) with a control group (the camouflaged mice normally resident in that area). Ideally, the experimental and control groups differ only in the one factor the experiment is designed to test—in our example, the effect of mouse coloration on the behavior of predators. Without the control group, the researchers would not have been able to rule out other factors as causes of the more frequent attacks on the non-camouflaged mice—such as different numbers of predators or different temperatures in the different test areas. The clever experimental design left coloration as the only factor that could account for the low predation rate on the camouflaged mice placed in their normal environment. It was not the absolute number of attacks on the non-camouflaged mice that counted, but the difference between that number and the number of attacks on the camouflaged mice.

A common misconception is that the term *controlled experiment* means that scientists control the experimental environment to keep everything constant except the one variable being tested. But that's impossible in field research and not realistic even in highly regulated laboratory environments. Researchers usually "control" unwanted variables not by *eliminating* them by regulating the environment, but by *canceling out* their effects using control groups.

### Theories in Science

"It's just a theory!" Our everyday use of the term *theory* often implies an untested speculation. But the term *theory* has a different meaning in science. What is a scientific theory, and how is it different from a hypothesis or from mere speculation?

First, a scientific **theory** is much broader in scope than a hypothesis. *This* is a hypothesis: "A match of the coloration of a mouse's coat to its environment is an adaptation that protects mice from predators." But *this* is a theory: "Evolutionary adaptations arise by natural selection." Darwin's theory of natural selection accounts for an enormous diversity of adaptations, of which coat color in mice is one example.

Second, a theory is general enough to spin off many new, testable hypotheses. For example, the theory of natural selection motivated two researchers at Princeton University, Peter and Rosemary Grant, to test the specific hypothesis that the beaks of Galápagos finches evolve in response to changes in the types of available food.

And third, compared to any one hypothesis, a theory is generally supported by a much greater body of evidence. Those theories that become widely adopted in science (such as the theory of natural selection) explain a great diversity of observations and are supported by a vast accumulation of evidence.

In spite of the body of evidence supporting a widely accepted theory, scientists must sometimes modify or even reject theories when new research methods produce results that don't fit. For example, biologists once lumped bacteria and archaea together as a kingdom of prokaryotes. When new methods for comparing cells and molecules could be used to test such relationships, the evidence led scientists to reject the theory that bacteria and archaea are members of the same kingdom. If there is "truth" in science, it is conditional, based on the weight of available evidence.

### Science as a Social Process: Community and Diversity

The great scientist Sir Isaac Newton once said: "To explain all nature is too difficult a task for any one man or even for any one age. 'Tis much better to do a little with certainty, and leave the rest for others that come after you. . . ." Anyone who becomes a scientist, driven by curiosity about nature, is sure to benefit from the rich storehouse of discoveries by others who have come before. In fact, while movies and cartoons sometimes portray scientists as loners working in isolated labs, science is an intensely social activity. Most scientists work in teams, which often include graduate and undergraduate students **(Figure 1.20)**.

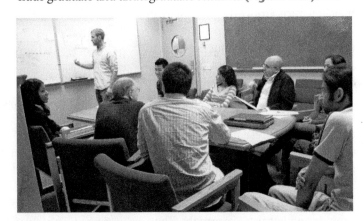

▲ **Figure 1.20  Science as a social process.** Lab members help each other interpret data, troubleshoot experiments, and plan future research.

Science is rarely perfectly objective, but it is continuously vetted through the expectation that observations and experiments be repeatable and hypotheses be falsifiable. Scientists working in the same research field often check one another's claims by attempting to confirm observations or repeat experiments. In fact, Hopi Hoekstra's experiment benefited from the work of another researcher, D. W. Kaufman, 40 years earlier. You can study the design of Kaufman's experiment and interpret the results in the **Scientific Skills Exercise**.

If experimental results cannot be repeated by scientific colleagues, this failure may reflect some underlying weakness in the original claim, which will then have to be revised. In this sense, science polices itself. Integrity and adherence to high professional standards in reporting results are central to the scientific endeavor. After all, the validity of experimental data is key to designing further lines of inquiry.

Biologists may approach questions from different angles. Some biologists focus on ecosystems, while others study natural phenomena at the level of organisms or cells. This text is divided into units that focus on biology at different levels. Yet any given problem can be addressed from many perspectives, which in fact complement each other. For example, Hoekstra's work uncovered at least one genetic mutation that underlies the differences between beach and inland mouse coloration. Her lab includes biologists with different specialties, allowing discoveries on topics that range from evolutionary adaptations to their molecular basis in DNA.

The research community is part of society at large. The relationship of science to society becomes clearer when we add technology to the picture. The goal of **technology** is to *apply* scientific knowledge for some specific purpose. Because scientists put new technology to work in their research, science and technology are interdependent.

In centuries past, many major technological innovations originated along trade routes, where a rich mix of different cultures ignited new ideas. For example, the printing press was invented by Johannes Gutenberg around 1440, living in what is now Germany. This invention relied on several innovations from China,

## Scientific Skills Exercise

# *Interpreting a Pair of Bar Graphs*

**How Much Does Camouflage Affect Predation on Mice by Owls with and without Moonlight?** Nearly half a century ago, D. W. Kaufman investigated the effect of prey camouflage on predation. Kaufman tested the hypothesis that the amount of contrast between the coat color of a mouse and the color of its surroundings would affect the rate of nighttime predation by owls. He also hypothesized that the color contrast would be affected by the amount of moonlight. In this exercise, you will analyze data from his owl-mouse predation studies.

**How the Experiment Was Done** Pairs of mice (*Peromyscus polionotus*) with different coat colors, one light brown and one dark brown, were released simultaneously into an enclosure that contained a hungry owl. The researcher recorded the color of the mouse that was first caught by the owl. If the owl did not catch either mouse within 15 minutes, the test was recorded as a zero. The release trials were repeated multiple times in enclosures with either a dark-colored soil surface or a light-colored soil surface. The presence or absence of moonlight during each assay was recorded.

**Data from the Experiment**

**Interpret the Data**

1. First, make sure you understand how the graphs are set up. Graph A shows data from the light-colored soil enclosure and Graph B from the dark-colored enclosure, but in all other respects the graphs are the same. (a) There is more than one independent variable in these graphs. What are the independent variables, the variables that were tested by the researcher? Which axis of the graphs has the independent variables? (b) What is the dependent variable, the response to the variables being tested? Which axis of the graphs has the dependent variable?

2. (a) How many dark brown mice were caught in the light-colored soil enclosure on a moonlit night? (b) How many dark brown mice were caught in the dark-colored soil enclosure on a moonlit night? (c) On a moonlit night, would a dark brown mouse be more likely to escape predation by owls on dark- or light-colored soil? Explain your answer.

3. (a) Is a dark brown mouse on dark-colored soil more likely to escape predation under a full moon or with no moon? (b) A light brown mouse on light-colored soil? Explain.

4. (a) Under which conditions would a dark brown mouse be most likely to escape predation at night? (b) A light brown mouse?

5. (a) What combination of independent variables led to the highest predation level in enclosures with light-colored soil? (b) What combination of independent variables led to the highest predation level in enclosures with dark-colored soil? (c) What relationship, if any, do you see in your answers to parts (a) and (b)?

6. What conditions are most deadly for both colors of mice?

7. Combining the data shown in both graphs, estimate the total number of mice caught in moonlight versus no-moonlight conditions. Which condition is optimal for predation by the owl on mice? Explain your answer.

**Data from** D. W. Kaufman, Adaptive coloration in *Peromyscus polionotus*: Experimental selection by owls, *Journal of Mammalogy* 55:271–283 (1974).

(MB) A version of this Scientific Skills Exercise can be assigned in MasteringBiology.

including paper and ink, and from Iraq, where technology was developed for the mass production of paper. Like technology, science stands to gain much from embracing a diversity of backgrounds and viewpoints among its practitioners.

The scientific community reflects the customs and behaviors of society at large. It is therefore not surprising that until recently, women and certain minorities have faced huge obstacles in their pursuit to become professional scientists. Over the past 50 years, changing attitudes about career choices have increased the proportion of women in biology and several other sciences, and now women constitute roughly half of undergraduate biology majors and biology Ph.D. students. The pace has been slow at higher levels in the profession, however, and women and many racial and ethnic groups are still significantly underrepresented in many branches of science. This lack of diversity hampers the progress of science. The more voices that are heard at the table, the more robust and productive the scientific conversation will be. The authors of this textbook welcome all students to the community of biologists, wishing you the joys and satisfactions of this exciting field of science.

**CONCEPT CHECK 1.3**

1. Contrast inductive reasoning with deductive reasoning.
2. What variable was tested in Hoekstra's mouse experiment?
3. Why is natural selection called a theory rather than a hypothesis?
4. How does science differ from technology?

For suggested answers, see Appendix A.

# 1 Chapter Review

## SUMMARY OF KEY CONCEPTS

### CONCEPT 1.1

**Studying the diverse forms of life reveals common themes (pp. 2–7)**

**Theme: Organization**

- The hierarchy of life unfolds as follows: biosphere > ecosystem > community > population > organism > organ system > organ > tissue > cell > organelle > molecule > atom. With each step up, new properties emerge (**emergent properties**) as a result of interactions among components at the lower levels.
- Structure and function are correlated at all levels of biological organization. The cell is the lowest level of organization that can perform all activities required for life. Cells are either prokaryotic or eukaryotic. **Eukaryotic cells** have a DNA-containing nucleus and other membrane-enclosed organelles. **Prokaryotic cells** lack such organelles.

**Theme: Information**

- Genetic information is encoded in the nucleotide sequences of **DNA**. It is DNA that transmits heritable information from parents to offspring. DNA sequences (called **genes**) program a cell's protein production by being transcribed into RNA and then translated into specific proteins, a process called **gene expression**. Gene expression also produces RNAs that are not translated into protein but serve other important functions.

**Theme: Energy and Matter**

- Energy flows through an ecosystem. All organisms must perform work, which requires energy. Producers convert energy from sunlight to chemical energy, some of which is then passed on to consumers (the rest is lost from the ecosystem as heat). Chemicals cycle between organisms and the environment.

**Theme: Interactions**

- Organisms interact continuously with physical factors. Plants take up nutrients from the soil and chemicals from the air and use energy from the sun. Interactions among plants, animals, and other organisms affect the participants in varying ways.

**Core Theme: Evolution**

- Evolution accounts for the unity and diversity of life and also for the match of organisms to their environments.

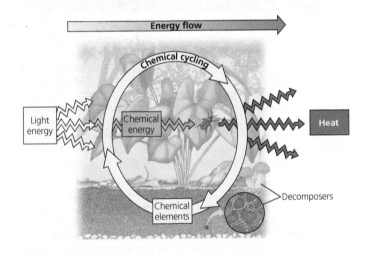

**?** *Thinking about the muscles and nerves in your hand, how does the activity of text messaging reflect the five unifying themes of biology described in this chapter?*

### CONCEPT 1.2

**The Core Theme: Evolution accounts for the unity and diversity of life (pp. 7–11)**

- Biologists classify species according to a system of broader and broader groups. Domain **Bacteria** and domain **Archaea** consist of prokaryotes. Domain **Eukarya**, the eukaryotes, includes various groups of protists as well as plants, fungi, and animals. As diverse as life is, there is also evidence of remarkable unity, which is revealed in the similarities between different kinds of organisms.
- Darwin proposed **natural selection** as the mechanism for evolutionary adaptation of populations to their environments. Each species is one twig of a branching tree of life extending back in time through ancestral species more and more remote. All of life is connected through its long evolutionary history.

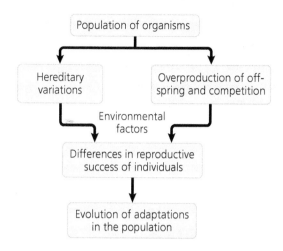

Population of organisms

→ Hereditary variations

→ Overproduction of off-spring and competition

Environmental factors

Differences in reproductive success of individuals

Evolution of adaptations in the population

**?** *How could natural selection have led to the evolution of adaptations such as camouflaging coat color in beach mice?*

**CONCEPT** 1.3

## Biological inquiry entails forming and testing hypotheses based on observations of nature (pp. 11–16)

- In scientific **inquiry**, scientists make observations (collect **data**) and use **inductive reasoning** to draw a general conclusion, which can be developed into a testable **hypothesis**. **Deductive reasoning** makes predictions that can be used to test hypotheses. Scientific hypotheses must be falsifiable.
- **Controlled experiments**, such as the study investigating coat color in mouse populations, are designed to demonstrate the effect of one variable by testing control groups and experimental groups that differ in only that one variable.
- A scientific **theory** is broad in scope, generates new hypotheses, and is supported by a large body of evidence.
- Scientists must be able to repeat each other's results, so integrity is key. Biologists approach questions at different levels; their approaches complement each other. **Technology** is a method or device that applies scientific knowledge for some specific purpose that affects society as well as for scientific research. Diversity among scientists promotes progress in science.

**?** *What are the roles of inductive and deductive reasoning in scientific inquiry?*

## TEST YOUR UNDERSTANDING

### Level 1: Knowledge/Comprehension

1. All the organisms on your campus make up
   a. an ecosystem.
   b. a community.
   c. a population.
   d. an experimental group.
   e. a domain.

2. Which of the following best demonstrates the unity among all organisms?
   a. identical DNA sequences
   b. descent with modification
   c. the structure and function of DNA
   d. natural selection
   e. emergent properties

3. A controlled experiment is one that
   a. proceeds slowly enough that a scientist can make careful records of the results.
   b. tests experimental and control groups in parallel.
   c. is repeated many times to make sure the results are accurate.
   d. keeps all variables constant.
   e. is supervised by an experienced scientist.

4. Which of the following statements best distinguishes hypotheses from theories in science?
   a. Theories are hypotheses that have been proved.
   b. Hypotheses are guesses; theories are correct answers.
   c. Hypotheses usually are relatively narrow in scope; theories have broad explanatory power.
   d. Hypotheses and theories are essentially the same thing.
   e. Theories are proved true; hypotheses are often falsified.

### Level 2: Application/Analysis

5. Which of the following is an example of qualitative data?
   a. The temperature decreased from 20°C to 15°C.
   b. The plant's height is 25 centimeters (cm).
   c. The fish swam in a zigzag motion.
   d. The six pairs of robins hatched an average of three chicks.
   e. The contents of the stomach are mixed every 20 seconds.

6. Which of the following best describes the logic of scientific inquiry?
   a. If I generate a testable hypothesis, tests and observations will support it.
   b. If my prediction is correct, it will lead to a testable hypothesis.
   c. If my observations are accurate, they will support my hypothesis.
   d. If my hypothesis is correct, I can expect certain test results.
   e. If my experiments are set up right, they will lead to a testable hypothesis.

7. **DRAW IT** With rough sketches, draw a biological hierarchy similar to the one in Figure 1.3 but using a coral reef as the ecosystem, a fish as the organism, its stomach as the organ, and DNA as the molecule. Include all levels in the hierarchy.

### Level 3: Synthesis/Evaluation

8. **SCIENTIFIC INQUIRY**
   Based on the results of the mouse coloration case study, suggest another hypothesis to extend the investigation.

9. **FOCUS ON EVOLUTION**
   In a short essay (100–150 words), discuss Darwin's view of how natural selection resulted in both unity and diversity of life on Earth. Include in your discussion some of his evidence. (A suggested grading rubric and tips for writing good essays can be found in the Study Area of MasteringBiology.)

10. **FOCUS ON INFORMATION**
    A typical prokaryotic cell has about 3,000 genes in its DNA, while a human cell has about 20,500 genes. About 1,000 of these genes are present in both types of cells. Based on your understanding of evolution, explain how such different organisms could have this same subset of genes. What sorts of functions might these shared genes have?

*For selected answers, see Appendix A.*

## MasteringBiology®

**Students** Go to **MasteringBiology** for assignments, the eText, and the Study Area with practice tests, animations, and activities.

**Instructors** Go to **MasteringBiology** for automatically graded tutorials and questions that you can assign to your students, plus Instructor Resources.

# Carbon and the Molecular Diversity of Life

*See all tables.*
*And the online question.*

OVERVIEW

## Carbon Compounds and Life

Water is the universal medium for life on Earth, but water aside, living organisms are made up of chemicals based mostly on the element carbon. Of all chemical elements, carbon is unparalleled in its ability to form molecules that are large, complex, and varied. Hydrogen (H), oxygen (O), nitrogen (N), sulfur (S), and phosphorus (P) are other common ingredients of these compounds, but it is the element carbon (C) that accounts for the enormous variety of biological molecules. For historical reasons, a compound containing carbon is said to be an **organic compound**; furthermore, almost all organic compounds associated with life contain hydrogen atoms in addition to carbon atoms. Different species of organisms and even different individuals within a species are distinguished by variations in their large organic compounds.

Given the rich complexity of life on Earth, it may surprise you to learn that the critically important large molecules of all living things—from bacteria to elephants—fall into just four main classes: carbohydrates, lipids, proteins, and nucleic acids. On the molecular scale, members of three of these classes—carbohydrates, proteins, and nucleic acids—are huge and are therefore called **macromolecules**. For example, a protein may consist of thousands of atoms that form a molecular colossus with a mass well over 100,000 daltons. Considering the size and complexity of macromolecules, it is noteworthy that biochemists have determined the detailed structure of so many of them. The scientist in the foreground of **Figure 2.1** is using 3-D glasses to help her visualize the structure of the protein displayed on her screen. The structures of macromolecules can provide important information about their functions.

In this chapter, we'll first investigate the properties of small organic molecules and then go on to discuss the larger biological molecules. After considering how macromolecules are built, we'll examine the structure and function of all four classes of large biological molecules. The architecture of a large biological molecule helps explain how that molecule works. Like small molecules, large biological molecules exhibit unique emergent properties arising from the orderly arrangement of their atoms.

▼ **Figure 2.2 The shapes of three simple organic molecules.**

| Name and Comment | Molecular Formula | Structural Formula | Ball-and-Stick Model (molecular shape in pink) | Space-Filling Model |
|---|---|---|---|---|
| **(a) Methane.** When a carbon atom has four single bonds to other atoms, the molecule is tetrahedral. | $CH_4$ | H — C — H with H above and H below | | |
| **(b) Ethane.** A molecule may have more than one tetrahedral group of single-bonded atoms. (Ethane consists of two such groups.) | $C_2H_6$ | H — C — C — H with H's above and below | | |
| **(c) Ethene (ethylene).** When two carbon atoms are joined by a double bond, all atoms attached to those carbons are in the same plane; the molecule is flat. | $C_2H_4$ | C = C with H's attached | | |

**CONCEPT 2.1**

# Carbon atoms can form diverse molecules by bonding to four other atoms

The key to an atom's chemical characteristics is its electron configuration. This configuration determines the kinds and number of bonds an atom will form with other atoms, and it is the source of carbon's versatility.

## The Formation of Bonds with Carbon

Carbon has 6 electrons, with 2 in the first electron shell and 4 in the second shell; thus, it has 4 valence electrons in a shell that holds 8 electrons. A carbon atom usually completes its valence shell by sharing its 4 electrons with other atoms so that 8 electrons are present. Each pair of shared electrons constitutes a covalent bond. In organic molecules, carbon usually forms single or double covalent bonds. Each carbon atom acts as an intersection point from which a molecule can branch off in as many as four directions. This ability is one facet of carbon's versatility that makes large, complex molecules possible.

When a carbon atom forms four single covalent bonds, the bonds angle toward the corners of an imaginary tetrahedron. The bond angles in methane ($CH_4$) are 109.5° **(Figure 2.2a)**, and they are roughly the same in any group of atoms where carbon has four single bonds. For example, ethane ($C_2H_6$) is

shaped like two overlapping tetrahedrons **(Figure 2.2b)**. In molecules with more carbons, every grouping of a carbon bonded to four other atoms has a tetrahedral shape. But when two carbon atoms are joined by a double bond, as in ethene ($C_2H_4$), the atoms joined to those carbons are in the same plane as the carbons **(Figure 2.2c)**. We find it convenient to write molecules as structural formulas, as if the molecules being represented are two-dimensional, but keep in mind that molecules are three-dimensional and that the shape of a molecule often determines its function.

The electron configuration of carbon gives it covalent compatibility with many different elements. **Figure 2.3** shows electron distribution diagrams for carbon and its most frequent partners—hydrogen, oxygen, and nitrogen. These are the four major atomic components of organic molecules. The number of unpaired electrons in the valence shell of an atom is generally equal to the atom's **valence**, the number of covalent bonds it can form. Let's consider how valence and

| Hydrogen (valence = 1) | Oxygen (valence = 2) | Nitrogen (valence = 3) | Carbon (valence = 4) |
|---|---|---|---|
| H | O | N | C |

▲ **Figure 2.3 Valences of the major elements of organic molecules.** Valence is the number of covalent bonds an atom can form. It is generally equal to the number of electrons required to complete the valence (outermost) shell (see Figure 2.6). Note that carbon can form four bonds.

the rules of covalent bonding apply to carbon atoms with partners other than hydrogen. We'll first look at the simple example of carbon dioxide.

In the carbon dioxide molecule ($CO_2$), a single carbon atom is joined to two atoms of oxygen by double covalent bonds. The structural formula for $CO_2$ is shown here:

$$O=C=O$$

Each line in a structural formula represents a pair of shared electrons. Thus, the two double bonds in $CO_2$ have the same number of shared electrons as four single bonds. The arrangement completes the valence shells of all atoms in the molecule. Because $CO_2$ is a very simple molecule and lacks hydrogen, it is often considered inorganic, even though it contains carbon. Whether we call $CO_2$ organic or inorganic, however, it is clearly important to the living world as the source of carbon for all organic molecules in organisms.

Carbon dioxide is a molecule with only one carbon atom. But as Figure 2.2 shows, a carbon atom can also use one or more valence electrons to form covalent bonds to other carbon atoms, linking the atoms into chains of seemingly infinite variety.

## Molecular Diversity Arising from Variation in Carbon Skeletons

Carbon chains form the skeletons of most organic molecules. The skeletons vary in length and may be straight, branched, or arranged in closed rings **(Figure 2.4)**. Some carbon skeletons have double bonds, which vary in number and location. Such variation in carbon skeletons is one important source of the molecular complexity and diversity that characterize living matter. In addition, atoms of other elements can be bonded to the skeletons at available sites.

All of the molecules shown in Figures 2.2 and 2.4 are **hydrocarbons**, organic molecules consisting of only carbon and hydrogen. Atoms of hydrogen are attached to the carbon skeleton wherever electrons are available for covalent bonding. Hydrocarbons are the major components of petroleum, which is called a fossil fuel because it consists of the partially decomposed remains of organisms that lived millions of years ago. Although hydrocarbons are not prevalent in most living organisms, many of a cell's organic molecules have regions consisting of only carbon and hydrogen. For example, the molecules known as fats have long hydrocarbon tails attached to a nonhydrocarbon component (as you will see in Figure 2.12). Neither petroleum nor fat dissolves in water; both are hydrophobic compounds because the great majority of their bonds are relatively nonpolar carbon-to-hydrogen linkages. Another characteristic of hydrocarbons is that they can undergo reactions that release a relatively large amount of energy. The gasoline that fuels a car consists of hydrocarbons, and the hydrocarbon tails of fats serve as stored fuel for animals.

▼ **Figure 2.4 Four ways that carbon skeletons can vary.**

**(a) Length**

Ethane  Propane

Carbon skeletons vary in length.

**(b) Branching**

Butane  2-Methylpropane (commonly called isobutane)

Skeletons may be unbranched or branched.

**(c) Double bond position**

1-Butene  2-Butene

The skeleton may have double bonds, which can vary in location.

**(d) Presence of rings**

Cyclohexane  Benzene

Some carbon skeletons are arranged in rings. In the abbreviated structural formula for each compound (at the right), each corner represents a carbon and its attached hydrogens.

## The Chemical Groups Most Important to Life

The distinctive properties of an organic molecule depend not only on the arrangement of its carbon skeleton but also on the chemical groups attached to that skeleton **(Figure 2.5)**. We can think of hydrocarbons, the simplest organic molecules, as the underlying framework for more complex organic molecules. A number of chemical groups can replace one or more of the hydrogens bonded to the carbon skeleton of the hydrocarbon. The number and arrangement of chemical groups help give each organic molecule its unique properties.

▼ Figure 2.5 **Some biologically important chemical groups.**

| Chemical Group | Compound Name | Examples |
|---|---|---|
| **Hydroxyl group** (—OH)<br>(may be written HO—) | **Alcohol**<br>(The specific name usually ends in -ol.) | **Ethanol**, the alcohol present in alcoholic beverages |
| **Carbonyl group** ($\diagup$C$=$O) | **Ketone** if the carbonyl group is within a carbon skeleton<br>**Aldehyde** if the carbonyl group is at the end of a carbon skeleton | **Acetone**, the simplest ketone    **Propanal**, an aldehyde |
| **Carboxyl group** (—COOH) | **Carboxylic acid,** or organic acid | **Acetic acid**, which gives vinegar its sour taste    Ionized form of —COOH (carboxylate ion), found in cells |
| **Amino group** (—NH$_2$) | **Amine** | **Glycine**, an amino acid (note its carboxyl group)    Ionized form of —NH$_2$, found in cells |
| **Sulfhydryl group** (—SH)<br>(may be written HS—) | **Thiol** | **Cysteine**, a sulfur-containing amino acid |
| **Phosphate group** (—OPO$_3^{2-}$) | **Organic phosphate** | **Glycerol phosphate**, which takes part in many important chemical reactions in cells |
| **Methyl group** (—CH$_3$) | **Methylated compound** | **5-Methyl cytosine**, a component of DNA that has been modified by addition of a methyl group |

In some cases, chemical groups contribute to function primarily by affecting the molecule's shape. This is true for the steroid sex hormones estradiol (a type of estrogen) and testosterone, which differ in attached chemical groups.

**Estradiol**

**Testosterone**

In other cases, the chemical groups affect molecular function by being directly involved in chemical reactions; these important chemical groups are known as **functional groups**. Each functional group participates in chemical reactions in a characteristic way.

The seven chemical groups most important in biological processes are the hydroxyl, carbonyl, carboxyl, amino, sulfhydryl, phosphate, and methyl groups (see Figure 2.5). The first six groups can act as functional groups; also, except for the sulfhydryl, they are hydrophilic and thus increase the solubility of organic compounds in water. The last group, the methyl group, is not reactive, but instead often serves as a recognizable tag on biological molecules. Before reading further, study Figure 2.5 to familiarize yourself with these biologically important chemical groups. Notice the ionized forms of the amino group and carboxyl group; these are the forms of these groups at normal cellular pH.

## ATP: An Important Source of Energy for Cellular Processes

The "phosphate group" row in Figure 2.5 shows a simple example of an organic phosphate molecule. A more complicated organic phosphate, **adenosine triphosphate**, or **ATP**, is worth mentioning here because its function in the cell is so important. ATP consists of an organic molecule called adenosine attached to a string of three phosphate groups:

Where three phosphates are present in series, as in ATP, one phosphate may be split off as a result of a reaction with water. This inorganic phosphate ion, $HOPO_3^{2-}$, is often abbreviated $\text{\textcircled{P}}_i$ in this book, and a phosphate group in an organic molecule is often written as $\text{\textcircled{P}}$. Having lost one phosphate, ATP becomes adenosine *di*phosphate, or ADP. Although ATP is sometimes said to store energy, it is more accurate to think of it as storing the potential to react with

water. This reaction releases energy that can be used by the cell. (You will learn about this in more detail in Chapter 5.)

**CONCEPT CHECK 2.1**

1. How are gasoline and fat chemically similar?
2. What does the term *amino acid* signify about the structure of such a molecule?
3. **WHAT IF?** Suppose you had an organic molecule such as cysteine (see Figure 2.5, sulfhydryl group example), and you chemically removed the —$NH_2$ group and replaced it with —COOH. How would this change the chemical properties of the molecule?

For suggested answers, see Appendix A.

### CONCEPT 2.2

# Macromolecules are polymers, built from monomers

The macromolecules in three of the four classes of life's organic compounds—carbohydrates, proteins, and nucleic acids—are chain-like molecules called polymers (from the Greek *polys*, many, and *meros*, part). A **polymer** is a long molecule consisting of many similar or identical building blocks linked by covalent bonds, much as a train consists of a chain of cars. The repeating units that serve as the building blocks of a polymer are smaller molecules called **monomers** (from the Greek *monos*, single). Some of the molecules that serve as monomers also have other functions of their own.

## The Synthesis and Breakdown of Polymers

Although each class of polymer is made up of a different type of monomer, the chemical mechanisms by which cells make and break down polymers are basically the same in all cases. In cells, these processes are facilitated by **enzymes**, specialized macromolecules (usually proteins) that speed up chemical reactions. Monomers are connected by a reaction in which two molecules are covalently bonded to each other, with the loss of a water molecule; this is known as a **dehydration reaction** (**Figure 2.6a**). When a bond forms between two monomers, each monomer contributes part of the water molecule that is released during the reaction: One monomer provides a hydroxyl group (—OH), while the other provides a hydrogen (—H). This reaction is repeated as monomers are added to the chain one by one, making a polymer.

Polymers are disassembled to monomers by **hydrolysis**, a process that is essentially the reverse of the dehydration reaction (**Figure 2.6b**). Hydrolysis means breakage using water

▼ **Figure 2.6 The synthesis and breakdown of polymers.**

**(a) Dehydration reaction: synthesizing a polymer**

Short polymer

Unlinked monomer

Dehydration removes a water molecule, forming a new bond.

$H_2O$

Longer polymer

**(b) Hydrolysis: breaking down a polymer**

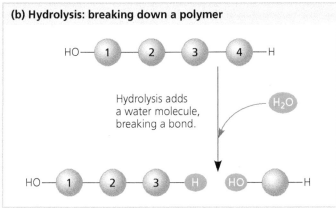

Hydrolysis adds a water molecule, breaking a bond.

$H_2O$

What is the basis for such diversity in life's polymers? These molecules are constructed from only 40 to 50 common monomers and some others that occur rarely. Building a huge variety of polymers from such a limited number of monomers is analogous to constructing hundreds of thousands of words from only 26 letters of the alphabet. The key is arrangement— the particular linear sequence that the units follow. However, this analogy falls far short of describing the great diversity of macromolecules because most biological polymers have many more monomers than the number of letters in the longest word. Proteins, for example, are built from 20 kinds of amino acids arranged in chains that are typically hundreds of amino acids long. The molecular logic of life is simple but elegant: Small molecules common to all organisms are ordered into unique macromolecules.

Despite this immense diversity, molecular structure and function can still be grouped roughly by class. Let's examine each of the four major classes of large biological molecules. For each class, the large molecules have emergent properties not found in their individual building blocks.

**CONCEPT CHECK 2.2**

1. How many molecules of water are needed to completely hydrolyze a polymer that is ten monomers long?
2. **WHAT IF?** Suppose you eat a serving of fish. What reactions must occur for the amino acid monomers in the protein of the fish to be converted to new proteins in your body?

For suggested answers, see Appendix A.

(from the Greek *hydro*, water, and *lysis*, break). The bond between the monomers is broken by the addition of a water molecule, with a hydrogen from the water attaching to one monomer and the hydroxyl group attaching to the adjacent monomer. An example of hydrolysis working within our bodies is the process of digestion. The bulk of the organic material in our food is in the form of polymers that are much too large to enter our cells. Within the digestive tract, various enzymes attack the polymers, speeding up hydrolysis. The released monomers are then absorbed into the bloodstream for distribution to all body cells. Those cells can then use dehydration reactions to assemble the monomers into new, different polymers that can perform specific functions required by the cell.

## The Diversity of Polymers

Each cell has thousands of different macromolecules; the collection varies from one type of cell to another even in the same organism. The inherent differences between, for example, human siblings reflect small variations in polymers, particularly DNA and proteins. Molecular differences between unrelated individuals are more extensive and those between species greater still. The diversity of macromolecules in the living world is vast, and the possible variety is effectively limitless.

# Carbohydrates serve as fuel and building material

**Carbohydrates** include both sugars and polymers of sugars. The simplest carbohydrates are the monosaccharides, or simple sugars; these are the monomers from which more complex carbohydrates are constructed. Disaccharides are double sugars, consisting of two monosaccharides joined by a covalent bond. Carbohydrates also include macromolecules called polysaccharides, polymers composed of many sugar building blocks joined together by dehydration reactions.

## Sugars

**Monosaccharides** (from the Greek *monos*, single, and *sacchar*, sugar) generally have molecular formulas that are some multiple of the unit $CH_2O$. Glucose ($C_6H_{12}O_6$), the most common monosaccharide, is of central importance in the chemistry of life. In the structure of glucose, we can see the trademarks of a sugar: The molecule has a carbonyl group

▼ **Figure 2.7 Examples of monosaccharides.** Sugars vary in the location of their carbonyl groups (orange) and the length of their carbon skeletons.

| Triose: 3-carbon sugar ($C_3H_6O_3$) | Pentose: 5-carbon sugar ($C_5H_{10}O_5$) | Hexoses: 6-carbon sugars ($C_6H_{12}O_6$) |
|---|---|---|
|  |  | |
| **Glyceraldehyde**<br>An initial breakdown<br>product of glucose in cells | **Ribose**<br>A component of RNA | **Glucose**   **Fructose**<br>Energy sources for organisms |

(C=O) and multiple hydroxyl groups (—OH) **(Figure 2.7)**. The carbonyl group can be on the end of the linear sugar molecule, as in glucose, or attached to an interior carbon, as in fructose. (Thus, sugars are either aldehydes or ketones; see Figure 2.5.) The carbon skeleton of a sugar molecule ranges from three to seven carbons long. Glucose, fructose, and other sugars that have six carbons are called hexoses. Trioses (three-carbon sugars) and pentoses (five-carbon sugars) are also common. Note that most names for sugars end in *-ose*.

Although it is convenient to draw glucose with a linear carbon skeleton, this representation is not completely accurate. In aqueous solutions, glucose molecules, as well as most other five- and six-carbon sugars, form rings **(Figure 2.8)**.

Monosaccharides, particularly glucose, are major nutrients for cells. In the process known as cellular respiration, cells extract energy from glucose in a series of reactions that break down its molecules. Also, the carbon skeletons of sugars serve as raw material for the synthesis of other types of small organic molecules, such as amino acids. Sugar molecules that are not immediately used in these ways are generally incorporated as monomers into disaccharides or polysaccharides.

A **disaccharide** consists of two monosaccharides joined by a **glycosidic linkage**, a covalent bond formed between two monosaccharides by a dehydration reaction. The most prevalent disaccharide is sucrose, which is table sugar. Its two monomers are glucose and fructose **(Figure 2.9)**. Plants generally transport carbohydrates from leaves to roots and other nonphotosynthetic organs in the form of sucrose. Other disaccharides are lactose, the sugar present in milk, and maltose, an ingredient used in making beer.

**(a) Linear and ring forms.** Chemical equilibrium between the linear and ring structures greatly favors the formation of rings. The carbons of the sugar are numbered 1 to 6, as shown. To form the glucose ring, carbon 1 bonds to the oxygen attached to carbon 5.

**(b) Abbreviated ring structure.** Each corner represents a carbon. The ring's thicker edge indicates that you are looking at the ring edge-on; the components attached to the ring lie above or below the plane of the ring.

▲ **Figure 2.8 Linear and ring forms of glucose.**

**DRAW IT** *Start with the linear form of fructose (see Figure 2.7) and draw the formation of the fructose ring in two steps. First, number the carbons starting at the top of the linear structure. Then attach carbon 5 via its oxygen to carbon 2. Compare the number of carbons in the fructose and glucose rings.*

▶ **Figure 2.9 Disaccharide synthesis.** Sucrose is a disaccharide formed from glucose and fructose by a dehydration reaction. Notice that fructose, though a hexose like glucose, forms a five-sided ring.

**DRAW IT** *Referring to Figure 2.8, number the carbons in each sugar in this figure. Show how the numbering is consistent with the name of the glycosidic linkage.*

**Glucose**          **Fructose**          **Sucrose**

## Polysaccharides

**Polysaccharides** are macromolecules, polymers with a few hundred to a few thousand monosaccharides joined by glycosidic linkages. Some polysaccharides serve as storage material, hydrolyzed as needed to provide sugar for cells. Other polysaccharides serve as building material for structures that protect the cell or the whole organism. The structure and function of a polysaccharide are determined by its sugar monomers and by the positions of its glycosidic linkages.

### Storage Polysaccharides

Both plants and animals store sugars for later use in the form of storage polysaccharides **(Figure 2.10)**. Plants store **starch**, a polymer of glucose monomers, as granules within cells.

Synthesizing starch enables the plant to stockpile surplus glucose. Because glucose is a major cellular fuel, starch represents stored energy. The sugar can later be withdrawn from this carbohydrate "bank" by hydrolysis, which breaks the bonds between the glucose monomers. Most animals, including humans, also have enzymes that can hydrolyze plant starch, making glucose available as a nutrient for cells. Potato tubers and grains—the fruits of wheat, maize (corn), rice, and other grasses—are the major sources of starch in the human diet.

Most of the glucose monomers in starch are joined by 1–4 linkages (number 1 carbon to number 4 carbon). The simplest form of starch, amylose, is unbranched, as shown in Figure 2.10. Amylopectin, a more complex starch, is a branched polymer with 1–6 linkages at the branch points.

Starch granules in a potato tuber cell

Glycogen granules in muscle tissue

Cellulose microfibrils in a plant cell wall

Cellulose molecules

**Starch** (amylose)

Glucose monomer

**Glycogen**

**Cellulose**

Hydrogen bonds between —OH groups (not shown) attached to carbons 3 and 6

▲ **Figure 2.10 Polysaccharides of plants and animals.** The polysaccharides shown are composed entirely of glucose monomers, represented here by hexagons. In starch and glycogen, the polymer chains tend to form helices in unbranched regions because of the angle of the 1–4 linkage between the glucose monomers. Cellulose, with a different kind of 1–4 linkage, is always unbranched.

Animals store a polysaccharide called **glycogen**, a polymer of glucose that is like amylopectin but more extensively branched. Humans and other vertebrates store glycogen mainly in liver and muscle cells. Hydrolysis of glycogen in these cells releases glucose when the demand for sugar increases. This stored fuel cannot sustain an animal for long, however. In humans, for example, glycogen stores are depleted in about a day unless they are replenished by eating.

### Structural Polysaccharides

Organisms build strong materials from structural polysaccharides. The polysaccharide called **cellulose** is a major component of the tough walls that enclose plant cells (see Figure 2.10). On a global scale, plants produce almost $10^{14}$ kg (100 billion tons) of cellulose per year; it is the most abundant organic compound on Earth. Like starch and glycogen, cellulose is a polymer of glucose with 1–4 glycosidic linkages, but the linkages in cellulose are different. The difference is based on the fact that there are actually two slightly different ring structures for glucose (**Figure 2.11a**). When glucose forms a ring, the hydroxyl group attached to the number 1 carbon is positioned either below or above the plane of the ring. These two ring forms for glucose are called alpha ($\alpha$) and beta ($\beta$), respectively. In starch, all the glucose monomers are in the $\alpha$ configuration (**Figure 2.11b**), the arrangement we saw in Figure 2.8. In contrast, the glucose monomers of cellulose are all in the $\beta$ configuration, making every glucose monomer "upside down" with respect to its neighbors (**Figure 2.11c**).

The differing glycosidic linkages in starch and cellulose give the two molecules distinct three-dimensional shapes. Whereas starch (and glycogen) molecules are largely helical, a cellulose molecule is straight. Cellulose is never branched, and some hydroxyl groups on its glucose monomers are free to hydrogen-bond with the hydroxyls of other cellulose molecules lying parallel to it. In plant cell walls, parallel cellulose molecules held together in this way are grouped into units called microfibrils (see Figure 2.10). These cable-like microfibrils are a strong building material for plants and an important substance for humans because cellulose is the major component of paper and the only constituent of cotton.

Enzymes that digest starch by hydrolyzing its $\alpha$ linkages are unable to hydrolyze the $\beta$ linkages of cellulose because of the distinctly different shapes of these two molecules. In fact, few organisms possess enzymes that can digest cellulose. Animals, including humans, do not; the cellulose in our food passes through the digestive tract and is eliminated with the feces. Along the way, the cellulose abrades the wall of the digestive tract and stimulates the lining to secrete mucus, which aids in the smooth passage of food through the tract. Thus, although cellulose is not a nutrient for humans, it is an important part of a healthful diet. Most fresh fruits, vegetables, and whole grains are rich in cellulose. On food packages, "insoluble fiber" refers mainly to cellulose.

Some microorganisms can digest cellulose, breaking it down into glucose monomers. A cow harbors cellulose-digesting prokaryotes and protists in its stomach. These microbes hydrolyze the cellulose of hay and grass and convert the glucose to other compounds that nourish the cow. Similarly, a termite, which is unable to digest cellulose by itself, has prokaryotes or protists living in its gut that can make a meal of wood. Some fungi can also digest cellulose, thereby helping recycle chemical elements within Earth's ecosystems.

**(a) $\alpha$ and $\beta$ glucose ring structures.** These two interconvertible forms of glucose differ in the placement of the hydroxyl group (highlighted in blue) attached to the number 1 carbon.

$\alpha$ Glucose

$\beta$ Glucose

**(b) Starch: 1–4 linkage of $\alpha$ glucose monomers.** All monomers are in the same orientation. Compare the positions of the —OH groups highlighted in yellow with those in cellulose (c).

**(c) Cellulose: 1–4 linkage of $\beta$ glucose monomers.** In cellulose, every $\beta$ glucose monomer is upside down with respect to its neighbors.

▲ **Figure 2.11 Monomer structures of starch and cellulose.**

Another important structural polysaccharide is **chitin**, the carbohydrate used by arthropods (insects, spiders, crustaceans, and related animals) to build their exoskeletons—hard cases that surround the soft parts of these animals. Chitin is also found in many fungi, which use this polysaccharide as the building material for their cell walls. Chitin is similar to cellulose except that the glucose monomer of chitin has a nitrogen-containing appendage.

### CONCEPT CHECK 2.3

1. Write the formula for a monosaccharide that has three carbons.
2. A dehydration reaction joins two glucose molecules to form maltose. The formula for glucose is $C_6H_{12}O_6$. What is the formula for maltose?
3. **WHAT IF?** After a cow is given antibiotics to treat an infection, a vet gives the animal a drink of "gut culture" containing various prokaryotes. Why is this necessary?

For suggested answers, see Appendix A.

## CONCEPT 2.4

# Lipids are a diverse group of hydrophobic molecules

Lipids are the one class of large biological molecules that does not include true polymers, and they are generally not big enough to be considered macromolecules. The compounds called **lipids** are grouped together because they share one important trait: They mix poorly, if at all, with water. The hydrophobic behavior of lipids is based on their molecular structure. Although they may have some polar bonds associated with oxygen, lipids consist mostly of hydrocarbon regions. Lipids are varied in form and function. They include waxes and certain pigments, but we will focus on the most biologically important types of lipids: fats, phospholipids, and steroids.

## Fats

Although fats are not polymers, they are large molecules assembled from smaller molecules by dehydration reactions. A **fat** is constructed from two kinds of smaller molecules: glycerol and fatty acids **(Figure 2.12a)**. Glycerol is an alcohol; each of its three carbons bears a hydroxyl group. A **fatty acid** has a long carbon skeleton, usually 16 or 18 carbon atoms in length. The carbon at one end of the skeleton is part of a carboxyl group, the functional group that gives these molecules the name fatty *acid*. The rest of the skeleton consists of a hydrocarbon chain. The relatively nonpolar C—H bonds in the hydrocarbon chains of fatty acids are the reason fats are hydrophobic. Fats separate from water because the water molecules hydrogen-bond to one another and exclude the fats. This is the reason that vegetable oil (a liquid fat) separates from the aqueous vinegar solution in a bottle of salad dressing.

**Glycerol**

**(a) One of three dehydration reactions in the synthesis of a fat**

Ester linkage

**(b) Fat molecule (triacylglycerol)**

▲ **Figure 2.12 The synthesis and structure of a fat, or triacylglycerol.** The molecular building blocks of a fat are one molecule of glycerol and three molecules of fatty acids. **(a)** One water molecule is removed for each fatty acid joined to the glycerol. **(b)** A fat molecule with three fatty acid units, two of them identical. The carbons of the fatty acids are arranged zigzag to suggest the actual orientations of the four single bonds extending from each carbon (see Figure 2.2a).

In making a fat, three fatty acid molecules are each joined to glycerol by an ester linkage, a bond between a hydroxyl group and a carboxyl group. The resulting fat, also called a **triacylglycerol**, thus consists of three fatty acids linked to one glycerol molecule. (Still another name for a fat is *triglyceride*, a word often found in the list of ingredients on packaged foods.) The fatty acids in a fat can be the same, or they can be of two or three different kinds, as in **Figure 2.12b**.

The terms *saturated fats* and *unsaturated fats* are commonly used in the context of nutrition. These terms refer to the structure of the hydrocarbon chains of the fatty acids. If there are no double bonds between carbon atoms composing a chain, then as many hydrogen atoms as possible are bonded to the carbon skeleton. Such a structure is said to be *saturated* with hydrogen, and the resulting fatty acid is called a **saturated fatty acid**. An **unsaturated fatty acid** has one or more double bonds, with one fewer hydrogen atom on each double-bonded carbon. Nearly every double bond in naturally occurring fatty acids has an orientation that creates a kink in the hydrocarbon chain.

A fat made from saturated fatty acids is called a saturated fat. Most animal fats are saturated: The hydrocarbon chains of their fatty acids—the "tails" of the fat molecules—lack double bonds, and their flexibility allows the fat molecules to pack together tightly. Saturated animal fats—such as lard and butter—are solid at room temperature (Figure 2.13a). In contrast, the fats of plants and fishes are generally unsaturated, meaning that they are built of one or more types of unsaturated fatty acids. Usually liquid at room temperature, plant and fish fats are referred to as oils—olive oil and cod

liver oil are examples (Figure 2.13b). The kinks where the double bonds are located prevent the molecules from packing together closely enough to solidify at room temperature. The phrase "hydrogenated vegetable oils" on food labels means that unsaturated fats have been converted to saturated fats by adding hydrogen.

The major function of fats is energy storage. The hydrocarbon chains of fats are similar to gasoline molecules and just as rich in energy. A gram of fat stores more than twice as much energy as a gram of a polysaccharide, such as starch. Because plants are relatively immobile, they can function with bulky energy storage in the form of starch. (Vegetable oils are generally obtained from seeds, where more compact storage is an asset to the plant.) Animals, however, must carry their energy stores with them, so there is an advantage to having a more compact reservoir of fuel—fat.

## Phospholipids

Cells could not exist without another type of lipid—**phospholipid**. Phospholipids are essential for cells because they are major constituents of cell membranes. Their structure provides a classic example of how form fits function at the molecular level. As shown in **Figure 2.14**, a phospholipid is similar to a fat molecule but has only two fatty acids attached to glycerol rather than three. The third hydroxyl group of glycerol is joined to a phosphate group, which has a negative electrical charge in the cell. Additional small molecules, which are usually charged or polar, can be linked to the phosphate group to form a variety of phospholipids.

The two ends of a phospholipid exhibit different behavior toward water. The hydrocarbon tails are hydrophobic and are excluded from water. However, the phosphate group and its attachments form a hydrophilic head that has an affinity for water. When phospholipids are added to water, they self-assemble into double-layered structures called "bilayers," shielding their hydrophobic portions from water (see Figure 2.14d).

At the surface of a cell, phospholipids are arranged in a similar bilayer. The hydrophilic heads of the molecules are on the outside of the bilayer, in contact with the aqueous solutions inside and outside of the cell. The hydrophobic tails point toward the interior of the bilayer, away from the water. The phospholipid bilayer forms a boundary between the cell and its external environment; the existence of cells depends on phospholipids.

## Steroids

**Steroids** are lipids characterized by a carbon skeleton consisting of four fused rings. Different steroids are distinguished by the particular chemical groups attached to this ensemble of rings. Shown in **Figure 2.15**, **cholesterol** is a crucial steroid in animals. It is a common component of animal cell membranes and is also the precursor from which other steroids are synthesized, such as the vertebrate sex hormones estrogen and testosterone (see Concept 2.1).

▼ Figure 2.13 **Saturated and unsaturated fats and fatty acids.**

**(a) Saturated fat**

At room temperature, the molecules of a saturated fat, such as the fat in butter, are packed closely together, forming a solid.

Structural formula of a saturated fat molecule (Each hydrocarbon chain is represented as a zigzag line, where each bend represents a carbon atom and hydrogens are not shown.)

Space-filling model of stearic acid, a saturated fatty acid (red = oxygen, black = carbon, gray = hydrogen)

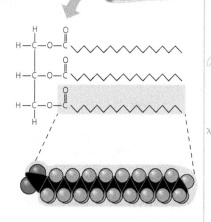

**(b) Unsaturated fat**

At room temperature, the molecules of an unsaturated fat such as olive oil cannot pack together closely enough to solidify because of the kinks in some of their fatty acid hydrocarbon chains.

Structural formula of an unsaturated fat molecule

Space-filling model of oleic acid, an unsaturated fatty acid

Double bond causes bending.

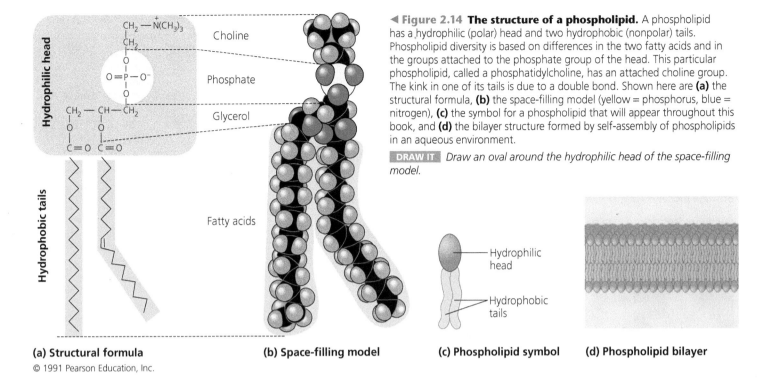

◄ **Figure 2.14** **The structure of a phospholipid.** A phospholipid has a hydrophilic (polar) head and two hydrophobic (nonpolar) tails. Phospholipid diversity is based on differences in the two fatty acids and in the groups attached to the phosphate group of the head. This particular phospholipid, called a phosphatidylcholine, has an attached choline group. The kink in one of its tails is due to a double bond. Shown here are **(a)** the structural formula, **(b)** the space-filling model (yellow = phosphorus, blue = nitrogen), **(c)** the symbol for a phospholipid that will appear throughout this book, and **(d)** the bilayer structure formed by self-assembly of phospholipids in an aqueous environment.

**DRAW IT** *Draw an oval around the hydrophilic head of the space-filling model.*

**(a) Structural formula**   **(b) Space-filling model**   **(c) Phospholipid symbol**   **(d) Phospholipid bilayer**

© 1991 Pearson Education, Inc.

▲ **Figure 2.15 Cholesterol, a steroid.** Cholesterol is the molecule from which other steroids, including the sex hormones, are synthesized. Steroids vary in the chemical groups attached to their four interconnected rings (shown in gold).

In vertebrates, cholesterol is synthesized in the liver and is also obtained from the diet. A high level of cholesterol in the blood may contribute to atherosclerosis. In fact, saturated fats exert their negative impact on health by affecting cholesterol levels.

**CONCEPT CHECK 2.4**

1. Compare the structure of a fat (triacylglycerol) with that of a phospholipid.
2. Why are human sex hormones considered lipids?
3. **WHAT IF?** Suppose a membrane surrounded an oil droplet, as it does in the cells of plant seeds. Describe and explain the form it might take.

For suggested answers, see Appendix A.

**CONCEPT** 2.5 *polymer of aminoacid monomer*

# Proteins include a diversity of structures, resulting in a wide range of functions

Nearly every dynamic function of a living being depends on proteins. In fact, the importance of proteins is underscored by their name, which comes from the Greek word *proteios*, meaning "first," or "primary." Proteins account for more than 50% of the dry mass of most cells, and they are instrumental in almost everything organisms do. Some proteins speed up chemical reactions, while others play a role in defense, storage, transport, cellular communication, movement, or structural support. **Figure 2.16** shows examples of proteins with these functions (which you'll learn more about in later chapters).

Life would not be possible without enzymes, most of which are proteins. Enzymatic proteins regulate metabolism by acting as **catalysts**, chemical agents that selectively speed up chemical reactions without being consumed by the reaction. Because an enzyme can perform its function over and over again, these molecules can be thought of as workhorses that keep cells running by carrying out the processes of life.

A human has tens of thousands of different proteins, each with a specific structure and function; proteins, in fact, are the most structurally sophisticated molecules known. Consistent with their diverse functions, they vary extensively in structure, each type of protein having a unique three-dimensional shape.

**Enzymatic proteins**

**Function:** Selective acceleration of chemical reactions
**Example:** Digestive enzymes catalyze the hydrolysis of bonds in food molecules.

**Storage proteins**

**Function:** Storage of amino acids
**Examples:** Casein, the protein of milk, is the major source of amino acids for baby mammals. Plants have storage proteins in their seeds. Ovalbumin is the protein of egg white, used as an amino acid source for the developing embryo.

**Hormonal proteins**

**Function:** Coordination of an organism's activities
**Example:** Insulin, a hormone secreted by the pancreas, causes other tissues to take up glucose, thus regulating blood sugar concentration.

**Contractile and motor proteins**

**Function:** Movement
**Examples:** Motor proteins are responsible for the undulations of cilia and flagella. Actin and myosin proteins are responsible for the contraction of muscles.

**Defensive proteins**

**Function:** Protection against disease
**Example:** Antibodies inactivate and help destroy viruses and bacteria.

**Transport proteins**

**Function:** Transport of substances
**Examples:** Hemoglobin, the iron-containing protein of vertebrate blood, transports oxygen from the lungs to other parts of the body. Other proteins transport molecules across cell membranes.

**Receptor proteins**

**Function:** Response of cell to chemical stimuli
**Example:** Receptors built into the membrane of a nerve cell detect signaling molecules released by other nerve cells.

**Structural proteins**

**Function:** Support
**Examples:** Keratin is the protein of hair, horns, feathers, and other skin appendages. Insects and spiders use silk fibers to make their cocoons and webs, respectively. Collagen and elastin proteins provide a fibrous framework in animal connective tissues.

Proteins are made up of polymers of amino acids called **polypeptides**. A **protein** is a biologically functional molecule that consists of one or more polypeptides folded and coiled into a specific three-dimensional structure.

## Amino Acids

Polypeptides are all unbranched polymers constructed from the same set of 20 amino acids, and all amino acids share a common structure. An **amino acid** is an organic molecule with both an amino group and a carboxyl group. The figure at the right shows the general formula for an amino acid. At the center of the amino acid is a carbon atom called the *alpha (α) carbon*. Its four different partners are an amino group, a carboxyl group, a hydrogen atom, and a variable group symbolized by R. The R group, also called the side chain, differs with each amino acid (**Figure 2.17**).

# ▼ Figure 2.17 The 20 amino acids of proteins.

The amino acids are grouped here according to the properties of their side chains (R groups) and shown in their prevailing ionic forms at pH 7.2, the pH within a cell. The three-letter and one-letter abbreviations for the amino acids are in parentheses.

## Nonpolar side chains; hydrophobic

## Polar side chains; hydrophilic

## Electrically charged side chains; hydrophilic

The 20 amino acids in Figure 2.17 are the ones cells use to build their proteins. Here the amino groups and carboxyl groups are all depicted in ionized form, the way they usually exist at the pH found in a cell. The side chain (R group) may be as simple as a hydrogen atom, as in the amino acid glycine, or it may be a carbon skeleton with various functional groups attached, as in glutamine.

The physical and chemical properties of the side chain determine the unique characteristics of a particular amino acid, thus affecting its functional role in a polypeptide. In Figure 2.17, the amino acids are grouped according to the properties of their side chains. One group consists of amino acids with nonpolar side chains, which are hydrophobic. Another group consists of amino acids with polar side chains, which are hydrophilic. Acidic amino acids are those with side chains that are generally negative in charge owing to the presence of a carboxyl group, which is usually dissociated (ionized) at cellular pH. Basic amino acids have amino groups in their side chains that are generally positive in charge. (Notice that *all* amino acids have carboxyl groups and amino groups; the terms *acidic* and *basic* in this context refer only to groups on the side chains.) Because they are charged, acidic and basic side chains are also hydrophilic.

## Polypeptides

Now that we have examined amino acids, let's see how they are linked to form polymers (**Figure 2.18**). When two amino acids are positioned so that the carboxyl group of one is adjacent to the amino group of the other, they can become joined by a dehydration reaction, with the removal of a water molecule. The resulting covalent bond is called a **peptide bond**. Repeated over and over, this process yields a polypeptide, a polymer of many amino acids linked by peptide bonds.

The repeating sequence of atoms highlighted in purple in Figure 2.18 is called the polypeptide backbone. Extending from this backbone are the different side chains (R groups) of the amino acids. Polypeptides range in length from a few amino acids to a thousand or more. Each specific polypeptide has a unique linear sequence of amino acids. Note that one end of the polypeptide chain has a free amino group, while the opposite end has a free carboxyl group. Thus, a polypeptide of any length has a single amino end (N-terminus) and a single carboxyl end (C-terminus). In a polypeptide of any significant size, the side chains far outnumber the terminal groups, so the chemical nature of the molecule as a whole is determined by the kind and sequence of the side chains. The immense variety of polypeptides in nature illustrates an important concept introduced earlier—that cells can make many different polymers by linking a limited set of monomers into diverse sequences.

▲ **Figure 2.18 Making a polypeptide chain.** Peptide bonds are formed by dehydration reactions, which link the carboxyl group of one amino acid to the amino group of the next. The peptide bonds are formed one at a time, starting with the amino acid at the amino end (N-terminus). The polypeptide has a repetitive backbone (purple) from which the amino acid side chains (yellow and green) extend.

**DRAW IT** *At the top of the figure, circle and label the carboxyl and amino groups that will form the new peptide bond.*

## Protein Structure and Function

The specific activities of proteins result from their intricate three-dimensional architecture, the simplest level of which is the sequence of their amino acids. What can the amino acid sequence of a polypeptide tell us about the three-dimensional structure (commonly referred to simply as "the structure") of the protein and its function? The term *polypeptide* is not synonymous with the term *protein*. Even for a protein consisting of a single polypeptide, the relationship is somewhat analogous to that between a long strand of yarn and a sweater of particular size and shape that can be knit from the yarn. A functional protein is not *just* a polypeptide chain, but one or more polypeptides precisely twisted, folded, and coiled into a molecule of unique shape (**Figure 2.19**). And it is the amino acid sequence of each polypeptide that determines what three-dimensional structure the protein will have under normal cellular conditions.

(a) A **ribbon model** shows how the single polypeptide chain folds and coils to form the functional protein. (The yellow lines represent disulfide bridges that stabilize the protein's shape.)

(b) A **space-filling model** shows more clearly the globular shape seen in many proteins, as well as the specific three-dimensional structure unique to lysozyme.

▲ **Figure 2.19 Structure of a protein, the enzyme lysozyme.** Present in our sweat, tears, and saliva, lysozyme is an enzyme that helps prevent infection by binding to and catalyzing the destruction of specific molecules on the surface of many kinds of bacteria. The groove is the part of the protein that recognizes and binds to the target molecules on bacterial walls.

When a cell synthesizes a polypeptide, the chain generally folds spontaneously, assuming the functional structure for that protein. This folding is driven and reinforced by the formation of various bonds between parts of the chain, which in turn depend on the sequence of amino acids. Many proteins are roughly spherical (*globular proteins*), while others are shaped like long fibers (*fibrous proteins*). Even within these broad categories, countless variations exist.

A protein's specific structure determines how it works. In almost every case, the function of a protein depends on its ability to recognize and bind to some other molecule. In an especially striking example of the marriage of form and function, **Figure 2.20** shows the exact match of shape between an antibody (a protein in the body) and the particular foreign substance on a flu virus that the antibody binds to and marks for destruction.

Another example of molecules with matching shapes is that of endorphin molecules—or morphine molecules—that fit into receptor molecules on the surface of brain cells in humans, producing euphoria and relieving pain. Morphine, heroin, and other opiate drugs are able to mimic endorphins because they all share a similar shape with endorphins and can thus fit into and bind to endorphin receptors in the brain. This fit is very specific, something like a lock and key. The endorphin receptor, like other receptor molecules, is a protein. The function of a protein—for instance, the ability of a receptor protein to bind to a particular pain-relieving signaling molecule—is an emergent property resulting from exquisite molecular order.

Antibody protein          Protein from flu virus

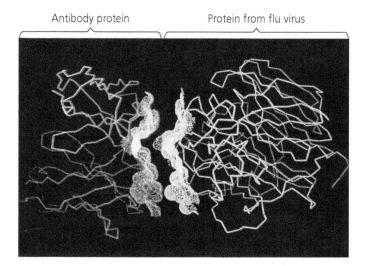

▲ **Figure 2.20 An antibody binding to a protein from a flu virus.** A technique called X-ray crystallography was used to generate a computer model of an antibody protein (blue and orange, left) bound to a flu virus protein (green and yellow, right). Computer software was then used to back the images away from each other, revealing the exact complementarity of shape between the two protein surfaces.

### Four Levels of Protein Structure

In spite of their great diversity, all proteins share three superimposed levels of structure, known as primary, secondary, and tertiary structure. A fourth level, quaternary structure, arises when a protein consists of two or more polypeptide chains. **Figure 2.21** describes these four levels of protein structure. Be sure to study this figure thoroughly before going on to the next section.

## Primary Structure

### Linear chain of amino acids

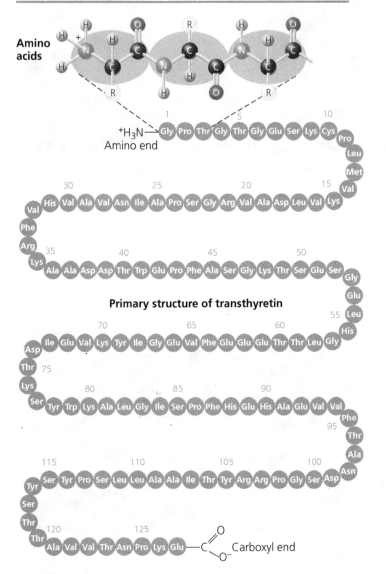

Primary structure of transthyretin

## Secondary Structure

### Regions stabilized by hydrogen bonds between atoms of the polypeptide backbone

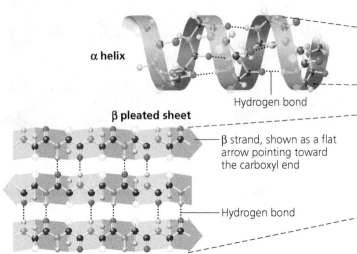

The **primary structure** of a protein is its sequence of amino acids. As an example, let's consider transthyretin, a globular blood protein that transports vitamin A and one of the thyroid hormones throughout the body. Transthyretin is made up of four identical polypeptide chains, each composed of 127 amino acids. Shown here is one of these chains unraveled for a closer look at its primary structure. Each of the 127 positions along the chain is occupied by one of the 20 amino acids, indicated here by its three-letter abbreviation.

The primary structure is like the order of letters in a very long word. If left to chance, there would be $20^{127}$ different ways of making a polypeptide chain 127 amino acids long. However, the precise primary structure of a protein is determined not by the random linking of amino acids, but by inherited genetic information. The primary structure in turn dictates secondary and tertiary structure, due to the chemical nature of the backbone and the side chains (R groups) of the amino acids along the polypeptide.

Most proteins have segments of their polypeptide chains repeatedly coiled or folded in patterns that contribute to the protein's overall shape. These coils and folds, collectively referred to as **secondary structure**, are the result of hydrogen bonds between the repeating constituents of the polypeptide backbone (not the amino acid side chains). Within the backbone, the oxygen atoms have a partial negative charge, and the hydrogen atoms attached to the nitrogens have a partial positive charge; therefore, hydrogen bonds can form between these atoms. Individually, these hydrogen bonds are weak, but because they are repeated many times over a relatively long region of the polypeptide chain, they can support a particular shape for that part of the protein.

One such secondary structure is the **α helix**, a delicate coil held together by hydrogen bonding between every fourth amino acid, as shown above. Although each transthyretin polypeptide has only one α helix region (see tertiary structure), other globular proteins have multiple stretches of α helix separated by nonhelical regions (see hemoglobin). Some fibrous proteins, such as α-keratin, the structural protein of hair, have the α helix formation over most of their length.

The other main type of secondary structure is the **β pleated sheet**. As shown above, in this structure two or more segments of the polypeptide chain lying side by side (called β strands) are connected by hydrogen bonds between parts of the two parallel segments of polypeptide backbone. β pleated sheets make up the core of many globular proteins, as is the case for transthyretin (see tertiary structure), and dominate some fibrous proteins, including the silk protein of a spider's web. The teamwork of so many hydrogen bonds makes each spider silk fiber stronger than a steel strand of the same weight.

▼ Spiders secrete silk fibers made of a structural protein containing β pleated sheets, which allow the spider web to stretch and recoil.

<table>
<tr><td>

## Tertiary Structure

### Three-dimensional shape stabilized by interactions between side chains

</td><td>

## Quaternary Structure

### Association of two or more polypeptides (some proteins only)

</td></tr>
</table>

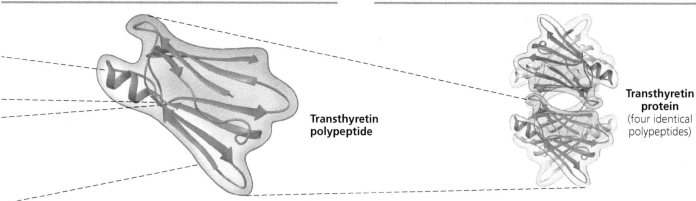

Transthyretin polypeptide

**Transthyretin protein**
(four identical polypeptides)

Superimposed on the patterns of secondary structure is a protein's tertiary structure, shown above in a ribbon model of the transthyretin polypeptide. While secondary structure involves interactions between backbone constituents, **tertiary structure** is the overall shape of a polypeptide resulting from interactions between the side chains (R groups) of the various amino acids. One type of interaction that contributes to tertiary structure is called—somewhat misleadingly—a **hydrophobic interaction**. As a polypeptide folds into its functional shape, amino acids with hydrophobic (nonpolar) side chains usually end up in clusters at the core of the protein, out of contact with water. Thus, a "hydrophobic interaction" is actually caused by the exclusion of nonpolar substances by water molecules. Once nonpolar amino acid side chains are close together, van der Waals interactions help hold them together. Meanwhile, hydrogen bonds between polar side chains and ionic bonds between positively and negatively charged side chains also help stabilize tertiary structure. These are all weak interactions in the aqueous cellular environment, but their cumulative effect helps give the protein a unique shape.

Covalent bonds called **disulfide bridges** may further reinforce the shape of a protein. Disulfide bridges form where two cysteine monomers, which have sulfhydryl groups (—SH) on their side chains (see Figure 2.5), are brought close together by the folding of the protein. The sulfur of one cysteine bonds to the sulfur of the second, and the disulfide bridge (—S—S—) rivets parts of the protein together (see yellow lines in Figure 2.19a). All of these different kinds of interactions can contribute to the tertiary structure of a protein, as shown here in a small part of a hypothetical protein:

Some proteins consist of two or more polypeptide chains aggregated into one functional macromolecule. **Quaternary structure** is the overall protein structure that results from the aggregation of these polypeptide subunits. For example, shown above is the complete globular transthyretin protein, made up of its four polypeptides.

Another example is collagen, shown below, which is a fibrous protein that has three identical helical polypeptides intertwined into a larger triple helix, giving the long fibers great strength. This suits collagen fibers to their function as the girders of connective tissue in skin, bone, tendons, ligaments, and other body parts. (Collagen accounts for 40% of the protein in a human body.)

SDH

**Collagen**

Hemoglobin, the oxygen-binding protein of red blood cells shown below, is another example of a globular protein with quaternary structure. It consists of four polypeptide subunits, two of one kind (α) and two of another kind (β). Both α and β subunits consist primarily of α-helical secondary structure. Each subunit has a nonpolypeptide component, called heme, with an iron atom that binds oxygen.

Heme
Iron
β subunit
α subunit
α subunit
β subunit
**Hemoglobin**

Hydrogen bond
Hydrophobic interactions and van der Waals interactions
Disulfide bridge
Ionic bond
Polypeptide backbone

| | Primary Structure | Secondary and Tertiary Structures | Quaternary Structure | Function | Red Blood Cell Shape |
|---|---|---|---|---|---|
| **Normal hemoglobin** | 1 Val<br>2 His<br>3 Leu<br>4 Thr<br>5 Pro<br>6 Glu<br>7 Glu | β subunit | Normal hemoglobin<br>α β<br>α β | Molecules do not associate with one another; each carries oxygen. | Normal red blood cells are full of individual hemoglobin molecules, each carrying oxygen.<br>5 μm |
| **Sickle-cell hemoglobin** | 1 Val<br>2 His<br>3 Leu<br>4 Thr<br>5 Pro<br>6 Val<br>7 Glu | Exposed hydrophobic region<br>β subunit | Sickle-cell hemoglobin<br>α β<br>α β | Molecules interact with one another and crystallize into a fiber; capacity to carry oxygen is greatly reduced. | Fibers of abnormal hemoglobin deform red blood cell into sickle shape.<br>5 μm |

▲ **Figure 2.22  A single amino acid substitution in a protein causes sickle-cell disease.**

**MAKE CONNECTIONS**  *Considering the chemical characteristics of the amino acids valine and glutamic acid (see Figure 2.17), propose a possible explanation for the dramatic effect on protein function that occurs when valine is substituted for glutamic acid.*

## Sickle-Cell Disease: A Change in Primary Structure

Even a slight change in primary structure can affect a protein's shape and ability to function. For instance, **sickle-cell disease**, an inherited blood disorder, is caused by the substitution of one amino acid (valine) for the normal one (glutamic acid) at a particular position in the primary structure of hemoglobin, the protein that carries oxygen in red blood cells. Normal red blood cells are disk-shaped, but in sickle-cell disease, the abnormal hemoglobin molecules tend to crystallize, deforming some of the cells into a sickle shape **(Figure 2.22)**. A person with the disease has periodic "sickle-cell crises" when the angular cells clog tiny blood vessels, impeding blood flow. The toll taken on such patients is a dramatic example of how a simple change in protein structure can have devastating effects on protein function.

## What Determines Protein Structure?

You've learned that a unique shape endows each protein with a specific function. But what are the key factors determining protein structure? You already know most of the answer: A polypeptide chain of a given amino acid sequence can spontaneously arrange itself into a three-dimensional shape determined and maintained by the interactions responsible for secondary and tertiary structure. This folding normally occurs as the protein is being synthesized in the crowded environment within a cell, aided by other proteins. However, protein structure also depends on the physical and chemical conditions of the protein's environment. If the pH, salt concentration, temperature, or other aspects of its environment are altered, the weak chemical bonds and interactions within a protein may be destroyed, causing the protein to unravel and lose its native shape, a change called **denaturation** **(Figure 2.23)**. Because it is misshapen, the denatured protein is biologically inactive.

Most proteins become denatured if they are transferred from an aqueous environment to a nonpolar solvent, such as

Normal protein    *Denaturation →*    Denatured protein
*← Renaturation*

▲ **Figure 2.23  Denaturation and renaturation of a protein.** High temperatures or various chemical treatments will denature a protein, causing it to lose its shape and hence its ability to function. If the denatured protein remains dissolved, it can sometimes renature when the chemical and physical aspects of its environment are restored to normal.

ether or chloroform; the polypeptide chain refolds so that its hydrophobic regions face outward toward the solvent. Other denaturation agents include chemicals that disrupt the hydrogen bonds, ionic bonds, and disulfide bridges that maintain a protein's shape. Denaturation can also result from excessive heat, which agitates the polypeptide chain enough to overpower the weak interactions that stabilize the structure. The white of an egg becomes opaque during cooking because the denatured proteins are insoluble and solidify. This also explains why excessively high fevers can be fatal: Proteins in the blood can denature at very high body temperatures.

When a protein in a test-tube solution has been denatured by heat or chemicals, it can sometimes return to its functional shape when the denaturing agent is removed. We can conclude that the information for building a specific shape is intrinsic to the protein's primary structure. The sequence of amino acids determines the protein's shape—where an α helix can form, where β pleated sheets can exist, where disulfide bridges are located, where ionic bonds can form, and so on. But how does protein folding occur in the cell?

### Protein Folding in the Cell

Biochemists now know the amino acid sequence for more than 10 million proteins and the three-dimensional shape for more than 20,000. Researchers have tried to correlate the primary structure of many proteins with their three-dimensional structure to discover the rules of protein folding. Unfortunately, however, the protein-folding process is not that simple. Most proteins probably go through several intermediate structures on their way to a stable shape, and looking at the mature structure does not reveal the stages of folding required to achieve that form. However, biochemists have developed methods for tracking a protein through such stages. They are still working to develop computer programs that can predict the 3-D structure of a polypeptide from its primary structure alone.

Misfolding of polypeptides is a serious problem in cells. Many diseases, such as Alzheimer's, Parkinson's, and mad cow disease, are associated with an accumulation of misfolded proteins. In fact, misfolded versions of the transthyretin protein featured in Figure 2.21 have been implicated in several diseases, including one form of senile dementia.

Even when scientists have a correctly folded protein in hand, determining its exact three-dimensional structure is not simple, for a single protein molecule has thousands of atoms. The method most commonly used to determine the 3-D shape of a protein is **X-ray crystallography**, which depends on the diffraction of an X-ray beam by the atoms of a crystallized molecule. Using this technique, scientists can build a 3-D model that shows the exact position of every atom in a protein molecule **(Figure 2.24)**. Nuclear magnetic resonance (NMR) spectroscopy and bioinformatics (see Chapter 1) are complementary approaches to understanding protein structure and function.

---

### ▼ Figure 2.24 Inquiry

## What can the 3-D shape of the enzyme RNA polymerase II tell us about its function?

**Experiment** In 2006, Roger Kornberg was awarded the Nobel Prize in Chemistry for using X-ray crystallography to determine the 3-D shape of RNA polymerase II, which binds to the DNA double helix and synthesizes RNA. After crystallizing a complex of all three components, Kornberg and his colleagues aimed an X-ray beam through the crystal. The atoms of the crystal diffracted (bent) the X-rays into an orderly array that a digital detector recorded as a pattern of spots called an X-ray diffraction pattern.

**Results** Using data from X-ray diffraction patterns, as well as the amino acid sequence determined by chemical methods, Kornberg and colleagues built a 3-D model of the complex with the help of computer software.

**Conclusion** By analyzing their model, the researchers developed a hypothesis about the functions of different regions of RNA polymerase II. For example, the region above the DNA may act as a clamp that holds the nucleic acids in place. (You'll learn more about RNA polymerase in Chapter 14.)

**Further Reading** A. L. Gnatt et al., Structural basis of transcription: an RNA polymerase II elongation complex at 3.3Å, *Science* 292:1876–1882 (2001).

**WHAT IF?** If you were one of the researchers and were describing the model, what type of protein structure would you call the small polypeptide spirals in RNA polymerase II?

---

**CONCEPT CHECK 2.5**

1. Why does a denatured protein no longer function normally?
2. What parts of a polypeptide participate in the bonds that hold together secondary structure? Tertiary structure?
3. **WHAT IF?** Where would you expect a polypeptide region that is rich in the amino acids valine, leucine, and isoleucine to be located in the folded polypeptide? Explain.

For suggested answers, see Appendix A.

# CONCEPT 2.6

## Nucleic acids store, transmit, and help express hereditary information

If the primary structure of polypeptides determines a protein's shape, what determines primary structure? The amino acid sequence of a polypeptide is programmed by a discrete unit of inheritance known as a **gene**. Genes consist of DNA, which belongs to the class of compounds called nucleic acids. **Nucleic acids** are polymers made of monomers called nucleotides.

### The Roles of Nucleic Acids

The two types of nucleic acids, **deoxyribonucleic acid (DNA)** and **ribonucleic acid (RNA)**, enable living organisms to reproduce their complex components from one generation to the next. Unique among molecules, DNA provides directions for its own replication. DNA also directs RNA synthesis and, through RNA, controls protein synthesis **(Figure 2.25)**.

DNA is the genetic material that organisms inherit from their parents. Each chromosome contains one long DNA molecule, usually carrying several hundred or more genes. When a cell reproduces itself by dividing, its DNA molecules are copied and passed along from one generation of cells to the next. Encoded in the structure of DNA is the information that

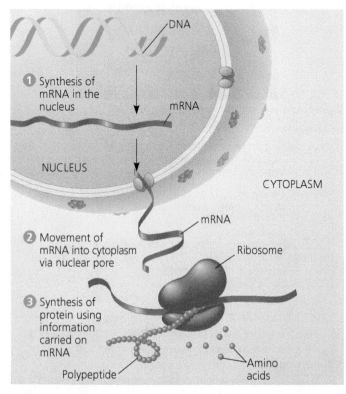

**1** Synthesis of mRNA in the nucleus

DNA

mRNA

NUCLEUS

CYTOPLASM

mRNA

**2** Movement of mRNA into cytoplasm via nuclear pore

Ribosome

**3** Synthesis of protein using information carried on mRNA

Polypeptide

Amino acids

▲ **Figure 2.25 DNA → RNA → protein.** In a eukaryotic cell, DNA in the nucleus programs protein production in the cytoplasm by dictating synthesis of messenger RNA (mRNA). (The cell nucleus is actually much larger relative to the other elements of this figure.)

programs all the cell's activities. The DNA, however, is not directly involved in running the operations of the cell, any more than computer software by itself can print a bank statement or read the bar code on a box of cereal. Just as a printer is needed to print out a statement and a scanner is needed to read a bar code, proteins are required to implement genetic programs. The molecular hardware of the cell—the tools for biological functions—consists mostly of proteins. For example, the oxygen carrier in red blood cells is the protein hemoglobin, not the DNA that specifies its structure.

How does RNA, the other type of nucleic acid, fit into gene expression, the flow of genetic information from DNA to pro-teins? Each gene along a DNA molecule directs synthesis of a type of RNA called *messenger RNA (mRNA)*. The mRNA molecule interacts with the cell's protein-synthesizing machinery to direct production of a polypeptide, which folds into all or part of a protein. We can summarize the flow of genetic information as DNA → RNA → protein (see Figure 2.25). The sites of protein synthesis are tiny structures called ribosomes. In a eukaryotic cell, ribosomes are in the cytoplasm, the region between the nucleus and a cell's outer membrane, but DNA resides in the nucleus. Messenger RNA conveys genetic instructions for building proteins from the nucleus to the cytoplasm. Prokaryotic cells lack nuclei but still use mRNA to convey a message from the DNA to ribosomes and other cellular equipment that translate the coded information into amino acid sequences. In recent years, the spotlight has been turned on other, previously unknown types of RNA that play many other roles in the cell. As is so often true in biology, the story is still being written!

### The Components of Nucleic Acids

Nucleic acids are macromolecules that exist as polymers called **polynucleotides (Figure 2.26a)**. As indicated by the name, each polynucleotide consists of monomers called **nucleotides**. A nucleotide, in general, is composed of three parts: a nitrogen-containing (nitrogenous) base, a five-carbon sugar (a pentose), and one or more phosphate groups **(Figure 2.26b)**. In a polynucleotide, each monomer has only one phosphate group. The portion of a nucleotide without any phosphate groups is called a *nucleoside*.

To build a nucleotide, let's first consider the nitrogenous bases **(Figure 2.26c)**. Each nitrogenous base has one or two rings that include nitrogen atoms. (They are called nitrogenous *bases* because the nitrogen atoms tend to take up H$^+$ from solution, thus acting as bases.) There are two families of nitrogenous bases: pyrimidines and purines. A **pyrimidine** has one six-membered ring of carbon and nitrogen atoms. The members of the pyrimidine family are cytosine (C), thymine (T), and uracil (U). **Purines** are larger, with a six-membered ring fused to a five-membered ring. The purines are adenine (A) and guanine (G). The specific pyrimidines and purines differ in

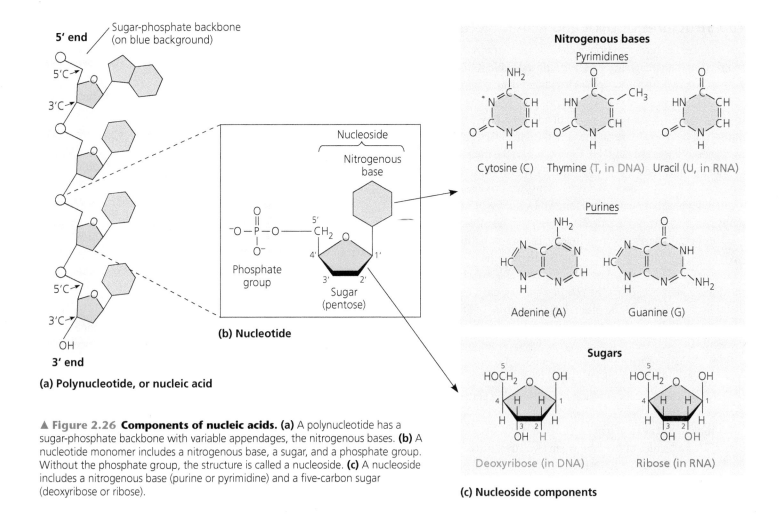

**(b) Nucleotide**

**(a) Polynucleotide, or nucleic acid**

▲ **Figure 2.26 Components of nucleic acids. (a)** A polynucleotide has a sugar-phosphate backbone with variable appendages, the nitrogenous bases. **(b)** A nucleotide monomer includes a nitrogenous base, a sugar, and a phosphate group. Without the phosphate group, the structure is called a nucleoside. **(c)** A nucleoside includes a nitrogenous base (purine or pyrimidine) and a five-carbon sugar (deoxyribose or ribose).

**(c) Nucleoside components**

the chemical groups attached to the rings. Adenine, guanine, and cytosine are found in both DNA and RNA; thymine is found only in DNA and uracil only in RNA.

Now let's add a sugar to the nitrogenous base. In DNA the sugar is **deoxyribose**; in RNA it is **ribose** (See Figure 2.26c). The only difference between these two sugars is that deoxyribose lacks an oxygen atom on the second carbon in the ring; hence the name *deoxy*ribose. To distinguish the numbers of the sugar carbons from those used for the ring atoms of the attached nitrogenous base, we add a prime (′) after the sugar carbon numbers of a nucleoside or nucleotide. Thus, the second carbon in the sugar ring is the 2′ ("2 prime") carbon, and the carbon that sticks up from the ring is called the 5′ carbon.

To complete the construction of a nucleotide, we attach a phosphate group to the 5′ carbon of the sugar (see Figure 2.26b). The molecule is now a nucleoside monophosphate, better known as a nucleotide.

## Nucleotide Polymers

Now let's see how these nucleotides are linked together to build a polynucleotide. Adjacent nucleotides are joined by a phosphodiester linkage, which consists of a phosphate group that links the sugars of two nucleotides. This bonding results

in a backbone with a repeating pattern of sugar-phosphate units (see Figure 2.26a). (Note that the nitrogenous bases are not part of the backbone.) The two free ends of the polymer are distinctly different from each other. One end has a phosphate attached to a 5′ carbon, and the other end has a hydroxyl group on a 3′ carbon; we refer to these as the 5′ end and the 3′ end, respectively. We can say that a polynucleotide has a built-in directionality along its sugar-phosphate backbone, from 5′ to 3′, somewhat like a one-way street. All along this sugar-phosphate backbone are appendages consisting of the nitrogenous bases.

The sequence of bases along a DNA (or mRNA) polymer is unique for each gene and provides very specific information to the cell. Because genes are hundreds to thousands of nucleotides long, the number of possible base sequences is effectively limitless. A gene's meaning to the cell is encoded in its specific sequence of the four DNA bases. For example, the sequence 5′-AGGTAACTT-3′ means one thing, whereas the sequence 5′-CGCTTTAAC-3′ has a different meaning. (Entire genes, of course, are much longer.) The linear order of bases in a gene specifies the amino acid sequence—the primary structure—of a protein, which in turn specifies that protein's three-dimensional structure and its function in the cell.

## The Structures of DNA and RNA Molecules

DNA molecules have two polynucleotides, or "strands," that spiral around an imaginary axis, forming a **double helix (Figure 2.27a)**. The two sugar-phosphate backbones run in opposite $5' \rightarrow 3'$ directions from each other; this arrangement is referred to as **antiparallel**, somewhat like a divided highway. The sugar-phosphate backbones are on the outside of the helix, and the nitrogenous bases are paired in the interior of the helix. The two strands are held together by hydrogen bonds between the paired bases. Most DNA molecules are very long, with thousands or even millions of base pairs. One long DNA double helix includes many genes, each one a particular segment of the molecule.

Only certain bases in the double helix are compatible with each other. Adenine (A) always pairs with thymine (T), and guanine (G) always pairs with cytosine (C). The two strands of the double helix are said to be *complementary*, each the predictable counterpart of the other. It is this feature of DNA that makes it possible to generate two identical copies of each DNA molecule in a cell that is preparing to divide. When the cell divides, the copies are distributed to the daughter cells, making them genetically identical to the parent cell. Thus, the structure of DNA accounts for its function of transmitting genetic information whenever a cell reproduces.

Complementary base pairing can also occur between two RNA molecules or even between two stretches of nucleotides in the *same* RNA molecule. In fact, base pairing within an RNA molecule allows it to take on the particular three-dimensional shape necessary for its function. Consider, for example, the type of RNA called *transfer RNA (tRNA)*, which brings amino acids to the ribosome during the synthesis of a polypeptide. A tRNA molecule is about 80 nucleotides in length. Its functional shape results from base pairing between nucleotides where complementary stretches of the molecule run antiparallel to each other **(Figure 2.27b)**.

Note that in RNA, adenine (A) pairs with uracil (U); thymine (T) is not present in RNA. Another difference between RNA and DNA is that RNA molecules are more variable in shape. This variability arises because the extent and location of complementary base pairing within an RNA molecule differs with the type of RNA (as you will learn in Chapter 14).

## DNA and Proteins as Tape Measures of Evolution

**EVOLUTION** Biologists think of shared traits as evidence of shared ancestry. For example, we infer from the existence of hair and milk production in all mammalian species living today that the members of this group have inherited these traits from common ancestors that lived in the distant past.

Now we have additional kinds of evidence in the form of genes and their protein products, which like observable traits document the hereditary background of an organism. The linear sequences of nucleotides in DNA molecules are passed from parents to offspring; these sequences determine the

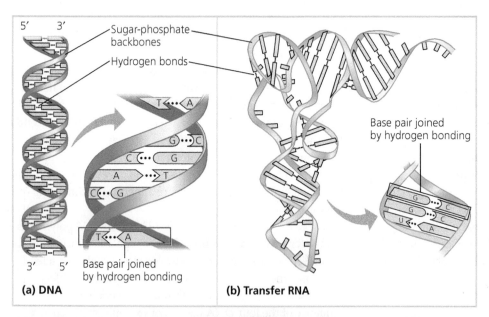

(a) DNA   (b) Transfer RNA

▲ **Figure 2.27 The structures of DNA and tRNA molecules. (a)** The DNA molecule is usually a double helix, with the sugar-phosphate backbones of the antiparallel polynucleotide strands (symbolized here by blue ribbons) on the outside of the helix. Holding the two strands together are pairs of nitrogenous bases attached to each other by hydrogen bonds. As illustrated here with symbolic shapes for the bases, adenine (A) can pair only with thymine (T), and guanine (G) can pair only with cytosine (C). Each DNA strand in this figure is the structural equivalent of the polynucleotide diagrammed in Figure 2.26a. **(b)** A tRNA molecule has a roughly L-shaped structure, with complementary base pairing of antiparallel stretches of RNA. In RNA, A pairs with U.

amino acid sequences of proteins. As a result, siblings have greater similarity in their DNA and proteins than do unrelated individuals of the same species. Given the validity of evolutionary theory, we can extend this concept of "molecular genealogy" to relationships between species: We would expect two species that appear to be closely related based on anatomical evidence (possibly including fossil evidence) to also share a greater proportion of their DNA and protein sequences than do more distantly related species. In fact, that is the case. An example is the comparison of the β polypeptide chain of human hemoglobin with the corresponding hemoglobin polypeptide in other vertebrates. In this chain of 146 amino acids, humans and gorillas differ in just 1 amino acid, while humans and frogs, more distantly related, differ in 67 amino acids. In the **Scientific Skills Exercise**, you can apply this sort of reasoning to additional species. Molecular biology has added a new tape measure to the toolkit biologists use to assess evolutionary kinship.

## CONCEPT CHECK 2.6

1. **DRAW IT** Go to Figure 2.26a and, for the top three nucleotides, number all the carbons in the sugars, circle the nitrogenous bases, and star the phosphates.

2. **DRAW IT** In a DNA double helix, a region along one DNA strand has the following sequence of nitrogenous bases: 5'-TAGGCCT-3'. Copy this sequence, and write down its complementary strand, clearly indicating the 5' and 3' ends of the complementary strand.

3. **WHAT IF?** (a) Suppose a substitution occurred in one DNA strand of the double helix in question 2, resulting in

   5'-TAAGCCT-3'
   3'-ATCCGGA-5'

   Copy these two strands, and circle and label the mismatched bases. (b) If the modified top strand is used by the cell to construct a complementary strand, what would that matching strand be?

For suggested answers, see Appendix A.

## Scientific Skills Exercise

# Analyzing Polypeptide Sequence Data

**Are Rhesus Monkeys or Gibbons More Closely Related to Humans?** As discussed in Concept 2.6, DNA and polypeptide sequences from closely related species are more similar to each other than are sequences from more distantly related species. In this exercise, you will look at amino acid sequence data for the β polypeptide chain of hemoglobin, often called β-globin. You will then interpret the data to hypothesize whether the monkey or the gibbon is more closely related to humans.

**How Such Experiments Are Done** Researchers can isolate the polypeptide of interest from an organism and then determine the amino acid sequence. More frequently, the DNA of the relevant gene is sequenced, and the amino acid sequence of the polypeptide is deduced from the DNA sequence of its gene.

**Data from the Experiments** In the data below, the letters give the sequence of the 146 amino acids in β-globin from humans, rhesus monkeys, and gibbons. Because a complete sequence would not fit on one line here, the sequences are broken into three segments. Note that the sequences for the three different species are aligned so that you can compare them easily. For example, you can see that for all three species, the first amino acid is V (valine; see Figure 2.17) and the 146th amino acid is H (histidine).

**Interpret the Data**

1. Scan along the monkey and gibbon sequences, letter by letter, circling any amino acids that do not match the human sequence. (a) How many amino acids differ between the monkey and the human sequences? (b) Between the gibbon and human?

2. For each nonhuman species, what percent of its amino acids are identical to the human sequence of β-globin?

3. Based on these data alone, state a hypothesis for which of these two species is more closely related to humans. What is your reasoning?

4. What other evidence could you use to support your hypothesis?

**Data from** Human: http://www.ncbi.nlm.nih.gov/protein/AAA21113.1; rhesus monkey: http://www.ncbi.nlm.nih.gov/protein/122634; gibbon: http://www.ncbi.nlm.nih.gov/protein/122616

(MB) A version of this Scientific Skills Exercise can be assigned in MasteringBiology.

| Species | Alignment of Amino Acid Sequences of β-globin |
|---|---|
| Human | 1 VHLTPEEKSA VTALWGKVNV DEVGGEALGR LLVVYPWTQR FFESFGDLST PDAVMGNPKV |
| Monkey | 1 VHLTPEEKNA VTTLWGKVNV DEVGGEALGR LLLVYPWTQR FFESFGDLSS PDAVMGNPKV |
| Gibbon | 1 VHLTPEEKSA VTALWGKVNV DEVGGEALGR LLVVYPWTQR FFESFGDLST PDAVMGNPKV |
| | |
| Human | 61 KAHGKKVLGA FSDGLAHLDN LKGTFATLSE LHCDKLHVDP ENFRLLGNVL VCVLAHHFGK |
| Monkey | 61 KAHGKKVLGA FSDGLNHLDN LKGTFAQLSE LHCDKLHVDP ENFKLLGNVL VCVLAHHFGK |
| Gibbon | 61 KAHGKKVLGA FSDGLAHLDN LKGTFAQLSE LHCDKLHVDP ENFRLLGNVL VCVLAHHFGK |
| | |
| Human | 121 EFTPPVQAAY QKVVAGVANA LAHKYH |
| Monkey | 121 EFTPQVQAAY QKVVAGVANA LAHKYH |
| Gibbon | 121 EFTPQVQAAY QKVVAGVANA LAHKYH |

# 2 Chapter Review

## SUMMARY OF KEY CONCEPTS

CONCEPT 2.1

### Carbon atoms can form diverse molecules by bonding to four other atoms (pp. 19–22)

- Carbon, with a **valence** of 4, can bond to various other atoms, including O, H, and N. Carbon can also bond to other carbon atoms, forming the carbon skeletons of **organic compounds**. These skeletons vary in length and shape.
- Chemical groups attached to the carbon skeletons of organic molecules participate in chemical reactions (**functional groups**) or contribute to function by affecting molecular shape.
- **ATP (adenosine triphosphate)** can react with water, releasing energy that can be used by the cell.

> [?] *In what ways does a methyl group differ chemically from the other six important chemical groups shown in Figure 2.5?*

CONCEPT 2.2

### Macromolecules are polymers, built from monomers (pp. 22–23)

- Proteins, nucleic acids, and large carbohydrates (polysaccharides) are **polymers**, which are chains of **monomers**. Monomers form larger molecules by **dehydration reactions**, in which water molecules are released. Polymers can disassemble by the reverse process, **hydrolysis**. In cells, dehydration reactions and hydrolysis are catalyzed by enzymes. An immense variety of polymers can be built from a small set of monomers.

> [?] *What is the fundamental basis for the differences between carbohydrates, proteins, and nucleic acids?*

| Large Biological Molecules | Components | Examples | Functions |
|---|---|---|---|
| CONCEPT 2.3<br>**Carbohydrates serve as fuel and building material (pp. 23–27)**<br><br>[?] *Compare the composition, structure, and function of starch and cellulose. What roles do starch and cellulose play in the human body?* | Monosaccharide monomer | **Monosaccharides:** glucose, fructose<br><br>**Disaccharides:** lactose, sucrose | Fuel; carbon sources that can be converted to other molecules or combined into polymers |
| | | **Polysaccharides:**<br>• Cellulose (plants)<br>• Starch (plants)<br>• Glycogen (animals)<br>• Chitin (animals and fungi) | • Strengthens plant cell walls<br>• Stores glucose for energy in plants<br>• Stores glucose for energy in animals<br>• Strengthens exoskeletons and fungal cell walls |
| CONCEPT 2.4<br>**Lipids are a diverse group of hydrophobic molecules (pp. 27–29)**<br><br>[?] *Why are lipids not considered to be macromolecules or polymers?* | Glycerol — 3 fatty acids | **Triacylglycerols** (fats or oils): glycerol + 3 fatty acids | Important energy source |
| | Head with ℗ — 2 fatty acids | **Phospholipids:** phosphate group + glycerol + 2 fatty acids | Lipid bilayers of membranes<br>Hydrophilic heads / Hydrophobic tails |
| | Steroid backbone | **Steroids:** four fused rings with attached chemical groups | • Component of cell membranes (cholesterol)<br>• Signaling molecules that travel through the body (hormones) |
| CONCEPT 2.5<br>**Proteins include a diversity of structures, resulting in a wide range of functions (pp. 29–37)**<br><br>[?] *Explain the basis for the great diversity of proteins.* | Amino acid monomer (20 types) | • Enzymes<br>• Structural proteins<br>• Storage proteins<br>• Transport proteins<br>• Hormones<br>• Receptor proteins<br>• Motor proteins<br>• Defensive proteins | • Catalyze chemical reactions<br>• Provide structural support<br>• Store amino acids<br>• Transport substances<br>• Coordinate organismal responses<br>• Receive signals from outside cell<br>• Function in cell movement<br>• Protect against disease |

| Large Biological Molecules | Components | Examples | Functions |
|---|---|---|---|
| **CONCEPT** 2.6 <br> **Nucleic acids store, transmit, and help express hereditary information (pp. 38–41)** <br> ? *What role does complementary base pairing play in the functions of nucleic acids?* |  <br> Nitrogenous base <br> Phosphate group <br> Ⓟ—CH₂ O <br> Sugar <br> Nucleotide monomer | **DNA:** <br> • Sugar = deoxyribose <br> • Nitrogenous bases = C, G, A, T <br> • Usually double-stranded | Stores hereditary information |
| | | **RNA:** <br> • Sugar = ribose <br> • Nitrogenous bases = C, G, A, U <br> • Usually single-stranded | Various functions in gene expression, including carrying instructions from DNA to ribosomes |

## TEST YOUR UNDERSTANDING

### Level 1: Knowledge/Comprehension

1. Which functional group is *not* present in this molecule?
   a. carboxyl
   **b.** sulfhydryl
   c. hydroxyl
   d. amino

   HO   C═O
         |   H
   H—C—C—OH
      |   |
      N   H
     / \
    H   H

2. **MAKE CONNECTIONS** Which chemical group is most likely to be responsible for an organic molecule behaving as a base?
   a. hydroxyl
   b. carbonyl
   c. carboxyl
   d. amino
   e. phosphate

3. Which of the following categories includes all others in the list?
   a. monosaccharide
   b. disaccharide
   c. starch
   d. carbohydrate
   e. polysaccharide

4. Which of the following statements concerning *unsaturated* fats is true?
   a. They are more common in animals than in plants.
   b. They have double bonds in the carbon chains of their fatty acids.
   c. They generally solidify at room temperature.
   d. They contain more hydrogen than do saturated fats having the same number of carbon atoms.
   e. They have fewer fatty acid molecules per fat molecule.

5. The structural level of a protein *least* affected by a disruption in hydrogen bonding is the
   a. primary level.
   b. secondary level.
   c. tertiary level.
   d. quaternary level.
   e. All structural levels are equally affected.

### Level 2: Application/Analysis

6. Which of the following hydrocarbons has a double bond in its carbon skeleton?
   a. $C_3H_8$
   b. $C_2H_6$
   c. $CH_4$
   d. $C_2H_4$
   e. $C_2H_2$

7. The molecular formula for glucose is $C_6H_{12}O_6$. What would be the molecular formula for a polymer made by linking ten glucose molecules together by dehydration reactions?
   a. $C_{60}H_{120}O_{60}$
   b. $C_6H_{12}O_6$
   c. $C_{60}H_{102}O_{51}$
   d. $C_{60}H_{100}O_{50}$
   e. $C_{60}H_{111}O_{51}$

   $C_{60}H_{120}O_{60}$
   $-9(H_2O)$
   $18 - 9$

8. Rewrite the following table. Start with the left column, and then rearrange the terms in the second and third columns so they line up correctly. Label the columns and rows.

| Monosaccharides | Polypeptides | Phosphodiester linkages |
| Fatty acids | Triacylglycerols | Peptide bonds |
| Amino acids | Polynucleotides | Glycosidic linkages |
| Nucleotides | Polysaccharides | Ester linkages |

### Level 3: Synthesis/Evaluation

9. **SCIENTIFIC INQUIRY**
   Suppose you are a research assistant in a lab studying DNA-binding proteins. You have been given the amino acid sequences of all the proteins encoded by the genome of a certain species and have been asked to find candidate proteins that could bind DNA. What type of amino acids would you expect to see in the DNA-binding regions of such proteins? Why?

10. **FOCUS ON EVOLUTION**
    Comparisons of amino acid sequences can shed light on the evolutionary divergence of related species. If you were comparing two living species, would you expect all proteins to show the same degree of divergence? Why or why not?

11. **FOCUS ON ORGANIZATION**
    Proteins, which have diverse functions in a cell, are all polymers of the same kinds of monomers—amino acids. Write a short essay (100–150 words) that discusses how the structure of amino acids allows this one type of polymer to perform so many functions.

*For selected answers, see Appendix A.*

## MasteringBiology®

**Students** Go to **MasteringBiology** for assignments, the eText, and the Study Area with practice tests, animations, and activities.

**Instructors** Go to **MasteringBiology** for automatically graded tutorials and questions that you can assign to your students, plus Instructor Resources.

# 3

# A Tour of the Cell

OVERVIEW

## The Fundamental Units of Life

Given the scope of biology, you may wonder sometimes how you will ever learn all the material in this course! The answer involves cells, which are as fundamental to the living systems of biology as the atom is to chemistry. The contraction of muscle cells moves your eyes as you read this sentence. The words on the page are translated into signals that nerve cells carry to your brain, where they are passed on to still other nerve cells. **Figure 3.1** shows extensions from one nerve cell (purple) making contact with another nerve cell (orange) in the brain. As you study, your goal is to make connections like these that solidify memories and permit learning to occur.

All organisms are made of cells. In the hierarchy of biological organization, the cell is the simplest collection of matter that can be alive. Indeed, many forms of life exist as single-celled organisms. (You may be familiar with single-celled eukaryotic organisms that live in pond water, such as paramecia.) Larger, more complex organisms, including plants and animals, are multicellular; their bodies are cooperatives of many kinds of specialized cells that could not survive for long on their own. Even when cells are arranged into higher levels of organization, such as tissues and organs, the cell remains the organism's basic unit of structure and function.

All cells are related by their descent from earlier cells. Furthermore, they have been modified in many different ways during the long evolutionary history of life on Earth. But although cells can differ substantially from one another, they share common features. It is these features that we focus on in most of this chapter.

We begin the chapter with a discussion of microscopy and some other techniques used by cell biologists. Next comes an overview of the cellular structures revealed by these methods. In the rest of the chapter, we explore cellular structures and their functions in more detail.

▼ **Figure 3.1** How do your brain cells help you learn about biology?

# Biologists use microscopes and the tools of biochemistry to study cells

How can cell biologists investigate the inner workings of a cell, usually too small to be seen by the unaided eye? Before we tour the cell, it will be helpful to learn how cells are studied.

## Microscopy

The development of instruments that extend the human senses has gone hand in hand with the advance of science. The discovery and early study of cells progressed with the invention of microscopes in 1590 and their refinement during the 1600s. Cell walls were first seen by Robert Hooke in 1665 as he looked through a microscope at dead cells from the bark of an oak tree. But it took the wonderfully crafted lenses of Antoni van Leeuwenhoek to visualize living cells. Imagine Hooke's awe when he visited van Leeuwenhoek in 1674 and the world of microorganisms—what his host called "very little animalcules"—was revealed to him.

The microscopes first used by Renaissance scientists, as well as the microscopes you are likely to use in the laboratory, are all light microscopes. In a **light microscope (LM)**, visible light is passed through the specimen and then through glass lenses. The lenses refract (bend) the light in such a way that the image of the specimen is magnified as it is projected into the eye or into a camera (see Appendix D).

Three important parameters in microscopy are magnification, resolution, and contrast. *Magnification* is the ratio of an object's image size to its real size. Light microscopes can magnify effectively to about 1,000 times the actual size of the specimen; at greater magnifications, additional details cannot be seen clearly. *Resolution* is a measure of the clarity of the image; it is the minimum distance two points can be separated and still be distinguished as separate points. For example, what appears to the unaided eye as one star in the sky may be resolved as twin stars with a telescope, which has a higher resolving ability than the eye. Similarly, using standard techniques, the light microscope cannot resolve detail finer than about 0.2 micrometer (µm), or 200 nanometers (nm), regardless of the magnification **(Figure 3.2)**. The third parameter, *contrast*, is the difference in brightness between the light and dark areas of an image. Methods for enhancing contrast in light microscopy include staining or labeling cell components to stand out visually. **Figure 3.3** shows some different types of microscopy; study this figure as you read the rest of this section.

Until recently, the resolution barrier prevented cell biologists from using standard light microscopy to study **organelles**, the membrane-enclosed structures within eukaryotic cells. To see these structures in any detail required the development of a new instrument. In the 1950s, the

1 centimeter (cm) = $10^{-2}$ meter (m) = 0.4 inch
1 millimeter (mm) = $10^{-3}$ m
1 micrometer (µm) = $10^{-3}$ mm = $10^{-6}$ m
1 nanometer (nm) = $10^{-3}$ µm = $10^{-9}$ m

▲ **Figure 3.2 The size range of cells and how we view them.** Most cells are between 1 and 100 µm in diameter (yellow region of chart), and their components are even smaller, as are viruses. Notice that the scale along the left side is logarithmic to accommodate the range of sizes shown. Starting at the top of the scale with 10 m, each reference measurement marks a tenfold decrease in diameter or length. For a complete table of the metric system, see Appendix C.

electron microscope was introduced to biology. Rather than using light, an **electron microscope (EM)** focuses a beam of electrons through a specimen or onto its surface (see Appendix D). Resolution is inversely related to the wavelength of the radiation a microscope uses for imaging, and electron beams have much shorter wavelengths than visible light. Modern electron microscopes can theoretically achieve a resolution of about 0.002 nm, though in practice they usually cannot resolve structures smaller than about 2 nm across. Still, this is a hundredfold improvement over the standard light microscope.

# Light Microscopy (LM)

**Brightfield (unstained specimen).** Light passes directly through the specimen. Unless the cell is naturally pigmented or artificially stained, the image has little contrast.

**Brightfield (stained specimen).** Staining with various dyes enhances contrast. Most staining procedures require that cells be fixed (preserved), thereby killing them.

**Phase-contrast.** Variations in density within the specimen are amplified to enhance contrast in unstained cells; this is especially useful for examining living, unpigmented cells.

**Differential-interference contrast (Nomarski).** As in phase-contrast microscopy, optical modifications are used to exaggerate differences in density; the image appears almost 3-D.

The light micrographs above show human cheek epithelial cells; the scale bar pertains to all four micrographs.

**Fluorescence.** The locations of specific molecules in the cell can be revealed by labeling the molecules with fluorescent dyes or antibodies; some cells have molecules that fluoresce on their own. Fluorescent substances absorb ultraviolet radiation and emit visible light. In this fluorescently labeled uterine cell, nuclear material is blue, organelles called mitochondria are orange, and the cell's "skeleton" is green.

**Confocal.** The left image is a standard fluorescence micrograph of fluorescently labeled nervous tissue (nerve cells are green, support cells are orange, and regions of overlap are yellow); at right is a confocal image of the same tissue. Using a laser, this "optical sectioning" technique eliminates out-of-focus light from a thick sample, creating a single plane of fluorescence in the image. By capturing sharp images at many different planes, a 3-D reconstruction can be created. The standard image is blurry because out-of-focus light is not excluded.

# Electron Microscopy (EM)

**Scanning electron microscopy (SEM).** Micrographs taken with a scanning electron microscope show a 3-D image of the surface of a specimen. This image shows the surface of a cell from a trachea (windpipe) covered with cilia. (Beating of the cilia helps move inhaled debris upward toward the throat.) The two micrographs shown here have been artificially colorized. Electron micrographs are black and white but are often artificially colorized to highlight particular structures.

Abbreviations used in figure legends throughout this book:
LM = Light Micrograph
SEM = Scanning Electron Micrograph
TEM = Transmission Electron Micrograph

Cilia

Longitudinal section of cilium

Cross section of cilium

2 µm

2 µm

**Transmission electron microscopy (TEM).** A transmission electron microscope profiles a thin section of a specimen. Here we see a section through a tracheal cell, revealing its internal structure. In preparing the specimen, some cilia were cut along their lengths, creating longitudinal sections, while other cilia were cut straight across, creating cross sections.

The **transmission electron microscope (TEM)** is used to study the internal structure of cells (see Figure 3.3). The TEM aims an electron beam through a very thin section of a specimen, much as a light microscope aims light through a sample on a slide. For the TEM, the specimen has been stained with atoms of heavy metals, which attach to certain cellular structures, thus enhancing the electron density of some parts of the cell more than others. The electrons passing through the specimen are scattered more in the denser regions, so fewer are transmitted. The image displays the pattern of transmitted electrons. Instead of using glass lenses, the TEM uses electromagnets as lenses to bend the paths of the electrons, ultimately focusing the image onto a monitor for viewing.

The **scanning electron microscope (SEM)** is especially useful for detailed study of the topography of a specimen (see Figure 3.3). Controlled by electromagnetic "lenses" as in a TEM, an electron beam scans the surface of the sample, usually coated with a thin film of gold. The beam excites electrons on the surface, and these secondary electrons are detected by a device that translates the pattern of electrons into an electronic signal to a video screen. The result is an image of the specimen's surface that appears three-dimensional.

Electron microscopes have revealed many organelles and other subcellular structures that were impossible to resolve with the light microscope. But the light microscope offers advantages, especially in studying living cells. A disadvantage of electron microscopy is that the methods used to prepare the specimen kill the cells. Specimen preparation for any type of microscopy can introduce artifacts, structural features seen in micrographs that do not exist in the living cell.

In the past several decades, light microscopy has been revitalized by major technical advances. Labeling individual cellular molecules or structures with fluorescent markers has made it possible to see such structures with increasing detail. In addition, confocal and other newer types of fluorescent light microscopy have produced sharpened images of three-dimensional tissues and cells. Finally, new techniques and labeling molecules have in recent years allowed researchers to break the resolution barrier and distinguish subcellular structures as small as 10–20 nm across. As this "super-resolution microscopy" becomes more widespread, the images we'll see of living cells may well be as awe-inspiring to us as van Leeuwenhoek's were to Robert Hooke 350 years ago.

Microscopes are the most important tools of *cytology*, the study of cell structure. To understand the function of each structure, however, required the integration of cytology and *biochemistry*, the study of the chemical processes of cells.

## Cell Fractionation

A useful technique for studying cell structure and function is **cell fractionation**. Broken-up cells are placed in a tube that is spun in a centrifuge. The resulting force causes the largest cell

components to settle to the bottom of the tube, forming a pellet. The liquid above the pellet is poured into a new tube and centrifuged at a higher speed for a longer time. This process is repeated several times, resulting in a series of pellets that consist of nuclei, mitochondria (and chloroplasts if the cells are from a photosynthetic organism), pieces of membrane, and ribosomes, the smallest components.

Cell fractionation enables researchers to prepare specific cell components in bulk and identify their functions, a task not usually possible with intact cells. For example, in one of the cell fractions resulting from centrifugation, biochemical tests showed the presence of enzymes involved in cellular respiration, while electron microscopy revealed large numbers of the organelles called mitochondria. Together, these data helped biologists determine that mitochondria are the sites of cellular respiration. Biochemistry and cytology thus complement each other in correlating cell function with structure.

**CONCEPT CHECK 3.1**

1. How do stains used for light microscopy compare with those used for electron microscopy?
2. **WHAT IF?** Which type of microscope would you use to study (a) the changes in shape of a living white blood cell and (b) the details of surface texture of a hair?

For suggested answers, see Appendix A.

---

CONCEPT 3.2

# Eukaryotic cells have internal membranes that compartmentalize their functions

Cells—the basic structural and functional units of every organism—are of two distinct types: prokaryotic and eukaryotic. Organisms of the domains Bacteria and Archaea consist of prokaryotic cells. Protists, fungi, animals, and plants all consist of eukaryotic cells.

## Comparing Prokaryotic and Eukaryotic Cells

All cells share certain basic features: They are all bounded by a selective barrier, called the *plasma membrane*. Inside all cells is a semifluid, jellylike substance called **cytosol**, in which subcellular components are suspended. All cells contain *chromosomes*, which carry genes in the form of DNA. And all cells have *ribosomes*, tiny complexes that make proteins according to instructions from the genes.

A major difference between prokaryotic and eukaryotic cells is the location of their DNA. In a **eukaryotic cell**, most of the DNA is in an organelle called the *nucleus*, which is bounded by a double membrane (see Figure 3.7). In a **prokaryotic cell**, the DNA is concentrated in the **nucleoid**,

**Fimbriae:** attachment structures on the surface of some prokaryotes

**Nucleoid:** region where the cell's DNA is located (not enclosed by a membrane)

**Ribosomes:** complexes that synthesize proteins

**Plasma membrane:** membrane enclosing the cytoplasm

**Cell wall:** rigid structure outside the plasma membrane

**Capsule:** jellylike outer coating of many prokaryotes

Bacterial chromosome

**(a) A typical rod-shaped bacterium**

**Flagella:** locomotion organelles of some bacteria

0.5 μm

**(b) A thin section through the bacterium *Bacillus coagulans* (TEM)**

▲ **Figure 3.4 A prokaryotic cell.** Lacking a true nucleus and the other membrane-enclosed organelles of the eukaryotic cell, the prokaryotic cell is much simpler in structure. Prokaryotes include bacteria and archaea; the general cell structure of the two domains is essentially the same.

a region that is not bounded by a membrane **(Figure 3.4)**. The word *eukaryotic* means "true nucleus" (from the Greek *eu*, true, and *karyon*, kernel, here referring to the nucleus), and the word *prokaryotic* means "before nucleus" (from the Greek *pro*, before), reflecting the fact that prokaryotic cells evolved before eukaryotic cells.

The interior of either type of cell is called the **cytoplasm**; in eukaryotic cells, this term refers only to the region between the nucleus and the plasma membrane. Within the cytoplasm of a eukaryotic cell, suspended in cytosol, are a variety of organelles of specialized form and function. These membrane-bounded structures are absent in prokaryotic cells. Thus, the presence or absence of a true nucleus is just one aspect of the disparity in structural complexity between the two types of cells.

Eukaryotic cells are generally much larger than prokaryotic cells (see Figure 3.2). Size is a general feature of cell structure that relates to function. The logistics of carrying out cellular metabolism sets limits on cell size. At the lower limit, the smallest cells known are bacteria called mycoplasmas, which have diameters between 0.1 and 1.0 μm. These are perhaps the smallest packages with enough DNA to program metabolism and enough enzymes and other cellular equipment to carry out the activities necessary for a cell to sustain itself and

reproduce. Typical bacteria are 1–5 μm in diameter, about ten times the size of mycoplasmas. Eukaryotic cells are typically 10–100 μm in diameter.

Metabolic requirements also impose theoretical upper limits on the size that is practical for a single cell. At the boundary of every cell, the **plasma membrane** functions as a selective barrier that allows passage of enough oxygen, nutrients, and wastes to service the entire cell **(Figure 3.5)**. For each square micrometer of membrane, only a limited amount of a particular substance can cross per second, so the ratio of surface area to volume is critical. As a cell (or any other object) increases in size, its volume grows proportionately more than its surface area. (Area is proportional to a linear dimension squared, whereas volume is proportional to the linear dimension cubed.) Thus, a smaller object has a greater ratio of surface area to volume **(Figure 3.6)**. The **Scientific Skills Exercise** for this chapter (on p. 52) gives you a chance to calculate the volumes and surface areas of two actual cells—a mature yeast cell and a cell budding from it.

The need for a surface area sufficiently large to accommodate the volume helps explain the microscopic size of most cells and the narrow, elongated shapes of others, such as nerve cells. Larger organisms do not generally have *larger*

**(a) TEM of a plasma membrane.** The plasma membrane, here in a red blood cell, appears as a pair of dark bands separated by a light band.

Outside of cell

Inside of cell |—| 0.1 μm

Carbohydrate side chains

Hydrophilic region

Hydrophobic region

Hydrophilic region

Phospholipid

Proteins

**(b) Structure of the plasma membrane**

© 1996 Pearson Education, Inc.

▲ **Figure 3.5 The plasma membrane.** The plasma membrane and the membranes of organelles consist of a double layer (bilayer) of phospholipids with various proteins attached to or embedded in it. The hydrophobic parts, including phospholipid tails and interior portions of membrane proteins, are found in the interior of the membrane. The hydrophilic parts, including phospholipid heads, exterior portions of proteins, and channels of proteins, are in contact with aqueous solution. Carbohydrate side chains may be attached to proteins or lipids on the outer surface of the plasma membrane.

**MAKE CONNECTIONS** *Review Figure 3.14 and describe the characteristics of phospholipids that allow them to function as the major material of the plasma membrane.*

cells than smaller organisms—they simply have *more* cells. A sufficiently high ratio of surface area to volume is especially important in cells that exchange a lot of material with their surroundings, such as intestinal cells. Such cells may have many thin projections from their surface called *microvilli*, which increase surface area without an appreciable increase in volume.

The evolutionary relationships between prokaryotic and eukaryotic cells will be discussed later in this chapter. Most of the discussion of cell structure that follows in this chapter applies to eukaryotic cells.

## A Panoramic View of the Eukaryotic Cell

In addition to the plasma membrane at its outer surface, a eukaryotic cell has extensive and elaborately arranged internal membranes. These membranes divide the cell into compartments—the organelles mentioned earlier. The cell's compartments provide different local environments that facilitate specific metabolic functions, so incompatible processes can go on simultaneously inside a single cell. The plasma membrane and organelle membranes also participate

Surface area increases while total volume remains constant

| | 1 | 5 | 1 |
|---|---|---|---|
| **Total surface area** [sum of the surface areas (height × width) of all box sides × number of boxes] | 6 | 150 | 750 |
| **Total volume** [height × width × length × number of boxes] | 1 | 125 | 125 |
| **Surface-to-volume ratio** [surface area ÷ volume] | 6 | 1.2 | 6 |

▲ **Figure 3.6 Geometric relationships between surface area and volume.** In this diagram, cells are represented as boxes. Using arbitrary units of length, we can calculate the cell's surface area (in square units, or units$^2$), volume (in cubic units, or units$^3$), and ratio of surface area to volume. A high surface-to-volume ratio facilitates the exchange of materials between a cell and its environment.

directly in the cell's metabolism, because many enzymes are built right into the membranes.

The basic fabric of most biological membranes is a double layer of phospholipids and other lipids. Embedded in this lipid bilayer or attached to its surface are diverse proteins (see Figure 3.5). However, each type of membrane has a unique composition of lipids and proteins suited to that membrane's specific functions. For example, enzymes embedded in the membranes of the organelles called mitochondria function in cellular respiration.

Before continuing with this chapter, examine the eukaryotic cells in **Figure 3.7**. The generalized diagrams of an animal cell and a plant cell introduce the various organelles and highlight the key differences between animal and plant cells. The micrographs at the bottom of the figure give you a glimpse of cells from different types of eukaryotic organisms.

**CONCEPT CHECK 3.2**

1. After carefully reviewing Figure 3.7, briefly describe the structure and function of the nucleus, the mitochondrion, the chloroplast, and the endoplasmic reticulum.

2. **WHAT IF?** Imagine an elongated cell (such as a nerve cell) that measures 125 × 1 × 1 arbitrary units. Predict how its surface-to-volume ratio would compare with those in Figure 3.6. Then calculate the ratio and check your prediction.

For suggested answers, see Appendix A.

# Animal Cell (cutaway view of generalized cell)

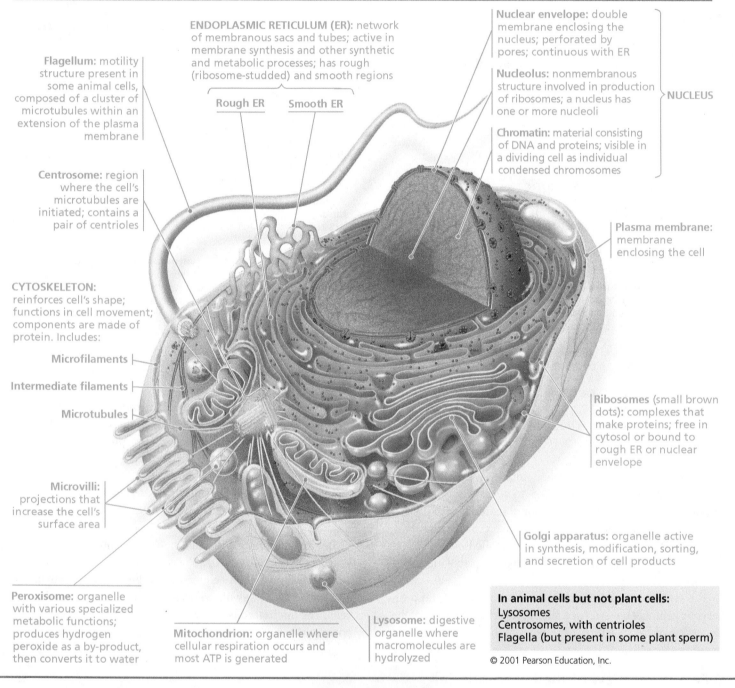

**Flagellum:** motility structure present in some animal cells, composed of a cluster of microtubules within an extension of the plasma membrane

**Centrosome:** region where the cell's microtubules are initiated; contains a pair of centrioles

**CYTOSKELETON:** reinforces cell's shape; functions in cell movement; components are made of protein. Includes:

**Microfilaments** ├

**Intermediate filaments** ├

**Microtubules** ├

**Microvilli:** projections that increase the cell's surface area

**ENDOPLASMIC RETICULUM (ER):** network of membranous sacs and tubes; active in membrane synthesis and other synthetic and metabolic processes; has rough (ribosome-studded) and smooth regions

Rough ER    Smooth ER

**Nuclear envelope:** double membrane enclosing the nucleus; perforated by pores; continuous with ER

**Nucleolus:** nonmembranous structure involved in production of ribosomes; a nucleus has one or more nucleoli

**Chromatin:** material consisting of DNA and proteins; visible in a dividing cell as individual condensed chromosomes

} **NUCLEUS**

**Plasma membrane:** membrane enclosing the cell

**Ribosomes** (small brown dots): complexes that make proteins; free in cytosol or bound to rough ER or nuclear envelope

**Golgi apparatus:** organelle active in synthesis, modification, sorting, and secretion of cell products

**Peroxisome:** organelle with various specialized metabolic functions; produces hydrogen peroxide as a by-product, then converts it to water

**Mitochondrion:** organelle where cellular respiration occurs and most ATP is generated

**Lysosome:** digestive organelle where macromolecules are hydrolyzed

**In animal cells but not plant cells:**
Lysosomes
Centrosomes, with centrioles
Flagella (but present in some plant sperm)

© 2001 Pearson Education, Inc.

**Animal Cells**

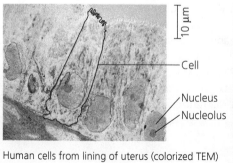

10 μm

— Cell

— Nucleus
— Nucleolus

Human cells from lining of uterus (colorized TEM)

**Fungal Cells**

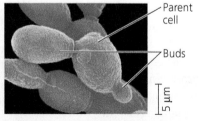

Parent cell

Buds

5 μm

Yeast cells: reproducing by budding (above, colorized SEM) and a single cell (right, colorized TEM)

1 μm

— Cell wall

— Vacuole

— Nucleus

— Mitochondrion

# Plant Cell (cutaway view of generalized cell)

ANIMATION

**BioFlix** Visit the Study Area in **MasteringBiology** for the BioFlix® 3-D Animations Tour of an Animal Cell and Tour of a Plant Cell.

**NUCLEUS** {
- Nuclear envelope
- Nucleolus
- Chromatin
}

Rough endoplasmic reticulum

Smooth endoplasmic reticulum

Ribosomes (small brown dots)

**Central vacuole:** prominent organelle in older plant cells; functions include storage, breakdown of waste products, hydrolysis of macromolecules; enlargement of vacuole is a major mechanism of plant growth

Golgi apparatus

Microfilaments

Intermediate filaments

CYTOSKELETON

Microtubules

Mitochondrion

Peroxisome

Plasma membrane

**Cell wall:** outer layer that maintains cell's shape and protects cell from mechanical damage; made of cellulose, other polysaccharides, and protein

Wall of adjacent cell

**Chloroplast:** photosynthetic organelle; converts energy of sunlight to chemical energy stored in sugar molecules

**Plasmodesmata:** channels through cell walls that connect the cytoplasms of adjacent cells

**In plant cells but not animal cells:**
Chloroplasts
Central vacuole
Cell wall
Plasmodesmata

© 2001 Pearson Education, Inc.

**Plant Cells**

- Cell
- Cell wall
- Chloroplast
- Mitochondrion
- Nucleus
- Nucleolus

5 μm

Cells from duckweed (*Spirodela oligorrhiza*), a floating plant (colorized TEM)

**Protistan Cells**

8 μm

Unicellular green alga *Chlamydomonas* (above, colorized SEM; right, colorized TEM)

1 μm

- Flagella
- Nucleus
- Nucleolus
- Vacuole
- Chloroplast
- Cell wall

## Using a Scale Bar to Calculate Volume and Surface Area of a Cell

**How Much New Cytoplasm and Plasma Membrane Are Made by a Growing Yeast Cell?** The unicellular yeast *Saccharomyces cerevisiae* divides by budding off a small new cell that then grows to full size. During its growth, the new cell synthesizes new cytoplasm, which increases its volume, and new plasma membrane, which increases its surface area.

In this exercise, you will use a scale bar to determine the sizes of a mature parent yeast cell and a cell budding from it. You will then calculate the volume and surface area of each cell. You will use your calculations to determine how much cytoplasm and plasma membrane the new cell needs to synthesize to grow to full size.

**How the Experiment Was Done** Yeast cells were grown under conditions that promoted division by budding. The cells were then viewed with a differential interference contrast light microscope and photographed.

**Data from the Experiment** This light micrograph shows a budding yeast cell about to be released from the mature parent cell:

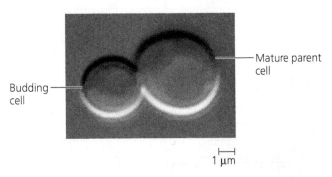

Budding cell — Mature parent cell

1 µm

**Interpret the Data**

1. Examine the micrograph of the yeast cells. The scale bar under the photo is labeled 1 µm. The scale bar works the same way as a scale on a map, where, for example, 1 inch equals 1 mile. In this case the bar represents a much smaller distance. Using the scale bar as a basic unit, determine the diameter of the mature parent cell and the new cell. Start by measuring the scale bar and then

each cell diameter. The units you use are irrelevant, but working in millimeters is convenient. Divide each diameter by the length of the scale bar and then multiply by the scale bar's label to give you the diameter in micrometers.

2. The shape of a yeast cell can be approximated by a sphere.
(a) Calculate the volume of each cell using the formula for the volume of a sphere:

$$V = \frac{4}{3}\pi r^3$$

Note that π (the Greek letter pi) is a constant with an approximate value of 3.14, *d* stands for diameter, and *r* stands for radius, which is half the diameter. (b) How much new cytoplasm will the new cell have to synthesize as it matures? To determine this, calculate the difference between the volume of the full-size cell and the volume of the new cell.

3. As the new cell grows, its plasma membrane needs to expand to contain the increased volume of the cell. (a) Calculate the surface area of each cell using the formula for the surface area of a sphere:

$$A = 4\pi r^2$$

(b) How much area of new plasma membrane will the new cell have to synthesize as it matures?

4. When the new cell matures, it will be approximately how many times greater in volume and how many times greater in surface area than its current size?

**Micrograph from** Kelly Tatchell, using yeast cells grown for experiments described in L. Kozubowski et al., Role of the septin ring in the asymmetric localization of proteins at the mother-bud neck in *Saccharomyces cerevisiae*, *Molecular Biology of the Cell* 16:3455–3466 (2005).

(MB) A version of this Scientific Skills Exercise can be assigned in MasteringBiology.

---

**CONCEPT** 3.3

# The eukaryotic cell's genetic instructions are housed in the nucleus and carried out by the ribosomes

On the first stop of our detailed tour of the cell, let's look at two cellular components involved in the genetic control of the cell: the nucleus, which houses most of the cell's DNA, and the ribosomes, which use information from the DNA to make proteins.

## The Nucleus: Information Central

The **nucleus** contains most of the genes in the eukaryotic cell. (Some genes are located in mitochondria and chloroplasts.) It is generally the most conspicuous organelle in a eukaryotic cell, averaging about 5 µm in diameter. The **nuclear envelope** encloses the nucleus (**Figure 3.8**), separating its contents from the cytoplasm.

The nuclear envelope is a *double* membrane. The two membranes, each a lipid bilayer with associated proteins, are separated by a space of 20–40 nm. The envelope is perforated by pore structures that are about 100 nm in diameter. At the lip of each pore, the inner and outer membranes of the nuclear envelope are continuous. An intricate protein structure called a

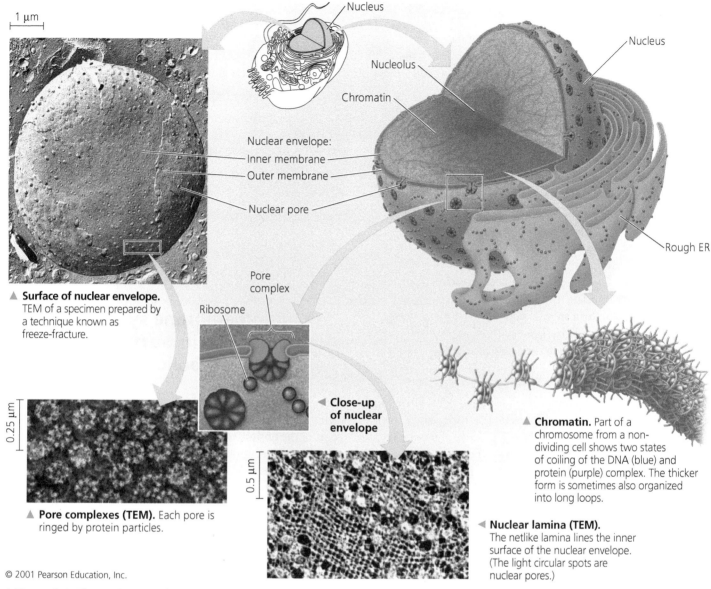

**1 μm**

Nucleus

Nucleolus

Chromatin

Nuclear envelope:
Inner membrane
Outer membrane
Nuclear pore

Nucleus

Rough ER

▲ **Surface of nuclear envelope.** TEM of a specimen prepared by a technique known as freeze-fracture.

Pore complex

Ribosome

◀ **Close-up of nuclear envelope**

**0.25 μm**

▲ **Pore complexes (TEM).** Each pore is ringed by protein particles.

**0.5 μm**

▲ **Chromatin.** Part of a chromosome from a non-dividing cell shows two states of coiling of the DNA (blue) and protein (purple) complex. The thicker form is sometimes also organized into long loops.

◀ **Nuclear lamina (TEM).** The netlike lamina lines the inner surface of the nuclear envelope. (The light circular spots are nuclear pores.)

© 2001 Pearson Education, Inc.

▲ **Figure 3.8 The nucleus and its envelope.** Within the nucleus are the chromosomes, which appear as a mass of chromatin (DNA and associated proteins), and one or more nucleoli (singular, *nucleolus*), which function in ribosome synthesis. The nuclear envelope, which consists of two membranes separated by a narrow space, is perforated with pores and lined by the nuclear lamina.

**MAKE CONNECTIONS** *Since the chromosomes contain the genetic material and reside in the nucleus, how does the rest of the cell get access to the information they carry? See Figure 3.25.*

*pore complex* lines each pore and plays an important role in the cell by regulating the entry and exit of proteins and RNAs, as well as large complexes of macromolecules. Except at the pores, the nuclear side of the envelope is lined by the **nuclear lamina**, a netlike array of protein filaments that maintains the shape of the nucleus by mechanically supporting the nuclear envelope.

Within the nucleus, the DNA is organized into discrete units called **chromosomes**, structures that carry the genetic information. Each chromosome contains one long DNA molecule associated with proteins. Some of the proteins help coil the

DNA molecule of the chromosome, reducing its length and allowing it to fit into the nucleus. The complex of DNA and proteins making up chromosomes is called **chromatin**. When a cell is not dividing, stained chromatin appears as a diffuse mass in micrographs, and the chromosomes cannot be distinguished from one another, even though discrete chromosomes are present. As a cell prepares to divide, however, the chromosomes coil (condense) further, becoming thick enough to be distinguished as separate structures. Each eukaryotic species has a characteristic number of chromosomes. For example, a typical human cell has 46 chromosomes in its nucleus; the exceptions are the sex cells (eggs and sperm), which have only 23 chromosomes in humans.

A prominent structure within the nondividing nucleus is the **nucleolus** (plural, *nucleoli*), which appears through the electron microscope as a mass of densely stained granules and fibers adjoining part of the chromatin. Here a type of RNA called *ribosomal RNA* (*rRNA*) is synthesized from instructions in the DNA. Also in the nucleolus, proteins imported from the cytoplasm are assembled with rRNA into large and small subunits of ribosomes. These subunits then exit the nucleus through the nuclear pores to the cytoplasm, where a large and a small subunit can assemble into a ribosome. Sometimes there are two or more nucleoli.

The nucleus directs protein synthesis by synthesizing messenger RNA (mRNA) according to instructions provided by the DNA. The mRNA is then transported to the cytoplasm via the nuclear pores. Once an mRNA molecule reaches the cytoplasm, ribosomes translate the mRNA's genetic message into the primary structure of a specific polypeptide. (This process of transcribing and translating genetic information is outlined in Figure 2.25 and described in detail in Chapter 14.)

## Ribosomes: Protein Factories

**Ribosomes**, which are complexes made of ribosomal RNA and protein, are the cellular components that carry out protein synthesis **(Figure 3.9)**. Cells that have high rates of protein synthesis have particularly large numbers of ribosomes. Not surprisingly, cells active in protein synthesis also have prominent nucleoli.

Ribosomes build proteins in two cytoplasmic locales. At any given time, *free ribosomes* are suspended in the cytosol, while *bound ribosomes* are attached to the outside of the endoplasmic reticulum or nuclear envelope (see Figure 3.9). Bound and free ribosomes are structurally identical, and ribosomes can alternate between the two roles. Most of the proteins made on free ribosomes function within the cytosol; examples are enzymes that catalyze the first steps of sugar breakdown. Bound ribosomes generally make proteins that are destined for insertion into membranes, for packaging

within certain organelles such as lysosomes (see Figure 3.7), or for export from the cell (secretion). Cells that specialize in protein secretion—for instance, the cells of the pancreas that secrete digestive enzymes—frequently have a high proportion of bound ribosomes. (You will learn more about ribosome structure and function in Chapter 14.)

**CONCEPT** 3.4

# The endomembrane system regulates protein traffic and performs metabolic functions in the cell

*Proteins that will be secreted will almost always enclosed by a membrane before secretion*

Many of the different membranes of the eukaryotic cell are part of the **endomembrane system**, which includes the nuclear envelope, the endoplasmic reticulum, the Golgi apparatus, lysosomes, various kinds of vesicles and vacuoles, and the plasma membrane. This system carries out a variety of tasks in the cell, including synthesis of proteins, transport of proteins into membranes and organelles or out of the cell, metabolism and movement of lipids, and detoxification of poisons. The membranes of this system are related either through direct physical continuity or by the transfer of membrane segments as tiny **vesicles** (sacs made of membrane). Despite these relationships, the various membranes are not identical in structure and function. Moreover, the thickness, molecular composition, and types of chemical reactions carried out in a given membrane are not fixed, but may be modified several times during

▶ **Figure 3.9  Ribosomes.** This electron micrograph of part of a pancreas cell shows many ribosomes, both free (in the cytosol) and bound (to the endoplasmic reticulum). The simplified diagram of a ribosome shows its two subunits.

**DRAW IT**  *After you have read the section on ribosomes, circle a ribosome in the micrograph that might be making a protein that will be secreted.*

TEM showing ER and ribosomes        Diagram of a ribosome

the membrane's life. Having already discussed the nuclear envelope, we will now focus on the endoplasmic reticulum and the other endomembranes to which the endoplasmic reticulum gives rise.

## The Endoplasmic Reticulum: Biosynthetic Factory

The **endoplasmic reticulum (ER)** is such an extensive network of membranes that it accounts for more than half the total membrane in many eukaryotic cells. (The word *endoplasmic* means "within the cytoplasm," and *reticulum* is Latin for "little net.") The ER consists of a network of membranous tubules and sacs called cisternae (from the Latin *cisterna*, a reservoir for a liquid). The ER membrane separates the internal compartment of the ER, called the ER lumen (cavity) or cisternal space, from the cytosol. And because the ER membrane is continuous with the nuclear envelope, the space between the two membranes of the envelope is continuous with the lumen of the ER **(Figure 3.10)**.

There are two distinct, though connected, regions of the ER that differ in structure and function: smooth ER and rough ER. **Smooth ER** is so named because its outer surface lacks ribosomes. **Rough ER** is studded with ribosomes on the outer surface of the membrane and thus appears rough through the electron microscope. As already mentioned, ribosomes are also attached to the cytoplasmic side of the nuclear envelope's outer membrane, which is continuous with rough ER.

### Functions of Smooth ER

The smooth ER functions in diverse metabolic processes, which vary with cell type. These processes include synthesis of lipids, metabolism of carbohydrates, detoxification of drugs and poisons, and storage of calcium ions.

Enzymes of the smooth ER are important in the synthesis of lipids, including oils, phospholipids, and steroids. Among the steroids produced by the smooth ER in animal cells are the sex hormones of vertebrates and the various steroid hormones secreted by the adrenal glands. The cells that synthesize and secrete these hormones—in the testes and ovaries, for example—are rich in smooth ER, a structural feature that fits the function of these cells.

Other enzymes of the smooth ER help detoxify drugs and poisons, especially in liver cells. Detoxification usually involves adding hydroxyl groups to drug molecules, making them more soluble and easier to flush from the body. The sedative phenobarbital and other barbiturates are examples of drugs metabolized in this manner by smooth ER in liver cells. In fact, barbiturates, alcohol, and many other drugs induce the proliferation of smooth ER and its associated detoxification enzymes, thus increasing the rate of detoxification. This, in turn, increases tolerance to the drugs, meaning that higher doses are required to achieve a particular effect, such as sedation. Also, because some of the detoxification enzymes have relatively

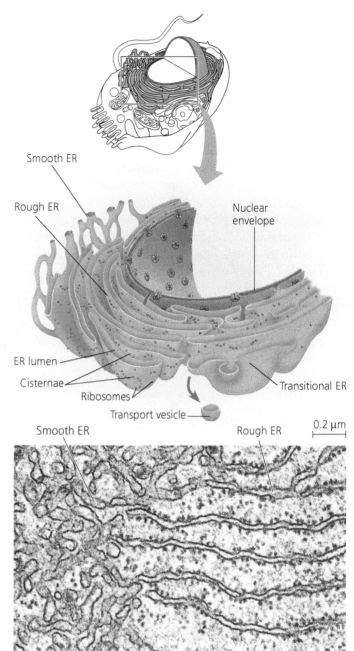

Smooth ER

Rough ER

Nuclear envelope

ER lumen

Cisternae

Ribosomes

Transitional ER

Transport vesicle

Smooth ER

Rough ER

0.2 μm

▲ **Figure 3.10 Endoplasmic reticulum (ER).** A membranous system of interconnected tubules and flattened sacs called cisternae, the ER is also continuous with the nuclear envelope. (The drawing is a cutaway view.) The membrane of the ER encloses a continuous compartment called the ER lumen (or cisternal space). Rough ER, which is studded on its outer surface with ribosomes, can be distinguished from smooth ER in the electron micrograph (TEM). Transport vesicles bud off from a region of the rough ER called transitional ER and travel to the Golgi apparatus and other destinations.

broad action, the proliferation of smooth ER in response to one drug can increase tolerance to other drugs as well. Barbiturate abuse, for example, can decrease the effectiveness of certain antibiotics and other useful drugs.

The smooth ER also stores calcium ions. In muscle cells, for example, the smooth ER membrane pumps calcium ions from the cytosol into the ER lumen. When a muscle cell is stimulated by a nerve impulse, calcium ions rush back across the ER membrane into the cytosol and trigger contraction of the muscle cell.

### Functions of Rough ER

Many types of cells secrete proteins produced by ribosomes attached to rough ER. For example, certain pancreatic cells synthesize the protein insulin in the ER and secrete this hormone into the bloodstream. As a polypeptide chain grows from a bound ribosome, the chain is threaded into the ER lumen through a pore formed by a protein complex in the ER membrane. As the new polypeptide enters the ER lumen, it folds into its functional shape. Most secretory proteins are **glycoproteins**, proteins that have carbohydrates covalently bonded to them. The carbohydrates are attached to the proteins in the ER by enzymes built into the ER membrane.

After secretory proteins are formed, the ER membrane keeps them separate from proteins that are produced by free ribosomes and that will remain in the cytosol. Secretory proteins depart from the ER wrapped in the membranes of vesicles that bud like bubbles from a specialized region called transitional ER (see Figure 3.10). Vesicles in transit from one part of the cell to another are called **transport vesicles**; we will discuss their fate shortly.

In addition to making secretory proteins, rough ER is a membrane factory for the cell; it grows in place by adding membrane proteins and phospholipids to its own membrane. As polypeptides destined to be membrane proteins grow from the ribosomes, they are inserted into the ER membrane itself and anchored there by their hydrophobic portions. Like the smooth ER, the rough ER also makes membrane phospholipids; enzymes built into the ER membrane assemble phospholipids from precursors in the cytosol. The ER membrane expands, and portions of it are transferred in the form of transport vesicles to other components of the endomembrane system.

## The Golgi Apparatus: Shipping and Receiving Center

After leaving the ER, many transport vesicles travel to the **Golgi apparatus**. We can think of the Golgi primarily as a warehouse for receiving, sorting, and shipping, although some manufacturing also occurs there. In the Golgi, products of the ER, such as proteins, are modified and stored and then sent to other destinations. Not surprisingly, the Golgi apparatus is especially extensive in cells specialized for secretion.

The Golgi apparatus consists of flattened membranous sacs—cisternae—looking like a stack of pita bread (**Figure 3.11**). A cell may have many, even hundreds, of these stacks. The membrane of each cisterna in a stack separates its internal space from the cytosol. Vesicles concentrated in the vicinity of the Golgi apparatus are engaged in the transfer of material between parts of the Golgi and other structures.

▼ **Figure 3.11** **The Golgi apparatus.** The Golgi apparatus consists of stacks of flattened sacs, or cisternae, which, unlike ER cisternae, are not physically connected. (The drawing is a cutaway view.) A Golgi stack receives and dispatches transport vesicles and the products they contain. A Golgi stack has a structural and functional directionality, with a *cis* face that receives vesicles containing ER products and a *trans* face that dispatches vesicles. The cisternal maturation model proposes that the Golgi cisternae themselves "mature," moving from the *cis* to the *trans* face while carrying some proteins along. In addition, some vesicles recycle enzymes that had been carried forward in moving cisternae, transporting them "backward" to a less mature region where their functions are needed.

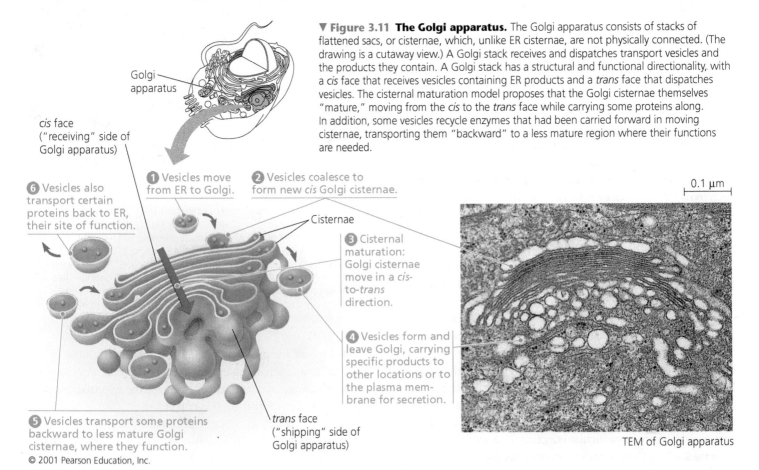

Golgi apparatus

*cis* face ("receiving" side of Golgi apparatus)

**6** Vesicles also transport certain proteins back to ER, their site of function.

**1** Vesicles move from ER to Golgi.

**2** Vesicles coalesce to form new *cis* Golgi cisternae.

Cisternae

**3** Cisternal maturation: Golgi cisternae move in a *cis*-to-*trans* direction.

**4** Vesicles form and leave Golgi, carrying specific products to other locations or to the plasma membrane for secretion.

**5** Vesicles transport some proteins backward to less mature Golgi cisternae, where they function.

*trans* face ("shipping" side of Golgi apparatus)

0.1 μm

TEM of Golgi apparatus

© 2001 Pearson Education, Inc.

A Golgi stack has a distinct structural directionality, with the membranes of cisternae on opposite sides of the stack differing in thickness and molecular composition. The two sides of a Golgi stack are referred to as the *cis* face and the *trans* face; these act, respectively, as the receiving and shipping departments of the Golgi apparatus. The *cis* face is usually located near the ER. Transport vesicles move material from the ER to the Golgi apparatus. A vesicle that buds from the ER can add its membrane and the contents of its lumen to the *cis* face by fusing with a Golgi membrane. The *trans* face gives rise to vesicles that pinch off and travel to other sites.

Products of the endoplasmic reticulum are usually modified during their transit from the *cis* region to the *trans* region of the Golgi apparatus. For example, glycoproteins formed in the ER have their carbohydrates modified, first in the ER itself, then as they pass through the Golgi. The Golgi removes some sugar monomers and substitutes others, producing a large variety of carbohydrates. Membrane phospholipids may also be altered in the Golgi.

In addition to its finishing work, the Golgi apparatus also manufactures some macromolecules. Many polysaccharides secreted by cells are Golgi products. For example, pectins and certain other noncellulose polysaccharides are made in the Golgi of plant cells and then incorporated along with cellulose into their cell walls. Like secretory proteins, nonprotein Golgi products that will be secreted depart from the *trans* face of the Golgi inside transport vesicles that eventually fuse with the plasma membrane.

The Golgi manufactures and refines its products in stages, with different cisternae containing unique teams of enzymes. Until recently, biologists viewed the Golgi as a static structure, with products in various stages of processing transferred from one cisterna to the next by vesicles. While this may occur, recent research has given rise to a new model of the Golgi as a more dynamic structure. According to the *cisternal maturation model*, the cisternae of the Golgi actually progress forward from the *cis* to the *trans* face, carrying and modifying their cargo as they move. Figure 3.11 shows the details of this model.

Before a Golgi stack dispatches its products by budding vesicles from the *trans* face, it sorts these products and targets them for various parts of the cell. Molecular identification tags, such as phosphate groups added to the Golgi products, aid in sorting by acting like ZIP codes on mailing labels. Finally, transport vesicles budded from the Golgi may have external molecules on their membranes that recognize "docking sites" on the surface of specific organelles or on the plasma membrane, thus targeting the vesicles appropriately.

## Lysosomes: Digestive Compartments

A **lysosome** is a membranous sac of hydrolytic enzymes that an animal cell uses to digest (hydrolyze) macromolecules. Lysosomal enzymes work best in the acidic environment found in lysosomes. If a lysosome breaks open or leaks its contents,

the released enzymes are not very active because the cytosol has a neutral pH. However, excessive leakage from a large number of lysosomes can destroy a cell by self-digestion.

Hydrolytic enzymes and lysosomal membrane are made by rough ER and then transferred to the Golgi apparatus for further processing. At least some lysosomes probably arise by budding from the *trans* face of the Golgi apparatus (see Figure 3.11). How are the proteins of the inner surface of the lysosomal membrane and the digestive enzymes themselves spared from destruction? Apparently, the three-dimensional shapes of these lysosomal proteins protect vulnerable bonds from enzymatic attack.

Lysosomes carry out intracellular digestion in a variety of circumstances. Amoebas and many other protists eat by engulfing smaller organisms or food particles, a process called **phagocytosis** (from the Greek *phagein*, to eat, and *kytos*, vessel, referring here to the cell). The *food vacuole* formed in this way then fuses with a lysosome, whose enzymes digest the food (**Figure 3.12**, bottom). Digestion products, including simple sugars, amino acids, and other monomers, pass into the

**① Lysosome contains active hydrolytic enzymes.**

**② Food vacuole fuses with lysosome.**

**③ Hydrolytic enzymes digest food particles.**

▲ **Figure 3.12 Lysosomes: Phagocytosis.** In phagocytosis, lysosomes digest (hydrolyze) materials taken into the cell. *Top*: In this macrophage (a type of white blood cell) from a rat, the lysosomes are very dark because of a stain that reacts with one of the products of digestion inside the lysosome (TEM). Macrophages ingest bacteria and viruses and destroy them using lysosomes. *Bottom*: This diagram shows a lysosome fusing with a food vacuole during the process of phagocytosis by a protist.

cytosol and become nutrients for the cell. Some human cells also carry out phagocytosis. Among them are macrophages, a type of white blood cell that helps defend the body by engulfing and destroying bacteria and other invaders (see Figure 3.12, top, and Figure 3.28).

Lysosomes also use their hydrolytic enzymes to recycle the cell's own organic material, a process called *autophagy*. During autophagy, a damaged organelle or small amount of cytosol becomes surrounded by a double membrane, and a lysosome fuses with the outer membrane of this vesicle (Figure 3.13). The lysosomal enzymes dismantle the enclosed material, and the resulting small organic compounds are released to the cytosol for reuse. With the help of lysosomes, the cell continually renews itself. A human liver cell, for example, recycles half of its macromolecules each week.

The cells of people with inherited lysosomal storage diseases lack a functioning hydrolytic enzyme normally present in lysosomes. The lysosomes become engorged with indigestible material, which begins to interfere with other cellular activities. In Tay-Sachs disease, for example, a lipid-digesting enzyme is missing or inactive, and the brain becomes impaired by an accumulation of lipids in the cells. Fortunately, lysosomal storage diseases are rare in the general population.

## Vacuoles: Diverse Maintenance Compartments

**Vacuoles** are large vesicles derived from the endoplasmic reticulum and Golgi apparatus. Thus, vacuoles are an integral part of a cell's endomembrane system. Like all cellular membranes, the vacuolar membrane is selective in transporting solutes; as a result, the solution inside a vacuole differs in composition from the cytosol.

Vacuoles perform a variety of functions in different kinds of cells. **Food vacuoles**, formed by phagocytosis, have already been mentioned (see Figure 3.12). Many freshwater protists have **contractile vacuoles** that pump excess water out of the cell, thereby maintaining a suitable concentration of ions and molecules inside the cell. In plants and fungi, certain vacuoles carry out enzymatic hydrolysis, a function shared by lysosomes in animal cells. (In fact, some biologists consider these hydrolytic vacuoles to be a type of lysosome.) In plants, small vacuoles can hold reserves of important organic compounds, such as the proteins stockpiled in the storage cells in seeds. Vacuoles may also help protect the plant against herbivores by storing compounds that are poisonous or unpalatable to animals. Some plant vacuoles contain pigments, such as the red and blue pigments of petals that help attract pollinating insects to flowers.

Mature plant cells generally contain a large **central vacuole** (Figure 3.14), which develops by the coalescence of smaller vacuoles. The solution inside the central vacuole, called cell sap, is the plant cell's main repository of inorganic ions, including potassium and chloride. The central vacuole plays a major role in the growth of plant cells, which enlarge as the vacuole absorbs water, enabling the cell to become larger with a minimal investment in new cytoplasm. The cytosol often occupies only a thin layer between the central vacuole and the plasma

❶ Lysosome fuses with vesicle containing damaged organelles.

❷ Hydrolytic enzymes digest organelle components.

Vesicle containing two damaged organelles

1 μm

Mitochondrion fragment

Peroxisome fragment

Lysosome

Peroxisome

Mitochondrion

Vesicle

Digestion

▲ **Figure 3.13 Lysosomes: Autophagy.** In autophagy, lysosomes recycle intracellular materials. *Top*: In the cytoplasm of this rat liver cell is a vesicle containing two disabled organelles; the vesicle will fuse with a lysosome in the process of autophagy (TEM). *Bottom*: This diagram shows fusion of such a vesicle with a lysosome and the subsequent digestion of the damaged organelles.

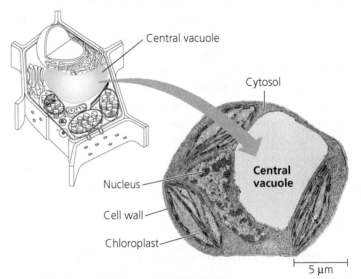

Central vacuole

Cytosol

Nucleus

Cell wall

Chloroplast

Central vacuole

5 μm

▲ **Figure 3.14 The plant cell vacuole.** The central vacuole is usually the largest compartment in a plant cell; the rest of the cytoplasm is often confined to a narrow zone between the vacuolar membrane and the plasma membrane (TEM).

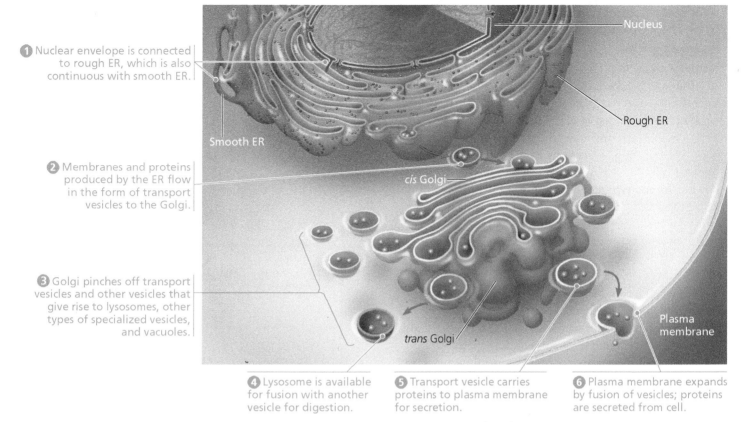

① Nuclear envelope is connected to rough ER, which is also continuous with smooth ER.

Nucleus

Rough ER

Smooth ER

② Membranes and proteins produced by the ER flow in the form of transport vesicles to the Golgi.

*cis* Golgi

③ Golgi pinches off transport vesicles and other vesicles that give rise to lysosomes, other types of specialized vesicles, and vacuoles.

Plasma membrane

*trans* Golgi

④ Lysosome is available for fusion with another vesicle for digestion.

⑤ Transport vesicle carries proteins to plasma membrane for secretion.

⑥ Plasma membrane expands by fusion of vesicles; proteins are secreted from cell.

▲ **Figure 3.15 Review: relationships among organelles of the endomembrane system.** The red arrows show some of the migration pathways for membranes and the materials they enclose.

membrane, so the ratio of plasma membrane surface to cytosolic volume is sufficient, even for a large plant cell.

### The Endomembrane System: *A Review*

**Figure 3.15** reviews the endomembrane system, showing the flow of membrane lipids and proteins through the various organelles. As the membrane moves from the ER to the Golgi and then elsewhere, its molecular composition and metabolic functions are modified, along with those of its contents. The endomembrane system is a complex and dynamic player in the cell's compartmental organization.

We'll continue our tour of the cell with some organelles that are not closely related to the endomembrane system but play crucial roles in the energy transformations carried out by cells.

**CONCEPT CHECK 3.4**

1. Describe the structural and functional distinctions between rough and smooth ER.
2. Describe how transport vesicles integrate the endomembrane system.
3. **WHAT IF?** Imagine a protein that functions in the ER but requires modification in the Golgi apparatus before it can achieve that function. Describe the protein's path through the cell, starting with the mRNA molecule that specifies the protein.

For suggested answers, see Appendix A.

**CONCEPT** 3.5

# Mitochondria and chloroplasts change energy from one form to another

Organisms transform the energy they acquire from their surroundings. In eukaryotic cells, mitochondria and chloroplasts are the organelles that convert energy to forms that cells can use for work. **Mitochondria** (singular, *mitochondrion*) are the sites of cellular respiration, the metabolic process that uses oxygen to generate ATP by extracting energy from sugars, fats, and other fuels. **Chloroplasts**, found in plants and algae, are the sites of photosynthesis. These organelles convert solar energy to chemical energy by absorbing sunlight and using it to drive the synthesis of organic compounds such as sugars from carbon dioxide and water.

In addition to having related functions, mitochondria and chloroplasts share similar evolutionary origins, which we'll discuss briefly before describing their structures. In this section, we will also consider the peroxisome, an oxidative organelle. The evolutionary origin of the peroxisome, as well as its relation to other organelles, is still under debate.

## The Evolutionary Origins of Mitochondria and Chloroplasts

**EVOLUTION** Mitochondria and chloroplasts display similarities with bacteria that led to the **endosymbiont theory**, illustrated in **Figure 3.16**. This theory states that an early ancestor of eukaryotic cells engulfed an oxygen-using nonphotosynthetic prokaryotic cell. Eventually, the engulfed cell formed a relationship with the host cell in which it was enclosed, becoming an *endosymbiont* (a cell living within another cell). Indeed, over the course of evolution, the host cell and its endosymbiont merged into a single organism, a eukaryotic cell with a mitochondrion. At least one of these cells may have then taken up a photosynthetic prokaryote, becoming the ancestor of eukaryotic cells that contain chloroplasts.

This theory is consistent with many structural features of mitochondria and chloroplasts. First, rather than being bounded by a single membrane like organelles of the endomembrane system, mitochondria and typical chloroplasts have two membranes surrounding them. (Chloroplasts also have an internal system of membranous sacs.) There is evidence that the ancestral engulfed prokaryotes had two outer membranes, which became the double membranes of mitochondria and chloroplasts. Second, like prokaryotes, mitochondria and chloroplasts contain ribosomes, as well as multiple circular DNA molecules attached to their inner membranes. The DNA in these organelles programs the synthesis of some of their own proteins, which are made on the ribosomes inside the organelles. Third, also consistent with their probable evolutionary origins as cells, mitochondria and chloroplasts are autonomous (somewhat independent) organelles that grow and reproduce within the cell.

Next we focus on the structure of mitochondria and chloroplasts, while providing an overview of their functions.

▲ **Figure 3.16 The endosymbiont theory of the origin of mitochondria and chloroplasts in eukaryotic cells.** According to this theory, the proposed ancestors of mitochondria were oxygen-using nonphotosynthetic prokaryotes, while the proposed ancestors of chloroplasts were photosynthetic prokaryotes. The large arrows represent change over evolutionary time; the small arrows inside the cells show the process of the endosymbiont becoming an organelle.

## Mitochondria: Chemical Energy Conversion

Each of the two membranes enclosing a mitochondrion is a phospholipid bilayer with a unique collection of embedded proteins **(Figure 3.17)**. The outer membrane is smooth, but the inner membrane is convoluted, with infoldings called

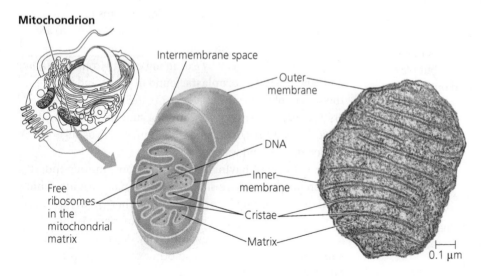

◀ **Figure 3.17 The mitochondrion, site of cellular respiration.** The inner and outer membranes of the mitochondrion are evident in this drawing and electron micrograph (TEM). The cristae are infoldings of the inner membrane, which increase its surface area. The cutaway drawing shows the two compartments bounded by the membranes: the intermembrane space and the mitochondrial matrix. Many respiratory enzymes are found in the inner membrane and the matrix. Free ribosomes are also present in the matrix. The circular DNA molecules are attached to the inner mitochondrial membrane.

cristae. The inner membrane divides the mitochondrion into two internal compartments. The first is the intermembrane space, the narrow region between the inner and outer membranes. The second compartment, the **mitochondrial matrix**, is enclosed by the inner membrane. The matrix contains many different enzymes as well as the mitochondrial DNA and ribosomes. Enzymes in the matrix catalyze some of the steps of cellular respiration. Other proteins that function in respiration, including the enzyme that makes ATP, are built into the inner membrane. As highly folded surfaces, the cristae give the inner mitochondrial membrane a large surface area, thus enhancing the productivity of cellular respiration. This is another example of structure fitting function. (Chapter 6 discusses cellular respiration in detail.)

Mitochondria are found in nearly all eukaryotic cells, including those of plants, animals, fungi, and most protists. Some cells have a single large mitochondrion, but more often a cell has hundreds or even thousands of mitochondria; the number correlates with the cell's level of metabolic activity. For example, cells that move or contract have proportionally more mitochondria per volume than less active cells.

Mitochondria are generally in the range of 1–10 μm long. Time-lapse films of living cells reveal mitochondria moving around, changing their shapes, and fusing or dividing in two, unlike the static structures seen in electron micrographs of dead cells.

## Chloroplasts: Capture of Light Energy

Chloroplasts contain the green pigment chlorophyll, along with enzymes and other molecules that function in the photo-synthetic production of sugar. These lens-shaped organelles, about 3–6 μm in length, are found in leaves and other green organs of plants and in algae (**Figure 3.18**).

The contents of a chloroplast are partitioned from the cytosol by an envelope consisting of two membranes separated by a very narrow intermembrane space. Inside the chloroplast is another membranous system in the form of flattened, interconnected sacs called **thylakoids**. In some regions, thylakoids are stacked like poker chips; each stack is called a **granum** (plural, *grana*). The fluid outside the thylakoids is the **stroma**, which contains the chloroplast DNA and ribosomes as well as many enzymes. The membranes of the chloroplast divide the chloroplast space into three compartments: the intermembrane space, the stroma, and the thylakoid space. This compartmental organization enables the chloroplast to convert light energy to chemical energy during photosynthesis.

As with mitochondria, the static and rigid appearance of chloroplasts in micrographs or schematic diagrams is not true to their dynamic behavior in the living cell. Their shape is changeable, and they grow and occasionally pinch in two, reproducing themselves. They are mobile and, along with mitochondria and other organelles, move around the cell along tracks of the cytoskeleton, a structural network we will consider later in this chapter.

The chloroplast is a specialized member of a family of closely related plant organelles called **plastids**. One type of plastid, the *amyloplast*, is a colorless organelle that stores starch (amylose), particularly in roots and tubers. Another is the *chromoplast*, which has pigments that give fruits and flowers their orange and yellow hues.

▼ Figure 3.18 **The chloroplast, site of photosynthesis.** (a) Many plants have disk-shaped choloroplasts, as shown here. A typical chloroplast has three compartments: the intermembrane space, the stroma, and the thylakoid space. Free ribosomes are present in the stroma, as are copies of chloroplast DNA molecules. (b) This fluorescence micrograph shows a cell of the green alga *Spirogyra crassa*, which is named for its spiral chloroplasts. Under natural light the chloroplasts appear green, but under ultraviolet light they naturally fluoresce red, as shown here.

Chloroplast

Ribosomes

Stroma

Inner and outer membranes

Granum

Thylakoid

DNA

Intermembrane space

50 μm

Chloroplasts (red)

1 μm

**(a) Diagram and TEM of chloroplast**

**(b) Chloroplasts in an algal cell**

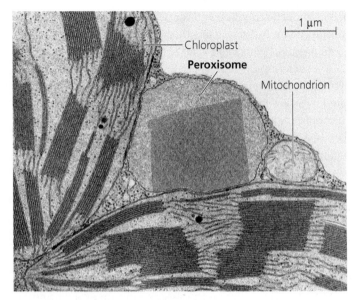

▲ **Figure 3.19 A peroxisome.** Peroxisomes are roughly spherical and often have a granular or crystalline core that is thought to be a dense collection of enzyme molecules. This peroxisome is in a leaf cell (TEM). Notice its proximity to two chloroplasts and a mitochondrion. These organelles cooperate with peroxisomes in certain metabolic functions.

*multiply by splitting into two.*

## Peroxisomes: Oxidation

The **peroxisome** is a specialized metabolic compartment bounded by a single membrane **(Figure 3.19)**. Peroxisomes contain enzymes that remove hydrogen atoms from certain molecules and transfer them to oxygen ($O_2$), producing hydrogen peroxide ($H_2O_2$). These reactions have many different functions. For example, peroxisomes in the liver detoxify alcohol and other harmful compounds by transferring hydrogen from the poisons to oxygen. The $H_2O_2$ formed by peroxisomes is itself toxic, but the organelle also contains an enzyme that converts $H_2O_2$ to water. This is an excellent example of how the cell's compartmental structure is crucial to its functions: The enzymes that produce $H_2O_2$ and those that dispose of this toxic compound are sequestered from other cellular components that could be damaged.

Peroxisomes grow larger by incorporating proteins made in the cytosol and ER, as well as lipids made in the ER and within the peroxisome itself. But how peroxisomes increase in number and how they arose in evolution are still open questions.

### CONCEPT CHECK 3.5

1. Describe two characteristics that chloroplasts and mitochondria have in common. Consider both function and membrane structure.
2. Do plant cells have mitochondria? Explain.
3. **WHAT IF?** A classmate proposes that mitochondria and chloroplasts should be classified in the endomembrane system. Argue against the proposal.

For suggested answers, see Appendix A.

**CONCEPT** 3.6

# The cytoskeleton is a network of fibers that organizes structures and activities in the cell

In the early days of electron microscopy, biologists thought that the organelles of a eukaryotic cell floated freely in the cytosol. But improvements in both light microscopy and electron microscopy have revealed the **cytoskeleton**, a network of fibers extending throughout the cytoplasm **(Figure 3.20)**. The cytoskeleton plays a major role in organizing the structures and activities of the cell.

## Roles of the Cytoskeleton: Support and Motility

The most obvious function of the cytoskeleton is to give mechanical support to the cell and maintain its shape. This is especially important for animal cells, which lack walls. The remarkable strength and resilience of the cytoskeleton as a whole is based on its architecture. Like a dome tent, the cytoskeleton is stabilized by a balance between opposing forces exerted by its elements. And just as the skeleton of an animal helps fix the positions of other body parts, the cytoskeleton provides anchorage for many organelles and even cytosolic enzyme molecules. The cytoskeleton is more dynamic than an animal skeleton, however. It can be quickly dismantled in one part of the cell and reassembled in a new location, changing the shape of the cell.

Several types of cell motility (movement) also involve the cytoskeleton. The term *cell motility* encompasses both changes in cell location and more limited movements of parts of the cell. Cell motility generally requires the interaction of

▲ **Figure 3.20 The cytoskeleton.** As shown in this fluorescence micrograph, the cytoskeleton extends throughout the cell. The cytoskeletal elements have been tagged with different fluorescent molecules: green for microtubules and red for microfilaments (which look orangish here). A third component of the cytoskeleton, intermediate filaments, is not evident. (The blue area is DNA in the nucleus.)

**(a)** Motor proteins that attach to receptors on vesicles can "walk" the vesicles along the cytoskeletal fibers called microtubules or, in some cases, along microfilaments. ATP powers the movement.

Microtubule        Vesicles                    0.25 μm

**(b)** In this SEM of a squid giant axon (a nerve cell extension), two vesicles containing neurotransmitters migrate toward the tip of the axon via the mechanism shown in (a).

▲ **Figure 3.21 Motor proteins and the cytoskeleton.**

the cytoskeleton with **motor proteins**. Examples of such cell motility abound. Cytoskeletal elements and motor proteins work together with plasma membrane molecules to allow whole cells to move along fibers outside the cell. Inside the cell, vesicles and other organelles often use motor protein "feet" to "walk" to their destinations along a track provided by the cytoskeleton. For example, this is how vesicles containing neurotransmitter molecules migrate to the tips of axons, the long extensions of nerve cells that release these molecules as chemical signals to adjacent nerve cells **(Figure 3.21)**. The vesicles that bud off from the ER also travel along cytoskeletal tracks as they make their way to the Golgi. And the cytoskeleton can manipulate the plasma membrane so that it bends inward to form food vacuoles or other phagocytic vesicles.

## Components of the Cytoskeleton

Let's look more closely at the three main types of fibers that make up the cytoskeleton: *Microtubules* are the thickest, *microfilaments* (actin filaments) are the thinnest, and *intermediate filaments* are fibers with diameters in a middle range. **Table 3.1** (next page) summarizes the properties of these fibers.

### *Microtubules*

All eukaryotic cells have **microtubules**, hollow rods constructed from a globular protein called tubulin. Each

tubulin protein is a *dimer*, a molecule made up of two subunits. A tubulin dimer consists of two slightly different polypeptides, α-tubulin and β-tubulin. Microtubules grow in length by adding tubulin dimers; they can also be disassembled and their tubulin used to build microtubules elsewhere in the cell.

Microtubules shape and support the cell and serve as tracks along which organelles equipped with motor proteins can move (see Figure 3.21). Microtubules are also involved in the separation of chromosomes during cell division.

**Centrosomes and Centrioles** In animal cells, microtubules grow out from a **centrosome**, a region that is often located near the nucleus and is considered a "microtubule-organizing center." These microtubules function as compression-resisting girders of the cytoskeleton. Within the centrosome is a pair of **centrioles**, each composed of nine sets of triplet microtubules arranged in a ring **(Figure 3.22)**. Before an animal cell divides, the centrioles replicate. Although centrosomes with centrioles may help organize microtubule assembly in animal cells, they are not essential for this function in all eukaryotes; fungi and almost all plant cells lack centrosomes with centrioles but have well-organized microtubules. Apparently, other microtubule-organizing centers play the role of centrosomes in these cells.

**Cilia and Flagella** In eukaryotes, a specialized arrangement of microtubules is responsible for the beating of **flagella** (singular, *flagellum*) and **cilia** (singular, *cilium*), microtubule-containing extensions that project from some cells. (The bacterial flagellum, shown in Figure 3.4, has a completely different

▲ **Figure 3.22 Centrosome containing a pair of centrioles.** Most animal cells have a centrosome, a region near the nucleus where the cell's microtubules are initiated. Within the centrosome is a pair of centrioles, each about 250 nm (0.25 μm) in diameter. The two centrioles are at right angles to each other, and each is made up of nine sets of three microtubules. The blue portions of the drawing represent nontubulin proteins that connect the microtubule triplets.

**?** *How many microtubules are in a centrosome? In the drawing, circle and label one microtubule and describe its structure. Circle and label a triplet.*

**Table 3.1 The Structure and Function of the Cytoskeleton**

| Property | Microtubules (Tubulin Polymers) | Microfilaments (Actin Filaments) | Intermediate Filaments |
|---|---|---|---|
| Structure | Hollow tubes; wall consists of 13 columns of tubulin molecules | Two intertwined strands of actin, each a polymer of actin subunits | Fibrous proteins supercoiled into thicker cables |
| Diameter | 25 nm with 15-nm lumen | 7 nm | 8–12 nm |
| Protein subunits | Tubulin, a dimer consisting of α-tubulin and β-tubulin | Actin | One of several different proteins (such as keratins), depending on cell type |
| Main functions | Maintenance of cell shape | Maintenance of cell shape | Maintenance of cell shape |
| | Cell motility (as in cilia or flagella) | Changes in cell shape | Anchorage of nucleus and certain other organelles |
| | Chromosome movements in cell division | Muscle contraction | Formation of nuclear lamina |
| | Organelle movements | Cytoplasmic streaming in plants | |
| | | Cell motility (as in amoeboid movement) | |
| | | Division of animal cells | |

Column of tubulin dimers

25 nm

α  β  Tubulin dimer

Actin subunit

7 nm

Keratin proteins

Fibrous subunit (keratins coiled together)

8–12 nm

© 2000 Pearson Education, Inc.

structure.) Many unicellular eukaryotes are propelled through water by cilia or flagella that act as locomotor appendages, and the sperm of animals, algae, and some plants have flagella. When cilia or flagella extend from cells that are held in place as part of a tissue layer, they can move fluid over the surface of the tissue. For example, the ciliated lining of the trachea (windpipe) sweeps mucus containing debris out of the lungs (see the EMs in Figure 3.3). In a woman's reproductive tract, the cilia lining the oviducts help move an egg toward the uterus.

Motile cilia usually occur in large numbers on the cell surface. Flagella are usually limited to just one or a few per cell, and they are longer than cilia. Flagella and cilia also differ in their beating patterns. A flagellum has an undulating motion like the tail of a fish. In contrast, cilia work more like oars, with alternating power and recovery strokes.

A cilium may also act as a signal-receiving antenna for the cell. Cilia that have this function are generally nonmotile, and there is only one per cell. (In fact, in vertebrate animals, it appears that almost all cells have such a cilium, which is called a *primary cilium*.) Membrane proteins on this kind of cilium transmit molecular signals from the cell's environment to its interior, triggering signaling pathways that may lead to changes in the cell's activities. Cilium-based signaling appears to be crucial to brain function and to embryonic development.

Though different in length, number per cell, and beating pattern, motile cilia and flagella share a common structure. Each motile cilium or flagellum has a group of microtubules sheathed in an extension of the plasma membrane (Figure 3.23). Nine doublets of microtubules are arranged in a ring; in the center of the ring are two single microtubules. This arrangement, referred to as the "9 + 2" pattern, is found in nearly all eukaryotic flagella and motile cilia. (Nonmotile primary cilia have a "9 + 0" pattern, lacking the central pair of microtubules.) The microtubule assembly of a cilium or flagellum is anchored in the cell by a **basal body**, which is structurally like a centriole, with microtubule triplets in a "9 + 0" pattern. In fact, in many animals (including humans), the basal body of the fertilizing sperm's flagellum enters the egg and becomes a centriole.

How does the microtubule assembly produce the bending movements of flagella and motile cilia? Bending involves large motor proteins called **dyneins** (red in the diagram) that are attached along each outer microtubule doublet. A typical dynein protein has two "feet" that "walk" along the microtubule of the adjacent doublet, using ATP for energy. One foot maintains contact while the other releases and reattaches farther along the microtubule (see Figure 3.21). The outer doublets and two central microtubules are held together by flexible cross-linking

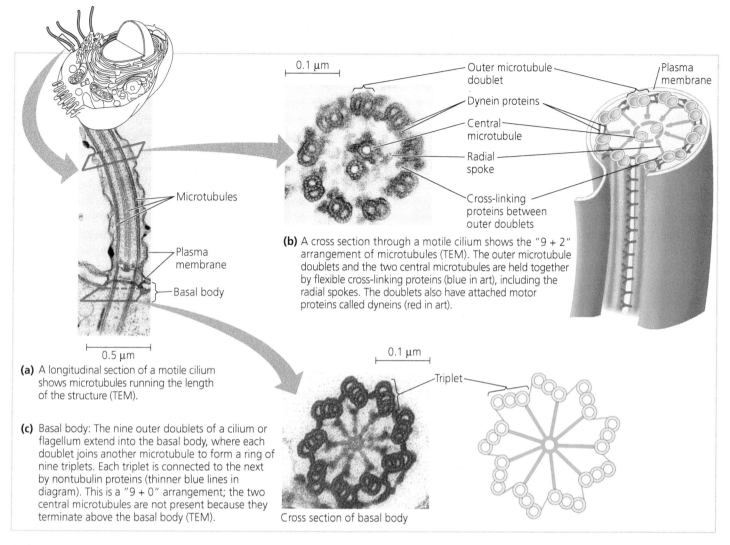

**(a)** A longitudinal section of a motile cilium shows microtubules running the length of the structure (TEM).

**(b)** A cross section through a motile cilium shows the "9 + 2" arrangement of microtubules (TEM). The outer microtubule doublets and the two central microtubules are held together by flexible cross-linking proteins (blue in art), including the radial spokes. The doublets also have attached motor proteins called dyneins (red in art).

**(c)** Basal body: The nine outer doublets of a cilium or flagellum extend into the basal body, where each doublet joins another microtubule to form a ring of nine triplets. Each triplet is connected to the next by nontubulin proteins (thinner blue lines in diagram). This is a "9 + 0" arrangement; the two central microtubules are not present because they terminate above the basal body (TEM).

Cross section of basal body

▲ **Figure 3.23 Structure of a flagellum or motile cilium.**

**DRAW IT** *In **(a)**, circle the central pair of microtubules. Show where they terminate, and explain why they aren't seen in the cross section of the basal body in **(c)**.*

proteins. If the doublets were not held in place, the walking action would make them slide past each other. Instead, the movements of the dynein feet cause the microtubules—and the organelle as a whole—to bend.

## Microfilaments (Actin Filaments)

**Microfilaments** are thin solid rods. They are also called actin filaments because they are built from molecules of **actin**, a globular protein. A microfilament is a twisted double chain of actin subunits (see Table 3.1). Besides occurring as linear filaments, microfilaments can form structural networks when certain proteins bind along the side of such a filament and allow a new filament to extend as a branch.

The structural role of microfilaments in the cytoskeleton is to bear tension (pulling forces). A three-dimensional network formed by microfilaments just inside the plasma membrane helps support the cell's shape. In some kinds of animal cells, such as nutrient-absorbing intestinal cells, bundles of microfilaments make up the core of microvilli, delicate projections that increase the cell's surface area (**Figure 3.24**).

▲ **Figure 3.24 A structural role of microfilaments.** The surface area of this intestinal cell is increased by its many microvilli (singular, *microvillus*), cellular extensions reinforced by bundles of microfilaments (TEM).

Microfilaments are well known for their role in cell motility. Thousands of actin filaments and thicker filaments of a motor protein called **myosin** interact to cause contraction of muscle cells. In the protist *Amoeba* and some of our white blood cells, localized contractions brought about by actin and myosin are involved in the amoeboid (crawling) movement of the cells. In plant cells, actin-myosin interaction contributes to *cytoplasmic streaming,* a circular flow of cytoplasm within cells. This movement, which is especially common in large plant cells, speeds the distribution of materials within the cell.

### Intermediate Filaments

**Intermediate filaments** are named for their diameter, which is larger than the diameter of microfilaments but smaller than that of microtubules (see Table 3.1). Specialized for bearing tension (like microfilaments), intermediate filaments are a diverse class of cytoskeletal elements. Each type is constructed from a particular molecular subunit belonging to a family of proteins whose members include the keratins in hair and nails.

Intermediate filaments are more permanent fixtures of cells than are microfilaments and microtubules, which are often disassembled and reassembled in various parts of a cell. Even after cells die, intermediate filament networks often persist; for example, the outer layer of our skin consists of dead skin cells full of keratin filaments. Intermediate filaments are especially sturdy and play an important role in reinforcing the shape of a cell and fixing the position of certain organelles. For instance, the nucleus typically sits within a cage made of intermediate filaments. Other intermediate filaments make up the nuclear lamina, which lines the interior of the nuclear envelope (see Figure 3.8). In general, the various kinds of intermediate filaments seem to function together as the permanent framework of the entire cell.

**CONCEPT CHECK 3.6**

1. How do cilia and flagella bend?
2. **WHAT IF?** Males afflicted with Kartagener's syndrome are sterile because of immotile sperm, and they tend to suffer from lung infections. This disorder has a genetic basis. Suggest what the underlying defect might be.

For suggested answers, see Appendix A.

**CONCEPT** 3.7

# Extracellular components and connections between cells help coordinate cellular activities

Having crisscrossed the cell to explore its interior components, we complete our tour of the cell by returning to the surface of this microscopic world, where there are additional structures with important functions. The plasma membrane is usually regarded as the boundary of the living cell, but most cells synthesize and secrete materials to their extracellular side, external to the plasma membrane. Although these materials and the structures they form are outside the cell, their study is important to cell biology because they are involved in a great many cellular functions.

## Cell Walls of Plants

The **cell wall** is an extracellular structure of plant cells that distinguishes them from animal cells (see Figure 3.7). The wall protects the plant cell, maintains its shape, and prevents excessive uptake of water. On the level of the whole plant, the strong walls of specialized cells hold the plant up against the force of gravity.

Plant cell walls are much thicker than the plasma membrane, ranging from 0.1 μm to several micrometers. The exact chemical composition of the wall varies from species to species and even from one cell type to another in the same plant, but the basic design of the wall is consistent. Microfibrils made of the polysaccharide cellulose (see Figure 2.10) are synthesized by an enzyme called cellulose synthase and secreted to the extracellular space, where they become embedded in a matrix of other polysaccharides and proteins. This combination of materials, strong fibers in a "ground substance" (matrix), is the same basic architectural design found in steel-reinforced concrete and in fiberglass.

A young plant cell first secretes a relatively thin and flexible wall called the **primary cell wall** (**Figure 3.25**). Between primary walls of adjacent cells is the **middle lamella**, a thin layer rich in sticky polysaccharides called pectins. The middle lamella glues adjacent cells together. (Pectin is used as a thickening agent in fruit jellies.) When the cell matures and stops growing, it strengthens its wall. Some plant cells do this simply by secreting hardening substances into the primary wall. Other cells add a **secondary cell wall** between the plasma membrane and the primary wall. The secondary wall, often deposited in several laminated layers, has a strong and durable matrix that affords the cell protection and support. Wood, for example, consists mainly of secondary walls. Plant cell walls are usually perforated by channels between adjacent cells called plasmodesmata, which will be discussed shortly.

## The Extracellular Matrix (ECM) of Animal Cells

Although animal cells lack walls akin to those of plant cells, they do have an elaborate **extracellular matrix (ECM)**. The main ingredients of the ECM are glycoproteins and other carbohydrate-containing molecules secreted by the cells. (Recall that glycoproteins are proteins with covalently bonded carbohydrates.) The most abundant glycoprotein in the ECM of most animal cells is **collagen**, which forms strong fibers outside the cells (see Figure 2.21, carbohydrate not shown). In fact, collagen accounts for about 40% of the total protein in the human

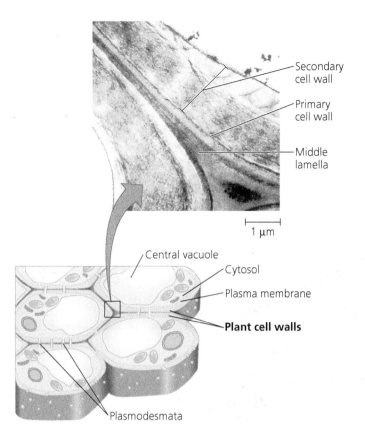

Secondary cell wall

Primary cell wall

Middle lamella

1 μm

Central vacuole

Cytosol

Plasma membrane

**Plant cell walls**

Plasmodesmata

▲ **Figure 3.25 Plant cell walls.** The drawing shows several cells, each with a large vacuole, a nucleus, and several chloroplasts and mitochondria. The transmission electron micrograph shows the cell walls where two cells come together. The multilayered partition between plant cells consists of adjoining walls individually secreted by the cells. Plasmodesmata are channels through cell walls that connect the cytoplasm of adjacent plant cells.

body. The collagen fibers are embedded in a network woven of secreted **proteoglycans (Figure 3.26)**. A proteoglycan molecule consists of a small protein with many carbohydrate chains covalently attached; it may be up to 95% carbohydrate. Large proteoglycan complexes can form when hundreds of proteoglycan molecules become noncovalently attached to a single long polysaccharide molecule, as shown in Figure 3.26. Some cells are attached to the ECM by ECM glycoproteins such as **fibronectin**. Fibronectin and other ECM proteins bind to cell-surface receptor proteins called **integrins** that are built into the plasma membrane. Integrins span the membrane and bind on their cytoplasmic side to associated proteins attached to microfilaments of the cytoskeleton. The name *integrin* is based on the word *integrate*: Integrins are in a position to transmit signals between the ECM and the cytoskeleton and thus to integrate changes occurring outside and inside the cell.

Current research is revealing the influential role of the ECM in the lives of cells. By communicating with a cell through integrins, the ECM can regulate a cell's behavior. For example, some cells in a developing embryo migrate along specific pathways by matching the orientation of their microfilaments to the "grain" of fibers in the extracellular matrix. Researchers have also learned that the extracellular matrix around a cell can influence the activity of genes in the nucleus. Information about the ECM probably reaches the nucleus by a combination of mechanical and chemical signaling pathways. Mechanical signaling involves fibronectin, integrins, and microfilaments of the cytoskeleton. Changes in the cytoskeleton may in turn trigger chemical signaling pathways inside the cell, leading to changes in the set of proteins being made by

Collagen fibers are embedded in a web of proteoglycan complexes.

EXTRACELLULAR FLUID

A **proteoglycan complex** consists of hundreds of proteoglycan molecules attached noncovalently to a single long polysaccharide molecule.

Polysaccharide molecule

Carbohydrates

Core protein

Proteoglycan molecule

Proteoglycan complex

Fibronectin attaches the ECM to integrins embedded in the plasma membrane.

Plasma membrane

Micro-filaments

CYTOPLASM

**Integrins**, membrane proteins with two subunits, bind to the ECM on one side and to associated proteins attached to microfilaments on the other. This linkage can transmit signals between the cell's external environment and its interior and can result in changes in cell behavior.

▲ **Figure 3.26 Extracellular matrix (ECM) of an animal cell.** The molecular composition and structure of the ECM vary from one cell type to another. In this example, three different types of ECM molecules are present: proteoglycans, collagen, and fibronectin.

the cell and therefore changes in the cell's function. In this way, the extracellular matrix of a particular tissue may help coordinate the behavior of all the cells of that tissue. Direct connections between cells also function in this coordination, as we discuss next.

## Cell Junctions

Neighboring cells in an animal or plant often adhere, interact, and communicate via sites of direct physical contact.

### Plasmodesmata in Plant Cells

It might seem that the nonliving cell walls of plants would isolate plant cells from one another. But in fact, as shown in Figure 3.25, cell walls are perforated with **plasmodesmata** (singular, *plasmodesma*; from the Greek *desma*, bond),

membrane-lined channels filled with cytosol. By joining adjacent cells, plasmodesmata unify most of a plant into one living continuum. The plasma membranes of adjacent cells line the channel of each plasmodesma and thus are continuous. Water and small solutes can pass freely from cell to cell, and recent experiments have shown that in some circumstances, certain proteins and RNA molecules can as well. The macromolecules transported to neighboring cells appear to reach the plasmodesmata by moving along fibers of the cytoskeleton.

### Tight Junctions, Desmosomes, and Gap Junctions in Animal Cells

In animals, there are three main types of cell junctions: *tight junctions*, *desmosomes*, and *gap junctions* (**Figure 3.27**). All three types of cell junctions are especially common in

---

Tight junctions prevent fluid from moving across a layer of cells

Tight junction

Tight junction

**Tight junction**

Intermediate filaments

**Desmosome**

**Gap junction**

Ions or small molecules

Space between cells

Plasma membranes of adjacent cells

Extracellular matrix

## Tight Junctions

At **tight junctions**, the plasma membranes of neighboring cells are very tightly pressed against each other, bound together by specific proteins (purple). Forming continuous seals around the cells, tight junctions prevent leakage of extracellular fluid across a layer of epithelial cells. For example, tight junctions between skin cells make us watertight by preventing leakage between cells in our sweat glands.

TEM   0.5 μm

## Desmosomes

**Desmosomes** (also called anchoring junctions) function like rivets, fastening cells together into strong sheets. Intermediate filaments made of sturdy keratin proteins anchor desmosomes in the cytoplasm. Desmosomes attach muscle cells to each other in a muscle. Some "muscle tears" involve the rupture of desmosomes.

TEM   1 μm

## Gap Junctions

**Gap junctions** (also called communicating junctions) provide cytoplasmic channels from one cell to an adjacent cell and in this way are similar in their function to the plasmodesmata in plants. Gap junctions consist of membrane proteins that surround a pore through which ions, sugars, amino acids, and other small molecules may pass. Gap junctions are necessary for communication between cells in many types of tissues, such as heart muscle, and in animal embryos.

TEM   0.1 μm

epithelial tissue, which lines the external and internal surfaces of the body. Figure 3.27 uses epithelial cells of the intestinal lining to illustrate these junctions. (Gap junctions are most like the plasmodesmata of plants, although gap junction pores are not lined with membrane.)

CONCEPT CHECK 3.7

1. In what way are the cells of plants and animals structurally different from single-celled eukaryotes?
2. **WHAT IF?** If the plant cell wall or the animal extracellular matrix were impermeable, what effect would this have on cell function?
3. **MAKE CONNECTIONS** The polypeptide chain that makes up a tight junction weaves back and forth through the membrane four times, with two extracellular loops, and one loop plus short C-terminal and N-terminal tails in the cytoplasm. Looking at Figure 2.17, what would you predict about the amino acids making up the tight-junction protein?

For suggested answers, see Appendix A.

## The Cell: A Living Unit Greater Than the Sum of Its Parts

From our panoramic view of the cell's compartmental organization to our close-up inspection of each organelle's architecture, this tour of the cell has provided many opportunities to correlate structure with function. But even as we dissect the cell, remember that none of its components works alone. As an example of cellular integration, consider the microscopic scene in **Figure 3.28**. The large cell is a macrophage (see Figure 3.12). It helps defend the mammalian body against infections by ingesting bacteria (the smaller cells) into

phagocytic vesicles. The macrophage crawls along a surface and reaches out to the bacteria with thin cell extensions called pseudopodia (specifically, filopodia). Actin filaments interact with other elements of the cytoskeleton in these movements. After the macrophage engulfs the bacteria, they are destroyed by lysosomes. The elaborate endomembrane system produces the lysosomes. The digestive enzymes of the lysosomes and the proteins of the cytoskeleton are all made on ribosomes. And the synthesis of these proteins is programmed by genetic messages dispatched from the DNA in the nucleus. All these processes require energy, which mitochondria supply in the form of ATP. Cellular functions arise from cellular order: The cell is a living unit greater than the sum of its parts.

▲ **Figure 3.28 The emergence of cellular functions.** The ability of this macrophage (brown) to recognize, apprehend, and destroy bacteria (yellow) is a coordinated activity of the whole cell. Its cytoskeleton, lysosomes, and plasma membrane are among the components that function in phagocytosis (colorized SEM).

# 3 Chapter Review

## SUMMARY OF KEY CONCEPTS

### CONCEPT 3.1
### Biologists use microscopes and the tools of biochemistry to study cells (pp. 45–47)

- Improvements in microscopy that affect the parameters of magnification, resolution, and contrast have catalyzed progress in the study of cell structure. The **light microscope** (LM) and **electron microscope** (EM), as well as other types, remain important tools.
- Cell biologists can obtain pellets enriched in particular cellular components by centrifuging disrupted cells at sequential speeds, a process known as **cell fractionation**. Larger cellular components are in the pellet after lower-speed centrifugation, and smaller components are in the pellet after higher-speed centrifugation.

? *How do microscopy and biochemistry complement each other to reveal cell structure and function?*

### CONCEPT 3.2
### Eukaryotic cells have internal membranes that compartmentalize their functions (pp. 47–52)

- All cells are bounded by a **plasma membrane**.
- **Prokaryotic cells** lack nuclei and other membrane-enclosed **organelles**, while **eukaryotic cells** have internal membranes that compartmentalize cellular functions.
- The surface-to-volume ratio is an important parameter affecting cell size and shape.
- Plant and animal cells have most of the same organelles: a nucleus, endoplasmic reticulum, Golgi apparatus, and mitochondria. Some organelles are found only in plant or in animal cells. Chloroplasts are present only in cells of photosynthetic eukaryotes.

? *Explain how the compartmental organization of a eukaryotic cell contributes to its biochemical functioning.*

| | Cell Component | Structure | Function |
|---|---|---|---|
| **CONCEPT** 3.3<br><br>**The eukaryotic cell's genetic instructions are housed in the nucleus and carried out by the ribosomes (pp. 52–54)**<br><br>[?] *Describe the relationship between the nucleus and ribosomes.* | Nucleus<br><br>(ER) | Surrounded by nuclear envelope (double membrane) perforated by nuclear pores; nuclear envelope continuous with endoplasmic reticulum (ER) | Houses chromosomes, which are made of chromatin (DNA and proteins); contains nucleoli, where ribosomal subunits are made; pores regulate entry and exit of materials |
| | Ribosome | Two subunits made of ribosomal RNA and proteins; can be free in cytosol or bound to ER | Protein synthesis |
| **CONCEPT** 3.4<br><br>**The endomembrane system regulates protein traffic and performs metabolic functions in the cell (pp. 54–59)**<br><br>[?] *Describe the key role played by transport vesicles in the endo-membrane system.* | Endoplasmic reticulum<br><br>(Nuclear envelope) | Extensive network of membrane-bounded tubules and sacs; membrane separates lumen from cytosol; continuous with nuclear envelope | Smooth ER: synthesis of lipids, metabolism of carbohydrates, $Ca^{2+}$ storage, detoxification of drugs and poisons<br><br>Rough ER: aids in synthesis of secretory and other proteins from bound ribosomes; adds carbohydrates to proteins to make glycoproteins; produces new membrane |
| | Golgi apparatus | Stacks of flattened membranous sacs; has polarity (*cis* and *trans* faces) | Modification of proteins, carbohydrates on proteins, and phospholipids; synthesis of many polysaccharides; sorting of Golgi products, which are then released in vesicles |
| | Lysosome | Membranous sac of hydrolytic enzymes (in animal cells) | Breakdown of ingested substances, cell macromolecules, and damaged organelles for recycling |
| | Vacuole | Large membrane-bounded vesicle | Digestion, storage, waste disposal, water balance, plant cell growth and protection |
| **CONCEPT** 3.5<br><br>**Mitochondria and chloroplasts change energy from one form to another (pp. 59–62)**<br><br>[?] *What is the endosymbiont theory?* | Mitochondrion | Bounded by double membrane; inner membrane has infoldings (cristae) | Cellular respiration |
| | Chloroplast | Typically two membranes around fluid stroma, which contains thylakoids stacked into grana (in cells of photosynthetic eukaryotes, including plants) | Photosynthesis |
| | Peroxisome | Specialized metabolic compartment bounded by a single membrane | Contains enzymes that transfer hydrogen atoms from certain molecules to oxygen, producing hydrogen peroxide ($H_2O_2$) as a by-product; $H_2O_2$ is converted to water by another enzyme |

**The cytoskeleton is a network of fibers that organizes structures and activities in the cell (pp. 62–66)**

- The **cytoskeleton** functions in structural support for the cell and in motility and signal transmission.
- **Microtubules** shape the cell, guide organelle movement, and separate chromosomes in dividing cells. **Cilia** and **flagella** are motile appendages containing microtubules. *Primary cilia* play sensory and signaling roles. **Microfilaments** are thin rods functioning in muscle contraction, amoeboid movement, cytoplasmic streaming, and support of microvilli. **Intermediate filaments** support cell shape and fix organelles in place.

**?** *Describe the role of motor proteins inside the eukaryotic cell and in whole-cell movement.*

**CONCEPT 3.7**

**Extracellular components and connections between cells help coordinate cellular activities (pp. 66–69)**

- Plant **cell walls** are made of cellulose fibers embedded in other polysaccharides and proteins.
- Animal cells secrete glycoproteins and proteoglycans that form the **extracellular matrix (ECM)**, which functions in support, adhesion, movement, and regulation.
- Cell junctions connect neighboring cells in plants and animals. Plants have **plasmodesmata** that pass through adjoining cell walls. Animal cells have **tight junctions**, **desmosomes**, and **gap junctions**.

**?** *Compare the composition and functions of a plant cell wall and the extracellular matrix of an animal cell.*

# TEST YOUR UNDERSTANDING

## Level 1: Knowledge/Comprehension

1. Which structure is *not* part of the endomembrane system?
   a. nuclear envelope
   b. chloroplast
   c. Golgi apparatus
   d. plasma membrane
   e. ER

2. Which structure is common to plant *and* animal cells?
   a. chloroplast
   b. wall made of cellulose
   c. central vacuole
   d. mitochondrion
   e. centriole

3. Which of the following is present in a prokaryotic cell?
   a. mitochondrion
   b. ribosome
   c. nuclear envelope
   d. chloroplast
   e. ER

4. Which structure-function pair is *mismatched*?
   a. nucleolus; production of ribosomal subunits
   b. lysosome; intracellular digestion
   c. ribosome; protein synthesis
   d. Golgi; protein trafficking
   e. microtubule; muscle contraction

## Level 2: Application/Analysis

5. Cyanide binds to at least one molecule involved in producing ATP. If a cell is exposed to cyanide, most of the cyanide will be found within the
   a. mitochondria.
   b. ribosomes.
   c. peroxisomes.
   d. lysosomes.
   e. endoplasmic reticulum.

6. What is the most likely pathway taken by a newly synthesized protein that will be secreted by a cell?
   a. ER → Golgi → nucleus
   b. Golgi → ER → lysosome
   c. nucleus → ER → Golgi
   d. ER → Golgi → vesicles that fuse with plasma membrane
   e. ER → lysosomes → vesicles that fuse with plasma membrane

7. Which cell would be best for studying lysosomes?
   a. muscle cell          d. leaf cell of a plant
   b. nerve cell           e. bacterial cell
   c. phagocytic white blood cell

8. **DRAW IT** From memory, draw two eukaryotic cells, labeling the structures listed here and showing any physical connections between the internal structures of each cell: nucleus, rough ER, smooth ER, mitochondrion, centrosome, chloroplast, vacuole, lysosome, microtubule, cell wall, ECM, microfilament, Golgi apparatus, intermediate filament, plasma membrane, peroxisome, ribosome, nucleolus, nuclear pore, vesicle, flagellum, microvilli, plasmodesma.

## Level 3: Synthesis/Evaluation

9. **SCIENTIFIC INQUIRY**
   In studying micrographs of an unusual protist (single-celled eukaryote) that you found in a sample of pond water, you spot an organelle that you can't recognize. You successfully develop a method for growing this organism in liquid in the laboratory. Describe how you would go about finding out what this organelle is and what it does in the cell. Assume that you would make use of additional microscopy, cell fractionation, and biochemical tests.

10. **FOCUS ON EVOLUTION**
    Which aspects of cell structure best reveal evolutionary unity? What are some examples of specialized modifications?

11. **FOCUS ON ORGANIZATION**
    Considering some of the characteristics that define life and drawing on your new knowledge of cellular structures and functions, write a short essay (100–150 words) that discusses this statement: Life is an emergent property that appears at the level of the cell. (Review the section on emergent properties in Concept 1.1.)

*For selected answers, see Appendix A.*

# MasteringBiology®

**Students** Go to **MasteringBiology** for assignments, the eText, and the Study Area with practice tests, animations, and activities.

**Instructors** Go to **MasteringBiology** for automatically graded tutorials and questions that you can assign to your students, plus Instructor Resources.

# Membrane Structure and Function

OVERVIEW

## Life at the Edge

The plasma membrane is the edge of life, the boundary that separates the living cell from its surroundings and controls traffic into and out of the cell it surrounds. Like all biological membranes, the plasma membrane exhibits **selective permeability**; that is, it allows some substances to cross it more easily than others. The ability of the cell to discriminate in its chemical exchanges with its environment is fundamental to life, and it is the plasma membrane and its component molecules that make this selectivity possible.

In this chapter, you will learn how cellular membranes control the passage of substances. The image in **Figure 4.1** shows a computer model of water molecules (red and gray) passing through a short section of membrane. The blue ribbons within the lipid bilayer (green) represent helical regions of a membrane protein called an aquaporin. One molecule of this protein enables billions of water molecules to pass through the membrane every second, many more than could cross on their own. Found in many cells, aquaporins are but one example of how the plasma membrane and its proteins enable cells to survive and function. To understand how membranes work, we'll begin by examining their structure. Then, in the rest of the chapter, we'll describe in some detail how plasma membranes control transport into and out of cells, sometimes through proteins like the ion channel to the left.

▼ **Figure 4.1** How do cell membrane proteins help regulate chemical traffic?

# Cellular membranes are fluid mosaics of lipids and proteins

*[handwritten: most abundant – phospholipid lipids/steroid]*

Lipids and proteins are the staple ingredients of membranes, although carbohydrates are also important. The most abundant lipids in most membranes are phospholipids. The ability of phospholipids to form membranes is inherent in their molecular structure. A phospholipid is an **amphipathic** molecule, meaning it has both a hydrophilic region and a hydrophobic region. Other types of membrane lipids are also amphipathic. A phospholipid bilayer can exist as a stable boundary between two aqueous compartments because the molecular arrangement shelters the hydrophobic tails of the phospholipids from water while exposing the hydrophilic heads to water (**Figure 4.2**).

Like membrane lipids, most membrane proteins are amphipathic. Such proteins can reside in the phospholipid bilayer with their hydrophilic regions protruding. This molecular orientation maximizes contact of hydrophilic regions

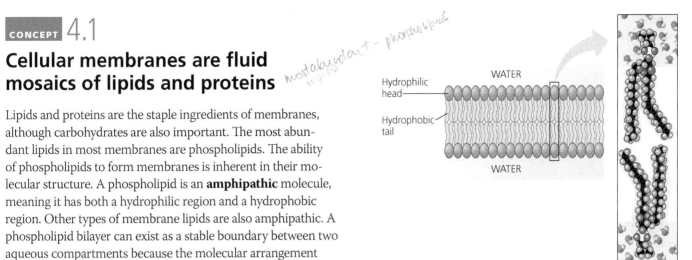

▲ **Figure 4.2 Phospholipid bilayer (cross section).**

of proteins with water in the cytosol and extracellular fluid, while providing their hydrophobic parts with a nonaqueous environment. **Figure 4.3** shows the currently accepted model

▲ **Figure 4.3 Updated model of an animal cell's plasma membrane (cutaway view).**

of the arrangement of molecules in the plasma membrane. In this **fluid mosaic model**, the membrane is a mosaic of protein molecules bobbing in a fluid bilayer of phospholipids. The proteins are not randomly distributed in the membrane, however. Groups of proteins are often associated in long-lasting, specialized patches, where they carry out common functions. The lipids themselves appear to form defined regions as well. Also, in some regions the membrane may be much more packed with proteins than shown in Figure 4.3. Like all models, the fluid mosaic model is continually being refined as new research reveals more about membrane structure.

## The Fluidity of Membranes

Membranes are not static sheets of molecules locked rigidly in place. A membrane is held together primarily by hydrophobic interactions, which are much weaker than covalent bonds. Most of the lipids and some of the proteins can shift about laterally—that is, in the plane of the membrane, like partygoers elbowing their way through a crowded room. Very rarely, also, a lipid may flip-flop across the membrane, switching from one phospholipid layer to the other.

The lateral movement of phospholipids within the membrane is rapid. Adjacent phospholipids switch positions about $10^7$ times per second, which means that a phospholipid can travel about 2 μm—the length of many bacterial cells—in 1 second. Proteins are much larger than lipids and move more slowly, but some membrane proteins do drift, as shown in a classic experiment described in **Figure 4.4**. Some membrane proteins seem to move in a highly directed manner, perhaps driven along cytoskeletal fibers in the cell by motor proteins

connected to the membrane proteins' cytoplasmic regions. However, many other membrane proteins seem to be held immobile by their attachment to the cytoskeleton or to the extracellular matrix (see Figure 4.3).

A membrane remains fluid as temperature decreases until the phospholipids settle into a closely packed arrangement and the membrane solidifies, much as bacon grease forms lard when it cools. The temperature at which a membrane solidifies depends on the types of lipids it is made of. The membrane remains fluid to a lower temperature if it is rich in phospholipids with unsaturated hydrocarbon tails. Because of kinks in the tails where double bonds are located, unsaturated hydrocarbon tails cannot pack together as closely as saturated hydrocarbon tails, making the membrane more fluid (**Figure 4.5a**).

The steroid cholesterol, which is wedged between phospholipid molecules in the plasma membranes of animal cells, has different effects on membrane fluidity at different temperatures (**Figure 4.5b**). At relatively high temperatures—at 37°C, the body temperature of humans, for example—cholesterol makes the membrane less fluid by restraining phospholipid movement. However, because cholesterol also hinders the close packing of phospholipids, it lowers the temperature required for the membrane to solidify. Thus, cholesterol can be thought of as a "fluidity buffer" for the membrane, resisting changes in membrane fluidity that can be caused by changes in temperature.

Membranes must be fluid to work properly; the fluidity of a membrane affects both its permeability and the ability of membrane proteins to move to where their function is needed. Usually, membranes are about as fluid as salad oil. When a membrane solidifies, its permeability changes, and enzymatic proteins in the membrane may become inactive if their activity requires movement within the membrane. However, membranes that are too fluid cannot support protein function either. Therefore, extreme environments pose a challenge for life, resulting in evolutionary adaptations that include differences in membrane lipid composition.

## Evolution of Differences in Membrane Lipid Composition

**EVOLUTION** Variations in the cell membrane lipid compositions of many species appear to be evolutionary adaptations that maintain the appropriate membrane fluidity under specific environmental conditions. For instance, fishes that live in extreme cold have membranes with a high proportion of unsaturated hydrocarbon tails, enabling their membranes to remain fluid (see Figure 4.5a). At the

---

▼ **Figure 4.4** **Inquiry**

### Do membrane proteins move?

**Experiment** Larry Frye and Michael Edidin, at Johns Hopkins University, labeled the plasma membrane proteins of a mouse cell and a human cell with two different markers and fused the cells. Using a microscope, they observed the markers on the hybrid cell.

**Results**

Membrane proteins

Mouse cell + Human cell → Hybrid cell → Mixed proteins after 1 hour

**Conclusion** The mixing of the mouse and human membrane proteins indicates that at least some membrane proteins move sideways within the plane of the plasma membrane.

**Source** L. D. Frye and M. Edidin, The rapid intermixing of cell surface antigens after formation of mouse-human heterokaryons, Journal of Cell Science 7:319 (1970).

**WHAT IF?** Suppose the proteins did not mix in the hybrid cell, even many hours after fusion. Would you be able to conclude that proteins don't move within the membrane? What other explanation could there be?

**(a) Unsaturated versus saturated hydrocarbon tails.**

Fluid

Viscous

Unsaturated hydrocarbon tails (kinked) prevent packing, enhancing membrane fluidity.

Saturated hydrocarbon tails pack together, increasing membrane viscosity.

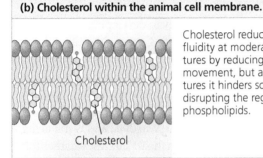

**(b) Cholesterol within the animal cell membrane.**

Cholesterol reduces membrane fluidity at moderate temperatures by reducing phospholipid movement, but at low temperatures it hinders solidification by disrupting the regular packing of phospholipids.

Cholesterol

other extreme, some bacteria and archaea thrive at temperatures greater than 90°C (194°F) in thermal hot springs and geysers. Their membranes include unusual lipids that may prevent excessive fluidity at such high temperatures.

The ability to change the lipid composition of cell membranes in response to changing temperatures has evolved in organisms that live where temperatures vary. In many plants that tolerate extreme cold, such as winter wheat, the percentage of unsaturated phospholipids increases in autumn, an adjustment that keeps the membranes from solidifying during winter. Certain bacteria and archaea can also change the proportion of unsaturated phospholipids in their cell membranes, depending on the temperature at which they are growing. Overall, natural selection has apparently favored organisms whose mix of membrane lipids ensures an appropriate level of membrane fluidity for their environment.

## Membrane Proteins and Their Functions

Now we come to the *mosaic* aspect of the fluid mosaic model. Somewhat like a tile mosaic, a membrane is a collage of different proteins, often clustered together in groups, embedded in the fluid matrix of the lipid bilayer (see Figure 4.3). In the plasma membrane of red blood cells alone, for example, more than 50 kinds of proteins have been found so far. Phospholipids form the main fabric of the membrane, but proteins determine most of the membrane's functions. Different types of cells contain different sets of membrane proteins, and the

various membranes within a cell each have a unique collection of proteins.

Notice in Figure 4.3 that there are two major populations of membrane proteins: integral proteins and peripheral proteins. **Integral proteins** penetrate the hydrophobic interior of the lipid bilayer. The majority are *transmembrane proteins*, which span the membrane; other integral proteins extend only partway into the hydrophobic interior. The hydrophobic regions of an integral protein consist of one or more stretches of nonpolar amino acids, usually coiled into α helices (**Figure 4.6**). The hydrophilic parts of the molecule are exposed to the aqueous solutions on either side of the membrane. Some proteins also have one or more hydrophilic channels that allow passage through the membrane of hydrophilic substances (even of water itself; see Figure 4.1). **Peripheral proteins** are not embedded in the lipid bilayer at all; they are appendages loosely bound to the surface of the membrane, often to exposed parts of integral proteins (see Figure 4.3).

On the cytoplasmic side of the plasma membrane, some membrane proteins are held in place by attachment to the cytoskeleton. And on the extracellular side, certain membrane proteins are attached to fibers of the extracellular matrix. These attachments combine to give animal cells a stronger framework than the plasma membrane alone could provide.

A single cell may have cell surface membrane proteins that carry out several different functions, such as transport through the cell membrane, enzymatic activity, or attaching a cell to either a neighboring cell or the extracellular matrix. Furthermore, a single membrane protein may itself carry out multiple functions. Thus, the membrane is not only a structural mosaic, but also a functional mosaic. **Figure 4.7** illustrates six major functions performed by proteins of the plasma membrane.

▶ **Figure 4.6 The structure of a transmembrane protein.**
Bacteriorhodopsin (a bacterial transport protein) has a distinct orientation in the membrane, with its N-terminus outside the cell and its C-terminus inside. This ribbon model highlights the α-helical secondary structure of the hydrophobic parts, which lie mostly within the hydrophobic interior of the membrane. The protein includes seven transmembrane helices. The nonhelical hydrophilic segments are in contact with the aqueous solutions on the extracellular and cytoplasmic sides of the membrane. Although shown as simple purple shapes in many figures in this book, each protein has its own unique structure.

EXTRACELLULAR SIDE

N-terminus

α helix

C-terminus

CYTOPLASMIC SIDE

**(a) Transport.** *Left:* A protein that spans the membrane may provide a hydrophilic channel across the membrane that is selective for a particular solute. *Right:* Other transport proteins shuttle a substance from one side to the other by changing shape (see Figure 4.14b). Some of these proteins hydrolyze ATP as an energy source to actively pump substances across the membrane.

**(b) Enzymatic activity.** A protein built into the membrane may be an enzyme with its active site exposed to substances in the adjacent solution. In some cases, several enzymes in a membrane are organized as a team that carries out sequential steps of a metabolic pathway.

Enzymes

**(c) Signal transduction.** A membrane protein (receptor) may have a binding site with a specific shape that fits the shape of a chemical messenger, such as a hormone. The external messenger (signaling molecule) may cause the protein to change shape, allowing it to relay the message to the inside of the cell, usually by binding to a cytoplasmic protein (see Figure 8.6).

Signaling molecule

Receptor

Signal transduction

**(d) Cell-cell recognition.** Some glyco-proteins serve as identification tags that are specifically recognized by membrane proteins of other cells. This type of cell-cell binding is usually short-lived compared to that shown in (e).

Glyco-protein

**(e) Intercellular joining.** Membrane proteins of adjacent cells may hook together in various kinds of junctions, such as gap junctions or tight junctions. This type of binding is more long-lasting than that shown in (d).

**(f) Attachment to the cytoskeleton and extracellular matrix (ECM).** Microfilaments or other elements of the cytoskeleton may be noncovalently bound to membrane proteins, a function that helps maintain cell shape and stabilizes the location of certain membrane proteins. Proteins that can bind to ECM molecules can coordinate extracellular and intracellular changes.

▲ **Figure 4.7 Some functions of membrane proteins.** In many cases, a single protein performs multiple tasks.

*Some transmembrane proteins can bind to a particular ECM molecule and, when bound, transmit a signal into the cell. Use the proteins shown in (c) and (f) to explain how this might occur.*

    Proteins on a cell's surface are important in the medical field. For example, a protein called CD4 on the surface of immune cells helps the human immunodeficiency virus (HIV) infect these cells, leading to acquired immune deficiency syndrome (AIDS). Despite multiple exposures to HIV, however, a small number of people do not develop AIDS and show no evidence of HIV-infected cells. Comparing their genes with the genes of infected individuals, researchers learned that resistant people have an unusual form of a gene that codes for an immune cell-surface protein called CCR5. Further work showed although CD4 is the main HIV receptor, HIV must also bind to CCR5 as a "co-receptor" to infect most cells **(Figure 4.8a)**. An absence of CCR5 on the cells of resistant individuals, due to the gene alteration, prevents the virus from entering the cells **(Figure 4.8b)**.

    This information has been key to developing a treatment for HIV infection. Interfering with CD4 could cause dangerous side effects because it performs many important functions in cells. Discovery of the CCR5 co-receptor provided a safer target for development of drugs that mask this protein and block HIV entry. One such drug, maraviroc (brand name Selzentry), was approved for treatment of HIV in 2007 and is still being used today. A clinical trial began in 2012 to test whether this drug might also work to prevent HIV infection in uninfected, at-risk patients.

## The Role of Membrane Carbohydrates in Cell-Cell Recognition

Cell-cell recognition, a cell's ability to distinguish one type of neighboring cell from another, is crucial to the functioning of an organism. It is important, for example, in the sorting of cells into tissues and organs in an animal embryo. It is also the basis for the rejection of foreign cells by the immune system, an important line of defense in vertebrate animals. Cells recognize

HIV

Receptor (CD4)

Co-receptor (CCR5)

Receptor (CD4) but no CCR5

Plasma membrane

**(a)**          **(b)**

▲ **Figure 4.8 The genetic basis for HIV resistance. (a)** HIV can infect a cell with CCR5 on its surface, as in most people. **(b)** HIV cannot infect a cell lacking CCR5 on its surface, as in resistant individuals.

**MAKE CONNECTIONS** *Study Figures, both of which show pairs of molecules binding to each other. What would you predict about CCR5 that would allow HIV to bind to it? How could a drug molecule interfere with this binding?*

other cells by binding to molecules, often containing carbohydrates, on the extracellular surface of the plasma membrane (see Figure 4.7d).

Membrane carbohydrates are usually short, branched chains of fewer than 15 sugar units. Some are covalently bonded to lipids, forming molecules called **glycolipids**. (Recall that *glyco* refers to the presence of carbohydrate.) However, most are covalently bonded to proteins, which are thereby **glycoproteins** (see Figure 4.3).

The carbohydrates on the extracellular side of the plasma membrane vary from species to species, among individuals of the same species, and even from one cell type to another in a single individual. The diversity of the molecules and their location on the cell's surface enable membrane carbohydrates to function as markers that distinguish one cell from another. For example, the four human blood types designated A, B, AB, and O reflect variation in the carbohydrate part of glycoproteins on the surface of red blood cells.

## Synthesis and Sidedness of Membranes

Membranes have distinct inside and outside faces. The two lipid layers may differ in lipid composition, and each protein has directional orientation in the membrane (see Figure 4.6). **Figure 4.9** shows how membrane sidedness arises: The asymmetrical arrangement of proteins, lipids, and their associated carbohydrates in the plasma membrane is determined as the membrane is being built by the endoplasmic reticulum (ER) and Golgi apparatus, components of the endomembrane system.

### CONCEPT CHECK 4.1

1. Plasma membrane proteins have carbohydrates attached to them in the ER and Golgi apparatus, then are transported in vesicles to the cell surface. On which side of the vesicle membrane are the carbohydrates?

2. **WHAT IF?** How would the membrane lipid composition of a native grass found in very warm soil around hot springs compare with that of a native grass found in cooler soil? Explain.

For suggested answers, see Appendix A.

## CONCEPT 4.2

# Membrane structure results in selective permeability

The biological membrane is an exquisite example of a supramolecular structure—many molecules ordered into a higher level of organization—with emergent properties beyond those of the individual molecules. The remainder of this chapter focuses on one of those properties: the ability to regulate transport across cellular boundaries, a function essential to the cell's existence. We will see once again that form fits function: The fluid mosaic model helps explain how membranes regulate the cell's molecular traffic.

A steady traffic of small molecules and ions moves across the plasma membrane in both directions. Consider the chemical exchanges between a muscle cell and the extracellular fluid that bathes it. Sugars, amino acids, and other nutrients

▼ **Figure 4.9 Synthesis of membrane components and their orientation in the membrane.** The cytoplasmic (orange) face of the plasma membrane differs from the extracellular (aqua) face. The latter arises from the inside face of ER, Golgi, and vesicle membranes.

① Membrane proteins and lipids are synthesized in the endoplasmic reticulum (ER). Carbohydrates (green) are added to the transmembrane proteins (purple dumbbells), making them glycoproteins. The carbohydrate portions may then be modified.

② Inside the Golgi apparatus, the glycoproteins undergo further carbohydrate modification, and lipids acquire carbohydrates, becoming glycolipids.

③ The glycoproteins, glycolipids, and secretory proteins (purple spheres) are transported in vesicles to the plasma membrane.

④ As vesicles fuse with the plasma membrane, the outside face of the vesicle becomes continuous with the inside (cytoplasmic) face of the plasma membrane. This releases the secretory proteins from the cell, a process called *exocytosis*, and positions the carbohydrates of membrane glycoproteins and glycolipids on the outside (extracellular) face of the plasma membrane.

**DRAW IT** *Draw an integral membrane protein extending from partway through the ER membrane into the ER lumen. Next, draw the protein where it would be located in a series of numbered steps ending at the plasma membrane. Would the protein contact the cytoplasm or the extracellular fluid? Explain.*

enter the cell, and metabolic waste products leave it. The cell takes in $O_2$ for use in cellular respiration and expels $CO_2$. Also, the cell regulates its concentrations of inorganic ions, such as $Na^+$, $K^+$, $Ca^{2+}$, and $Cl^-$, by shuttling them one way or the other across the plasma membrane. Although the heavy traffic through them may seem to suggest otherwise, cell membranes are selectively permeable, and substances do not cross the barrier indiscriminately. The cell is able to take up some small molecules and ions and exclude others.

## The Permeability of the Lipid Bilayer

Nonpolar molecules, such as hydrocarbons, $CO_2$, and $O_2$, are hydrophobic. They can therefore dissolve in the lipid bilayer of the membrane and cross it easily, without the aid of membrane proteins. However, the hydrophobic interior of the membrane impedes direct passage through the membrane of ions and polar molecules, which are hydrophilic. Polar molecules such as glucose and other sugars pass only slowly through a lipid bilayer, and even water, a very small polar molecule, does not cross rapidly. A charged atom or molecule and its surrounding shell of water are even less likely to penetrate the hydrophobic interior of the membrane. Furthermore, the lipid bilayer is only one aspect of the gatekeeper system responsible for a cell's selective permeability. Proteins built into the membrane play key roles in regulating transport.

## Transport Proteins

Specific ions and a variety of polar molecules can't move through cell membranes on their own. However, these hydrophilic substances can avoid contact with the lipid bilayer by passing through **transport proteins** that span the membrane.

Some transport proteins, called *channel proteins*, function by having a hydrophilic channel that certain molecules or atomic ions use as a tunnel through the membrane (see Figure 4.7a, left). For example, the passage of water molecules through the membrane in certain cells is greatly facilitated by channel proteins known as **aquaporins** (see Figure 4.1). Each aquaporin allows entry of up to *3 billion* ($3 \times 10^9$) water molecules per second, passing single file through its central channel, which fits ten at a time. Without aquaporins, only a tiny fraction of these water molecules would pass through the same area of the cell membrane in a second, so the channel protein brings about a tremendous increase in rate. Other transport proteins, called *carrier proteins*, hold onto their passengers and change shape in a way that shuttles them across the membrane (see Figure 4.7a, right).

A transport protein is specific for the substance it translocates (moves), allowing only a certain substance (or a small group of related substances) to cross the membrane. For example, a specific carrier protein in the plasma membrane of red blood cells transports glucose across the membrane 50,000 times faster than glucose can pass through on its own. This "glucose transporter" is so selective that it even rejects fructose, a structural isomer of glucose.

Thus, the selective permeability of a membrane depends on both the discriminating barrier of the lipid bilayer and the specific transport proteins built into the membrane. But what establishes the *direction* of traffic across a membrane? At a given time, what determines whether a particular substance will enter the cell or leave the cell? And what mechanisms actually drive molecules across membranes? We will address these questions next as we explore two modes of membrane traffic: passive transport and active transport.

**CONCEPT 4.3**

# Passive transport is diffusion of a substance across a membrane with no energy investment

Molecules have a type of energy called thermal energy, due to their constant motion. One result of this motion is **diffusion**, the movement of particles of any substance so that they spread out into the available space. Each molecule moves randomly, yet diffusion of a *population* of molecules may be directional. To understand this process, let's imagine a synthetic membrane separating pure water from a solution of a dye in water. Study **Figure 4.10a** carefully to appreciate how diffusion would result in both solutions having equal concentrations of the dye molecules. Once that point is reached, there will be a dynamic equilibrium, with roughly as many dye molecules crossing the membrane each second in one direction as in the other.

We can now state a simple rule of diffusion: In the absence of other forces, a substance will diffuse from where it is more concentrated to where it is less concentrated. Put another way, any substance will diffuse down its **concentration gradient**, the region along which the density of a chemical substance increases or decreases (in this case, decreases). No work must be done to make this happen;

Molecules of dye — Membrane (cross section)

WATER

Net diffusion | Net diffusion | Equilibrium

**(a) Diffusion of one solute.** The membrane has pores large enough for molecules of dye to pass through. Random movement of dye molecules will cause some to pass through the pores; this will happen more often on the side with more dye molecules. The dye diffuses from where it is more concentrated to where it is less concentrated (called diffusing down a concentration gradient). This leads to a dynamic equilibrium: The solute molecules continue to cross the membrane, but at roughly equal rates in both directions.

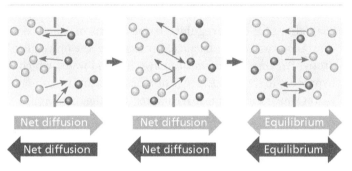

Net diffusion | Net diffusion | Equilibrium

Net diffusion | Net diffusion | Equilibrium

**(b) Diffusion of two solutes.** Solutions of two different dyes are separated by a membrane that is permeable to both. Each dye diffuses down its own concentration gradient. There will be a net diffusion of the purple dye toward the left, even though the *total* solute concentration was initially greater on the left side.

▲ **Figure 4.10 The diffusion of solutes across a synthetic membrane.** Each of the large arrows under the diagrams shows the net diffusion of the dye molecules of that color.

diffusion is a spontaneous process, needing no input of energy. Note that each substance diffuses down its *own* concentration gradient, unaffected by the concentration gradients of other substances **(Figure 4.10b)**.

Much of the traffic across cell membranes occurs by diffusion. When a substance is more concentrated on one side of a membrane than on the other, there is a tendency for the substance to diffuse across the membrane down its concentration gradient (assuming that the membrane is permeable to that substance). One important example is the uptake of oxygen by a cell performing cellular respiration. Dissolved oxygen diffuses into the cell across the plasma membrane. As long as cellular respiration consumes the $O_2$ as it enters, diffusion into the cell will continue because the concentration gradient favors movement in that direction.

The diffusion of a substance across a biological membrane is called **passive transport** because the cell does not have to expend energy to make it happen. The concentration gradient itself represents potential energy and drives diffusion. Remember, however, that membranes are selectively permeable and

therefore have different effects on the rates of diffusion of various molecules. In the case of water, aquaporins allow water to diffuse very rapidly across the membranes of certain cells. As we'll see next, the movement of water across the plasma membrane has important consequences for cells.

## Effects of Osmosis on Water Balance

To see how two solutions with different solute concentrations interact, picture a U-shaped glass tube with a selectively permeable artificial membrane separating two sugar solutions **(Figure 4.11)**. Pores in this synthetic membrane are too small for sugar molecules to pass through but large enough for water molecules. However, tight clustering of water molecules around the hydrophilic solute molecules makes some of the water unavailable to cross the membrane. As a result, the solution with a higher solute concentration has a lower *free* water concentration. Water diffuses across the membrane from the

Lower concentration of solute (sugar) | Higher concentration of solute | More similar concentrations of solute

Sugar molecule

$H_2O$

Selectively permeable membrane

Water molecules can pass through pores, but sugar molecules cannot.

Water molecules cluster around sugar molecules.

This side has fewer solute molecules, more free water molecules.

This side has more solute molecules, fewer free water molecules.

Osmosis

Water moves from an area of higher to lower free water concentration (lower to higher solute concentration).

▲ **Figure 4.11 Osmosis.** Two sugar solutions of different concentrations are separated by a membrane that the solvent (water) can pass through but the solute (sugar) cannot. Water molecules move randomly and may cross in either direction, but overall, water diffuses from the solution with less concentrated solute to that with more concentrated solute. This passive transport of water, or osmosis, makes the sugar concentrations on both sides more nearly equal. (The concentrations are prevented from being exactly equal due to the effect of water pressure on the higher side, which is not discussed here for simplicity.)

**WHAT IF?** *If an orange dye capable of passing through the membrane was added to the left side of the tube above, how would it be distributed at the end of the experiment? (See Figure 4.10.) Would the final solution levels in the tube be affected?*

region of higher free water concentration (lower solute concentration) to that of lower free water concentration (higher solute concentration) until the solute concentrations on both sides of the membrane are more nearly equal. The diffusion of free water across a selectively permeable membrane, whether artificial or cellular, is called **osmosis**. The movement of water across cell membranes and the balance of water between the cell and its environment are crucial to organisms. Let's now apply what we've learned in this system to living cells.

### Water Balance of Cells Without Cell Walls

To explain the behavior of a cell in a solution, we must consider both solute concentration and membrane permeability. Both factors are taken into account in the concept of **tonicity**, the ability of a surrounding solution to cause a cell to gain or lose water. The tonicity of a solution depends in part on its concentration of solutes that cannot cross the membrane (nonpenetrating solutes) relative to that inside the cell. If there is a higher concentration of nonpenetrating solutes in the surrounding solution, water will tend to leave the cell, and vice versa.

If a cell without a cell wall, such as an animal cell, is immersed in an environment that is **isotonic** to the cell (*iso* means "same"), there will be no *net* movement of water across the plasma membrane. Water diffuses across the membrane, but at the same rate in both directions. In an isotonic environment, the volume of an animal cell is stable **(Figure 4.12a)**.

Let's transfer the cell to a solution that is **hypertonic** to the cell (*hyper* means "more," in this case referring to nonpenetrating solutes). The cell will lose water, shrivel, and probably die.

This is why an increase in the salinity (saltiness) of a lake can kill the animals there; if the lake water becomes hypertonic to the animals' cells, they might shrivel and die. However, taking up too much water can be just as hazardous as losing water. If we place the cell in a solution that is **hypotonic** to the cell (*hypo* means "less"), water will enter the cell faster than it leaves, and the cell will swell and lyse (burst) like an overfilled water balloon.

A cell without rigid cell walls can tolerate neither excessive uptake nor excessive loss of water. This problem of water balance is automatically solved if such a cell lives in isotonic surroundings. Seawater is isotonic to many marine invertebrates. The cells of most terrestrial (land-dwelling) animals are bathed in an extracellular fluid that is isotonic to the cells. In hypertonic or hypotonic environments, however, organisms that lack rigid cell walls must have other adaptations for **osmoregulation**, the control of solute concentrations and water balance. For example, the unicellular protist *Paramecium caudatum* lives in pond water, which is hypotonic to the cell. *P. caudatum* has a plasma membrane that is much less permeable to water than the membranes of most other cells, but this only slows the uptake of water, which continually enters the cell. The *P. caudatum* cell doesn't burst because it is also equipped with a contractile vacuole, an organelle that functions as a bilge pump to force water out of the cell as fast as it enters by osmosis **(Figure 4.13)**.

### Water Balance of Cells with Cell Walls

The cells of plants, prokaryotes, fungi, and some protists are surrounded by cell walls. When such a cell is immersed in a hypotonic solution—bathed in rainwater, for example—the cell wall helps maintain the cell's water balance. Consider a plant cell. Like an animal cell, the plant cell swells as water enters by osmosis **(Figure 4.12b)**. However, the relatively inelastic cell wall will expand only so much before it exerts a back pressure on the cell, called *turgor pressure*, that opposes further water uptake. At this point, the cell is **turgid** (very firm), which is the healthy state for most plant cells. Plants that are not woody, such as most houseplants, depend for mechanical support on cells kept turgid by a surrounding hypotonic solution. If a plant's cells and their surroundings are isotonic, there is no net tendency for water to enter, and the cells become **flaccid** (limp).

However, a cell wall is of no advantage if the cell is immersed in a

**(a) Animal cell.** An animal cell fares best in an isotonic environment unless it has special adaptations that offset the osmotic uptake or loss of water.

**(b) Plant cell.** Plant cells are turgid (firm) and generally healthiest in a hypotonic environment, where the uptake of water is eventually balanced by the wall pushing back on the cell.

**Hypotonic solution**    **Isotonic solution**    **Hypertonic solution**

H₂O — Lysed | H₂O → H₂O — Normal | H₂O → — Shriveled

Plasma membrane / Cell wall / H₂O — Turgid (normal) | H₂O / H₂O — Flaccid | Plasma membrane / H₂O — Plasmolyzed

▲ **Figure 4.12 The water balance of living cells.** How living cells react to changes in the solute concentration of their environment depends on whether or not they have cell walls. **(a)** Animal cells, such as this red blood cell, do not have cell walls. **(b)** Plant cells do. (Arrows indicate net water movement after the cells were first placed in these solutions.)

Contractile vacuole

50 μm

▲ **Figure 4.13 The contractile vacuole of _Paramecium caudatum_.** The vacuole collects fluid from a system of canals in the cytoplasm. When full, the vacuole and canals contract, expelling fluid from the cell (LM).

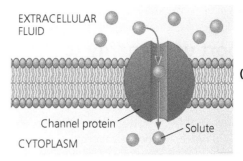

EXTRACELLULAR FLUID

Channel protein

CYTOPLASM

Solute

**(a)** A channel protein (purple) has a channel through which water molecules or a specific solute can pass.

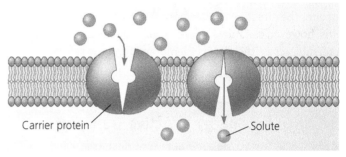

Carrier protein

Solute

**(b)** A carrier protein alternates between two shapes, moving a solute across the membrane during the shape change.

▲ **Figure 4.14 Two types of transport proteins that carry out facilitated diffusion.** In both cases, the protein can transport the solute in either direction, but the net movement is down the concentration gradient of the solute.

hypertonic environment. In this case, a plant cell, like an animal cell, will lose water to its surroundings and shrink. As the plant cell shrivels, its plasma membrane pulls away from the cell wall at multiple places. This phenomenon, called **plasmolysis**, causes the plant to wilt and can lead to plant death. The walled cells of bacteria and fungi also plasmolyze in hypertonic environments.

## Facilitated Diffusion: Passive Transport Aided by Proteins

Let's look more closely at how water and certain hydrophilic solutes cross a membrane. As mentioned earlier, many polar molecules and ions impeded by the lipid bilayer of the membrane diffuse passively with the help of transport proteins that span the membrane. This phenomenon is called **facilitated diffusion**. Cell biologists are still trying to learn exactly how various transport proteins facilitate diffusion. Most transport proteins are very specific: They transport some substances but not others.

As mentioned earlier, the two types of transport proteins are channel proteins and carrier proteins. Channel proteins simply provide corridors that allow specific molecules or ions to cross the membrane **(Figure 4.14a)**. The hydrophilic passageways provided by these proteins can allow water molecules or small ions to diffuse very quickly from one side of the membrane to the other. Aquaporins, the water channel proteins, facilitate the massive amounts of diffusion that occur in plant cells and in animal cells such as red blood cells (see Figure 4.12). Certain kidney cells also have a high number of aquaporins, allowing them to reclaim water from urine before it is excreted. If the kidneys did not perform this function, you would excrete about 180 L of urine per day—and have to drink an equal volume of water!

Channel proteins that transport ions are called **ion channels**. Many ion channels function as **gated channels**, which open or close in response to a stimulus. For some gated channels, the stimulus is electrical. In a nerve cell, for example, an ion channel opens in response to an electrical stimulus,

allowing a stream of potassium ions to leave the cell. (See the orange ion in the center of the ion channel shown at the bottom left of the chapter-opening page.) This restores the cell's ability to fire again. Other gated channels open or close when a specific substance other than the one to be transported binds to the channel. These are also important in the functioning of the nervous system.

Carrier proteins, such as the glucose transporter mentioned earlier, seem to undergo a subtle change in shape that somehow translocates the solute-binding site across the membrane **(Figure 4.14b)**. Such a change in shape may be triggered by the binding and release of the transported molecule. Like ion channels, carrier proteins involved in facilitated diffusion result in the net movement of a substance down its concentration gradient. No energy input is thus required: This is passive transport. The Scientific Skills Exercise gives you an opportunity to work with data from an experiment related to glucose transport.

**CONCEPT CHECK 4.3**

1. How do you think a cell performing cellular respiration rids itself of the resulting $CO_2$?

2. **WHAT IF?** If a Paramecium caudatum swims from a hypotonic to an isotonic environment, will its contractile vacuole become more active or less? Why?

For suggested answers, see Appendix A.

# Active transport uses energy to move solutes against their gradients

Despite the help of transport proteins, facilitated diffusion is considered passive transport because the solute is moving down its concentration gradient, a process that requires no energy. Facilitated diffusion speeds transport of a solute by providing efficient passage through the membrane, but it does not alter the direction of transport. Some other transport proteins, however, can move solutes against their concentration gradients, across the plasma membrane from the side where they are less concentrated (whether inside or outside) to the side where they are more concentrated.

## The Need for Energy in Active Transport

To pump a solute across a membrane against its gradient requires work; the cell must expend energy. Therefore, this type of membrane traffic is called **active transport**. The transport proteins that move solutes against their concentration

gradients are all carrier proteins rather than channel proteins. This makes sense because when channel proteins are open, they merely allow solutes to diffuse down their concentration gradients rather than picking them up and transporting them against their gradients.

Active transport enables a cell to maintain internal concentrations of small solutes that differ from concentrations in its environment. For example, compared with its surroundings, an animal cell has a much higher concentration of potassium ions ($K^+$) and a much lower concentration of sodium ions ($Na^+$). The plasma membrane helps maintain these steep gradients by pumping $Na^+$ out of the cell and $K^+$ into the cell.

As in other types of cellular work, ATP supplies the energy for most active transport. One way ATP can power active transport is by transferring its terminal phosphate group directly to the transport protein. This can induce the protein to change its shape in a manner that translocates a solute bound to the protein across the membrane. One transport system that works this way is the **sodium-potassium pump**, which exchanges $Na^+$ for $K^+$ across the plasma membrane of animal cells (**Figure 4.15**). The distinction between passive transport and active transport is reviewed in **Figure 4.16**.

---

## Scientific Skills Exercise

### *Interpreting a Scatter Plot with Two Sets of Data*

**Is Glucose Uptake into Cells Affected by Age?** Glucose, an important energy source for animals, is transported into cells by facilitated diffusion using protein carriers. In this exercise, you will interpret a graph with two sets of data from an experiment that examined glucose uptake over time in red blood cells from guinea pigs of different ages. You will determine if the age of the guinea pigs affected their cells' rate of glucose uptake.

**How the Experiment Was Done** Researchers incubated guinea pig red blood cells in a 300 mM (millimolar) radioactive glucose solution at pH 7.4 at 25°C. Every 10 or 15 minutes, they removed a sample of cells and measured the concentration of radioactive glucose inside those cells. The cells came from either a 15-day-old or 1-month-old guinea pig.

**Data from the Experiment** When you have multiple sets of data, it can be useful to plot them on the same graph for comparison. In the graph here, each set of dots (of the same color) forms a scatter plot, in which every data point represents two numerical values, one for each variable. For each data set, a curve that best fits the points has been drawn to make it easier to see the trends. (For additional information about graphs, see the Scientific Skills Review in the Study Area in MasteringBiology.)

**Interpret the Data**

1. First make sure you understand the parts of the graph. (a) Which variable is the independent variable—the variable controlled by the researchers? (b) Which variable is the dependent variable—the variable that depended on the treatment and was measured by the researchers? (c) What do the red dots represent? (d) the blue dots?

2. From the data points on the graph, construct a table of the data. Put "Incubation Time (min)" in the left column of the table.

Glucose Uptake Over Time in Guinea Pig Red Blood Cells

3. What does the graph show? Compare and contrast glucose uptake in red blood cells from 15-day-old and 1-month-old guinea pigs.

4. Develop a hypothesis to explain the difference between glucose uptake in red blood cells from 15-day-old and 1-month-old guinea pigs. (Think about how glucose gets into cells.)

5. Design an experiment to test your hypothesis.

**Data from** T. Kondo and E. Beutler, Developmental changes in glucose transport of guinea pig erythrocytes, *Journal of Clinical Investigation* 65:1–4 (1980).

(MB) A version of this Scientific Skills Exercise can be assigned in MasteringBiology.

► **Figure 4.15 The sodium-potassium pump: a specific case of active transport.** This transport system pumps ions against steep concentration gradients: Sodium ion concentration ([$Na^+$]) is high outside the cell and low inside, while potassium ion concentration ([$K^+$]) is low outside the cell and high inside. The pump oscillates between two shapes in a cycle that moves 3 $Na^+$ out of the cell for every 2 $K^+$ pumped into the cell. The two shapes have different affinities for $Na^+$ and $K^+$. ATP powers the shape change by transferring a phosphate group to the transport protein (phosphorylating the protein).

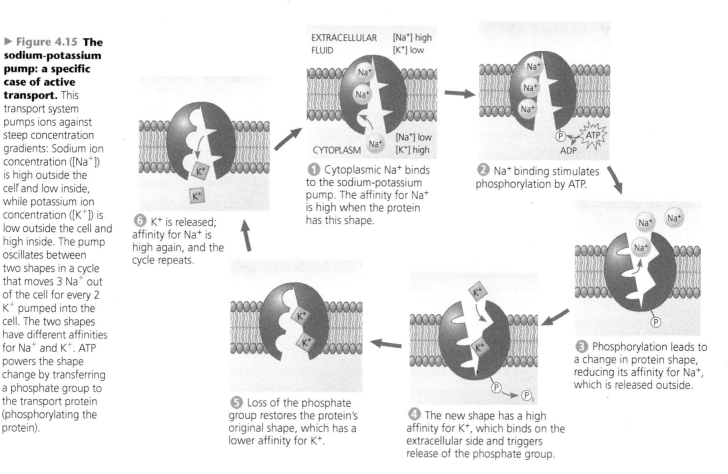

EXTRACELLULAR FLUID — [$Na^+$] high [$K^+$] low

CYTOPLASM — [$Na^+$] low [$K^+$] high

**1** Cytoplasmic $Na^+$ binds to the sodium-potassium pump. The affinity for $Na^+$ is high when the protein has this shape.

**2** $Na^+$ binding stimulates phosphorylation by ATP.

**3** Phosphorylation leads to a change in protein shape, reducing its affinity for $Na^+$, which is released outside.

**4** The new shape has a high affinity for $K^+$, which binds on the extracellular side and triggers release of the phosphate group.

**5** Loss of the phosphate group restores the protein's original shape, which has a lower affinity for $K^+$.

**6** $K^+$ is released; affinity for $Na^+$ is high again, and the cycle repeats.

▼ **Figure 4.16 Review: passive and active transport.**

**Passive transport.** Substances diffuse spontaneously down their concentration gradients, crossing a membrane with no expenditure of energy by the cell. The rate of diffusion can be greatly increased by transport proteins in the membrane.

**Diffusion.** Hydrophobic molecules and (at a slow rate) very small un-charged polar molecules can diffuse through the lipid bilayer.

**Facilitated diffusion.** Many hydrophilic substances diffuse through membranes with the assistance of transport proteins, either channel proteins (left) or carrier proteins (right).

**Active transport.** Some transport proteins act as pumps, moving substances across a membrane against their concentration (or electrochemical) gradients. Energy for this work is usually supplied by ATP.

ATP

**?** *For each solute in the right panel, describe its direction of movement, and state whether it is going with or against its concentration gradient.*

## How Ion Pumps Maintain Membrane Potential

All cells have voltages across their plasma membranes. Voltage is electrical potential energy—a separation of opposite charges. The cytoplasmic side of the membrane is negative in charge relative to the extracellular side because of an unequal distribution of anions and cations on the two sides. The voltage across a membrane, called a **membrane potential**, ranges from about $-50$ to $-200$ millivolts (mV). (The minus sign indicates that the inside of the cell is negative relative to the outside.)

The membrane potential acts like a battery, an energy source that affects the traffic of all charged substances across the membrane. Because the inside of the cell is negative compared with the outside, the membrane potential favors the passive transport of cations into the cell and anions out of the cell. Thus, *two* forces drive the diffusion of ions across a membrane: a chemical force (the ion's concentration gradient) and an electrical force (the effect of the membrane potential on the ion's movement). This combination of forces acting on an ion is called the **electrochemical gradient**.

In the case of ions, then, we must refine our concept of passive transport: An ion diffuses not simply down its *concentration* gradient but, more exactly, down its *electrochemical* gradient. For example, the concentration of $Na^+$ inside a rest-ing nerve cell is much lower than outside it. When the cell is stimulated, gated channels open that facilitate $Na^+$ diffusion. Sodium ions then "fall" down their electrochemical gradient, driven by the concentration gradient of $Na^+$ and by the attraction of these cations to the negative side (inside) of the membrane. In this example, both electrical and chemical contributions to the electrochemical gradient act in the same direction across the membrane, but this is not always so. In cases where electrical forces due to the membrane potential oppose the simple diffusion of an ion down its concentration gradient, active transport may be necessary.

Some membrane proteins that actively transport ions contribute to the membrane potential. An example is the sodium-potassium pump. Notice in Figure 4.15 that the pump does not translocate $Na^+$ and $K^+$ one for one, but pumps three sodium ions out of the cell for every two potassium ions it pumps into the cell. With each "crank" of the pump, there is a net transfer of one positive charge from the cytoplasm to the extracellular fluid, a process that stores energy as voltage. A transport protein that generates voltage across a membrane is called an **electrogenic pump**. The sodium-potassium pump appears to be the major electrogenic pump of animal cells. The main electrogenic pump of plants, fungi, and bacteria is a **proton pump**, which actively transports protons (hydrogen ions, $H^+$) out of the cell. The pumping of $H^+$ transfers positive charge from the cytoplasm to the extracellular solution (Figure 4.17). By generating voltage across membranes, electrogenic pumps help store energy that can be tapped for cellular work. One important use of proton gradients in the cell is for ATP synthesis during cellular respiration. Another is a type of membrane traffic called cotransport.

## Cotransport: Coupled Transport by a Membrane Protein

A solute that exists in different concentrations across a membrane can do work as it moves across that membrane by diffusion down its concentration gradient. This is analogous to water that has been pumped uphill and performs work as it flows back down. In a mechanism called **cotransport**, a transport protein (a cotransporter) can couple the "downhill" diffusion of the solute to the "uphill" transport of a second substance against its own concentration gradient. For instance, a plant cell uses the gradient of $H^+$ generated by its ATP-powered proton pumps to drive the active transport of amino acids, sugars, and several other nutrients into the cell. In the example shown in **Figure 4.18**, a cotransporter couples the return of $H^+$ to the transport of sucrose into the cell. This protein can translocate sucrose into the cell against its concentration gradient, but only if the sucrose molecule travels in the company of an $H^+$. The $H^+$ uses the transport protein as an avenue to diffuse down its own electrochemical gradient, which is maintained by the proton pump. Plants use sucrose-$H^+$ cotransport to load sucrose produced by photosynthesis into cells in the veins of leaves. The vascular tissue of the plant can then distribute the sugar to nonphotosynthetic organs, such as roots.

What we know about cotransport proteins in animal cells has helped us find more effective treatments for diarrhea, a serious problem in developing countries. Normally, sodium in waste is reabsorbed in the colon, maintaining constant levels in the body, but diarrhea expels waste so rapidly that reabsorption is not possible, and sodium levels fall precipitously. To treat this life-threatening condition, patients are given a solution to drink containing high concentrations of salt (NaCl) and glucose. The solutes are taken up by sodium-glucose cotransporters on the surface of intestinal cells and passed through the cells into the blood. This simple treatment has lowered infant mortality worldwide.

▲ **Figure 4.18 Cotransport: active transport driven by a concentration gradient.** A carrier protein, such as this sucrose-$H^+$ cotransporter in a plant cell (top), is able to use the diffusion of $H^+$ down its electrochemical gradient into the cell to drive the uptake of sucrose. (The cell wall is not shown.) Although not technically part of the cotransport process, an ATP-driven proton pump is shown here (bottom), which concentrates $H^+$ outside the cell. The resulting $H^+$ gradient represents potential energy that can be used for active transport—of sucrose, in this case. Thus, ATP indirectly provides the energy necessary for cotransport.

▲ **Figure 4.17 A proton pump.** Proton pumps are electrogenic pumps that store energy by generating voltage (charge separation) across membranes. A proton pump translocates positive charge in the form of hydrogen ions. The voltage and $H^+$ concentration gradient represent a dual energy source that can drive other processes, such as the uptake of nutrients. Most proton pumps are powered by ATP.

## CONCEPT CHECK 4.4

1. Sodium-potassium pumps help nerve cells establish a voltage across their plasma membranes. Do these pumps use ATP or produce ATP? Explain.

2. Explain why the sodium-potassium pump in Figure 4.15 would not be considered a cotransporter.

2. **MAKE CONNECTIONS** Given the internal environment of a lysosome, what transport protein might you expect to see in its membrane?

For suggested answers, see Appendix A.

*same direction
Symport against gradient
glucose uniporter - GLUT 2*

## CONCEPT 4.5

# Bulk transport across the plasma membrane occurs by exocytosis and endocytosis

Water and small solutes enter and leave the cell by diffusing through the lipid bilayer of the plasma membrane or by being pumped or moved across the membrane by transport proteins. However, large molecules—such as proteins and polysaccharides, as well as larger particles—generally cross the membrane in bulk, packaged in vesicles. Like active transport, these processes require energy.

## Exocytosis

As seen cell secretes certain molecules by the fusion of vesicles with the plasma membrane; this process is called **exocytosis**. A transport vesicle that has budded from the Golgi apparatus moves along microtubules of the cytoskeleton to the plasma membrane. When the vesicle membrane and plasma membrane come into contact, specific proteins rearrange the lipid molecules of the two bilayers so that the two membranes fuse. The contents of the vesicle spill out of the cell, and the vesicle membrane becomes part of the plasma membrane (see Figure 4.9, step 4).

Many secretory cells use exocytosis to export products. For example, cells in the pancreas that make insulin secrete it into the extracellular fluid by exocytosis. In another example, nerve cells use exocytosis to release neurotransmitters that signal other neurons or muscle cells. When plant cells are making cell walls, exocytosis delivers proteins and carbohydrates from Golgi vesicles to the outside of the cell.

## Endocytosis

In **endocytosis**, the cell takes in molecules and particulate matter by forming new vesicles from the plasma membrane.

Although the proteins involved in the processes are different, the events of endocytosis look like the reverse of exocytosis. First, a small area of the plasma membrane sinks inward to form a pocket. Then, as the pocket deepens, it pinches in, forming a vesicle containing material that had been outside the cell. Study **Figure 4.19** carefully to understand the three types of endocytosis: phagocytosis ("cellular eating"), pinocytosis ("cellular drinking"), and receptor-mediated endocytosis (which is considered a form of pinocytosis).

Human cells use receptor-mediated endocytosis to take in cholesterol for membrane synthesis and the synthesis of other steroids. Cholesterol travels in the blood in particles called low-density lipoproteins (LDLs), each a complex of lipids and a protein. LDLs bind to LDL receptors on plasma membranes and then enter the cells by endocytosis. (LDLs thus act as **ligands**, a term for any molecule that binds specifically to a receptor site on another molecule.) In the inherited disease familial hypercholesterolemia, characterized by a very high level of cholesterol in the blood, LDLs cannot enter cells because the LDL receptor proteins are defective or missing. Consequently, cholesterol accumulates in the blood, where it contributes to early atherosclerosis, the buildup of lipid deposits within the walls of blood vessels. This buildup narrows the space in the vessels and impedes blood flow, and can result in heart damage and stroke.

Vesicles not only transport substances to be released from the cell but also provide a mechanism for rejuvenating or remodeling the plasma membrane. Endocytosis and exocytosis occur continually in most eukaryotic cells, yet the amount of plasma membrane in a nongrowing cell remains fairly constant. The addition of membrane by one process appears to offset the loss of membrane by the other.

Energy and cellular work have figured prominently in our study of membranes. We have seen, for example, that active transport is powered by ATP. You will learn more about how cells acquire chemical energy to do the work of life.

## CONCEPT CHECK 4.5

1. As a cell grows, its plasma membrane expands. Does this involve endocytosis or exocytosis? Explain.

2. **DRAW IT** Return to Figure 4.9, and circle a patch of plasma membrane that is coming from a vesicle involved in exocytosis.

3. **MAKE CONNECTIONS** Describe the cellular pathway of synthesis and deposition of an ECM glycoprotein.

For suggested answers, see Appendix A.

## Phagocytosis

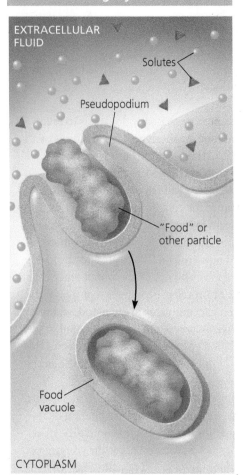

EXTRACELLULAR FLUID

Solutes

Pseudopodium

"Food" or other particle

Food vacuole

CYTOPLASM

In **phagocytosis**, a cell engulfs a particle by extending pseudopodia (singular, *pseudopodium*) around it and packaging it within a membranous sac called a food vacuole. The particle will be digested after the food vacuole fuses with a lysosome.

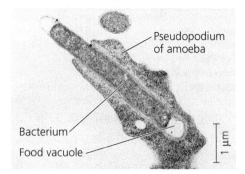

Pseudopodium of amoeba

Bacterium

Food vacuole

An amoeba engulfing a bacterium via phago-cytosis (TEM).

## Pinocytosis

Plasma membrane

Coat protein

Coated pit

Coated vesicle

In **pinocytosis**, a cell continually "gulps" droplets of extracellular fluid into tiny vesicles, formed by infoldings of the plasma membrane. In this way, the cell obtains molecules dissolved in the droplets. Because any and all solutes are taken into the cell, pinocytosis as shown here is nonspecific for the substances it transports. In many cases, as above, the parts of the plasma membrane that form vesicles are lined on their cytoplasmic side by a fuzzy layer of coat protein; the "pits" and resulting vesicles are said to be "coated."

Pinocytotic vesicles forming (TEMs).

## Receptor-Mediated Endocytosis

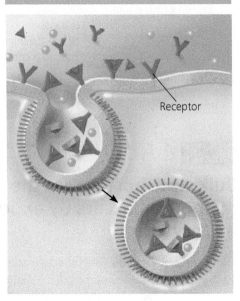

Receptor

**Receptor-mediated endocytosis** is a specialized type of pinocytosis that enables the cell to acquire bulk quantities of specific substances, even though those substances may not be very concentrated in the extracellular fluid. Embedded in the plasma membrane are proteins with receptor sites exposed to the extracellular fluid. Specific solutes bind to the sites. The receptor proteins then cluster in coated pits, and each coated pit forms a vesicle containing the bound molecules. Notice that there are relatively more bound molecules (purple triangles) inside the vesicle, but other molecules (green balls) are also present. After the ingested material is liberated from the vesicle, the emptied receptors are recycled to the plasma membrane by the same vesicle (not shown).

Plasma membrane

Coat protein

*Top*: A coated pit. *Bottom*: A coated vesicle forming during receptor-mediated endocytosis (TEMs).

**ANIMATION** **BioFlix** Visit the Study Area in **MasteringBiology** for the BioFlix® 3-D Animation on Membrane Transport. BioFlix Tutorials can also be assigned in MasteringBiology.

# 4 Chapter Review

## SUMMARY OF KEY CONCEPTS

CONCEPT 4.1

### Cellular membranes are fluid mosaics of lipids and proteins (pp. 73–77)

- In the **fluid mosaic model**, **amphipathic** proteins are embedded in the phospholipid bilayer. Proteins with related functions often cluster in patches.
- Phospholipids and some proteins move laterally within the membrane. The unsaturated hydrocarbon tails of some phospholipids keep membranes fluid at lower temperatures, while cholesterol helps membranes resist changes in fluidity caused by temperature changes. Differences in membrane lipid composition, as well as the ability to change lipid composition, are evolutionary adaptations that ensure membrane fluidity.
- **Integral proteins** are embedded in the lipid bilayer; **peripheral proteins** are attached to the membrane surface. The functions of membrane proteins include transport, enzymatic activity, signal transduction, cell-cell recognition, intercellular joining, and attachment to the cytoskeleton and extracellular matrix. Short chains of sugars linked to proteins (in **glycoproteins**) and lipids (in **glycolipids**) on the exterior side of the plasma membrane interact with surface molecules of other cells.
- Membrane proteins and lipids are synthesized in the ER and modified in the ER and Golgi apparatus. The inside and outside faces of membranes differ in molecular composition.

  **?** *In what ways are membranes crucial to life?*

CONCEPT 4.2

### Membrane structure results in selective permeability (pp. 77–78)

- A cell must exchange molecules and ions with its surroundings, a process controlled by the **selective permeability** of the plasma membrane. Hydrophobic substances are soluble in lipids and pass through membranes rapidly, whereas polar molecules and ions generally require specific **transport proteins** to cross the membrane.

  **?** *How do **aquaporins** affect the permeability of a membrane?*

CONCEPT 4.3

### Passive transport is diffusion of a substance across a membrane with no energy investment (pp. 78–81)

- **Diffusion** is the spontaneous movement of a substance down its **concentration gradient**. Water diffuses out through the permeable membrane of a cell (**osmosis**) if the solution outside has a higher solute concentration (**hypertonic**) than the cytosol; water enters the cell if the solution has a lower solute concentration (**hypotonic**). If the concentrations are equal (**isotonic**), no net osmosis occurs. Cell survival depends on balancing water uptake and loss. Cells lacking cell walls (as in animals and some protists) are isotonic with their environments or have adaptations for **osmoregulation**. Plants, prokaryotes, fungi, and some protists have relatively inelastic cell walls, so the cells don't burst in a hypotonic environment.

- In a type of **passive transport** called **facilitated diffusion**, a transport protein speeds the movement of water or a solute across a membrane down its concentration gradient. **Ion channels**, some of which are **gated channels**, facilitate the diffusion of ions across a membrane. Carrier proteins can undergo changes in shape that translocate bound solutes across the membrane.

  **?** *What happens to a cell placed in a hypertonic solution? Describe the free water concentration inside and out.*

Passive transport: Facilitated diffusion

Channel protein — Carrier protein

CONCEPT 4.4

### Active transport uses energy to move solutes against their gradients (pp. 82–84)

Active transport

- Specific membrane proteins use energy, usually in the form of ATP, to do the work of **active transport**. One example of such a protein is the **sodium-potassium pump**.
- Ions can have both a concentration (chemical) gradient and an electrical gradient (voltage). These gradients combine in the **electrochemical gradient**, which determines the net direction of ionic diffusion. **Electrogenic pumps**, such as the sodium-potassium pump and **proton pumps**, are transport proteins that contribute to electrochemical gradients.
- **Cotransport** of two solutes occurs when a membrane protein enables the "downhill" diffusion of one solute to drive the "uphill" transport of the other.

  **?** *ATP is not directly involved in the functioning of a cotransporter. Why, then, is cotransport considered active transport?*

## Bulk transport across the plasma membrane occurs by exocytosis and endocytosis (pp. 85–86)

• In **exocytosis**, transport vesicles migrate to the plasma membrane, fuse with it, and release their contents. In **endocytosis**, molecules enter cells within vesicles that pinch inward from the plasma membrane. The three types of endocytosis are **phagocytosis**, **pinocytosis**, and **receptor-mediated endocytosis**.

? *Which type of endocytosis involves ligands? What does this type of transport enable a cell to do?*

## TEST YOUR UNDERSTANDING

### Level 1: Knowledge/Comprehension

1. In what way do the membranes of a eukaryotic cell vary?
   a. Phospholipids are found only in certain membranes.
   b. Certain proteins are unique to each membrane.
   c. Only certain membranes of the cell are selectively permeable.
   d. Only certain membranes are constructed from amphipathic molecules.

2. According to the fluid mosaic model of membrane structure, proteins of the membrane are mostly
   a. spread in a continuous layer over the inner and outer surfaces of the membrane.
   b. confined to the hydrophobic interior of the membrane.
   c. embedded in a lipid bilayer.
   d. randomly oriented in the membrane, with no fixed inside-outside polarity.

3. Which of the following factors would tend to increase membrane fluidity?
   a. a greater proportion of unsaturated phospholipids
   b. a greater proportion of saturated phospholipids
   c. a lower temperature
   d. a relatively high protein content in the membrane

### Level 2: Application/Analysis

4. Which of the following processes includes all the others?
   a. osmosis
   b. diffusion of a solute across a membrane
   c. passive transport
   d. transport of an ion down its electrochemical gradient

5. Based on Figure 4.18, which of these experimental treatments would increase the rate of sucrose transport into a plant cell?
   a. decreasing extracellular sucrose concentration
   b. decreasing extracellular pH
   c. decreasing cytoplasmic pH
   d. adding a substance that makes the membrane more permeable to hydrogen ions

6. **DRAW IT** An artificial "cell" consisting of an aqueous solution enclosed in a selectively permeable membrane is immersed in a beaker containing a different solution, the "environment," as shown below. The membrane is permeable to water and to the simple sugars glucose and fructose but impermeable to the disaccharide sucrose.

"Cell"
0.03 *M* sucrose
0.02 *M* glucose

"Environment"
0.01 *M* sucrose
0.01 *M* glucose
0.01 *M* fructose

   a. Draw solid arrows to indicate the net movement of solutes into and/or out of the cell.
   b. Is the solution outside the cell isotonic, hypotonic, or hypertonic?
   c. Draw a dashed arrow to show the net osmosis, if any.
   d. Will the artificial cell become more flaccid, more turgid, or stay the same?
   e. Eventually, will the two solutions have the same or different solute concentrations?

### Level 3: Synthesis/Evaluation

7. **EVOLUTION CONNECTION**
   *Paramecium* and other protists that live in hypotonic environments have cell membranes that limit water uptake, while those living in isotonic environments have membranes that are more permeable to water. What adaptations might have evolved in protists in hypertonic habitats such as the Great Salt Lake? In habitats with changing salt concentration?

8. **SCIENTIFIC INQUIRY**
   An experiment is designed to study the mechanism of sucrose uptake by plant cells. Cells are immersed in a sucrose solution, and the pH of the solution is monitored. Samples of the cells are taken at intervals, and their sucrose concentration is measured. After a decrease in the pH of the solution to a steady, slightly acidic level, sucrose uptake begins. Propose a hypothesis for these results. What do you think would happen if an inhibitor of ATP regeneration by the cell were added to the beaker once the pH was at a steady level? Explain.

9. **SCIENCE, TECHNOLOGY, AND SOCIETY**
   Extensive irrigation in arid regions causes salts to accumulate in the soil. (When water evaporates, salts that were dissolved in the water are left behind in the soil.) Based on what you learned about water balance in plant cells, explain why increased soil salinity (saltiness) might be harmful to crops.

10. **WRITE ABOUT A THEME: INTERACTIONS**
    A human pancreatic cell obtains $O_2$, and necessary molecules such as glucose, amino acids, and cholesterol, from its environment, and it releases $CO_2$ as a waste product. In response to hormonal signals, the cell secretes digestive enzymes. It also regulates its ion concentrations by exchange with its environment. Based on what you have just learned about the structure and function of cellular membranes, write a short essay (100–150 words) that describes how such a cell accomplishes these interactions with its environment.

**11.**

In the supermarket, lettuce and other produce is often sprayed with water. Explain why this makes vegetables crisp.

*For selected answers, see Appendix A.*

## MasteringBiology®

**Students** Go to **MasteringBiology** for assignments, the eText, and the Study Area with practice tests, animations, and activities.

**Instructors** Go to **MasteringBiology** for automatically graded tutorials and questions that you can assign to your students, plus Instructor Resources.

# 5

# An Introduction to Metabolism

OVERVIEW

## The Energy of Life

The living cell is a chemical factory in miniature, where thousands of reactions occur within a microscopic space. Sugars can be converted to amino acids that are linked together into proteins when needed, and when food is digested, proteins are dismantled into amino acids that can be converted to sugars. The process called cellular respiration drives the cellular economy by extracting the energy stored in sugars and other fuels. Cells apply this energy to perform various types of work. Cells of the two firefly squid (*Watasenia scintillans*) shown mating in **Figure 5.1** convert the energy stored in organic molecules to light, a process called bioluminescence that aids in mate recognition. Such metabolic activities are precisely coordinated and controlled in the cell. In its complexity, its efficiency, and its responsiveness to subtle changes, the cell is peerless as a chemical factory. The concepts of metabolism that you learn in this chapter will help you understand how matter and energy flow during life's processes and how that flow is regulated.

▼ **Figure 5.1** What causes these two squid to glow?

CONCEPT 5.1

## An organism's metabolism transforms matter and energy

The totality of an organism's chemical reactions is called **metabolism** (from the Greek *metabole*, change). Metabolism is an emergent property of life that arises from orderly interactions between molecules.

### Metabolic Pathways

We can picture a cell's metabolism as an elaborate road map of many chemical reactions, arranged as intersecting metabolic pathways. In a **metabolic pathway**, a specific molecule is altered in a series of defined steps, resulting in a product. Each step of the pathway is catalyzed by a specific enzyme:

Analogous to the red, yellow, and green stoplights that control the flow of automobile traffic, mechanisms that regulate enzymes balance metabolic supply and demand.

Metabolism as a whole manages the material and energy resources of the cell. Some metabolic pathways release energy by breaking down complex molecules to simpler compounds. These degradative processes are called **catabolic pathways**, or breakdown pathways. A major pathway of catabolism is cellular respiration, in which the sugar glucose and other organic fuels are broken down in the presence of oxygen to carbon dioxide and water. Energy stored in the organic molecules becomes available to do the work of the cell, such as ciliary beating or membrane transport. **Anabolic pathways**, in contrast, consume energy to build complicated molecules from simpler ones; they are sometimes called biosynthetic pathways. Examples of anabolism are the synthesis of an amino acid from simpler molecules and the synthesis of a protein from amino acids. Catabolic and anabolic pathways are the "downhill" and "uphill" avenues of the metabolic landscape. Energy released from the downhill reactions of catabolic pathways can be stored and then used to drive the uphill reactions of anabolic pathways.

In this chapter, we will focus on mechanisms common to metabolic pathways. Because energy is fundamental to all metabolic processes, a basic knowledge of energy is necessary to understand how the living cell works. Although we will use some nonliving examples to study energy, the concepts demonstrated by these examples also apply to **bioenergetics**, the study of how energy flows through living organisms.

## Forms of Energy

**Energy** is the capacity to cause change. In everyday life, energy is important because some forms of energy can be used to do work—that is, to move matter against opposing forces, such as gravity and friction. Put another way, energy is the ability to rearrange a collection of matter. For example, you expend energy to turn the pages of this book, and your cells expend energy in transporting certain substances across membranes. Energy exists in various forms, and the work of life depends on the ability of cells to transform energy from one form to another.

Energy can be associated with the relative motion of objects; this energy is called **kinetic energy**. Moving objects can perform work by imparting motion to other matter: Water gushing through a dam turns turbines, and the contraction of leg muscles pushes bicycle pedals. **Thermal energy** is kinetic energy associated with the random movement of atoms or molecules; thermal energy in transfer from one object to another is called **heat**. Light is also a type of energy that can be harnessed to perform work, such as powering photosynthesis in green plants.

An object not presently moving may still possess energy. Energy that is not kinetic is called **potential energy**; it is energy that matter possesses because of its location or structure. Water behind a dam, for instance, possesses energy because of its altitude above sea level. Molecules possess energy because of the arrangement of electrons in the bonds between their atoms. **Chemical energy** is a term used by biologists to refer to the potential energy available for release in a chemical reaction. Recall that catabolic pathways release energy by breaking down complex molecules. Biologists say that these complex molecules, such as glucose, are high in chemical energy. During a catabolic reaction, some bonds are broken and others formed, releasing energy and resulting in lower-energy breakdown products. This transformation also occurs, for example, in the engine of a car when the hydrocarbons of gasoline react explosively with oxygen, releasing the energy that pushes the pistons and producing exhaust. Although less explosive, a similar reaction of food molecules with oxygen provides chemical energy in biological systems, producing carbon dioxide and water as waste products. Biochemical pathways, carried out in the context of cellular structures, enable cells to release chemical energy from food molecules and use the energy to power life processes.

How is energy converted from one form to another? Consider the divers in **Figure 5.2**. The young woman climbing the ladder to the diving platform is releasing chemical energy from the food she ate for lunch and using some of that energy to perform the work of climbing. The kinetic energy of muscle movement is thus being transformed into potential energy due to her increasing height above the water. The young man diving is converting his potential energy to kinetic energy, which is then transferred to the water as he enters it. A small amount of energy is lost as heat due to friction.

Now let's go back one step and consider the original source of the organic food molecules that provided the necessary

A diver has more potential energy on the platform than in the water.

Diving converts potential energy to kinetic energy.

Climbing up converts the kinetic energy of muscle movement to potential energy.

A diver has less potential energy in the water than on the platform.

▲ **Figure 5.2 Transformations between potential and kinetic energy.**

chemical energy for the diver to climb the steps. This chemical energy was itself derived from light energy by plants during photosynthesis. Organisms are energy transformers.

## The Laws of Energy Transformation

The study of the energy transformations that occur in a collection of matter is called **thermodynamics**. Scientists use the word *system* to denote the matter under study; they refer to the rest of the universe—everything outside the system—as the *surroundings*. An *isolated system*, such as that approximated by liquid in a thermos bottle, is unable to exchange either energy or matter with its surroundings. In an *open system*, energy and matter can be transferred between the system and its surroundings. Organisms are open systems. They absorb energy—for instance, light energy or chemical energy in the form of organic molecules—and release heat and metabolic waste products, such as carbon dioxide, to the surroundings. Two laws of thermodynamics govern energy transformations in organisms and all other collections of matter.

### The First Law of Thermodynamics

According to the **first law of thermodynamics**, the energy of the universe is constant: *Energy can be transferred and transformed, but it cannot be created or destroyed.* The first law is also known as the *principle of conservation of energy.* The electric company does not make energy, but merely converts it to a form that is convenient for us to use. By converting sunlight to chemical energy, a plant acts as an energy transformer, not an energy producer.

The brown bear in **Figure 5.3a** will convert the chemical energy of the organic molecules in its food to kinetic and other forms of energy as it carries out biological processes. What happens to this energy after it has performed work? The second law of thermodynamics helps to answer this question.

### The Second Law of Thermodynamics

If energy cannot be destroyed, why can't organisms simply recycle their energy over and over again? It turns out that during every energy transfer or transformation, some energy is converted to thermal energy and released as heat, becoming unavailable to do work. Only a small fraction of the chemical energy from the food in Figure 5.3a is transformed into the motion of the brown bear shown in **Figure 5.3b**; most is lost as heat, which dissipates rapidly through the surroundings.

A system can put thermal energy to work only when there is a temperature difference that results in the thermal energy flowing from a warmer location to a cooler one. If temperature is uniform, as it is in a living cell, then the heat generated during a chemical reaction will simply warm a body of matter, such as the organism. (This can make a room crowded with people uncomfortably warm, as each person is carrying out a multitude of chemical reactions!)

A logical consequence of the loss of usable energy during energy transfer or transformation is that each such event makes the universe more disordered. Scientists use a quantity called **entropy** as a measure of disorder, or randomness. The more randomly arranged a collection of matter is, the greater its entropy. We can now state the **second law of thermodynamics**: *Every energy transfer or transformation increases the entropy of the universe.* Although order can increase locally, there is an unstoppable trend toward randomization of the universe as a whole.

In many cases, increased entropy is evident in the physical disintegration of a system's organized structure. For example, you can observe increasing entropy in the gradual decay of an unmaintained building. Much of the increasing entropy of the universe is less apparent, however, because it appears as increasing amounts of heat and less ordered forms of matter. As the bear in Figure 5.3b converts chemical energy to kinetic energy, it is also increasing the disorder of its surroundings by

**(a) First law of thermodynamics:** Energy can be transferred or transformed but neither created nor destroyed. For example, chemical reactions in this brown bear will convert the chemical (potential) energy in the fish to the kinetic energy of running.

**(b) Second law of thermodynamics:** Every energy transfer or transformation increases the disorder (entropy) of the universe. For example, as the bear runs, disorder is increased around the bear by the release of heat and small molecules that are the by-products of metabolism. A brown bear can run at speeds up to 35 miles per hour (56 km/hr)—as fast as a racehorse.

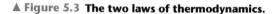

▲ **Figure 5.3 The two laws of thermodynamics.**

producing heat and small molecules, such as the $CO_2$ it exhales, that are the breakdown products of food.

The concept of entropy helps us understand why certain processes occur without any input of energy. It turns out that for a process to occur on its own, without outside help, it must increase the entropy of the universe. A process that can occur without an input of energy is called a **spontaneous process**. Note that as we're using it here, the word *spontaneous* does not imply that such a process would occur quickly; rather, the word signifies that the process is energetically favorable. (In fact, it may be helpful for you to think of the phrase "energetically favorable" when you read the formal term "spontaneous.") Some spontaneous processes, such as an explosion, may be virtually instantaneous, while others, such as the rusting of an old car over time, are much slower. A process that cannot occur on its own is said to be nonspontaneous; it will happen only if energy is added to the system. We know from experience that certain events occur spontaneously and others do not. For instance, we know that water flows downhill spontaneously but moves uphill only with an input of energy, such as when a machine pumps the water against gravity. This understanding gives us another way to state the second law: *For a process to occur spontaneously, it must increase the entropy of the universe.*

### Biological Order and Disorder

Living systems increase the entropy of their surroundings, as predicted by thermodynamic law. It is true that cells create ordered structures from less organized starting materials. For example, simpler molecules are ordered into the more complex structure of an amino acid, and amino acids are ordered into polypeptide chains. At the organismal level as well, complex and beautifully ordered structures result from biological processes that use simpler starting materials **(Figure 5.4)**. However, an organism also takes in organized forms of matter and energy from the surroundings and replaces them with less ordered forms. For example, an animal obtains starch, proteins, and other complex molecules from the food it eats. As catabolic pathways break these molecules down, the animal releases carbon dioxide and water—small molecules that possess less chemical energy than the food did. The depletion of chemical energy is accounted for by heat generated during metabolism. On a larger scale, energy flows into most ecosystems in the form of light and exits in the form of heat.

During the early history of life, complex organisms evolved from simpler ancestors. For example, we can trace the ancestry of the plant kingdom from much simpler organisms called green algae to more complex flowering plants. However, this increase in organization over time in no way violates the second law. The entropy of a particular system, such as an organism, may actually decrease as long as the total entropy of the *universe*—the system plus its surroundings—increases. Thus, organisms are islands of low entropy in an increasingly random universe. The evolution of biological order is perfectly consistent with the laws of thermodynamics.

▲ **Figure 5.4 Order as a characteristic of life.** Order is evident in the detailed structures of the sea urchin skeleton and the succulent plant shown here. As open systems, organisms can increase their order as long as the order of their surroundings decreases.

**CONCEPT CHECK 5.1**

1. **MAKE CONNECTIONS** How does the second law of thermodynamics help explain the diffusion of a substance across a membrane?
2. Describe the forms of energy found in an apple as it grows on a tree, then falls, then is digested by someone who eats it.

For suggested answers, see Appendix A.

**CONCEPT** 5.2

# The free-energy change of a reaction tells us whether or not the reaction occurs spontaneously

The laws of thermodynamics that we've just discussed apply to the universe as a whole. As biologists, we want to understand the chemical reactions of life—for example, which reactions occur spontaneously and which ones require some input of energy from outside. But how can we know this without assessing the energy and entropy changes in the entire universe for each separate reaction?

## Free-Energy Change (ΔG), Stability, and Equilibrium

Recall that the universe is really equivalent to "the system" plus "the surroundings." In 1878, J. Willard Gibbs, a professor at Yale, defined a very useful function called the Gibbs free energy of a system (without considering its surroundings), symbolized by the letter $G$. We'll refer to the Gibbs free energy simply as free energy. **Free energy** is the portion of a system's energy that can perform work when temperature and pressure are uniform throughout the system, as in a living cell. Biologists find it most informative to focus on the *change* in free energy ($\Delta G$) during the chemical reactions of life. $\Delta G$ represents the difference between the free energy of the final state and the free energy of the initial state:

$$\Delta G = G_{\text{final state}} - G_{\text{initial state}}$$

Using chemical methods, we can measure $\Delta G$ for any reaction. More than a century of experiments has shown that only reactions with a negative $\Delta G$ can occur with no input of energy, so the value of $\Delta G$ tells us whether a particular reaction is a spontaneous one. This principle is very important in the study of metabolism, where a major goal is to determine which reactions occur spontaneously and can be harnessed to supply energy for cellular work.

For a reaction to have a negative $\Delta G$, the system must lose free energy during the change from initial state to final state. Because it has less free energy, the system in its final state is less likely to change and is therefore more stable than it was previously. We can think of free energy as a measure of a system's instability—its tendency to change to a more stable state. Unstable systems (higher $G$) tend to change in such a way that they become more stable (lower $G$), as shown in **Figure 5.5**.

Another term that describes a state of maximum stability is chemical *equilibrium*. At equilibrium, the forward and reverse reactions occur at the same rate, and there is no further net change in the relative concentration of products and reactants. For a system at equilibrium, $G$ is at its lowest possible value in that system. We can think of the equilibrium state as a free-energy valley. Any change from the equilibrium position will have a positive $\Delta G$ and will not be spontaneous. For this reason, systems never spontaneously move away from equilibrium. Because a system at equilibrium cannot spontaneously change, it can do no work. *A process is spontaneous and can perform work only when it is moving toward equilibrium.*

## Free Energy and Metabolism

We can now apply the free-energy concept more specifically to the chemistry of life's processes.

### Exergonic and Endergonic Reactions in Metabolism

Based on their free-energy changes, chemical reactions can be classified as either exergonic ("energy outward") or endergonic ("energy inward"). An **exergonic reaction** proceeds with a net release of free energy **(Figure 5.6a)**. Because the chemical mixture loses free energy ($G$ decreases), $\Delta G$ is negative for an exergonic reaction. Using $\Delta G$ as a standard for spontaneity, exergonic reactions are those that occur spontaneously. (Remember, the word *spontaneous* implies that it is energetically favorable, not that it will occur rapidly.) The magnitude of $\Delta G$ for an exergonic reaction represents the maximum amount of work the reaction can perform (some of the free energy is released as heat and cannot do work). The greater the decrease in free energy, the greater the amount of work that can be done.

Consider the overall reaction for cellular respiration:

$$C_6H_{12}O_6 + 6\ O_2 \rightarrow 6\ CO_2 + 6\ H_2O$$
$$\Delta G = -686 \text{ kcal/mol } (-2{,}870 \text{ kJ/mol})$$

686 kcal (2,870 kJ) of energy are made available for work for each mole (180 g) of glucose broken down by respiration under "standard conditions" (1 $M$ of each reactant and product, 25°C, pH 7). Because energy must be conserved, the products of respiration store 686 kcal less free energy per mole than the reactants. The products are the "exhaust" of a process that tapped the free energy stored in the bonds of the sugar molecules.

- More free energy (higher $G$)
- Less stable
- Greater work capacity

In a **spontaneous change**
- The free energy of the system decreases ($\Delta G < 0$)
- The system becomes more stable
- The released free energy can be harnessed to do work

- Less free energy (lower $G$)
- More stable
- Less work capacity

**(a) Gravitational motion.** Objects move spontaneously from a higher altitude to a lower one.

**(b) Diffusion.** Molecules in a drop of dye diffuse until they are randomly dispersed.

**(c) Chemical reaction.** In a cell, a glucose molecule is broken down into simpler molecules.

▲ **Figure 5.5 The relationship of free energy to stability, work capacity, and spontaneous change.** Unstable systems (top) are rich in free energy, $G$. They have a tendency to change spontaneously to a more stable state (bottom), and it is possible to harness this "downhill" change to perform work.

## ▼ Figure 5.6 Free energy changes (ΔG) in exergonic and endergonic reactions.

### (a) Exergonic reaction: energy released, spontaneous

### (b) Endergonic reaction: energy required, nonspontaneous

It is important to realize that the breaking of bonds does not release energy; on the contrary, as you will soon see, it requires energy. The phrase "energy stored in bonds" is shorthand for the potential energy that can be released when new bonds are formed after the original bonds break, as long as the products are of lower free energy than the reactants.

An **endergonic reaction** is one that absorbs free energy from its surroundings **(Figure 5.6b)**. Because this kind of reaction essentially *stores* free energy in molecules (G increases), ΔG is positive. Such reactions are nonspontaneous, and the magnitude of ΔG is the quantity of energy required to drive the reaction. If a chemical process is exergonic (downhill), releasing energy in one direction, then the reverse process must be endergonic (uphill), using energy. A reversible process cannot be downhill in both directions. If ΔG = −686 kcal/mol for respiration, which converts glucose and oxygen to carbon dioxide and water, then the reverse process—the conversion of carbon dioxide and water to glucose and oxygen—must be strongly endergonic, with ΔG = +686 kcal/mol. Such a reaction would never happen by itself.

How, then, do plants make the sugar that organisms use for energy? Plants get the required energy—686 kcal to make a

**(a) An isolated hydroelectric system.** Water flowing downhill turns a turbine that drives a generator providing electricity to a lightbulb, but only until the system reaches equilibrium.

**(b) An open hydroelectric system.** Flowing water keeps driving the generator because intake and outflow of water keep the system from reaching equilibrium.

**(c) A multistep open hydroelectric system.** Cellular respiration is analogous to this system: Glucose is broken down in a series of exergonic reactions that power the work of the cell. The product of each reaction is used as the reactant for the next, so no reaction reaches equilibrium.

▲ **Figure 5.7 Equilibrium and work in isolated and open systems.**

mole of glucose—from the environment by capturing light and converting its energy to chemical energy. Next, in a long series of exergonic steps, they gradually spend that chemical energy to assemble glucose molecules.

### Equilibrium and Metabolism

Reactions in an isolated system eventually reach equilibrium and can then do no work, as illustrated by the isolated hydroelectric system in **Figure 5.7a**. The chemical reactions of metabolism are reversible, and they, too, would reach equilibrium if they occurred in the isolation of a test tube. Because systems at equilibrium are at a minimum of G and can do no work, a cell that has reached metabolic equilibrium is dead! The fact that metabolism as a whole is never at equilibrium is one of the defining features of life.

Like most systems, a living cell is not in equilibrium. The constant flow of materials in and out of the cell keeps the metabolic pathways from ever reaching equilibrium, and the cell continues to do work throughout its life. This principle is illustrated by the open (and more realistic) hydroelectric system in **Figure 5.7b**. However, unlike this simple single-step system, a catabolic pathway in a cell releases free energy in a series of reactions. An example is cellular respiration, illustrated by analogy in **Figure 5.7c**. Some of the reversible reactions of respiration are constantly "pulled" in one direction—that is, they are kept out of equilibrium. The key to maintaining this lack of equilibrium is that the product of a reaction does not accumulate but instead becomes a reactant in the next step; finally, waste products are expelled from the cell. The overall sequence of reactions is kept going by the huge free-energy difference between glucose and oxygen at the top of the energy "hill" and carbon dioxide and water at the "downhill" end. As long as our cells have a steady supply of glucose or other fuels and oxygen and are able to expel waste products to the surroundings, their metabolic pathways never reach equilibrium and can continue to do the work of life.

We see once again how important it is to think of organisms as open systems. Sunlight provides a daily source of free energy for an ecosystem's plants and other photosynthetic organisms. Animals and other nonphotosynthetic organisms in an ecosystem must have a source of free energy in the form of the organic products of photosynthesis. Now that we have applied the free-energy concept to metabolism, we are ready to see how a cell actually performs the work of life.

**CONCEPT CHECK 5.2**

1. Cellular respiration uses glucose and oxygen, which have high levels of free energy, and releases $CO_2$ and water, which have low levels of free energy. Is cellular respiration spontaneous or not? Is it exergonic or endergonic? What happens to the energy released from glucose?

2. **WHAT IF?** Some nighttime partygoers wear glow-in-the-dark necklaces. The necklaces start glowing once they are "activated" by snapping the necklace in a way that allows two chemicals to react and emit light in the form of chemiluminescence. Is this chemical reaction exergonic or endergonic? Explain your answer.

For suggested answers, see Appendix A.

CONCEPT 5.3

# ATP powers cellular work by coupling exergonic reactions to endergonic reactions

A cell does three main kinds of work:

- *Chemical work*, the pushing of endergonic reactions that would not occur spontaneously, such as the synthesis of polymers from monomers (chemical work will be discussed further in this chapter and in Chapter 6)

- *Transport work*, the pumping of substances across membranes against the direction of spontaneous movement

- *Mechanical work*, such as the beating of cilia (see Chapter 3), the contraction of muscle cells, and the movement of chromosomes during cellular reproduction

A key feature in the way cells manage their energy resources to do this work is **energy coupling**, the use of an exergonic process to drive an endergonic one. ATP is responsible for mediating most energy coupling in cells, and in most cases it acts as the immediate source of energy that powers cellular work.

## The Structure and Hydrolysis of ATP

**ATP (adenosine triphosphate)** contains the sugar ribose, with the nitrogenous base adenine and a chain of three phosphate groups bonded to it **(Figure 5.8a)**. In addition to its role in energy coupling, ATP is also one of the nucleoside triphosphates used to make RNA.

The bonds between the phosphate groups of ATP can be broken by hydrolysis. When the terminal phosphate bond is broken by the addition of a water molecule, a molecule of

**(a) The structure of ATP.** In the cell, most hydroxyl groups of phosphates are ionized (—O⁻).

**(b) The hydrolysis of ATP.** The reaction of ATP and water yields inorganic phosphate (Ⓟᵢ) and ADP and releases energy.

▲ **Figure 5.8 The structure and hydrolysis of adenosine triphosphate (ATP).**

inorganic phosphate ($HOPO_3^{2-}$, which is abbreviated Ⓟ$_i$ throughout this book) leaves the ATP. In this way, adenosine *tri*phosphate becomes adenosine *di*phosphate, or ADP **(Figure 5.8b)**. The reaction is exergonic and releases 7.3 kcal of energy per mole of ATP hydrolyzed:

$$ATP + H_2O \rightarrow ADP + Ⓟ_i$$
$$\Delta G = -7.3 \text{ kcal/mol } (-30.5 \text{ kJ/mol})$$

This is the free-energy change measured under standard conditions. In the cell, conditions do not conform to standard conditions, primarily because reactant and product concentrations differ from 1 $M$. For example, when ATP hydrolysis occurs under cellular conditions, the actual $\Delta G$ is about −13 kcal/mol, 78% greater than the energy released by ATP hydrolysis under standard conditions.

Because their hydrolysis releases energy, the phosphate bonds of ATP are sometimes referred to as high-energy phosphate bonds, but the term is misleading. The phosphate bonds of ATP are not unusually strong bonds, as "high-energy" may imply; rather, the reactants (ATP and water) themselves have high energy relative to the energy of the products (ADP and Ⓟ$_i$). The release of energy during the hydrolysis of ATP comes from the chemical change to a state of lower free energy, not from the phosphate bonds themselves.

ATP is useful to the cell because the energy it releases on losing a phosphate group is somewhat greater than the energy most other molecules could deliver. But why does this hydrolysis release so much energy? If we reexamine the ATP molecule in Figure 5.8a, we can see that all three phosphate groups are negatively charged. These like charges are crowded together, and their mutual repulsion contributes to the instability of this region of the ATP molecule. The triphosphate tail of ATP is the chemical equivalent of a compressed spring.

## How the Hydrolysis of ATP Performs Work

When ATP is hydrolyzed in a test tube, the release of free energy merely heats the surrounding water. In an organism, this same generation of heat can sometimes be beneficial. For instance, the process of shivering uses ATP hydrolysis during muscle contraction to warm the body. In most cases in the cell, however, the generation of heat alone would be an inefficient (and potentially dangerous) use of a valuable energy resource. Instead, the cell's proteins harness the energy released during ATP hydrolysis in several ways to perform the three types of cellular work—chemical, transport, and mechanical.

For example, with the help of specific enzymes, the cell is able to use the energy released by ATP hydrolysis directly to drive chemical reactions that, by themselves, are endergonic **(Figure 5.9)**. If the $\Delta G$ of an endergonic reaction is less than

**(a) Glutamic acid conversion to glutamine.** Glutamine synthesis from glutamic acid (Glu) by itself is endergonic ($\Delta G$ is positive), so it is not spontaneous.

$\Delta G_{Glu} = +3.4$ kcal/mol

**(b) Conversion reaction coupled with ATP hydrolysis.** In the cell, glutamine synthesis occurs in two steps, coupled by a phosphorylated intermediate. ❶ ATP phosphorylates glutamic acid, making it less stable. ❷ Ammonia displaces the phosphate group, forming glutamine.

**(c) Free-energy change for coupled reaction.** $\Delta G$ for the glutamic acid conversion to glutamine (+3.4 kcal/mol) plus $\Delta G$ for ATP hydrolysis (−7.3 kcal/mol) gives the free-energy change for the overall reaction (−3.9 kcal/mol). Because the overall process is exergonic (net $\Delta G$ is negative), it occurs spontaneously.

$\Delta G_{Glu} = +3.4$ kcal/mol

$\Delta G_{ATP} = -7.3$ kcal/mol

$\Delta G_{Glu} = +3.4$ kcal/mol
$+ \Delta G_{ATP} = -7.3$ kcal/mol
Net $\Delta G = -3.9$ kcal/mol

▲ **Figure 5.9 How ATP drives chemical work: energy coupling using ATP hydrolysis.** In this example, the exergonic process of ATP hydrolysis is used to drive an endergonic process—the cellular synthesis of the amino acid glutamine from glutamic acid and ammonia.

**MAKE CONNECTIONS** *Explain why glutamine is drawn as it is in this figure. (See Figure 2.17.)*

the amount of energy released by ATP hydrolysis, then the two reactions can be coupled so that, overall, the coupled reactions are exergonic. This usually involves phosphorylation, the transfer of a phosphate group from ATP to some other molecule, such as the reactant. The recipient with the phosphate group covalently bonded to it is then called a **phosphorylated intermediate**. The key to coupling exergonic and endergonic reactions is the formation of this phosphorylated intermediate, which is more reactive (less stable) than the original unphosphorylated molecule.

Transport and mechanical work in the cell are also nearly always powered by the hydrolysis of ATP. In these cases, ATP hydrolysis leads to a change in a protein's shape and often its ability to bind another molecule. Sometimes this occurs via a phosphorylated intermediate, as seen for the transport protein in **Figure 5.10a**. In most instances of mechanical work involving motor proteins "walking" along cytoskeletal elements **(Figure 5.10b)**, a cycle occurs in which ATP is first bound noncovalently to the motor protein. Next, ATP is hydrolyzed, releasing ADP and $P_i$. Another ATP molecule can then bind. At each stage, the motor protein changes its shape and ability to bind the cytoskeleton, resulting in movement of the protein along the cytoskeletal track. Phosphorylation and dephosphorylation also promote crucial protein shape changes during cell signaling.

Transport protein    Solute

ATP ⇨              ⇨              ⇨ ADP + $P_i$

Solute transported

**(a) Transport work:** ATP phosphorylates transport proteins.

Vesicle              Cytoskeletal track

ATP ⇨              ⇨ ATP            ⇨ ADP + $P_i$

Motor protein        Protein and
                     vesicle moved

**(b) Mechanical work:** ATP binds noncovalently to motor proteins and then is hydrolyzed.

▲ **Figure 5.10 How ATP drives transport and mechanical work.** ATP hydrolysis causes changes in the shapes and binding affinities of proteins. This can occur either **(a)** directly, by phosphorylation, as shown for a membrane protein carrying out active transport of a solute, or **(b)** indirectly, via noncovalent binding of ATP and its hydrolytic products, as is the case for motor proteins that move vesicles (and other organelles) along cytoskeletal "tracks" in the cell (see also Figure 3.20).

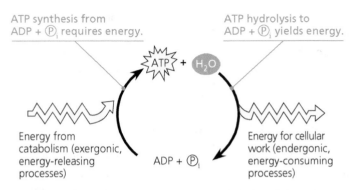

ATP synthesis from          ATP hydrolysis to
ADP + $P_i$ requires energy.   ADP + $P_i$ yields energy.

ATP + H₂O

Energy from                 Energy for cellular
catabolism (exergonic,      work (endergonic,
energy-releasing            energy-consuming
processes)                  processes)

ADP + $P_i$

▲ **Figure 5.11 The ATP cycle.** Energy released by breakdown reactions (catabolism) in the cell is used to phosphorylate ADP, regenerating ATP. Chemical potential energy stored in ATP drives most cellular work.

## The Regeneration of ATP

An organism at work uses ATP continuously, but ATP is a renewable resource that can be regenerated by the addition of phosphate to ADP **(Figure 5.11)**. The free energy required to phosphorylate ADP comes from exergonic breakdown reactions (catabolism) in the cell. This shuttling of inorganic phosphate and energy is called the ATP cycle, and it couples the cell's energy-yielding (exergonic) processes to the energy-consuming (endergonic) ones. The ATP cycle proceeds at an astonishing pace. For example, a working muscle cell recycles its entire pool of ATP in less than a minute. That turnover represents 10 million molecules of ATP consumed and regenerated per second per cell. If ATP could not be regenerated by the phosphorylation of ADP, humans would use up nearly their body weight in ATP each day.

Because both directions of a reversible process cannot be downhill, the regeneration of ATP from ADP and $P_i$ is necessarily endergonic:

$$ADP + P_i \rightarrow ATP + H_2O$$
$$\Delta G = +7.3 \text{ kcal/mol } (+30.5 \text{ kJ/mol}) \text{ (standard conditions)}$$

Since ATP formation from ADP and $P_i$ is not spontaneous, free energy must be spent to make it occur. Catabolic (exergonic) pathways, especially cellular respiration, provide the energy for the endergonic process of making ATP. Plants also use light energy to produce ATP. Thus, the ATP cycle is a revolving door through which energy passes during its transfer from catabolic to anabolic pathways.

**CONCEPT CHECK 5.3**

1. How does ATP typically transfer energy from exergonic to endergonic reactions in the cell?

2. Which of the following combinations has more free energy: glutamic acid + ammonia + ATP or glutamine + ADP + $P_i$? Explain your answer.

3. **MAKE CONNECTIONS** Does Figure 5.10a show passive or active transport? Explain.

For suggested answers, see Appendix A.

CONCEPT 5.4

# Enzymes speed up metabolic reactions by lowering energy barriers

The laws of thermodynamics tell us what will and will not happen under given conditions but say nothing about the rate of these processes. A spontaneous chemical reaction occurs without any requirement for outside energy, but it may occur so slowly that it is imperceptible. For example, even though the hydrolysis of sucrose (table sugar) to glucose and fructose is exergonic, occurring spontaneously with a release of free energy ($\Delta G = -7$ kcal/mol), a solution of sucrose dissolved in sterile water will sit for years at room temperature with no appreciable hydrolysis. However, if we add a small amount of the enzyme sucrase to the solution, then all the sucrose may be hydrolyzed within seconds, as shown below:

Sucrase

Sucrose ($C_{12}H_{22}O_{11}$) + $H_2O$ → Glucose ($C_6H_{12}O_6$) + Fructose ($C_6H_{12}O_6$)

How does the enzyme do this?

An **enzyme** is a macromolecule that acts as a **catalyst**, a chemical agent that speeds up a reaction without being consumed by the reaction. (In this chapter, we are focusing on enzymes that are proteins. Some RNA molecules, called ribozymes, can function as enzymes; these will be discussed in Chapter 14.) Without regulation by enzymes, chemical traffic through the pathways of metabolism would become terribly congested because many chemical reactions would take such a long time. In the next two sections, we will see what prevents a spontaneous reaction from occurring faster and how an enzyme changes the situation.

## The Activation Energy Barrier

Every chemical reaction between molecules involves both bond breaking and bond forming. For example, the hydrolysis of sucrose involves breaking the bond between glucose and fructose and one of the bonds of a water molecule and then forming two new bonds, as shown above. Changing one molecule into another generally involves contorting the starting molecule into a highly unstable state before the reaction can proceed. This contortion can be compared to the bending of a metal key ring when you pry it open to add a new key. The key ring is highly unstable in its opened form but returns to a stable state once the key is threaded all the way onto the ring. To reach the contorted state where bonds can change, reactant molecules must absorb energy from their surroundings. When the new bonds of the product molecules form, energy is released as heat, and the molecules return to stable shapes with lower energy than the contorted state.

The initial investment of energy for starting a reaction—the energy required to contort the reactant molecules so the bonds can break—is known as the *free energy of activation*, or **activation energy**, abbreviated $E_A$ in this book. We can think of activation energy as the amount of energy needed to push the reactants to the top of an energy barrier, or uphill, so that the "downhill" part of the reaction can begin. Activation energy is often supplied by heat in the form of thermal energy that the reactant molecules absorb from the surroundings. The absorption of thermal energy accelerates the reactant molecules, so they collide more often and more forcefully. It also agitates the atoms within the molecules, making the breakage of bonds more likely. When the molecules have absorbed enough energy for the bonds to break, the reactants are in an unstable condition known as the *transition state*.

**Figure 5.12** graphs the energy changes for a hypothetical exergonic reaction that swaps portions of two reactant molecules:

$$AB + CD \rightarrow AC + BD$$
Reactants    Products

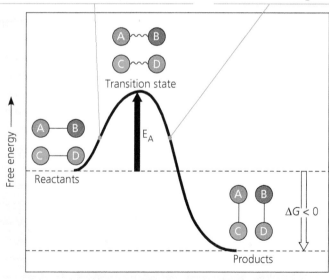

The reactants AB and CD must absorb enough energy from the surroundings to reach the unstable transition state, where bonds can break.

After bonds have broken, new bonds form, releasing energy to the surroundings.

▲ **Figure 5.12 Energy profile of an exergonic reaction.** The "molecules" are hypothetical, with A, B, C, and D representing portions of the molecules. Thermodynamically, this is an exergonic reaction, with a negative $\Delta G$, and the reaction occurs spontaneously. However, the activation energy ($E_A$) provides a barrier that determines the rate of the reaction.

**DRAW IT** *Graph the progress of an endergonic reaction in which EF and GH form products EG and FH, assuming that the reactants must pass through a transition state.*

The activation of the reactants is represented by the uphill portion of the graph, in which the free-energy content of the reactant molecules is increasing. At the summit, when energy equivalent to $E_A$ has been absorbed, the reactants are in the transition state: They are activated, and their bonds can be broken. As the atoms then settle into their new, more stable bonding arrangements, energy is released to the surroundings. This corresponds to the downhill part of the curve, which shows the loss of free energy by the molecules. The overall decrease in free energy means that $E_A$ is repaid with interest, as the formation of new bonds releases more energy than was invested in the breaking of old bonds.

The reaction shown in Figure 5.12 is exergonic and occurs spontaneously ($\Delta G < 0$). However, the activation energy provides a barrier that determines the rate of the reaction. The reactants must absorb enough energy to reach the top of the activation energy barrier before the reaction can occur. For some reactions, $E_A$ is modest enough that even at room temperature there is sufficient thermal energy for many of the reactant molecules to reach the transition state in a short time. In most cases, however, $E_A$ is so high and the transition state is reached so rarely that the reaction will hardly proceed at all. In these cases, the reaction will occur at a noticeable rate only if the reactants are heated. For example, the reaction of gasoline and oxygen is exergonic and will occur spontaneously, but energy is required for the molecules to reach the transition state and react. Only when the spark plugs fire in an automobile engine can there be the explosive release of energy that pushes the pistons. Without a spark, a mixture of gasoline hydrocarbons and oxygen will not react because the $E_A$ barrier is too high.

## How Enzymes Speed Up Reactions

Proteins, DNA, and other complex molecules of the cell are rich in free energy and have the potential to decompose spontaneously; that is, the laws of thermodynamics favor their breakdown. These molecules persist only because at temperatures typical for cells, few molecules can make it over the hump of activation energy. However, the barriers for selected reactions must occasionally be surmounted for cells to carry out the processes needed for life. Heat speeds a reaction by allowing reactants to attain the transition state more often, but this solution would be inappropriate for biological systems. First, high temperature denatures proteins and kills cells. Second, heat would speed up *all* reactions, not just those that are needed. Instead of heat, organisms use catalysis to speed up reactions.

An enzyme catalyzes a reaction by lowering the $E_A$ barrier **(Figure 5.13)**, enabling the reactant molecules to absorb enough energy to reach the transition state even at moderate temperatures. An enzyme cannot change the $\Delta G$ for a reaction; it cannot make an endergonic reaction exergonic. Enzymes can only hasten reactions that would eventually occur anyway, but this function makes it possible for the cell to have a dynamic metabolism, routing chemicals smoothly through the cell's

▲ **Figure 5.13 The effect of an enzyme on activation energy.** Without affecting the free-energy change ($\Delta G$) for a reaction, an enzyme speeds the reaction by reducing its activation energy ($E_A$).

metabolic pathways. And because enzymes are very specific for the reactions they catalyze, they determine which chemical processes will be going on in the cell at any particular time.

## Substrate Specificity of Enzymes

The reactant an enzyme acts on is referred to as the enzyme's **substrate**. The enzyme binds to its substrate (or substrates, when there are two or more reactants), forming an **enzyme-substrate complex**. While enzyme and substrate are joined, the catalytic action of the enzyme converts the substrate to the product (or products) of the reaction. The overall process can be summarized as follows:

$$\text{Enzyme} + \text{Substrate(s)} \rightleftharpoons \text{Enzyme-substrate complex} \rightleftharpoons \text{Enzyme} + \text{Product(s)}$$

For example, the enzyme sucrase (most enzyme names end in *-ase*) catalyzes the hydrolysis of the disaccharide sucrose into its two monosaccharides, glucose and fructose (see the illustrated equation on the previous page):

$$\text{Sucrase} + \text{Sucrose} + \text{H}_2\text{O} \rightleftharpoons \text{Sucrase-sucrose-H}_2\text{O complex} \rightleftharpoons \text{Sucrase} + \text{Glucose} + \text{Fructose}$$

The reaction catalyzed by each enzyme is very specific; an enzyme can recognize its specific substrate even among closely related compounds. For instance, sucrase will act only on sucrose and will not bind to other disaccharides, such as maltose. What accounts for this molecular recognition? Recall that most enzymes are proteins, and proteins are macromolecules with unique three-dimensional configurations. The specificity of an enzyme results from its shape, which is a consequence of its amino acid sequence.

Only a restricted region of the enzyme molecule actually binds to the substrate. This region, called the **active site**, is typically a pocket or groove on the surface of the enzyme where catalysis occurs **(Figure 5.14a)**. Usually, the active site is formed by only a few of the enzyme's amino acids, with the rest of the protein molecule providing a framework that determines the configuration of the active site. The specificity of an enzyme is attributed to a complementary fit between the shape of its active site and the shape of the substrate, like that seen in the binding of a signaling molecule to a receptor protein (see Concept 5.6).

An enzyme is not a stiff structure locked into a given shape. In fact, recent work by biochemists has shown clearly that enzymes (and other proteins as well) seem to "dance" between subtly different shapes in a dynamic equilibrium, with slight differences in free energy for each "pose." The shape that best fits the substrate isn't necessarily the one with the lowest energy, but during the very short time the enzyme takes on this shape, its active site can bind to the substrate. It has been known for more than 50 years that the active site itself is also not a rigid receptacle for the substrate. As the substrate enters the active site, the enzyme changes shape slightly due to interactions between the substrate's chemical groups and chemical groups on the side chains of the amino acids that form the active site. This shape change makes the active site fit even more snugly around the substrate **(Figure 5.14b)**. This **induced fit** is like a clasping handshake. Induced fit brings chemical groups of the active site into positions that enhance their ability to catalyze the chemical reaction.

## Catalysis in the Enzyme's Active Site

In most enzymatic reactions, the substrate is held in the active site by so-called weak interactions, such as hydrogen bonds and ionic bonds. R groups of a few of the amino acids that make up the active site catalyze the conversion of substrate to product, and the product departs from the active site. The enzyme is then free to take another substrate molecule into its active site. The entire cycle happens so fast that a single enzyme molecule typically acts on about a thousand substrate molecules per second, and some enzymes are even faster. Enzymes, like other catalysts, emerge from the reaction in their original form. Therefore, very small amounts of enzyme can have a huge metabolic impact by functioning over and over again in catalytic cycles. **Figure 5.15** shows a catalytic cycle involving two substrates and two products.

Most metabolic reactions are reversible, and an enzyme can catalyze either the forward or the reverse reaction, depending on which direction has a negative $\Delta G$. This in turn depends mainly on the relative concentrations of reactants and products. The net effect is always in the direction of equilibrium.

**Enzyme**

**Enzyme-substrate complex**

**(a)** In this computer graphic model, the active site of this enzyme (hexokinase, shown in blue) forms a groove on its surface. Its substrate is glucose (red).

**(b)** When the substrate enters the active site, it forms weak bonds with the enzyme, inducing a change in the shape of the enzyme. This change allows additional weak bonds to form, causing the active site to enfold the substrate and hold it in place.

▲ **Figure 5.14 Induced fit between an enzyme and its substrate.**

Enzymes use a variety of mechanisms that lower activation energy and speed up a reaction. First, in reactions involving two or more reactants, the active site provides a template on which the substrates can come together in the proper orientation for a reaction to occur between them (see Figure 5.15, step ❷). Second, as the active site of an enzyme clutches the bound substrates, the enzyme may stretch the substrate molecules toward their transition-state form, stressing and bending critical chemical bonds that must be broken during

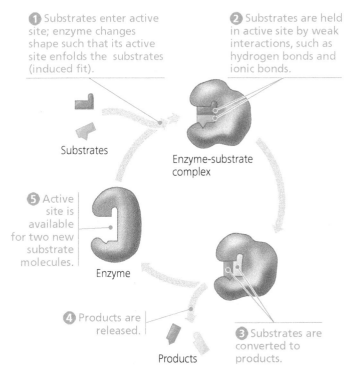

❶ Substrates enter active site; enzyme changes shape such that its active site enfolds the substrates (induced fit).

❷ Substrates are held in active site by weak interactions, such as hydrogen bonds and ionic bonds.

Substrates

Enzyme-substrate complex

❺ Active site is available for two new substrate molecules.

Enzyme

❹ Products are released.

Products

❸ Substrates are converted to products.

▲ **Figure 5.15 The active site and catalytic cycle of an enzyme.** An enzyme can convert one or more reactant molecules to one or more product molecules. The enzyme shown here converts two substrate molecules to two product molecules.

the reaction. Because $E_A$ is proportional to the difficulty of breaking the bonds, distorting the substrate helps it approach the transition state and thus reduces the amount of free energy that must be absorbed to achieve that state.

Third, the active site may also provide a microenvironment that is more conducive to a particular type of reaction than the solution itself would be without the enzyme. For example, if the active site has amino acids with acidic R groups, the active site may be a pocket of low pH in an otherwise neutral cell. In such cases, an acidic amino acid may facilitate $H^+$ transfer to the substrate as a key step in catalyzing the reaction.

A fourth mechanism of catalysis is the direct participation of the active site in the chemical reaction. Sometimes this process even involves brief covalent bonding between the substrate and the side chain of an amino acid of the enzyme. Subsequent steps of the reaction restore the side chains to their original states, so that the active site is the same after the reaction as it was before.

The rate at which a particular amount of enzyme converts substrate to product is partly a function of the initial concentration of the substrate: The more substrate molecules that are available, the more frequently they access the active sites of the enzyme molecules. However, there is a limit to how fast the reaction can be pushed by adding more substrate to a fixed concentration of enzyme. At some point, the concentration of substrate will be high enough that all enzyme molecules have their active sites engaged. As soon as the product exits an active site, another substrate molecule enters. At this substrate concentration, the enzyme is said to be *saturated*, and the rate of the reaction is determined by the speed at which the active site converts substrate to product. When an enzyme population is saturated, the only way to increase the rate of product formation is to add more enzyme. Cells often increase the rate of a reaction by producing more enzyme molecules. You can graph the progress of an enzymatic reaction in the **Scientific Skills Exercise**.

## Making a Line Graph and Calculating a Slope

**Does the Rate of Glucose 6-Phosphatase Activity Change over Time in Isolated Liver Cells?** Glucose 6-phosphatase, which is found in mammalian liver cells, is a key enzyme in control of blood glucose levels. The enzyme catalyzes the breakdown of glucose 6-phosphate into glucose and inorganic phosphate (Ⓟᵢ). These products are transported out of liver cells into the blood, increasing blood glucose levels. In this exercise, you will graph data from a time-course experiment that measured Ⓟᵢ concentration in the buffer outside isolated liver cells, thus indirectly measuring glucose 6-phosphatase activity inside the cells.

**How the Experiment Was Done** Isolated rat liver cells were placed in a dish with buffer at physiological conditions (pH 7.4, 37°C). Glucose 6-phosphate (the substrate) was added to the dish, where it was taken up by the cells. Then a sample of buffer was removed every 5 minutes and the concentration of Ⓟᵢ determined.

**Data from the Experiment**

| Time (min) | Concentration of Ⓟᵢ (μmol/mL) |
|:---:|:---:|
| 0 | 0 |
| 5 | 10 |
| 10 | 90 |
| 15 | 180 |
| 20 | 270 |
| 25 | 330 |
| 30 | 355 |
| 35 | 355 |
| 40 | 355 |

**Interpret the Data**

1. To see patterns in the data from a time-course experiment like this, it is helpful to graph the data. First, determine which set of data goes on each axis. (a) What did the researchers intentionally vary in the experiment? This is the independent variable, which goes on the x-axis. (b) What are the units (abbreviated) for the independent variable? Explain in words what the abbreviation stands for. (c) What was measured by the researchers? This is the dependent variable, which goes on the y-axis. (d) What does the units abbreviation stand for? Label each axis, including the units.

2. Next, you'll want to mark off the axes with just enough evenly spaced tick marks to accommodate the full set of data. Determine the range of data values for each axis. (a) What is the largest value to go on the x-axis? What is a reasonable spacing for the tick marks, and what should be the highest one? (b) What is the largest value to go on the y-axis? What is a reasonable spacing for the tick marks, and what should be the highest one?

3. Plot the data points on your graph. Match each x-value with its partner y-value and place a point on the graph at that coordinate. Draw a line that connects the points. (For additional information about graphs, see the Scientific Skills Review in Appendix F and in the Study Area in MasteringBiology.)

4. Examine your graph and look for patterns in the data. (a) Does the concentration of Ⓟᵢ increase evenly through the course of the experiment? To answer this question, describe the pattern you see in the graph. (b) What part of the graph shows the highest rate of enzyme activity? Consider that the rate of enzyme activity is related to the slope of the line, $\Delta y/\Delta x$ (the "rise" over the "run"), in μmol/mL·min, with the steepest slope indicating the highest rate of enzyme activity. Calculate the rate of enzyme activity (slope) where the graph is steepest. (c) Can you think of a biological explanation for the pattern you see?

5. If your blood sugar level is low from skipping lunch, what reaction (discussed in this exercise) will occur in your liver cells? Write out the reaction and put the name of the enzyme over the reaction arrow. How will this reaction affect your blood sugar level?

**Data from** S. R. Commerford et al., Diets enriched in sucrose or fat increase gluconeogenesis and G-6-Pase but not basal glucose production in rats, *American Journal of Physiology— Endocrinology and Metabolism* 283:E545–E555 (2002).

(MB) A version of this Scientific Skills Exercise can be assigned in MasteringBiology.

## Effects of Local Conditions on Enzyme Activity

The activity of an enzyme—how efficiently the enzyme functions—is affected by general environmental factors, such as temperature and pH. It can also be affected by chemicals that specifically influence that enzyme. In fact, researchers have learned much about enzyme function by employing such chemicals.

### Effects of Temperature and pH

The three-dimensional structures of proteins are sensitive to their environment (see Chapter 2). As a consequence, each enzyme works better under some conditions than under other conditions, because these *optimal conditions* favor the most active shape for the enzyme molecule.

Temperature and pH are environmental factors important in the activity of an enzyme. Up to a point, the rate of an enzymatic reaction increases with increasing temperature, partly because substrates collide with active sites more frequently when the molecules move rapidly. Above that temperature, however, the speed of the enzymatic reaction drops sharply. The thermal agitation of the enzyme molecule disrupts the hydrogen bonds, ionic bonds, and other weak interactions that stabilize the active shape of the enzyme, and the protein molecule eventually denatures. Each enzyme has an optimal temperature at which its reaction rate is greatest. Without denaturing the enzyme, this temperature allows the greatest number of molecular collisions and the fastest conversion of the reactants to product molecules. Most human enzymes have optimal temperatures of about 35–40°C (close to human body temperature). The thermophilic bacteria that live in hot springs contain enzymes with optimal temperatures of 70°C or higher **(Figure 5.16a)**.

Just as each enzyme has an optimal temperature, it also has a pH at which it is most active. The optimal pH values for most enzymes fall in the range of pH 6–8, but there are exceptions. For example, pepsin, a digestive enzyme in the human stomach, works best at pH 2. Such an acidic environment denatures most enzymes, but pepsin is adapted to maintain its functional three-dimensional structure in the acidic environment of the stomach. In contrast, trypsin, a digestive enzyme residing in the alkaline environment of the human intestine, has an optimal pH of 8 and would be denatured in the stomach **(Figure 5.16b)**.

### Cofactors

Apoenzyme + cofactor → holoenzyme.

Many enzymes require nonprotein helpers for catalytic activity. These adjuncts, called **cofactors**, may be bound tightly to the enzyme as permanent residents, or they may bind loosely and reversibly along with the substrate. The cofactors of some enzymes are inorganic, such as the metal atoms zinc, iron, and copper in ionic form. If the cofactor is an organic molecule, it is more specifically called a **coenzyme**. Most vitamins are important in nutrition because they act as coenzymes or raw materials from which coenzymes are made. Cofactors function

**(a) Optimal temperature for two enzymes**

**(b) Optimal pH for two enzymes**

▲ **Figure 5.16 Environmental factors affecting enzyme activity.** Each enzyme has an optimal **(a)** temperature and **(b)** pH that favor the most active shape of the protein molecule.

**DRAW IT** *Given that a mature lysosome has an internal pH of around 4.5, draw a curve in (b) showing what you would predict for a lysosomal enzyme, labeling its optimal pH.*

in various ways, but in all cases where they are used, they perform a crucial chemical function in catalysis. You'll encounter examples of cofactors later in the book.

### Enzyme Inhibitors

Certain chemicals selectively inhibit the action of specific enzymes, and we have learned a lot about enzyme function by studying the effects of these molecules. If the inhibitor attaches to the enzyme by covalent bonds, inhibition is usually irreversible.

Many enzyme inhibitors, however, bind to the enzyme by weak interactions, in which case inhibition is reversible. Some reversible inhibitors resemble the normal substrate molecule and compete for admission into the active site **(Figure 5.17a and b)**. These mimics, called **competitive inhibitors**, reduce the productivity of enzymes by blocking substrates from entering active sites. This kind of inhibition can be overcome by increasing the concentration of substrate so that as active sites become available, more substrate molecules than inhibitor molecules are around to gain entry to the sites.

In contrast, **noncompetitive inhibitors** do not directly compete with the substrate to bind to the enzyme at the active site. Instead, they impede enzymatic reactions by binding to another part of the enzyme. This interaction causes the

▼ **Figure 5.17 Inhibition of enzyme activity.**

**(a) Normal binding**

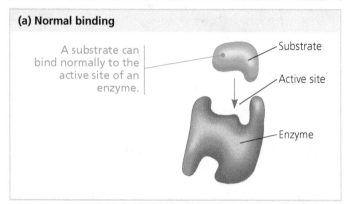

A substrate can bind normally to the active site of an enzyme.

Substrate

Active site

Enzyme

**(b) Competitive inhibition**

A competitive inhibitor mimics the substrate, competing for the active site.

Competitive inhibitor

**(c) Noncompetitive inhibition**

A noncompetitive inhibitor binds to the enzyme away from the active site, altering the shape of the enzyme so that even if the substrate can bind, the active site functions less effectively.

Noncompetitive inhibitor

enzyme molecule to change its shape in such a way that the active site becomes less effective at catalyzing the conversion of substrate to product **(Figure 5.17c)**.

Toxins and poisons are often irreversible enzyme inhibitors. An example is sarin, a nerve gas that caused the death of several people and injury to many others when it was released by terrorists in the Tokyo subway in 1995. This small molecule binds covalently to the R group on the amino acid serine, which is found in the active site of acetylcholinesterase, an enzyme important in the nervous system. Other examples include the pesticides DDT and parathion, inhibitors of key enzymes in the nervous system. Finally, many antibiotics are inhibitors of specific enzymes in bacteria. For instance, penicillin blocks the active site of an enzyme that many bacteria use to make their cell walls.

Citing enzyme inhibitors that are metabolic poisons may give the impression that enzyme inhibition is generally abnormal and harmful. In fact, molecules naturally present in the cell often regulate enzyme activity by acting as inhibitors. Such regulation—selective inhibition—is essential to the control of cellular metabolism, as we will discuss in Concept 5.5.

## The Evolution of Enzymes

**EVOLUTION**  Thus far, biochemists have discovered and named more than 4,000 different enzymes in various species, and this list probably represents the tip of the proverbial iceberg. How did this grand profusion of enzymes arise? Recall that most enzymes are proteins, and proteins are encoded by genes. A permanent change in a gene, known as a *mutation*, can result in a protein with one or more changed amino acids. In the case of an enzyme, if the changed amino acids are in the active site or some other crucial region, the altered enzyme might have a novel activity or might bind to a different substrate. Under environmental conditions where the new function benefits the organism, natural selection would tend to favor the mutated form of the gene, causing it to persist in the population. This simplified model is generally accepted as the main way in which the multitude of different enzymes arose over the past few billion years of life's history.

**CONCEPT CHECK 5.4**

1. Many spontaneous reactions occur very slowly. Why don't all spontaneous reactions occur instantly?
2. Why do enzymes act only on very specific substrates?
3. **WHAT IF?**  Malonate is an inhibitor of the enzyme succinate dehydrogenase. How would you determine whether malonate is a competitive or noncompetitive inhibitor?

For suggested answers, see Appendix A.

**CONCEPT** 5.5

# Regulation of enzyme activity helps control metabolism

Chemical chaos would result if all of a cell's metabolic pathways were operating simultaneously. Intrinsic to life's processes is a cell's ability to tightly regulate its metabolic pathways by controlling when and where its various enzymes are active. It does this either by switching on and off the genes that encode specific enzymes (as we will discuss in Unit Two) or, as we discuss next, by regulating the activity of enzymes once they are made.

## Allosteric Regulation of Enzymes

In many cases, the molecules that naturally regulate enzyme activity in a cell behave something like reversible noncompetitive inhibitors (see Figure 5.17c): These regulatory molecules change an enzyme's shape and the functioning of its active site by binding to a site elsewhere on the molecule, via noncovalent interactions. **Allosteric regulation** is the term used to describe any case in which a protein's function at one site is affected by the binding of a regulatory molecule to a separate site. It may result in either inhibition or stimulation of an enzyme's activity.

### Allosteric Activation and Inhibition

Most enzymes known to be allosterically regulated are constructed from two or more subunits, each composed of a polypeptide chain with its own active site. The entire complex oscillates between two different shapes, one catalytically active and the other inactive **(Figure 5.18a)**. In the simplest kind of allosteric regulation, an activating or inhibiting regulatory molecule binds to a regulatory site (sometimes called an allosteric site), often located where subunits join. The binding of an *activator* to a regulatory site stabilizes the shape that has functional active sites, whereas the binding of an *inhibitor* stabilizes the inactive form of the enzyme. The subunits of an allosteric enzyme fit together in such a way that a shape change in one subunit is transmitted to all others. Through this interaction of subunits, a single activator or inhibitor molecule that binds to one regulatory site will affect the active sites of all subunits.

Fluctuating concentrations of regulators can cause a sophisticated pattern of response in the activity of cellular enzymes. The products of ATP hydrolysis (ADP and $P_i$), for example, play a complex role in balancing the flow of traffic between anabolic and catabolic pathways by their effects on key enzymes. ATP binds to several catabolic enzymes allosterically, lowering their affinity for substrate and thus inhibiting their activity. ADP, however, functions as an activator of the same enzymes. This is logical because catabolism functions in regenerating ATP. If ATP production lags behind its use, ADP accumulates and activates the enzymes that speed up catabolism, producing more ATP. If the supply of ATP exceeds demand, then catabolism slows down as ATP molecules accumulate and bind to the same enzymes, inhibiting them. (You'll see specific examples of this type of regulation when you learn about cellular respiration in the next chapter.) ATP, ADP, and other related molecules also affect key enzymes in anabolic pathways. In this way, allosteric enzymes control the rates of important reactions in both sorts of metabolic pathways.

In another kind of allosteric activation, a *substrate* molecule binding to one active site in a multisubunit enzyme triggers a shape change in all the subunits, thereby increasing catalytic activity at the other active sites **(Figure 5.18b)**. Called **cooperativity**, this mechanism amplifies the response of enzymes to substrates: One substrate molecule primes an enzyme to act on additional substrate molecules more readily. Cooperativity is considered "allosteric" regulation because binding of the substrate to one active site affects catalysis in another active site.

▼ **Figure 5.18 Allosteric regulation of enzyme activity.**

**(a) Allosteric activators and inhibitors**

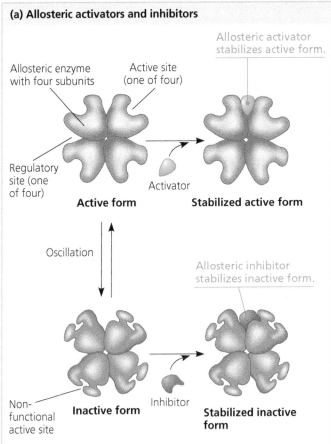

Allosteric enzyme with four subunits

Active site (one of four)

Allosteric activator stabilizes active form.

Regulatory site (one of four)

Activator

**Active form**

**Stabilized active form**

Oscillation

Allosteric inhibitor stabilizes inactive form.

Non-functional active site

**Inactive form**

Inhibitor

**Stabilized inactive form**

At low concentrations, activators and inhibitors dissociate from the enzyme. The enzyme can then oscillate again.

**(b) Cooperativity: another type of allosteric activation**

Binding of one substrate molecule to active site of one subunit locks all subunits in active conformation.

Substrate

**Inactive form**

**Stabilized active form**

The inactive form shown on the left oscillates with the active form when the active form is not stabilized by substrate.

Although the vertebrate oxygen transport protein hemoglobin is not an enzyme, classic studies of cooperative binding in this protein have elucidated the principle of cooperativity. Hemoglobin is made up of four subunits, each of which has an oxygen-binding site (see Figure 2.21). The binding of an oxygen molecule to one binding site increases the affinity for oxygen of the remaining binding sites. Thus, where oxygen is at high levels, such as in the lungs or gills, hemoglobin's affinity for oxygen increases as more binding sites are filled. In oxygen-deprived tissues, however, the release of each oxygen molecule decreases the oxygen affinity of the other binding sites, resulting in the release of oxygen where it is most needed. Cooperativity works similarly in multisubunit enzymes that have been studied.

### Feedback Inhibition

When ATP allosterically inhibits an enzyme in an ATP-generating pathway, as discussed earlier, the result is feedback inhibition, a common mode of metabolic control. In **feedback inhibition**, a metabolic pathway is switched off by the inhibitory binding of its end product to an enzyme that acts early in the pathway. **Figure 5.19** shows an example of this control mechanism operating on an anabolic pathway. Certain cells use this five-step pathway to synthesize the amino acid isoleucine from threonine, another amino acid. As isoleucine accumulates, it slows down its own synthesis by allosterically inhibiting the enzyme for the first step of the pathway. Feedback inhibition thereby prevents the cell from wasting chemical resources by making more isoleucine than is necessary.

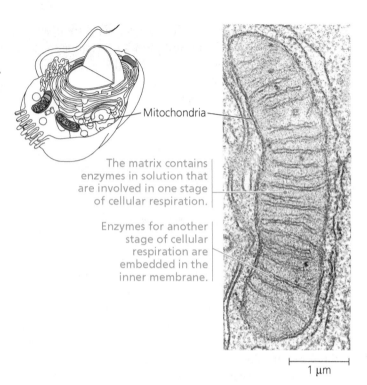

▲ **Figure 5.20 Organelles and structural order in metabolism.** Organelles such as the mitochondrion (TEM) contain enzymes that carry out specific functions, in this case cellular respiration.

## Specific Localization of Enzymes Within the Cell

The cell is not just a bag of chemicals with thousands of different kinds of enzymes and substrates in a random mix. The cell is compartmentalized, and cellular structures help bring order to metabolic pathways. In some cases, a team of enzymes for several steps of a metabolic pathway is assembled into a multienzyme complex. The arrangement facilitates the sequence of reactions, with the product from the first enzyme becoming the substrate for an adjacent enzyme in the complex, and so on, until the end product is released. Some enzymes and enzyme complexes have fixed locations within the cell and act as structural components of particular membranes. Others are in solution within particular membrane-enclosed eukaryotic organelles, each with its own internal chemical environment. For example, in eukaryotic cells, the enzymes for cellular respiration reside in specific locations within mitochondria (**Figure 5.20**).

In this chapter, you learned that metabolism, the intersecting set of chemical pathways characteristic of life, is a choreographed interplay of thousands of different kinds of cellular molecules. In the next chapter, we'll explore cellular respiration, the major catabolic pathway that breaks down organic molecules, releasing energy for the crucial processes of life.

**CONCEPT CHECK 5.5**

1. How do an activator and an inhibitor have different effects on an allosterically regulated enzyme?

   For suggested answers, see Appendix A.

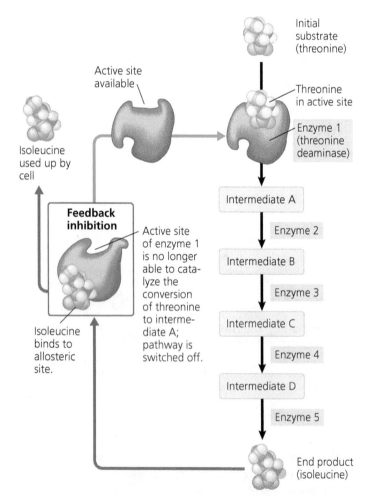

▲ **Figure 5.19 Feedback inhibition in isoleucine synthesis.**

# 5 Chapter Review

## SUMMARY OF KEY CONCEPTS

### CONCEPT 5.1
**An organism's metabolism transforms matter and energy (pp. 90–93)**

- **Metabolism** is the collection of chemical reactions that occur in an organism. Enzymes catalyze reactions in intersecting **metabolic pathways**, which may be **catabolic** (breaking down molecules, releasing energy) or **anabolic** (building molecules, consuming energy).
- **Energy** is the capacity to cause change; some forms of energy do work by moving matter. **Kinetic energy** is associated with motion and includes **thermal energy**, associated with the random motion of atoms or molecules. **Heat** is thermal energy in transfer from one object to another. **Potential energy** is related to the location or structure of matter and includes **chemical energy** possessed by a molecule due to its structure.
- The **first law of thermodynamics**, conservation of energy, states that energy cannot be created or destroyed, only transferred or transformed. The **second law of thermodynamics** states that **spontaneous processes**, those requiring no outside input of energy, increase the **entropy** (disorder) of the universe.

> ? *Explain how the highly ordered structure of a cell does not conflict with the second law of thermodynamics.*

### CONCEPT 5.2
**The free-energy change of a reaction tells us whether or not the reaction occurs spontaneously (pp. 93–96)**

- A living system's **free energy** is energy that can do work under cellular conditions. Organisms live at the expense of free energy. The change in free energy ($\Delta G$) during a biological process tells us if the process is spontaneous. During a spontaneous process, free energy decreases and the stability of a system increases. At maximum stability, the system is at equilibrium and can do no work.
- In an **exergonic** (spontaneous) chemical reaction, the products have less free energy than the reactants ($-\Delta G$). **Endergonic** (nonspontaneous) reactions require an input of energy ($+\Delta G$). The addition of starting materials and the removal of end products prevent metabolism from reaching equilibrium.

> ? *Why are spontaneous reactions important in the metabolism of a cell?*

### CONCEPT 5.3
**ATP powers cellular work by coupling exergonic reactions to endergonic reactions (pp. 96–98)**

- **ATP** is the cell's energy shuttle. Hydrolysis of its terminal phosphate yields ADP and $\textcircled{P}_i$ and releases free energy.
- Through **energy coupling**, the exergonic process of ATP hydrolysis drives endergonic reactions by transfer of a phosphate group to specific reactants, forming a **phosphorylated intermediate** that is more reactive. ATP hydrolysis (sometimes with protein phosphorylation) also causes changes in the shape and binding affinities of transport and motor proteins.
- Catabolic pathways drive regeneration of ATP from ADP + $\textcircled{P}_i$.

> ? *Describe the ATP cycle: How is ATP used and regenerated in a cell?*

### CONCEPT 5.4
**Enzymes speed up metabolic reactions by lowering energy barriers (pp. 99–104)**

- In a chemical reaction, the energy necessary to break the bonds of the reactants is the **activation energy**, $E_A$.
- **Enzymes** lower the $E_A$ barrier:

- Each type of enzyme has a unique **active site** that combines specifically with its **substrate(s)**, the reactant molecule(s) on which it acts. The enzyme changes shape slightly when it binds the substrate(s) (**induced fit**).
- The active site can lower an $E_A$ barrier by orienting substrates correctly, straining their bonds, providing a favorable microenvironment, or even covalently bonding with the substrate.
- Each enzyme has an optimal temperature and pH. Inhibitors reduce enzyme function. A **competitive inhibitor** binds to the active site, whereas a **noncompetitive inhibitor** binds to a different site on the enzyme.
- Natural selection, acting on organisms with mutant genes encoding altered enzymes, is a major evolutionary force responsible for the diverse array of enzymes found in organisms.

> ? *How do both activation energy barriers and enzymes help maintain the structural and metabolic order of life?*

### CONCEPT 5.5
**Regulation of enzyme activity helps control metabolism (pp. 104–106)**

- Many enzymes are subject to **allosteric regulation**: Regulatory molecules, either activators or inhibitors, bind to specific regulatory sites, affecting the shape and function of the enzyme. In **cooperativity**, binding of one substrate molecule can stimulate binding or activity at other active sites. In **feedback inhibition**, the end product of a metabolic pathway allosterically inhibits the enzyme for a previous step in the pathway.
- Some enzymes are grouped into complexes, some are incorporated into membranes, and some are contained inside organelles, increasing the efficiency of metabolic processes.

> ? *What roles do allosteric regulation and feedback inhibition play in the metabolism of a cell?*

# TEST YOUR UNDERSTANDING

## Level 1: Knowledge/Comprehension

**1.** Choose the pair of terms that correctly completes this sentence: Catabolism is to anabolism as _____ is to _____.
- **a.** exergonic; spontaneous
- **b.** exergonic; endergonic
- **c.** free energy; entropy
- **d.** work; energy
- **e.** entropy; heat

**2.** Most cells cannot harness heat to perform work because
- **a.** heat does not involve a transfer of energy.
- **b.** cells do not have much heat; they are relatively cool.
- **c.** temperature is usually uniform throughout a cell.
- **d.** heat can never be used to do work.
- **e.** heat must remain constant during work.

**3.** Which of the following metabolic processes can occur without a net influx of energy from some other process?
- **a.** $ADP + \textcircled{P}_i \rightarrow ATP + H_2O$
- **b.** $C_6H_{12}O_6 + 6\ O_2 \rightarrow 6\ CO_2 + 6\ H_2O$
- **c.** $6\ CO_2 + 6\ H_2O \rightarrow C_6H_{12}O_6 + 6\ O_2$
- **d.** amino acids $\rightarrow$ protein
- **e.** glucose + fructose $\rightarrow$ sucrose

**4.** If an enzyme in solution is saturated with substrate, the most effective way to obtain a faster yield of products is to
- **a.** add more of the enzyme.
- **b.** heat the solution to 90°C.
- **c.** add more substrate.
- **d.** add an allosteric inhibitor.
- **e.** add a noncompetitive inhibitor.

**5.** Some bacteria are metabolically active in hot springs because
- **a.** they are able to maintain a lower internal temperature.
- **b.** high temperatures make catalysis unnecessary.
- **c.** their enzymes have high optimal temperatures.
- **d.** their enzymes are completely insensitive to temperature.
- **e.** they use molecules other than proteins or RNAs as their main catalysts.

## Level 2: Application/Analysis

**6.** If an enzyme is added to a solution where its substrate and product are in equilibrium, what will occur?
- **a.** Additional product will be formed.
- **b.** Additional substrate will be formed.
- **c.** The reaction will change from endergonic to exergonic.
- **d.** The free energy of the system will change.
- **e.** Nothing; the reaction will stay at equilibrium.

## Level 3: Synthesis/Evaluation

**7.** **DRAW IT** Using a series of arrows, draw the branched metabolic reaction pathway described by the following statements. Then answer the question at the end. Use red arrows and minus signs to indicate inhibition.

L can form either M or N.
M can form O.
O can form either P or R.
P can form Q.
R can form S.
O inhibits the reaction of L to form M.
Q inhibits the reaction of O to form P.
S inhibits the reaction of O to form R.

Which reaction would prevail if both Q and S were present in the cell at high concentrations?
- **a.** L → M
- **b.** M → O
- **c.** L → N
- **d.** O → P
- **e.** R → S

**8. SCIENTIFIC INQUIRY**

**DRAW IT** A researcher has developed an assay to measure the activity of an important enzyme present in liver cells growing in culture. She adds the enzyme's substrate to a dish of cells and then measures the appearance of reaction products. The results are graphed as the amount of product on the y-axis versus time on the x-axis. The researcher notes four sections of the graph. For a short period of time, no products appear (section A). Then (section B) the reaction rate is quite high (the slope of the line is steep). Next, the reaction gradually slows down (section C). Finally, the graph line becomes flat (section D). Draw and label the graph, and propose a model to explain the molecular events occurring at each stage of this reaction profile.

**9. SCIENCE, TECHNOLOGY, AND SOCIETY**

Organophosphates (organic compounds containing phosophate groups) are commonly used as insecticides to improve crop yield. Organophosphates typically interfere with nerve signal transmission by inhibiting the enzymes that degrade transmitter molecules. They affect humans and other vertebrates as well as insects. Thus, the use of organophosphate pesticides poses some health risks. On the other hand, these molecules break down rapidly upon exposure to air and sunlight. As a consumer, what level of risk are you willing to accept in exchange for an abundant and affordable food supply?

**10. FOCUS ON EVOLUTION**

A recent revival of the antievolutionary "intelligent design" argument holds that biochemical pathways are too complex to have evolved, because all intermediate steps in a given pathway must be present to produce the final product. Critique this argument. How could you use the diversity of metabolic pathways that produce the same or similar products to support your case?

**11. FOCUS ON ENERGY AND MATTER**

Life requires energy. In a short essay (100–150 words), describe the basic principles of bioenergetics in an animal cell. How is the flow and transformation of energy different in a photosynthesizing cell? Include the role of ATP and enzymes in your discussion.

*For selected answers, see Appendix A.*

## MasteringBiology®

**Students** Go to **MasteringBiology** for assignments, the eText, and the Study Area with practice tests, animations, and activities.

**Instructors** Go to **MasteringBiology** for automatically graded tutorials and questions that you can assign to your students, plus Instructor Resources.

# 6 Cellular Respiration and Fermentation

OVERVIEW

## Life Is Work

Living cells require transfusions of energy from outside sources to perform their many tasks—for example, assembling polymers, pumping substances across membranes, moving, and reproducing. The giraffe in **Figure 6.1** obtains energy for its cells by eating plants; some animals feed on other organisms that eat plants. The energy stored in the organic molecules of food ultimately comes from the sun. Energy flows into an ecosystem as sunlight and exits as heat; in contrast, the chemical elements essential to life are recycled (**Figure 6.2**). Photosynthesis generates oxygen and organic molecules used by the mitochondria of eukaryotes (including plants and algae) as fuel for cellular respiration. Respiration breaks this fuel down, generating ATP. The waste products of this type of respiration, carbon dioxide and water, are the raw materials for photosynthesis.

In this chapter, we'll consider how cells harvest the chemical energy stored in organic molecules and use it to generate ATP, the molecule that drives most cellular work. After presenting some basics about respiration,

▼ **Figure 6.1** How do these leaves power the work of life for this giraffe?

▶ **Figure 6.2**
**Energy flow and chemical recycling in ecosystems.** Energy flows into an ecosystem as sunlight and ultimately leaves as heat, while the chemical elements essential to life are recycled.

Light energy

ECOSYSTEM

Photosynthesis in chloroplasts

$CO_2 + H_2O$

Organic molecules $+ O_2$

Cellular respiration in mitochondria

ATP

**ATP powers most cellular work**

Heat energy

we'll focus on three key pathways of respiration: glycolysis, the citric acid cycle, and oxidative phosphorylation. We'll also consider fermentation, a somewhat simpler pathway coupled to glycolysis that has deep evolutionary roots.

CONCEPT 6.1

# Catabolic pathways yield energy by oxidizing organic fuels

Metabolic pathways that release stored energy by breaking down complex molecules are called catabolic pathways (see Chapter 5). Electron transfer plays a major role in these pathways. In this section, we'll consider these processes, which are central to cellular respiration.

## Catabolic Pathways and Production of ATP

Organic compounds possess potential energy as a result of the arrangement of electrons in the bonds between their atoms. Compounds that can participate in exergonic reactions can act as fuels. With the help of enzymes, a cell systematically degrades complex organic molecules that are rich in potential energy to simpler waste products that have less energy. Some of the energy taken out of chemical storage can be used to do work; the rest is dissipated as heat.

One catabolic process, **fermentation**, is a partial degradation of sugars or other organic fuel that occurs without the use of oxygen. However, the most efficient catabolic pathway is **aerobic respiration**, in which oxygen is consumed as a reactant along with the organic fuel (*aerobic* is from the Greek *aer*, air, and *bios*, life). The cells of most eukaryotic and many prokaryotic organisms can carry out aerobic respiration. Some prokaryotes use substances other than oxygen as reactants in a similar process that harvests chemical energy without oxygen; this process is called *anaerobic respiration* (the prefix *an-* means "without"). Technically, the term **cellular respiration** includes both aerobic and anaerobic processes. However, it originated as a synonym for aerobic respiration because of the relationship of that process to organismal respiration, in which an animal breathes in oxygen. Thus, *cellular respiration* is often used to refer to the aerobic process, a practice we follow in most of this chapter.

Although very different in mechanism, aerobic respiration is in principle similar to the combustion of gasoline in an automobile engine after oxygen is mixed with the fuel (hydrocarbons). Food provides the fuel for respiration, and the exhaust is carbon dioxide and water. The overall process can be summarized as follows:

$$\text{Organic compounds} + \text{Oxygen} \rightarrow \text{Carbon dioxide} + \text{Water} + \text{Energy}$$

Carbohydrates, fats, and proteins can all be processed and consumed as fuel. A major source of carbohydrates in animal diets is the storage polysaccharide starch, which is broken down

into glucose ($C_6H_{12}O_6$) subunits. We will learn the steps of cellular respiration by tracking the degradation of the sugar glucose:

$$C_6H_{12}O_6 + 6\ O_2 \rightarrow 6\ CO_2 + 6\ H_2O + \text{Energy (ATP + heat)}$$

This breakdown of glucose is exergonic, having a free-energy change of –686 kcal (2,870 kJ) per mole of glucose decomposed ($\Delta G = -686$ kcal/mol). Recall that a negative $\Delta G$ indicates that the products of the chemical process store less energy than the reactants and that the reaction can happen spontaneously—in other words, without an input of energy.

Catabolic pathways do not directly move flagella, pump solutes across membranes, polymerize monomers, or perform other cellular work. Catabolism is linked to work by a chemical drive shaft—ATP (which you learned about in Chapters 2 and 5). To keep working, the cell must regenerate its supply of ATP from ADP and $\text{P}_i$ (see Figure 5.11). To understand how cellular respiration accomplishes this, let's examine the fundamental chemical processes known as oxidation and reduction.

## Redox Reactions: Oxidation and Reduction

How do the catabolic pathways that decompose glucose and other organic fuels yield energy? The answer is based on the transfer of electrons during the chemical reactions. The relocation of electrons releases energy stored in organic molecules, and this energy ultimately is used to synthesize ATP.

### The Principle of Redox

In many chemical reactions, there is a transfer of one or more electrons ($e^-$) from one reactant to another. These electron transfers are called oxidation-reduction reactions, or **redox reactions** for short. In a redox reaction, the loss of electrons from one substance is called **oxidation**, and the addition of electrons to another substance is known as **reduction**. (Note that *adding* electrons is called *reduction*; adding negatively charged electrons to an atom *reduces* the amount of positive charge of that atom.) To take a simple, nonbiological example, consider the reaction between the elements sodium (Na) and chlorine (Cl) that forms table salt:

$$\underbrace{\text{Na} + \text{Cl} \longrightarrow \text{Na}^+ + \text{Cl}^-}$$

becomes oxidized (loses electron)
becomes reduced (gains electron)

We could generalize a redox reaction this way:

$$\text{X}e^- + \text{Y} \longrightarrow \text{X} + \text{Y}e^-$$

becomes oxidized
becomes reduced

In the generalized reaction, substance $\text{X}e^-$, the electron donor, is called the **reducing agent**; it reduces Y, which accepts the donated electron. Substance Y, the electron acceptor, is the **oxidizing agent**; it oxidizes $\text{X}e^-$ by removing its electron. Because an electron transfer requires both a donor and an acceptor, oxidation and reduction always go together.

**Reactants**          **Products**

becomes oxidized

$$CH_4 \; + \; 2\,O_2 \; \longrightarrow \; CO_2 \; + \; Energy \; + \; 2\,H_2O$$

becomes reduced

Methane (reducing agent)    Oxygen (oxidizing agent)    Carbon dioxide    Water

▲ **Figure 6.3 Methane combustion as an energy-yielding redox reaction.** The reaction releases energy to the surroundings because the electrons lose potential energy when they end up being shared unequally, spending more time near electronegative atoms such as oxygen.

Not all redox reactions involve the complete transfer of electrons from one substance to another; some change the degree of electron sharing in covalent bonds. The reaction between methane and oxygen, shown in **Figure 6.3**, is an example. The covalent electrons in methane are shared nearly equally between the bonded atoms because carbon and hydrogen have about the same affinity for valence electrons; they are about equally electronegative. But when methane reacts with oxygen, forming carbon dioxide, electrons end up shared less equally between the carbon atom and its new covalent partners, the oxygen atoms, which are very electronegative. In effect, the carbon atom has partially "lost" its shared electrons; thus, methane has been oxidized.

Now let's examine the fate of the reactant $O_2$. The two atoms of the oxygen molecule ($O_2$) share their electrons equally. But when oxygen reacts with the hydrogen from methane, forming water, the electrons of the covalent bonds spend more time near the oxygen (see Figure 6.3). In effect, each oxygen atom has partially "gained" electrons, so the oxygen molecule has been reduced. Because oxygen is so electronegative, it is one of the most potent of all oxidizing agents.

Energy must be added to pull an electron away from an atom, just as energy is required to push a ball uphill. The more electronegative the atom (the stronger its pull on electrons), the more energy is required to take an electron away from it. An electron loses potential energy when it shifts from a less electronegative atom toward a more electronegative one, just as a ball loses potential energy when it rolls downhill. A redox reaction that moves electrons closer to oxygen, such as the burning (oxidation) of methane, therefore releases chemical energy that can be put to work.

### Oxidation of Organic Fuel Molecules During Cellular Respiration

The oxidation of methane by oxygen is the main combustion reaction that occurs at the burner of a gas stove. The combustion of gasoline in an automobile engine is also a redox reaction; the energy released pushes the pistons. But the energy-yielding redox process of greatest interest to biologists is respiration: the oxidation of glucose and other molecules in food. Examine again the summary equation for cellular respiration, but this time think of it as a redox process:

becomes oxidized

$$C_6H_{12}O_6 \; + \; 6\,O_2 \; \longrightarrow \; 6\,CO_2 \; + \; 6\,H_2O \; + \; Energy$$

becomes reduced

As in the combustion of methane or gasoline, the fuel (glucose) is oxidized and oxygen is reduced. The electrons lose potential energy along the way, and energy is released.

In general, organic molecules that have an abundance of hydrogen are excellent fuels because their bonds are a source of "hilltop" electrons, whose energy may be released as these electrons "fall" down an energy gradient when they are transferred to oxygen. The summary equation for respiration indicates that hydrogen is transferred from glucose to oxygen. But the important point, not visible in the summary equation, is that the energy state of the electron changes as hydrogen (with its electron) is transferred to oxygen. In respiration, the oxidation of glucose transfers electrons to a lower energy state, liberating energy that becomes available for ATP synthesis.

The main energy-yielding foods, carbohydrates and fats, are reservoirs of electrons associated with hydrogen. Only the barrier of activation energy holds back the flood of electrons to a lower energy state (see Figure 5.12). Without this barrier, a food substance like glucose would combine almost instantaneously with $O_2$. If we supply the activation energy by igniting glucose, it burns in air, releasing 686 kcal (2,870 kJ) of heat per mole of glucose (about 180 g). Body temperature is not high enough to initiate burning, of course. Instead, if you swallow some glucose, enzymes in your cells will lower the barrier of activation energy, allowing the sugar to be oxidized in a series of steps.

### Stepwise Energy Harvest via NAD⁺ and the Electron Transport Chain

If energy is released from a fuel all at once, it cannot be harnessed efficiently for constructive work. For example, if a gasoline tank explodes, it cannot drive a car very far. Cellular respiration does not oxidize glucose in a single explosive step either. Rather, glucose and other organic fuels are broken down in a series of steps, each one catalyzed by an enzyme. At key steps, electrons are stripped from the glucose. As is often the case in oxidation reactions, each electron travels with a proton—thus, as a hydrogen atom. The hydrogen atoms are not transferred directly to oxygen, but instead are usually passed first to an electron carrier, a coenzyme called **NAD⁺** (nicotinamide adenine dinucleotide, a derivative of the vitamin niacin). NAD⁺ is well suited as an electron carrier because it can cycle easily between oxidized (NAD⁺) and reduced (NADH) states. As an electron acceptor, NAD⁺ functions as an oxidizing agent during respiration.

How does NAD⁺ trap electrons from glucose and other organic molecules? Enzymes called dehydrogenases remove a

**NAD⁺** — Nicotinamide (oxidized form)

$2 e^- + 2 H^+$

$2 e^- + H^+$

$+ \quad 2[H]$ (from food)

Dehydrogenase
Reduction of NAD⁺
Oxidation of NADH

**NADH** — Nicotinamide (reduced form)

$+ \quad H^+$

$H^+$

◀ **Figure 6.4 NAD⁺ as an electron shuttle.** The full name for NAD⁺, nicotinamide adenine dinucleotide, describes its structure: The molecule consists of two nucleotides joined together at their phosphate groups (shown in yellow). (Nicotinamide is a nitrogenous base, although not one that is present in DNA or RNA.) The enzymatic transfer of 2 electrons and 1 proton (H⁺) from an organic molecule in food to NAD⁺ reduces the NAD⁺ to NADH; the second proton (H⁺) is released. Most of the electrons removed from food are transferred initially to NAD⁺.

pair of hydrogen atoms (2 electrons and 2 protons) from the substrate (glucose, in this example), thereby oxidizing it. The enzyme delivers the 2 electrons along with 1 proton to its coenzyme, NAD⁺ **(Figure 6.4)**. The other proton is released as a hydrogen ion (H⁺) into the surrounding solution:

$$H-\overset{|}{\underset{|}{C}}-OH + NAD^+ \xrightarrow{\text{Dehydrogenase}} \overset{|}{\underset{|}{C}}=O + NADH + H^+$$

By receiving 2 negatively charged electrons but only 1 positively charged proton, the nicotinamide portion of NAD⁺ has its charge neutralized when NAD⁺ is reduced to NADH. The name NADH shows the hydrogen that has been received in the reaction. NAD⁺ is the most versatile electron acceptor in cellular respiration and functions in several of the redox steps during the breakdown of glucose.

Electrons lose very little of their potential energy when they are transferred from glucose to NAD⁺. Each NADH molecule formed during respiration represents stored energy that can be tapped to make ATP when the electrons complete their "fall" down an energy gradient from NADH to oxygen.

How do electrons that are extracted from glucose and stored as potential energy in NADH finally reach oxygen? It will help to compare the redox chemistry of cellular respiration to a much simpler reaction: the reaction between hydrogen and oxygen to form water **(Figure 6.5a)**. Mix H₂ and O₂, provide a spark for activation

energy, and the gases combine explosively. In fact, combustion of liquid H₂ and O₂ was harnessed to help power the main engines of the Space Shuttle, boosting it into orbit. The explosion represents a release of energy as the electrons of hydrogen "fall" closer to the electronegative oxygen atoms. Cellular respiration also brings hydrogen and oxygen together to form water, but there are two important differences. First, in cellular respiration, the hydrogen that reacts with oxygen is derived from organic molecules rather than H₂. Second, instead of occurring

▲ **Figure 6.5 An introduction to electron transport chains. (a)** The one-step exergonic reaction of hydrogen with oxygen to form water releases a large amount of energy in the form of heat and light: an explosion. **(b)** In cellular respiration, the same reaction occurs in stages: An electron transport chain breaks the "fall" of electrons in this reaction into a series of smaller steps and stores some of the released energy in a form that can be used to make ATP. (The rest of the energy is released as heat.)

in one explosive reaction, respiration uses an electron transport chain to break the fall of electrons to oxygen into several energy-releasing steps (Figure 6.5b). An **electron transport chain** consists of a number of molecules, mostly proteins, built into the inner membrane of the mitochondria of eukaryotic cells and the plasma membrane of aerobically respiring prokaryotes. Electrons removed from glucose are shuttled by NADH to the "top," higher-energy end of the chain. At the "bottom," lower-energy end, $O_2$ captures these electrons along with hydrogen nuclei ($H^+$), forming water.

Electron transfer from NADH to oxygen is an exergonic reaction with a free-energy change of –53 kcal/mol (–222 kJ/mol). Instead of this energy being released and wasted in a single explosive step, electrons cascade down the chain from one carrier molecule to the next in a series of redox reactions, losing a small amount of energy with each step until they finally reach oxygen, the terminal electron acceptor, which has a very great affinity for electrons. Each "downhill" carrier is more electronegative than, and thus capable of oxidizing, its "uphill" neighbor, with oxygen at the bottom of the chain. Therefore, the electrons transferred from glucose to $NAD^+$ fall down an energy gradient in the electron transport chain to a far more stable location in the electronegative oxygen atom. Put another way, oxygen pulls electrons down the chain in an energy-yielding tumble analogous to gravity pulling objects downhill.

In summary, during cellular respiration, most electrons travel the following "downhill" route: glucose → NADH → electron transport chain → oxygen. Later in this chapter, you will learn more about how the cell uses the energy released from this exergonic electron fall to regenerate its supply of ATP. For now, having covered the basic redox mechanisms of cellular respiration, let's look at the entire process by which energy is harvested from organic fuels.

## The Stages of Cellular Respiration: *A Preview*

The harvesting of energy from glucose by cellular respiration is a cumulative function of three metabolic stages. We list them here along with a color-coding scheme that we will use throughout the chapter to help you keep track of the big picture.

1. Glycolysis (color-coded teal throughout the chapter)
2. Pyruvate oxidation and the citric acid cycle (color-coded salmon)
3. Oxidative phosphorylation: electron transport and chemiosmosis (color-coded violet)

Biochemists usually reserve the term *cellular respiration* for stages 2 and 3 together. In this text, we include glycolysis, however, because most respiring cells deriving energy from glucose use glycolysis to produce the starting material for the citric acid cycle.

As diagrammed in **Figure 6.6**, glycolysis and pyruvate oxidation followed by the citric acid cycle are the catabolic pathways that break down glucose and other organic fuels. **Glycolysis**, which occurs in the cytosol, begins the degradation process by breaking glucose into two molecules of a compound called pyruvate. In eukaryotes, pyruvate enters the mitochondrion and is oxidized to a compound called acetyl CoA, which enters the **citric acid cycle** (also called the Krebs cycle). There, the breakdown of glucose to carbon dioxide is completed. (In prokaryotes, these processes take place in the cytosol.) Thus, the carbon dioxide produced by respiration represents fragments of oxidized organic molecules.

Some of the steps of glycolysis and the citric acid cycle are redox reactions in which dehydrogenases transfer electrons from substrates to $NAD^+$, forming NADH. In the third stage of respiration, the electron transport chain accepts electrons

▶ Figure 6.6 **An overview of cellular respiration.** During glycolysis, each glucose molecule is broken down into two molecules of the compound pyruvate. In eukaryotic cells, as shown here, the pyruvate enters the mitochondrion. There it is oxidized to acetyl CoA, which is further oxidized to $CO_2$ in the citric acid cycle. NADH and a similar electron carrier, a coenzyme called $FADH_2$, transfer electrons derived from glucose to electron transport chains, which are built into the inner mitochondrial membrane. (In prokaryotes, the electron transport chains are located in the plasma membrane.) During oxidative phosphorylation, electron transport chains convert the chemical energy to a form used for ATP synthesis in the process called chemiosmosis.

**ANIMATION** **BioFlix** Visit the Study Area in **MasteringBiology** for the BioFlix® 3-D Animation on Cellular Respiration.

(most often via NADH) from the breakdown products of the first two stages and passes these electrons from one molecule to another. At the end of the chain, the electrons are combined with molecular oxygen and hydrogen ions ($H^+$), forming water (see Figure 6.5b). The energy released at each step of the chain is stored in a form the mitochondrion (or prokaryotic cell) can use to make ATP from ADP. This mode of ATP synthesis is called **oxidative phosphorylation** because it is powered by the redox reactions of the electron transport chain.

In eukaryotic cells, the inner membrane of the mitochondrion is the site of electron transport and chemiosmosis, the processes that together constitute oxidative phosphorylation. (In prokaryotes, these processes take place in the plasma membrane.) Oxidative phosphorylation accounts for almost 90% of the ATP generated by respiration. A smaller amount of ATP is formed directly in a few reactions of glycolysis and the citric acid cycle by a mechanism called **substrate-level phosphorylation (Figure 6.7)**. This mode of ATP synthesis occurs when an enzyme transfers a phosphate group from a substrate molecule to ADP, rather than adding an inorganic phosphate to ADP as in oxidative phosphorylation. "Substrate molecule" here refers to an organic molecule generated as an intermediate during the catabolism of glucose.

For each molecule of glucose degraded to carbon dioxide and water by respiration, the cell makes up to about 32 molecules of ATP, each with 7.3 kcal/mol of free energy. Respiration cashes in the large denomination of energy banked in a single molecule of glucose (686 kcal/mol) for the small change

▲ **Figure 6.7 Substrate-level phosphorylation.** Some ATP is made by direct transfer of a phosphate group from an organic substrate to ADP by an enzyme. (For examples in glycolysis, see Figure 6.9, steps 7 and 10.)

**MAKE CONNECTIONS** *Review Figure 5.8. Do you think the potential energy is higher for the reactants or the products in the reaction shown above? Explain.*

of many molecules of ATP, which is more practical for the cell to spend on its work.

This preview has introduced you to how glycolysis, the citric acid cycle, and oxidative phosphorylation fit into the process of cellular respiration. We are now ready to take a closer look at each of these three stages of respiration.

**CONCEPT CHECK 6.1**

1. Compare and contrast aerobic and anaerobic respiration.
2. Name and describe the two ways in which ATP is made during cellular respiration. During what stage(s) in the process does each type occur?
3. **WHAT IF?** If the following redox reaction occurred, which compound would be oxidized? Which reduced?

$$C_4H_6O_5 + NAD^+ \rightarrow C_4H_4O_5 + NADH + H^+$$

**For suggested answers, see Appendix A.**

▼ **Figure 6.9 A closer look at glycolysis.** Note that glycolysis is a source of ATP and NADH.

**Glycolysis: Energy Investment Phase**

Hexokinase transfers a phosphate group from ATP to glucose, making it more chemically reactive. The charge on the phosphate also traps the sugar in the cell. ①

Glucose 6-phosphate is converted to fructose 6-phosphate. ②

Phosphofructokinase transfers a phosphate group from ATP to the opposite end of the sugar, investing a second molecule of ATP. This is a key step for regulation of glycolysis. ③

Aldolase cleaves the sugar molecule into two different three-carbon sugars. ④

Conversion between DHAP and G3P: This reaction never reaches equilibrium; G3P is used in the next step as fast as it forms.

© 1996 Pearson Education, Inc.

# Glycolysis harvests chemical energy by oxidizing glucose to pyruvate

The word *glycolysis* means "sugar splitting," and that is exactly what happens during this pathway. Glucose, a six-carbon sugar, is split into two three-carbon sugars. These smaller sugars are then oxidized and their remaining atoms rearranged to form two molecules of pyruvate. (Pyruvate is the ionized form of pyruvic acid.)

As summarized in **Figure 6.8**, glycolysis can be divided into two phases: energy investment and energy payoff. During the energy investment phase, the cell actually spends ATP. This investment is repaid with interest during the energy payoff phase, when ATP is produced by substrate-level phosphorylation and $NAD^+$ is reduced to NADH by electrons released from the oxidation of glucose. The net energy yield from glycolysis, per glucose molecule, is 2 ATP plus 2 NADH.

Because glycolysis is a fundamental core process shared by bacteria, archaea, and eukaryotes alike, we will use it as an example of a biochemical pathway, detailing each of the enzyme-catalyzed reactions. The ten steps of the glycolytic pathway are shown in **Figure 6.9**, which begins on the previous page.

All of the carbon originally present in glucose is accounted for in the two molecules of pyruvate; no carbon is released as $CO_2$ during glycolysis. Glycolysis occurs whether or not $O_2$ is present. However, if $O_2$ *is* present, the chemical energy stored in pyruvate and NADH can be extracted by pyruvate oxidation, the citric acid cycle, and oxidative phosphorylation.

▼ **Figure 6.8** **The energy input and output of glycolysis.**

**CONCEPT CHECK 6.2**

1. During step 6 in Figure 6.9, which molecule acts as the oxidizing agent? The reducing agent?

For suggested answers, see Appendix A.

---

The energy payoff phase occurs after glucose is split into two three-carbon sugars. Thus, the coefficient 2 precedes all molecules in this phase.

## Glycolysis: Energy Payoff Phase

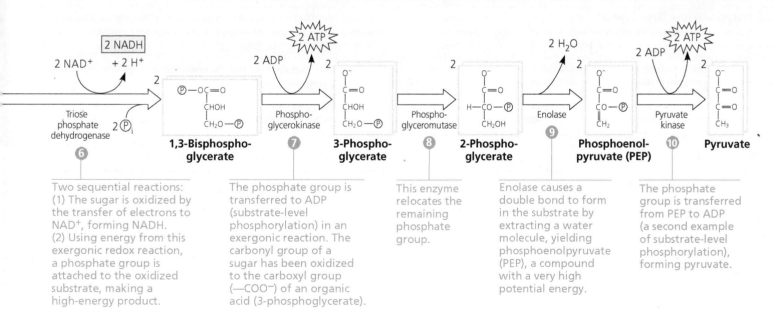

# CONCEPT 6.3

## After pyruvate is oxidized, the citric acid cycle completes the energy-yielding oxidation of organic molecules

Glycolysis releases less than a quarter of the chemical energy in glucose that can be harvested by cells; most of the energy remains stockpiled in the two molecules of pyruvate. If molecular oxygen is present, the pyruvate enters a mitochondrion (in eukaryotic cells), where the oxidation of glucose is completed. (In prokaryotic cells, this process occurs in the cytosol.)

Once inside the mitochondrion, pyruvate undergoes a series of enzymatic reactions that remove $CO_2$ and oxidizes the remaining fragment, forming NADH from $NAD^+$. The product is a highly reactive compound called acetyl coenzyme A, or **acetyl CoA**, which will feed its acetyl group into the citric acid cycle for further oxidation **(Figure 6.10)**.

The citric acid cycle (also known as the Krebs cycle) functions as a metabolic furnace that oxidizes organic fuel derived from pyruvate. Figure 6.10 summarizes the inputs and outputs as pyruvate is broken down to three $CO_2$ molecules, including the molecule of $CO_2$ released during the conversion of pyruvate to acetyl CoA. The cycle generates 1 ATP per turn by substrate-level phosphorylation, but most of the chemical energy is transferred to $NAD^+$ and a related electron carrier, the coenzyme FAD (flavin adenine dinucleotide, derived from riboflavin, a B vitamin), during the redox reactions. The reduced coenzymes, NADH and $FADH_2$, shuttle their cargo of high-energy electrons into the electron transport chain.

Now let's look at the citric acid cycle in more detail. The cycle has eight steps, each catalyzed by a specific enzyme. You can see in **Figure 6.11** that for each turn of the citric acid cycle, two carbons (red type) enter in the relatively reduced form of an acetyl group (step 1), and two different carbons (blue type) leave in the completely oxidized form of $CO_2$ molecules (steps 3 and 4). The acetyl group of acetyl CoA joins the cycle by combining with the compound oxaloacetate, forming citrate (step 1). (Citrate is the ionized form of citric acid, for which the cycle is named.) The next seven steps decompose the citrate back to oxaloacetate. It is this regeneration of oxaloacetate that makes this process a *cycle*.

Now let's tally the energy-rich molecules produced by the citric acid cycle. For each acetyl group entering the cycle, 3 $NAD^+$ are reduced to NADH (steps 3, 4, and 8). In step 6, electrons are transferred not to $NAD^+$, but to FAD, which accepts 2 electrons and 2 protons to become $FADH_2$. In many animal tissue cells, step 5 produces a guanosine triphosphate (GTP) molecule by substrate-level phosphorylation, as shown in Figure 6.11. GTP is a molecule similar to ATP in its structure and cellular function. This GTP may be used to make an ATP

▲ **Figure 6.10 An overview of pyruvate oxidation and the citric acid cycle.** The inputs and outputs per pyruvate molecule are shown. To calculate on a per-glucose basis, multiply by 2, because each glucose molecule is split during glycolysis into two pyruvate molecules.

molecule (as shown) or directly power work in the cell. In the cells of plants, bacteria, and some animal tissues, step 5 forms an ATP molecule directly by substrate-level phosphorylation. The output from step 5 represents the only ATP generated during the citric acid cycle.

Most of the ATP produced by respiration results from oxidative phosphorylation, when the NADH and $FADH_2$ produced by the citric acid cycle relay the electrons extracted from food to the electron transport chain. In the process, they supply the necessary energy for the phosphorylation of ADP to ATP. We will explore this process in the next section.

### CONCEPT CHECK 6.3

1. Name the molecules that conserve most of the energy from the citric acid cycle's redox reactions. How is this energy converted to a form that can be used to make ATP?
2. What processes in your cells produce the $CO_2$ that you exhale?

**For suggested answers, see Appendix A.**

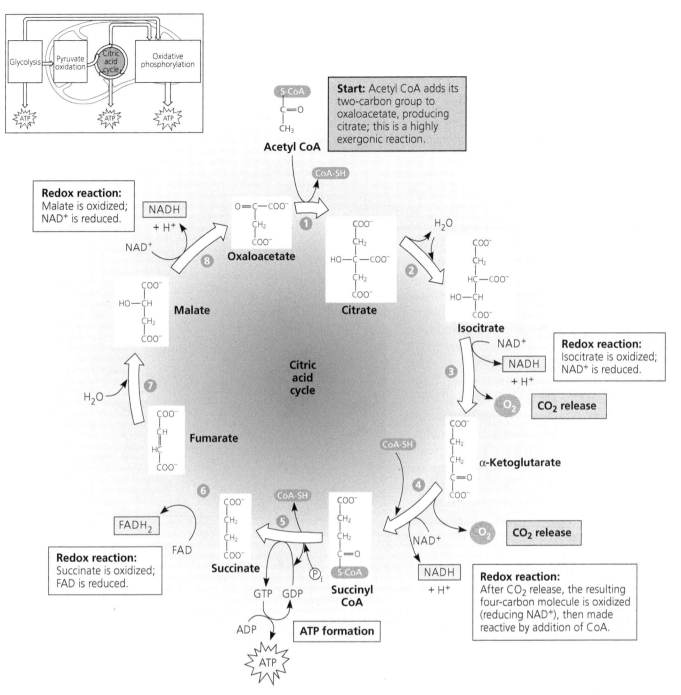

**Start:** Acetyl CoA adds its two-carbon group to oxaloacetate, producing citrate; this is a highly exergonic reaction.

**Redox reaction:** Malate is oxidized; $NAD^+$ is reduced.

**Redox reaction:** Isocitrate is oxidized; $NAD^+$ is reduced.

**Redox reaction:** Succinate is oxidized; FAD is reduced.

**Redox reaction:** After $CO_2$ release, the resulting four-carbon molecule is oxidized (reducing $NAD^+$), then made reactive by addition of CoA.

**ATP formation**

**CO₂ release**

Acetyl CoA

Oxaloacetate

Citrate

Isocitrate

α-Ketoglutarate

Succinyl CoA

Succinate

Fumarate

Malate

Citric acid cycle

▲ **Figure 6.11 A closer look at the citric acid cycle.** Key steps (redox reactions, $CO_2$ release, and ATP formation) are labeled. In the chemical structures, red type traces the fate of the two carbon atoms that enter the cycle via acetyl CoA (step 1), and blue type indicates the two carbons that exit the cycle as $CO_2$ in steps 3 and 4. (The red labeling goes only through step 5 because the succinate molecule is symmetrical; the two ends cannot be distinguished from each other.) Notice that the carbon atoms that enter the cycle from acetyl CoA do not leave the cycle in the same turn. They remain in the cycle, occupying a different location in the molecules on their next turn, after another acetyl group is added. As a consequence, the oxaloacetate that is regenerated at step 8 is composed of different carbon atoms each time around.

CONCEPT 6.4

# During oxidative phosphorylation, chemiosmosis couples electron transport to ATP synthesis

Our main objective in this chapter is to learn how cells harvest the energy of glucose and other nutrients in food to make ATP.

But the metabolic components of respiration we have dissected so far, glycolysis and the citric acid cycle, produce only 4 ATP molecules per glucose molecule, all by substrate-level phosphorylation: 2 net ATP from glycolysis and 2 ATP from the citric acid cycle. At this point, molecules of NADH (and $FADH_2$) account for most of the energy extracted from the glucose. These electron escorts link glycolysis and the citric acid cycle to the machinery of oxidative phosphorylation, which uses energy released by the electron transport chain to power

ATP synthesis. In this section, you will learn first how the electron transport chain works and then how electron flow down the chain is coupled to ATP synthesis.

## The Pathway of Electron Transport

The electron transport chain is a collection of molecules embedded in the inner membrane of the mitochondrion in eukaryotic cells. (In prokaryotes, these molecules reside in the plasma membrane.) The folding of the inner membrane to form cristae increases its surface area, providing space for thousands of copies of the chain in each mitochondrion. (Once again, we see that structure fits function—the infolded membrane with its placement of electron carrier molecules in a chain, one after the other, is well-suited for the series of sequential redox reactions that take place along the chain.) Most components of the chain are proteins, which exist in multiprotein complexes numbered I through IV. Tightly bound to these proteins are *prosthetic groups*, nonprotein components essential for the catalytic functions of certain enzymes.

Figure 6.12 shows the sequence of electron carriers in the electron transport chain and the drop in free energy as electrons travel down the chain. During electron transport along the chain, electron carriers alternate between reduced and oxidized states as they accept and donate electrons. Each component of the chain becomes reduced when it accepts electrons from its "uphill" neighbor, which has a lower affinity for electrons (is less electronegative). It then returns to its oxidized form as it passes electrons to its "downhill," more electronegative neighbor.

Now let's take a closer look at the electron transport chain in Figure 6.12. We'll first describe the passage of electrons through complex I in some detail as an illustration of the general principles involved in electron transport. Electrons removed from glucose by $NAD^+$ during glycolysis and the citric acid cycle are transferred from NADH to the first molecule of the electron transport chain in complex I. This molecule is a flavoprotein, so named because it has a prosthetic group called flavin mononucleotide (FMN). In the next redox reaction, the flavoprotein returns to its oxidized form as it passes electrons to an iron-sulfur protein (Fe • S in complex I), one of a family of proteins with both iron and sulfur tightly bound. The iron-sulfur protein then passes the electrons to a compound called ubiquinone (Q in Figure 6.12). This electron carrier is a small hydrophobic molecule, the only member of the electron transport chain that is not a protein. Ubiquinone is individually mobile within the membrane rather than residing in a particular complex. (Another name for ubiquinone is coenzyme Q, or CoQ; you may have seen it sold as a nutritional supplement.)

Most of the remaining electron carriers between ubiquinone and oxygen are proteins called **cytochromes**. Their prosthetic group, called a heme group, has an iron atom that accepts and donates electrons. (It is similar to the heme group in hemoglobin, the protein of red blood cells, except that the

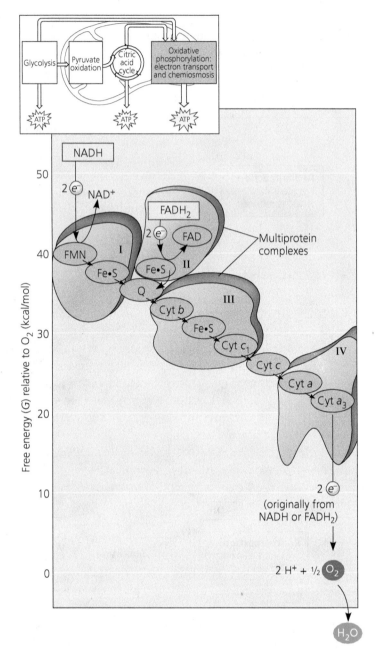

▲ **Figure 6.12 Free-energy change during electron transport.** The overall energy drop ($\Delta G$) for electrons traveling from NADH to oxygen is 53 kcal/mol, but this "fall" is broken up into a series of smaller steps by the electron transport chain. (An oxygen atom is represented here as $1/2 \, O_2$ to emphasize that the electron transport chain reduces molecular oxygen, $O_2$, not individual oxygen atoms.)

iron in hemoglobin carries oxygen, not electrons.) The electron transport chain has several types of cytochromes, each a different protein with a slightly different electron-carrying heme group. The last cytochrome of the chain, cyt $a_3$, passes its electrons to oxygen, which is *very* electronegative. Each oxygen atom also picks up a pair of hydrogen ions from the aqueous solution, forming water.

Another source of electrons for the transport chain is $FADH_2$, the other reduced product of the citric acid cycle.

Notice in Figure 6.12 that $FADH_2$ adds its electrons to the electron transport chain from within complex II, at a lower energy level than NADH does. Consequently, although NADH and $FADH_2$ each donate an equivalent number of electrons (2) for oxygen reduction, the electron transport chain provides about one-third less energy for ATP synthesis when the electron donor is $FADH_2$ rather than NADH. We'll see why in the next section.

The electron transport chain makes no ATP directly. Instead, it eases the fall of electrons from food to oxygen, breaking a large free-energy drop into a series of smaller steps that release energy in manageable amounts. How does the mitochondrion (or the prokaryotic plasma membrane) couple this electron transport and energy release to ATP synthesis? The answer is a mechanism called chemiosmosis.

## Chemiosmosis: The Energy-Coupling Mechanism

Populating the inner membrane of the mitochondrion or the prokaryotic plasma membrane are many copies of a protein complex called **ATP synthase**, the enzyme that actually makes ATP from ADP and inorganic phosphate. ATP synthase works like an ion pump running in reverse. Ion pumps usually use ATP as an energy source to transport ions against their gradients. (In fact, the proton pump shown in an ATP synthase.) Enzymes can catalyze a reaction in either direction, depending on the $\Delta G$ for the reaction, which is affected by the local concentrations of reactants and products (see Chapter 5). Rather than hydrolyzing ATP to pump protons against their concentration gradient, under the conditions of cellular respiration ATP synthase uses the energy of an existing ion gradient to power ATP synthesis. The power source for the ATP synthase is a difference in the concentration of $H^+$ on opposite sides of the inner mitochondrial membrane. (We can also think of this gradient as a difference in pH, since pH is a measure of $H^+$ concentration.) This process, in which energy stored in the form of a hydrogen ion gradient across a membrane is used to drive cellular work such as the synthesis of ATP, is called **chemiosmosis** (from the Greek *osmos*, push). We have previously used the word *osmosis* in discussing water transport, but here it refers to the flow of $H^+$ across a membrane.

From studying the structure of ATP synthase, scientists have learned how the flow of $H^+$ through this large enzyme powers ATP generation. ATP synthase is a multisubunit complex with four main parts, each made up of multiple polypeptides. Protons move one by one into binding sites on one of the parts (the rotor), causing it to spin in a way that catalyzes ATP production from ADP and inorganic phosphate **(Figure 6.13)**. The flow of protons thus behaves somewhat like a rushing stream that turns a waterwheel. ATP synthase is the smallest molecular rotary motor known in nature.

How does the inner mitochondrial membrane or the prokaryotic plasma membrane generate and maintain the $H^+$

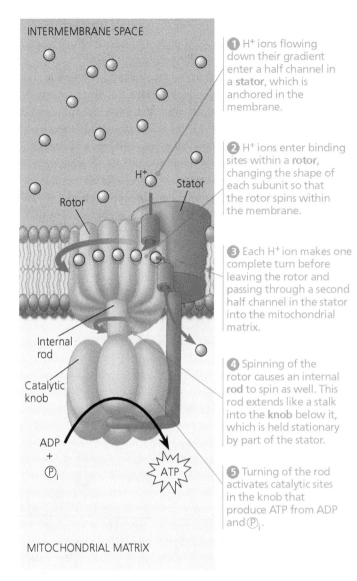

INTERMEMBRANE SPACE

1. $H^+$ ions flowing down their gradient enter a half channel in a **stator**, which is anchored in the membrane.

2. $H^+$ ions enter binding sites within a **rotor**, changing the shape of each subunit so that the rotor spins within the membrane.

$H^+$  Stator

Rotor

3. Each $H^+$ ion makes one complete turn before leaving the rotor and passing through a second half channel in the stator into the mitochondrial matrix.

Internal rod

Catalytic knob

4. Spinning of the rotor causes an internal **rod** to spin as well. This rod extends like a stalk into the **knob** below it, which is held stationary by part of the stator.

ADP + $\textcircled{P}_i$

ATP

5. Turning of the rod activates catalytic sites in the knob that produce ATP from ADP and $\textcircled{P}_i$.

MITOCHONDRIAL MATRIX

▲ **Figure 6.13 ATP synthase, a molecular mill.** The ATP synthase protein complex functions as a mill, powered by the flow of hydrogen ions. Multiple copies of this complex reside in mitochondrial and chloroplast membranes of eukaryotes and in the plasma membranes of prokaryotes. Each of the four parts of ATP synthase consists of a number of polypeptide subunits.

gradient that drives ATP synthesis by the ATP synthase protein complex? Establishing the $H^+$ gradient across the inner mitochondrial membrane is a major function of the electron transport chain **(Figure 6.14)**. The chain is an energy converter that uses the exergonic flow of electrons from NADH and $FADH_2$ to pump $H^+$ across the membrane, from the mitochondrial matrix into the intermembrane space. The $H^+$ has a tendency to move back across the membrane, diffusing down its gradient. And the ATP synthases are the only sites that provide a route through the membrane for $H^+$. As we described previously, the passage of $H^+$ through ATP synthase uses the exergonic flow of $H^+$ to drive the phosphorylation of ADP. Thus, the energy stored in an $H^+$ gradient across a membrane couples the redox reactions of the electron transport chain to ATP synthesis, an example of chemiosmosis (see Figure 6.14).

At this point, you may be wondering how the electron transport chain pumps hydrogen ions. Researchers have found that certain members of the electron transport chain accept and release protons ($H^+$) along with electrons. (The aqueous solutions inside and surrounding the cell are a ready source of $H^+$.) At certain steps along the chain, electron transfers cause $H^+$ to be taken up and released into the surrounding solution. In eukaryotic cells, the electron carriers are spatially arranged in the inner mitochondrial membrane in such a way that $H^+$ is accepted from the mitochondrial matrix and deposited in the intermembrane space (see Figure 6.14). The $H^+$ gradient that

results is referred to as a **proton-motive force**, emphasizing the capacity of the gradient to perform work. The force drives $H^+$ back across the membrane through the $H^+$ channels provided by ATP synthases.

In general terms, *chemiosmosis is an energy-coupling mechanism that uses energy stored in the form of an $H^+$ gradient across a membrane to drive cellular work.* In mitochondria, the energy for gradient formation comes from exergonic redox reactions, and ATP synthesis is the work performed. But chemiosmosis also occurs elsewhere and in other variations. Chloroplasts use chemiosmosis to generate ATP during photosynthesis; in these organelles, light (rather than chemical energy) drives both electron flow down an electron

▲ **Figure 6.14 Chemiosmosis couples the electron transport chain to ATP synthesis.** ❶ NADH and $FADH_2$ shuttle high-energy electrons extracted from food during glycolysis and the citric acid cycle into an electron transport chain built into the inner mitochondrial membrane. The gold arrows trace the transport of electrons, which are finally passed to oxygen at the "downhill" end of the chain, forming water. Most of the electron carriers of the chain are grouped into four complexes. Two mobile

carriers, ubiquinone (Q) and cytochrome c (Cyt c), move rapidly, ferrying electrons between the large complexes. As complexes shuttle electrons, they pump protons from the mitochondrial matrix into the intermembrane space. $FADH_2$ deposits its electrons via complex II and so results in fewer protons being pumped into the intermembrane space than occurs with NADH. Chemical energy originally harvested from food is transformed into a proton-motive force, a gradient of $H^+$ across the membrane.

❷ During chemiosmosis, the protons flow back down their gradient via ATP synthase, which is built into the membrane nearby. The ATP synthase harnesses the proton-motive force to phosphorylate ADP, forming ATP. Together, electron transport and chemiosmosis make up oxidative phosphorylation.

**WHAT IF?** *If complex IV were nonfunctional, could chemiosmosis produce any ATP, and if so, how would the rate of synthesis differ?*

transport chain and the resulting $H^+$ gradient formation. Prokaryotes, as already mentioned, generate $H^+$ gradients across their plasma membranes. They then tap the proton-motive force not only to make ATP inside the cell but also to rotate their flagella and to pump nutrients and waste products across the membrane. Because of its central importance to energy conversions in prokaryotes and eukaryotes, chemiosmosis has helped unify the study of bioenergetics. Peter Mitchell was awarded the Nobel Prize in 1978 for originally proposing the chemiosmotic model.

## An Accounting of ATP Production by Cellular Respiration

In the last few sections, we have looked rather closely at the key processes of cellular respiration. Now let's take a step back and remind ourselves of its overall function: harvesting the energy of glucose for ATP synthesis.

During respiration, most energy flows in this sequence: glucose → NADH → electron transport chain → proton-motive force → ATP. We can do some bookkeeping to calculate the ATP profit when cellular respiration oxidizes a molecule of glucose to six molecules of carbon dioxide. The three main departments of this metabolic enterprise are glycolysis, the citric acid cycle, and the electron transport chain, which drives oxidative phosphorylation. **Figure 6.15** gives a detailed accounting of the ATP yield per glucose molecule oxidized. The tally adds

the 4 ATP produced directly by substrate-level phosphorylation during glycolysis and the citric acid cycle to the many more molecules of ATP generated by oxidative phosphorylation. Each NADH that transfers a pair of electrons from glucose to the electron transport chain contributes enough to the proton-motive force to generate a maximum of about 3 ATP.

Why are the numbers in Figure 6.15 inexact? There are three reasons we cannot state an exact number of ATP molecules generated by the breakdown of one molecule of glucose. First, phosphorylation and the redox reactions are not directly coupled to each other, so the ratio of the number of NADH molecules to the number of ATP molecules is not a whole number. We know that 1 NADH results in 10 $H^+$ being transported out across the inner mitochondrial membrane, but the exact number of $H^+$ that must reenter the mitochondrial matrix via ATP synthase to generate 1 ATP has long been debated. Based on experimental data, however, most biochemists now agree that the most accurate number is 4 $H^+$. Therefore, a single molecule of NADH generates enough proton-motive force for the synthesis of 2.5 ATP. The citric acid cycle also supplies electrons to the electron transport chain via $FADH_2$, but since its electrons enter later in the chain, each molecule of this electron carrier is responsible for transport of only enough $H^+$ for the synthesis of 1.5 ATP. These numbers also take into account the slight energetic cost of moving the ATP formed in the mitochondrion out into the cytosol, where it will be used.

▲ **Figure 6.15 ATP yield per molecule of glucose at each stage of cellular respiration.**

? *Explain exactly how the numbers "26 or 28" in the yellow bar were calculated.*

Second, the ATP yield varies slightly depending on the type of shuttle used to transport electrons from the cytosol into the mitochondrion. The mitochondrial inner membrane is impermeable to NADH, so NADH in the cytosol is segregated from the machinery of oxidative phosphorylation. The 2 electrons of NADH captured in glycolysis must be conveyed into the mitochondrion by one of several electron shuttle systems. Depending on the kind of shuttle in a particular cell type, the electrons are passed either to $NAD^+$ or to FAD in the mitochondrial matrix (see Figure 6.15). If the electrons are passed to FAD, as in brain cells, only about 1.5 ATP can result from each NADH that was originally generated in the cytosol. If the electrons are passed to mitochondrial $NAD^+$, as in liver cells and heart cells, the yield is about 2.5 ATP per NADH.

A third variable that reduces the yield of ATP is the use of the proton-motive force generated by the redox reactions of respiration to drive other kinds of work. For example, the proton-motive force powers the mitochondrion's uptake of pyruvate from the cytosol. However, if *all* the proton-motive force generated by the electron transport chain were used to drive ATP synthesis, one glucose molecule could generate a maximum of 28 ATP produced by oxidative phosphorylation plus 4 ATP (net) from substrate-level phosphorylation to give a total yield of about 32 ATP (or only about 30 ATP if the less efficient shuttle were functioning).

We can now roughly estimate the efficiency of respiration—that is, the percentage of chemical energy in glucose that has been transferred to ATP. Recall that the complete oxidation of a mole of glucose releases 686 kcal of energy under standard conditions ($\Delta G = -686$ kcal/mol). Phosphorylation of ADP to form ATP stores at least 7.3 kcal per mole of ATP. Therefore, the efficiency of respiration is 7.3 kcal per mole of ATP times 32 moles of ATP per mole of glucose divided by 686 kcal per mole of glucose, which equals 0.34. Thus, about 34% of the potential chemical energy in glucose has been transferred to ATP; the actual percentage is bound to vary as $\Delta G$ varies under different cellular conditions. Cellular respiration is remarkably efficient in its energy conversion. By comparison, the most efficient automobile converts only about 25% of the energy stored in gasoline to energy that moves the car.

The rest of the energy stored in glucose is lost as heat. We humans use some of this heat to maintain our relatively high body temperature (37°C), and we dissipate the rest through sweating and other cooling mechanisms.

Surprisingly, perhaps, it is beneficial under certain conditions to reduce the efficiency of cellular respiration. A remarkable adaptation is shown by hibernating mammals, which overwinter in a state of inactivity and lowered metabolism. Although their internal body temperature is lower than normal, it still must be kept significantly higher than the external air temperature. One type of tissue, called brown fat, is made up of cells packed full of mitochondria. The inner mitochondrial membrane contains a channel protein called the uncoupling protein, which allows protons to flow back down their concentration gradient without generating ATP. Activation of these proteins in hibernating mammals results in ongoing oxidation of stored fuel stores (fats), generating heat without any ATP production. In the absence of such an adaptation, the ATP level would build up to a point that cellular respiration would be shut down due to regulatory mechanisms in the cell. In the **Scientific Skills Exercise**, you can work with data in a different case where a decrease in metabolic efficiency in cells is used to generate heat.

### CONCEPT CHECK 6.4

1. What effect would an absence of $O_2$ have on the process shown in Figure 6.14?
2. **WHAT IF?** In the absence of $O_2$, as in question 1, what do you think would happen if you decreased the pH of the intermembrane space of the mitochondrion? Explain your answer.
3. **MAKE CONNECTIONS** Membranes must be fluid to function properly. How does the operation of the electron transport chain support that assertion?

For suggested answers, see Appendix A.

---

**CONCEPT** 6.5

# Fermentation and anaerobic respiration enable cells to produce ATP without the use of oxygen

Because most of the ATP generated by cellular respiration is due to the work of oxidative phosphorylation, our estimate of ATP yield from aerobic respiration is contingent on an adequate supply of oxygen to the cell. Without the electronegative oxygen to pull electrons down the transport chain, oxidative phosphorylation eventually ceases. However, there are two general mechanisms by which certain cells can oxidize organic fuel and generate ATP *without* the use of oxygen: anaerobic respiration and fermentation. The distinction between these two is that an electron transport chain is used in anaerobic respiration but not in fermentation. (The electron transport chain is also called the respiratory chain because of its role in both types of cellular respiration.)

We have already mentioned anaerobic respiration, which takes place in certain prokaryotic organisms that live in environments without oxygen. These organisms have an electron transport chain but do not use oxygen as a final electron acceptor at the end of the chain. Oxygen performs this function very well because it is extremely electronegative, but other, less electronegative substances can also serve as final electron acceptors. Some "sulfate-reducing" marine bacteria, for instance, use the sulfate ion ($SO_4^{2-}$) at the end of their respiratory chain. Operation of the chain builds up a proton-motive force used to produce ATP, but $H_2S$ (hydrogen sulfide) is produced as a

# Making a Bar Graph and Evaluating a Hypothesis

**Does Thyroid Hormone Level Affect Oxygen Consumption in Cells?** Some animals, such as mammals and birds, maintain a relatively constant body temperature, above that of their environment, using heat produced as a by-product of metabolism. When the core temperature of these animals drops below an internal set point, their cells are triggered to reduce the efficiency of ATP produced by the electron transport chains in mitochondria. At lower efficiency, extra fuel must be consumed to produce the same number of ATPs, generating additional heat. Because this response is moderated by the endocrine system, researchers hypothesized that thyroid hormone might trigger this cellular response. In this exercise, you will use a bar graph to visualize data from an experiment that compared the metabolic rate (by measuring oxygen consumption) in mitochondria of cells from animals with different levels of thyroid hormone.

**How the Experiment Was Done** Liver cells were isolated from sibling rats that had low, normal, or elevated thyroid hormone levels. The oxygen consumption rate due to activity of the mitochondrial electron transport chains of each type of cell was measured under controlled conditions.

**Data from the Experiment**

| Thyroid Hormone Level | Oxygen Consumption Rate (nmol $O_2$/min·mg cells) |
|---|---|
| Low | 4.3 |
| Normal | 4.8 |
| Elevated | 8.7 |

**Interpret the Data**

1. To visualize any differences in oxygen consumption between cell types, it will be useful to graph the data in a bar graph. First, you'll set up the axes. (a) What is the independent variable (intentionally varied by the researchers), which goes on the x-axis? List the categories along the x-axis; because they are discrete rather than continuous, you can list them in any order. (b) What is the dependent variable (measured by the researchers), which goes on the y-axis? (c) What units (abbreviated) should go on the y-axis? Label the y-axis, including the units specified in the data table.

Determine the range of values of the data that will need to go on the y-axis. What is the largest value? Draw evenly spaced tick marks and label them, starting with 0 at the bottom.

2. Graph the data for each sample. Match each x-value with its y-value and place a mark on the graph at that coordinate, then draw a bar from the x-axis up to the correct height for each sample. Why is a bar graph more appropriate than a scatter plot or line graph? (For additional information about graphs, see the Scientific Skills Review in Appendix F and in the Study Area in MasteringBiology.)

3. Examine your graph and look for a pattern in the data. (a) Which cell type had the highest rate of oxygen consumption, and which had the lowest? (b) Does this support the researchers' hypothesis? Explain. (c) Based on what you know about mitochondrial electron transport and heat production, predict which rats had the highest, and which had the lowest, body temperature.

**Data from** M. E. Harper and M. D. Brand, The quantitative contributions of mitochondrial proton leak and ATP turnover reactions to the changed respiration rates of hepatocytes from rats of different thyroid status, *Journal of Biological Chemistry* 268:14850–14860 (1993).

(MB) A version of this Scientific Skills Exercise can be assigned in MasteringBiology.

---

by-product rather than water. The rotten-egg odor you may have smelled while walking through a salt marsh or a mudflat signals the presence of sulfate-reducing bacteria.

Fermentation is a way of harvesting chemical energy without using either oxygen or any electron transport chain—in other words, without cellular respiration. How can food be oxidized without cellular respiration? Remember, oxidation simply refers to the loss of electrons to an electron acceptor, so it does not need to involve oxygen. Glycolysis oxidizes glucose to two molecules of pyruvate. The oxidizing agent of glycolysis is $NAD^+$, and neither oxygen nor any electron transfer chain is involved. Overall, glycolysis is exergonic, and some of the energy made available is used to produce 2 ATP (net) by substrate-level phosphorylation. If oxygen *is* present, then additional ATP is made by oxidative phosphorylation when NADH passes

electrons removed from glucose to the electron transport chain. But glycolysis generates 2 ATP whether oxygen is present or not—that is, whether conditions are aerobic or anaerobic.

As an alternative to respiratory oxidation of organic nutrients, fermentation is an extension of glycolysis that allows continuous generation of ATP by the substrate-level phosphorylation of glycolysis. For this to occur, there must be a sufficient supply of $NAD^+$ to accept electrons during the oxidation step of glycolysis. Without some mechanism to recycle $NAD^+$ from NADH, glycolysis would soon deplete the cell's pool of $NAD^+$ by reducing it all to NADH and would shut itself down for lack of an oxidizing agent. Under aerobic conditions, $NAD^+$ is recycled from NADH by the transfer of electrons to the electron transport chain. An anaerobic alternative is to transfer electrons from NADH to pyruvate, the end product of glycolysis.

## Types of Fermentation

Fermentation consists of glycolysis plus reactions that regenerate $NAD^+$ by transferring electrons from NADH to pyruvate or derivatives of pyruvate. The $NAD^+$ can then be reused to oxidize sugar by glycolysis, which nets two molecules of ATP by substrate-level phosphorylation. There are many types of fermentation, differing in the end products formed from pyruvate. Two common types are alcohol fermentation and lactic acid fermentation.

In **alcohol fermentation (Figure 6.16a)**, pyruvate is converted to ethanol (ethyl alcohol) in two steps. The first step releases carbon dioxide from the pyruvate, which is converted to the two-carbon compound acetaldehyde. In the second step, acetaldehyde is reduced by NADH to ethanol. This regenerates the supply of $NAD^+$ needed for the continuation of glycolysis. Many bacteria carry out alcohol fermentation under anaerobic conditions. Yeast (a fungus) also carries out alcohol fermentation. For thousands of years, humans have used yeast in brewing, winemaking, and baking. The $CO_2$ bubbles generated by baker's yeast during alcohol fermentation allow bread to rise.

During **lactic acid fermentation (Figure 6.16b)**, pyruvate is reduced directly by NADH to form lactate as an end product, with no release of $CO_2$. (Lactate is the ionized form of lactic acid.) Lactic acid fermentation by certain fungi and bacteria is used in the dairy industry to make cheese and yogurt.

Human muscle cells make ATP by lactic acid fermentation when oxygen is scarce. This occurs during strenuous exercise, when sugar catabolism for ATP production outpaces the muscle's supply of oxygen from the blood. Under these conditions, the cells switch from aerobic respiration to fermentation. The lactate that accumulates was previously thought to cause muscle fatigue and pain, but recent research suggests instead that increased levels of potassium ions ($K^+$) may be to blame, while lactate appears to enhance muscle performance. In any case, the excess lactate is gradually carried away by the blood to the liver, where it is converted back to pyruvate by liver cells. Because oxygen is available, this pyruvate can then enter the mitochondria in liver cells and complete cellular respiration.

## Comparing Fermentation with Anaerobic and Aerobic Respiration

Fermentation, anaerobic respiration, and aerobic respiration are three alternative cellular pathways for producing ATP by harvesting the chemical energy of food. All three use glycolysis to oxidize glucose and other organic fuels to pyruvate, with a net production of 2 ATP by substrate-level phosphorylation. And in all three pathways, $NAD^+$ is the oxidizing agent that accepts electrons from food during glycolysis.

A key difference is the contrasting mechanisms for oxidizing NADH back to $NAD^+$, which is required to sustain glycolysis. In fermentation, the final electron acceptor is an organic molecule such as pyruvate (lactic acid fermentation) or acetaldehyde (alcohol fermentation). In cellular respiration,

**(a) Alcohol fermentation**

**(b) Lactic acid fermentation**

▲ **Figure 6.16 Fermentation.** In the absence of oxygen, many cells use fermentation to produce ATP by substrate-level phosphorylation. Pyruvate, the end product of glycolysis, serves as an electron acceptor for oxidizing NADH back to $NAD^+$, which can then be reused in glycolysis. Two of the common end products formed from fermentation are **(a)** ethanol and **(b)** lactate, the ionized form of lactic acid.

by contrast, electrons carried by NADH are transferred to an electron transport chain, which generates the $NAD^+$ required for glycolysis.

Another major difference is the amount of ATP produced. Fermentation yields two molecules of ATP, produced by substrate-level phosphorylation. In the absence of an electron transport chain, the energy stored in pyruvate is unavailable. In cellular respiration, however, pyruvate is completely oxidized in the mitochondrion. Most of the chemical energy from this process is shuttled by NADH and $FADH_2$ in the form of the electrons to the electron transport chain. There, the electrons move stepwise down a series of redox reactions to a final electron acceptor. (In aerobic respiration, the final electron is oxygen;

in anaerobic respiration, the final acceptor is another molecule that is electronegative, although less so than oxygen.) Stepwise electron transport drives oxidative phosphorylation, yielding ATPs. Thus, cellular respiration harvests much more energy from each sugar molecule than fermentation can. In fact, aerobic respiration yields up to 32 molecules of ATP per glucose molecule—up to 16 times as much as does fermentation.

Some organisms, called **obligate anaerobes**, carry out only fermentation or anaerobic respiration. In fact, these organisms cannot survive in the presence of oxygen. A few cell types can carry out only aerobic oxidation of pyruvate, not fermentation. Other organisms, including yeasts and many bacteria, can make enough ATP to survive using either fermentation or respiration. Such species are called **facultative anaerobes**. On the cellular level, our muscle cells behave as facultative anaerobes. In such cells, pyruvate is a fork in the metabolic road that leads to two alternative catabolic routes (**Figure 6.17**). Under aerobic conditions, pyruvate can be converted to acetyl CoA, which enters the citric acid cycle. Under anaerobic conditions, lactic acid fermentation occurs: Pyruvate is diverted from the citric acid cycle, serving instead as an electron acceptor to recycle NAD⁺. To make the same amount of ATP, a facultative anaerobe has to consume sugar at a much faster rate when fermenting than when respiring.

## The Evolutionary Significance of Glycolysis

**EVOLUTION** The role of glycolysis in both fermentation and respiration has an evolutionary basis. Ancient prokaryotes are thought to have used glycolysis to make ATP long before oxygen was present in Earth's atmosphere. The oldest known fossils of bacteria date back 3.5 billion years, but appreciable quantities of oxygen probably did not begin to accumulate in the atmosphere until about 2.7 billion years ago, produced by photosynthesizing cyanobacteria. Therefore, early prokaryotes may have generated ATP exclusively from glycolysis. The fact that glycolysis is today the most widespread metabolic pathway among Earth's organisms suggests that it evolved very early in the history of life. The cytosolic location of glycolysis also implies great antiquity; the pathway does not require any of the membrane-enclosed organelles of the eukaryotic cell, which evolved approximately 1 billion years after the prokaryotic cell. Glycolysis is a metabolic heirloom from early cells that continues to function in fermentation and as the first stage in the breakdown of organic molecules by respiration.

### CONCEPT CHECK 6.5

1. Consider the NADH formed during glycolysis. What is the final acceptor for its electrons during fermentation? What is the final acceptor for its electrons during aerobic respiration?

2. **WHAT IF?** A glucose-fed yeast cell is moved from an aerobic environment to an anaerobic one. How would its rate of glucose consumption change if ATP were to be generated at the same rate?

*For suggested answers, see Appendix A.*

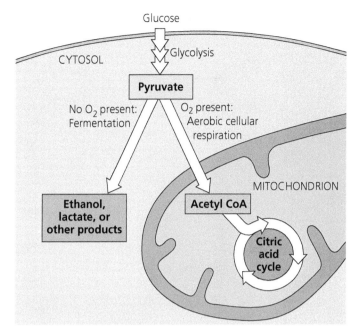

▲ Figure 6.17 **Pyruvate as a key juncture in catabolism.** Glycolysis is common to fermentation and cellular respiration. The end product of glycolysis, pyruvate, represents a fork in the catabolic pathways of glucose oxidation. In a facultative anaerobe or a muscle cell, which are capable of both aerobic cellular respiration and fermentation, pyruvate is committed to one of those two pathways, usually depending on whether or not oxygen is present.

---

**CONCEPT** 6.6

# Glycolysis and the citric acid cycle connect to many other metabolic pathways

So far, we have treated the oxidative breakdown of glucose in isolation from the cell's overall metabolic economy. In this section, you will learn that glycolysis and the citric acid cycle are major intersections of the cell's catabolic and anabolic (biosynthetic) pathways.

## The Versatility of Catabolism

Throughout this chapter, we have used glucose as an example of a fuel for cellular respiration. But free glucose molecules are not common in the diets of humans and other animals. We obtain most of our calories in the form of fats, proteins, sucrose and other disaccharides, and starch, a polysaccharide. All these organic molecules in food can be used by cellular respiration to make ATP (**Figure 6.18**).

Glycolysis can accept a wide range of carbohydrates for catabolism. In the digestive tract, starch is hydrolyzed to glucose, which can then be broken down in the cells by glycolysis and the citric acid cycle. Similarly, glycogen, the polysaccharide that humans and many other animals store in their liver and muscle cells, can be hydrolyzed to glucose between meals as fuel for respiration. The digestion of

**▲ Figure 6.18 The catabolism of various molecules from food.** Carbohydrates, fats, and proteins can all be used as fuel for cellular respiration. Monomers of these molecules enter glycolysis or the citric acid cycle at various points. Glycolysis and the citric acid cycle are catabolic funnels through which electrons from all kinds of organic molecules flow on their exergonic fall to oxygen.

disaccharides, including sucrose, provides glucose and other monosaccharides as fuel for respiration.

Proteins can also be used for fuel, but first they must be digested to their constituent amino acids. Many of the amino acids are used by the organism to build new proteins. Amino acids present in excess are converted by enzymes to intermediates of glycolysis and the citric acid cycle. Before amino acids can feed into glycolysis or the citric acid cycle, their amino groups must be removed, a process called *deamination*. The nitrogenous refuse is excreted from the animal in the form of ammonia ($NH_3$), urea, or other waste products.

Catabolism can also harvest energy stored in fats obtained either from food or from storage cells in the body. After fats are digested to glycerol and fatty acids, the glycerol is converted to glyceraldehyde 3-phosphate, an intermediate of glycolysis. Most of the energy of a fat is stored in the fatty acids. A metabolic sequence called **beta oxidation** breaks the fatty acids down to two-carbon fragments, which enter the citric acid cycle as

acetyl CoA. NADH and $FADH_2$ are also generated during beta oxidation, resulting in further ATP production. Fats make excellent fuel, in large part due to their chemical structure and the high energy level of their electrons compared to those of carbohydrates. A gram of fat oxidized by respiration produces more than twice as much ATP as a gram of carbohydrate.

## Biosynthesis (Anabolic Pathways)

Cells need substance as well as energy. Not all the organic molecules of food are destined to be oxidized as fuel to make ATP. In addition to calories, food must also provide the carbon skeletons that cells require to make their own molecules. Some organic monomers obtained from digestion can be used directly. For example, as previously mentioned, amino acids from the hydrolysis of proteins in food can be incorporated into the organism's own proteins. Often, however, the body needs specific molecules that are not present as such in food. Compounds formed as intermediates of glycolysis and the citric acid cycle can be diverted into anabolic pathways as precursors from which the cell can synthesize the molecules it requires. For example, humans can make about half of the 20 amino acids in proteins by modifying compounds siphoned away from the citric acid cycle; the rest are "essential amino acids" that must be obtained in the diet. Also, glucose can be made from pyruvate, and fatty acids can be synthesized from acetyl CoA. Of course, these anabolic, or biosynthetic, pathways do not generate ATP, but instead consume it.

In addition, glycolysis and the citric acid cycle function as metabolic interchanges that enable our cells to convert some kinds of molecules to others as we need them. For example, an intermediate compound generated during glycolysis, dihydroxyacetone phosphate (see Figure 6.9, step 5), can be converted to one of the major precursors of fats. If we eat more food than we need, we store fat even if our diet is fat-free. Metabolism is remarkably versatile and adaptable.

Cellular respiration and metabolic pathways play a role of central importance in organisms. Examine Figure 6.2 again to put cellular respiration into the broader context of energy flow and chemical cycling in ecosystems. The energy that keeps us alive is *released*, not *produced*, by cellular respiration. We are tapping energy that was stored in food by photosynthesis, which captures light and converts it to chemical energy.

---

**CONCEPT CHECK 6.6**

1. **MAKE CONNECTIONS** Compare the structure of a fat (see Figure 2.12) with that of a carbohydrate (see Figure 2.7). What features of their structures make fat a much better fuel?

2. Under what circumstances might your body synthesize fat molecules?

3. **WHAT IF?** During intense exercise, can a muscle cell use fat as a concentrated source of chemical energy? Explain. (Review Figures 6.17 and 6.18.)

For suggested answers, see Appendix A.

# 6 Chapter Review

## SUMMARY OF KEY CONCEPTS

### CONCEPT 6.1

#### Catabolic pathways yield energy by oxidizing organic fuels (pp. 110–114)

- Cells break down glucose and other organic fuels to yield chemical energy in the form of ATP. **Fermentation** is a partial degradation of glucose without the use of oxygen. **Cellular respiration** is a more complete breakdown of glucose; in **aerobic respiration**, oxygen is used as a reactant. The cell taps the energy stored in food molecules through **redox reactions**, in which one substance partially or totally shifts electrons to another. **Oxidation** is the loss of electrons from one substance, while **reduction** is the addition of electrons to the other.
- During aerobic respiration, glucose ($C_6H_{12}O_6$) is oxidized to $CO_2$, and $O_2$ is reduced to $H_2O$. Electrons lose potential energy during their transfer from glucose or other organic compounds to oxygen. Electrons are usually passed first to **NAD⁺**, reducing it to NADH, and then from NADH to an **electron transport chain**, which conducts them to $O_2$ in energy-releasing steps. The energy is used to make ATP.
- Aerobic respiration occurs in three stages: (1) **glycolysis**, (2) pyruvate oxidation and the **citric acid cycle**, and (3) **oxidative phosphorylation** (electron transport and chemiosmosis).

> **?** *Describe the difference between the two processes in cellular respiration that produce ATP: oxidative phosphorylation and substrate-level phosphorylation.*

### CONCEPT 6.2

#### Glycolysis harvests chemical energy by oxidizing glucose to pyruvate (pp. 114–115)

> **?** *What is the source of energy for the formation of ATP and NADH in glycolysis?*

### CONCEPT 6.3

#### After pyruvate is oxidized, the citric acid cycle completes the energy-yielding oxidation of organic molecules (pp. 116–117)

- In eukaryotic cells, pyruvate enters the mitochondrion and is oxidized to **acetyl CoA**, which is further oxidized in the citric acid cycle.

> **?** *What molecular products indicate the complete oxidation of glucose during cellular respiration?*

### CONCEPT 6.4

#### During oxidative phosphorylation, chemiosmosis couples electron transport to ATP synthesis (pp. 117–122)

- NADH and $FADH_2$ transfer electrons to the electron transport chain. Electrons move down the chain, losing energy in several energy-releasing steps. Finally, electrons are passed to $O_2$, reducing it to $H_2O$.

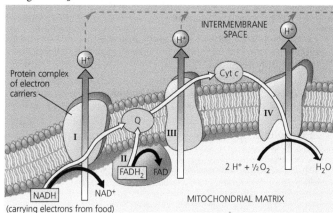

- At certain steps along the electron transport chain, electron transfer causes protein complexes to move H⁺ from the mitochondrial matrix (in eukaryotes) to the intermembrane space, storing energy as a **proton-motive force** (H⁺ gradient). As H⁺ diffuses back into the matrix through **ATP synthase**, its passage drives the phosphorylation of ADP, a process called **chemiosmosis**.
- About 34% of the energy stored in a glucose molecule is transferred to ATP during cellular respiration, producing a maximum of about 32 ATP.

> **?** *Briefly explain the mechanism by which ATP synthase produces ATP. List three locations in which ATP synthases are found.*

### CONCEPT 6.5

#### Fermentation and anaerobic respiration enable cells to produce ATP without the use of oxygen (pp. 122–125)

- Glycolysis nets 2 ATP by substrate-level phosphorylation, whether oxygen is present or not. Under anaerobic conditions, either anaerobic respiration or fermentation can take place. In anaerobic respiration, an electron transport chain is present with a final electron acceptor other than oxygen. In fermentation, the electrons from NADH are passed to pyruvate or a derivative of pyruvate, regenerating the NAD⁺ required to oxidize more glucose. Two common types of fermentation are **alcohol fermentation** and **lactic acid fermentation**.
- Fermentation, anaerobic respiration, and aerobic respiration all use glycolysis to oxidize glucose, but they differ in their final

electron acceptor and whether an electron transport chain is used (respiration) or not (fermentation). Respiration yields more ATP; aerobic respiration, with $O_2$ as the final electron acceptor, yields about 16 times as much ATP as does fermentation.

• Glycolysis occurs in nearly all organisms and is thought to have evolved in ancient prokaryotes before there was $O_2$ in the atmosphere.

**?** *Which process yields more ATP, fermentation or anaerobic respiration? Explain.*

CONCEPT 6.6

### Glycolysis and the citric acid cycle connect to many other metabolic pathways (pp. 125–126)

• Catabolic pathways funnel electrons from many kinds of organic molecules into cellular respiration. Many carbohydrates can enter glycolysis, most often after conversion to glucose. Amino acids of proteins must be deaminated before being oxidized. The fatty.acids of fats undergo **beta oxidation** to two-carbon fragments and then enter the citric acid cycle as acetyl CoA. Anabolic pathways can use small molecules from food directly or build other substances using intermediates of glycolysis or the citric acid cycle.

**?** *Describe how the catabolic pathways of glycolysis and the citric acid cycle intersect with anabolic pathways in the metabolism of a cell.*

## TEST YOUR UNDERSTANDING

### Level 1: Knowledge/Comprehension

1. The *immediate* energy source that drives ATP synthesis by ATP synthase during oxidative phosphorylation is the
   a. oxidation of glucose and other organic compounds.
   b. flow of electrons down the electron transport chain.
   c. affinity of oxygen for electrons.
   d. $H^+$ movement down its concentration gradient.
   e. transfer of phosphate to ADP.

2. Which metabolic pathway is common to both fermentation and cellular respiration of a glucose molecule?
   a. the citric acid cycle
   b. the electron transport chain
   c. glycolysis
   d. synthesis of acetyl CoA from pyruvate
   e. reduction of pyruvate to lactate

3. In mitochondria, exergonic redox reactions
   a. are the source of energy driving prokaryotic ATP synthesis.
   b. are directly coupled to substrate-level phosphorylation.
   c. provide the energy that establishes the proton gradient.
   d. reduce carbon atoms to carbon dioxide.
   e. use ATP to pump $H^+$ out of the mitochondrion.

4. The final electron acceptor of the electron transport chain that functions in aerobic oxidative phosphorylation is
   a. oxygen.               d. pyruvate.
   b. water.                e. ADP.
   c. $NAD^+$.

### Level 2: Application/Analysis

5. What is the oxidizing agent in the following reaction?

   Pyruvate + NADH + $H^+$ → Lactate + $NAD^+$

   a. oxygen                d. lactate
   b. NADH                 e. pyruvate
   c. $NAD^+$

6. When electrons flow along the electron transport chains of mitochondria, which of the following changes occurs?
   a. The pH of the matrix increases.
   b. ATP synthase pumps protons by active transport.
   c. The electrons gain free energy.
   d. The cytochromes phosphorylate ADP to form ATP.
   e. $NAD^+$ is oxidized.

7. Most $CO_2$ from catabolism is released during
   a. glycolysis.
   b. the citric acid cycle.
   c. lactate fermentation.
   d. electron transport.
   e. oxidative phosphorylation.

### Level 3: Synthesis/Evaluation

8. **DRAW IT** The graph here shows the pH difference across the inner mitochondrial membrane over time in an actively respiring cell. At the time indicated by the vertical arrow, a metabolic poison is added that specifically and completely inhibits all function of mitochondrial ATP synthase. Draw what you would expect to see for the rest of the graphed line.

9. **SCIENTIFIC INQUIRY**
   In the 1930s, some physicians prescribed low doses of a compound called dinitrophenol (DNP) to help patients lose weight. This unsafe method was abandoned after some patients died. DNP uncouples the chemiosmotic machinery by making the lipid bilayer of the inner mitochondrial membrane leaky to $H^+$. Explain how this could cause weight loss and death.

10. **FOCUS ON EVOLUTION**
    ATP synthases are found in the prokaryotic plasma membrane and in mitochondria and chloroplasts. What does this suggest about the evolutionary relationship of these eukaryotic organelles to prokaryotes? How might the amino acid sequences of the ATP synthases from the different sources support or refute your hypothesis?

11. **FOCUS ON ENERGY AND MATTER**
    In a short essay (100–150 words), explain how oxidative phosphorylation—the production of ATP using energy derived from the redox reactions of a spatially organized electron transport chain followed by chemiosmosis—is an example of how new properties emerge at each level of the biological hierarchy.

*For selected answers, see Appendix A.*

## MasteringBiology®

**Students** Go to **MasteringBiology** for assignments, the eText, and the Study Area with practice tests, animations, and activities.

**Instructors** Go to **MasteringBiology** for automatically graded tutorials and questions that you can assign to your students, plus Instructor Resources.

# 7 Photosynthesis

*(handwritten notes)* 5/ (-σ,σ) √x²+36  comparison of chemiosmosis in mitochondria and chloroplast

OVERVIEW

## The Process That Feeds the Biosphere

Life on Earth is solar powered. The chloroplasts in plants and other photosynthetic organisms capture light energy that has traveled 150 million kilometers from the sun and convert it to chemical energy that is stored in sugar and other organic molecules. This conversion process is called **photosynthesis**. Let's begin by placing photosynthesis in its ecological context.

Photosynthesis nourishes almost the entire living world directly or indirectly. An organism acquires the organic compounds it uses for energy and carbon skeletons by one of two major modes: autotrophic nutrition or heterotrophic nutrition. **Autotrophs** are "self-feeders" (*auto-* means "self," and *trophos* means "feeder"); they sustain themselves without eating anything derived from other living beings. Autotrophs produce their organic molecules from $CO_2$ and other inorganic raw materials obtained from the environment. They are the ultimate sources of organic compounds for all nonautotrophic organisms, and for this reason, biologists refer to autotrophs as the *producers* of the biosphere.

Almost all plants are autotrophs; the only nutrients they require are water and minerals from the soil and carbon dioxide from the air. Specifically, plants are *photo*autotrophs, organisms that use light as a source of energy to synthesize organic substances **(Figure 7.1)**. Photosynthesis also occurs in algae, certain other unicellular eukaryotes, and some prokaryotes

▶ Other organisms also benefit from photosynthesis.

(**Figure 7.2**). In this chapter, we will touch on these other groups in passing, but our emphasis will be on plants. Variations in autotrophic nutrition that occur in prokaryotes and algae.

**Heterotrophs** obtain organic material by the second major mode of nutrition. Unable to make their own food, they live on compounds produced by other organisms (*hetero-* means "other"). Heterotrophs are the biosphere's *consumers*. The most obvious "other-feeding" occurs when an animal eats plants or other animals. But heterotrophic nutrition may be more subtle. Some heterotrophs consume the remains of dead organisms by decomposing and feeding on organic litter such as carcasses, feces, and fallen leaves; these types of organisms are known as decomposers. Most fungi and many types of prokaryotes get their nourishment this way. Almost all heterotrophs, including humans, are completely dependent, either directly or indirectly, on photoautotrophs for food—and also for oxygen, a by-product of photosynthesis.

The Earth's supply of fossil fuels was formed from remains of organisms that died hundreds of millions of years ago. In a sense, then, fossil fuels represent stores of the sun's energy from the distant past. Because these resources are being used at a much higher rate than they are replenished, researchers are exploring methods of capitalizing on the photosynthetic process to provide alternative fuels (**Figure 7.3**).

In this chapter, you'll learn how photosynthesis works. After discussing general principles of photosynthesis, we'll consider the two stages of photosynthesis: the light reactions, which capture solar energy and transform it into chemical energy; and the Calvin cycle, which uses that chemical energy to make the organic molecules of food. Finally, we will consider some aspects of photosynthesis from an evolutionary perspective.

(a) Plants

(b) Multicellular alga

10 μm

(c) Unicellular eukaryotes

(d) Cyanobacteria     40 μm

1 μm

(e) Purple sulfur bacteria

▲ **Figure 7.2 Photoautotrophs.** These organisms use light energy to drive the synthesis of organic molecules from carbon dioxide and (in most cases) water. They feed themselves and the entire living world. **(a)** On land, plants are the predominant producers of food. In aquatic environments, photoautotrophs include unicellular and **(b)** multicellular algae, such as this kelp; **(c)** some non-algal unicellular eukaryotes, such as *Euglena*; **(d)** the prokaryotes called cyanobacteria; and **(e)** other photosynthetic prokaryotes, such as these purple sulfur bacteria, which produce sulfur (the yellow globules within the cells) (c–e, LMs).

▲ **Figure 7.3 Alternative fuels from algae.** The power of sunlight can be tapped to generate a sustainable alternative to fossil fuels. Species of unicellular algae that are prolific producers of plant oils can be cultured in long, transparent tanks called photobioreactors, such as the one shown here at Arizona State University. A simple chemical process can yield "biodiesel," which can be mixed with gasoline or used alone to power vehicles.

**WHAT IF?** *The main product of fossil fuel combustion is $CO_2$, and this is the source of the increase in atmospheric $CO_2$ concentration. Scientists have proposed strategically situating containers of these algae near industrial plants or near highly congested city streets. Considering the process of photosynthesis, how does this arrangement make sense?*

# Photosynthesis converts light energy to the chemical energy of food

The remarkable ability of an organism to harness light energy and use it to drive the synthesis of organic compounds emerges from structural organization in the cell: Photosynthetic enzymes and other molecules are grouped together in a biological membrane, enabling the necessary series of chemical reactions to be carried out efficiently. The process of photosynthesis most likely originated in a group of bacteria that had infolded regions of the plasma membrane containing clusters of such molecules. In existing photosynthetic bacteria, infolded photosynthetic membranes function similarly to the internal membranes of the chloroplast, a eukaryotic organelle. According to what has come to be known as the endosymbiont theory, the original chloroplast was a photosynthetic prokaryote that lived inside an ancestor of eukaryotic cells. Chloroplasts are present in a variety of photosynthesizing organisms (see some examples in Figure 7.2), but here we focus on chloroplasts in plants.

## Chloroplasts: The Sites of Photosynthesis in Plants

All green parts of a plant, including green stems and unripened fruit, have chloroplasts, but the leaves are the major sites of photosynthesis in most plants (**Figure 7.4**). There are about half a million chloroplasts in a chunk of leaf with a top surface area of 1 mm$^2$. Chloroplasts are found mainly in the cells of the **mesophyll**, the tissue in the interior of the leaf. Carbon dioxide enters the leaf, and oxygen exits, by way of microscopic pores called **stomata** (singular, *stoma*; from the Greek, meaning "mouth"). Water absorbed by the roots is delivered to the leaves in veins. Leaves also use veins to export sugar to roots and other nonphotosynthetic parts of the plant.

A typical mesophyll cell has about 30–40 chloroplasts, each measuring about 2–4 μm by 4–7 μm. A chloroplast has an envelope of two membranes surrounding a dense fluid called the **stroma**. Suspended within the stroma is a third membrane system, made up of sacs called **thylakoids**, which segregates the stroma from the *thylakoid space* inside these sacs. In some places, thylakoid sacs are stacked in columns called *grana* (singular, *granum*). **Chlorophyll**, the green pigment that gives leaves their color, resides in the thylakoid membranes of the chloroplast. (The internal photosynthetic membranes of some prokaryotes are also called thylakoid membranes.)

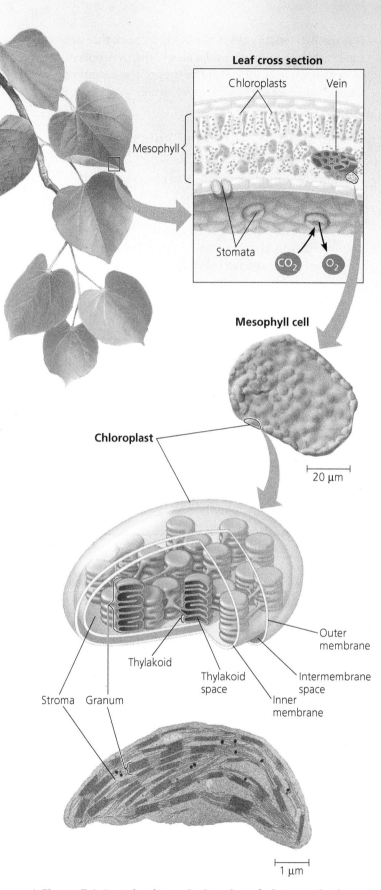

▲ Figure 7.4 **Zooming in on the location of photosynthesis in a plant.** Leaves are the major organs of photosynthesis in plants. These pictures take you into a leaf, then into a cell, and finally into a chloroplast, the organelle where photosynthesis occurs (middle, LM; bottom, TEM).

It is the light energy absorbed by chlorophyll that drives the synthesis of organic molecules in the chloroplast. Now that we have looked at the sites of photosynthesis in plants, we are ready to look more closely at the process of photosynthesis.

## Tracking Atoms Through Photosynthesis: *Scientific Inquiry*

Scientists have tried for centuries to piece together the process by which plants make food. Although some of the steps are still not completely understood, the overall photosynthetic equation has been known since the 1800s: In the presence of light, the green parts of plants produce organic compounds and oxygen from carbon dioxide and water. Using molecular formulas, we can summarize the complex series of chemical reactions in photosynthesis with this chemical equation:

$$6\ CO_2 + 12\ H_2O + \text{Light energy} \rightarrow C_6H_{12}O_6 + 6\ O_2 + 6\ H_2O$$

We use glucose ($C_6H_{12}O_6$) here to simplify the relationship between photosynthesis and respiration, but the direct product of photosynthesis is actually a three-carbon sugar that can be used to make glucose. Water appears on both sides of the equation because 12 molecules are consumed and 6 molecules are newly formed during photosynthesis. We can simplify the equation by indicating only the net consumption of water:

$$6\ CO_2 + 6\ H_2O + \text{Light energy} \rightarrow C_6H_{12}O_6 + 6\ O_2$$

Writing the equation in this form, we can see that the overall chemical change during photosynthesis is the reverse of the one that occurs during cellular respiration. Both of these metabolic processes occur in plant cells. However, as you will soon learn, chloroplasts do not synthesize sugars by simply reversing the steps of respiration.

Now let's divide the photosynthetic equation by 6 to put it in its simplest possible form:

$$CO_2 + H_2O \rightarrow [CH_2O] + O_2$$

Here, the brackets indicate that $CH_2O$ is not an actual sugar but represents the general formula for a carbohydrate. In other words, we are imagining the synthesis of a sugar molecule one carbon at a time. Six repetitions would theoretically produce a glucose molecule ($C_6H_{12}O_6$). Let's now see how researchers tracked the elements C, H, and O from the reactants of photosynthesis to the products.

### The Splitting of Water

One of the first clues to the mechanism of photosynthesis came from the discovery that the $O_2$ given off by plants is derived from $H_2O$ and not from $CO_2$. The chloroplast splits water into hydrogen and oxygen. Before this discovery, the prevailing hypothesis was that photosynthesis split carbon dioxide ($CO_2 \rightarrow C + O_2$) and then added water to the carbon ($C + H_2O \rightarrow [CH_2O]$). This hypothesis predicted that the $O_2$ released during photosynthesis came from $CO_2$. This idea was challenged in the 1930s by C. B. van Niel, of Stanford University. Van Niel was investigating photosynthesis in bacteria that make their carbohydrate from $CO_2$ but do not release $O_2$. He concluded that, at least in these bacteria, $CO_2$ is not split into carbon and oxygen. One group of bacteria used hydrogen sulfide ($H_2S$) rather than water for photosynthesis, forming yellow globules of sulfur as a waste product (these globules are visible in Figure 7.2e). Here is the chemical equation for photosynthesis in these sulfur bacteria:

$$CO_2 + 2\ H_2S \rightarrow [CH_2O] + H_2O + 2\ S$$

Van Niel reasoned that the bacteria split $H_2S$ and used the hydrogen atoms to make sugar. He then generalized that idea, proposing that all photosynthetic organisms require a hydrogen source but that the source varies:

$$\begin{aligned}\text{Sulfur bacteria: } & CO_2 + 2\ H_2S \rightarrow [CH_2O] + H_2O + 2\ S\\ \text{Plants: } & CO_2 + 2\ H_2O \rightarrow [CH_2O] + H_2O + O_2\\ \text{General: } & CO_2 + 2\ H_2X \rightarrow [CH_2O] + H_2O + 2\ X\end{aligned}$$

Thus, van Niel hypothesized that plants split $H_2O$ as a source of electrons from hydrogen atoms, releasing $O_2$ as a by-product.

Nearly 20 years later, scientists confirmed van Niel's hypothesis by using oxygen-18 ($^{18}O$), a heavy isotope, as a tracer to follow the fate of oxygen atoms during photosynthesis. The experiments showed that the $O_2$ from plants was labeled with $^{18}O$ *only* if water was the source of the tracer (experiment 1). If the $^{18}O$ was introduced to the plant in the form of $CO_2$, the label did not turn up in the released $O_2$ (experiment 2). In the following summary, red denotes labeled atoms of oxygen ($^{18}O$):

$$\begin{aligned}\text{Experiment 1: } & CO_2 + 2\ H_2O \rightarrow [CH_2O] + H_2O + O_2\\ \text{Experiment 2: } & CO_2 + 2\ H_2O \rightarrow [CH_2O] + H_2O + O_2\end{aligned}$$

A significant result of the shuffling of atoms during photosynthesis is the extraction of hydrogen from water and its incorporation into sugar. The waste product of photosynthesis, $O_2$, is released to the atmosphere. **Figure 7.5** shows the fates of all atoms in photosynthesis.

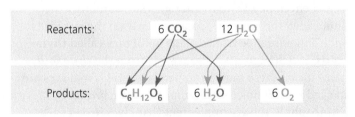

▲ **Figure 7.5 Tracking atoms through photosynthesis.** The atoms from $CO_2$ are shown in magenta, and the atoms from $H_2O$ are shown in blue.

### Photosynthesis as a Redox Process

Let's briefly compare photosynthesis with cellular respiration. Both processes involve redox reactions. During cellular respiration, energy is released from sugar when electrons associated with hydrogen are transported by carriers to oxygen, forming water as a by-product. The electrons lose potential energy as they "fall" down the electron transport chain toward electronegative oxygen, and the mitochondrion harnesses that energy to synthesize ATP. Photosynthesis reverses the direction of electron flow. Water is split, and electrons are transferred along with hydrogen ions from the water to carbon dioxide, reducing it to sugar.

$$\text{Energy} + 6\,CO_2 + 6\,H_2O \longrightarrow C_6H_{12}O_6 + 6\,O_2$$

becomes reduced

becomes oxidized

Because the electrons increase in potential energy as they move from water to sugar, this process requires energy—in other words is endergonic. This energy boost that occurs during photosynthesis is provided by light.

## The Two Stages of Photosynthesis: *A Preview*

The equation for photosynthesis is a deceptively simple summary of a very complex process. Actually, photosynthesis is not a single process, but two processes, each with multiple steps. These two stages of photosynthesis are known as the **light reactions** (the *photo* part of photosynthesis) and the **Calvin cycle** (the *synthesis* part) **(Figure 7.6)**.

The light reactions are the steps of photosynthesis that convert solar energy to chemical energy. Water is split, providing a source of electrons and protons (hydrogen ions, H$^+$) and giving off O$_2$ as a by-product. Light absorbed by chlorophyll drives a transfer of the electrons and hydrogen ions from water to an acceptor called **NADP$^+$** (nicotinamide adenine dinucleotide phosphate), where they are temporarily stored. The electron acceptor NADP$^+$ is first cousin to NAD$^+$, which functions as an electron carrier in cellular respiration; the two molecules differ only by the presence of an extra phosphate group in the NADP$^+$ molecule. The light reactions use solar energy to reduce NADP$^+$ to NADPH by adding a pair of electrons along with an H$^+$. The light reactions also generate ATP, using chemiosmosis to power the addition of a phosphate group to ADP, a process called **photophosphorylation**. Thus, light energy is initially converted to chemical energy in the form of two compounds: NADPH and ATP. NADPH, a source of electrons, acts as "reducing power" that can be passed along to an electron acceptor, reducing it, while ATP is the versatile energy currency of cells. Notice that the light reactions produce no sugar; that happens in the second stage of photosynthesis, the Calvin cycle.

The Calvin cycle is named for Melvin Calvin, who, along with his colleagues James Bassham and Andrew Benson, began to elucidate its steps in the late 1940s. The cycle begins by incorporating CO$_2$ from the air into organic molecules already present in the chloroplast. This initial incorporation of carbon into organic compounds is known as **carbon fixation**. The Calvin cycle then reduces the fixed carbon

▶ **Figure 7.6 An overview of photosynthesis: cooperation of the light reactions and the Calvin cycle.** In the chloroplast, the thylakoid membranes (green) are the sites of the light reactions, whereas the Calvin cycle occurs in the stroma (gray). The light reactions use solar energy to make ATP and NADPH, which supply chemical energy and reducing power, respectively, to the Calvin cycle. The Calvin cycle incorporates CO$_2$ into organic molecules, which are converted to sugar. (Recall that most simple sugars have formulas that are some multiple of CH$_2$O.)

**ANIMATION**

*BioFlix* Visit the Study Area in **MasteringBiology** for the BioFlix® 3-D Animation on Photosynthesis. BioFlix Tutorials can also be assigned in MasteringBiology.

to carbohydrate by the addition of electrons. The reducing power is provided by NADPH, which acquired its cargo of electrons in the light reactions. To convert $CO_2$ to carbohydrate, the Calvin cycle also requires chemical energy in the form of ATP, which is also generated by the light reactions. Thus, it is the Calvin cycle that makes sugar, but it can do so only with the help of the NADPH and ATP produced by the light reactions. The metabolic steps of the Calvin cycle are sometimes referred to as the dark reactions, or light-independent reactions, because none of the steps requires light *directly*. Nevertheless, the Calvin cycle in most plants occurs during daylight, for only then can the light reactions provide the NADPH and ATP that the Calvin cycle requires. In essence, the chloroplast uses light energy to make sugar by coordinating the two stages of photosynthesis.

As Figure 7.6 indicates, the thylakoids of the chloroplast are the sites of the light reactions, while the Calvin cycle occurs in the stroma. On the outside of the thylakoids, molecules of $NADP^+$ and ADP pick up electrons and phosphate, respectively, and NADPH and ATP are then released to the stroma, where they play crucial roles in the Calvin cycle. The two stages of photosynthesis are treated in this figure as metabolic modules that take in ingredients and crank out products. In the next two sections, we'll look more closely at how the two stages work, beginning with the light reactions.

**CONCEPT CHECK 7.1**

1. How do the reactant molecules of photosynthesis reach the chloroplasts in leaves?
2. How did the use of an oxygen isotope help elucidate the chemistry of photosynthesis?
3. **WHAT IF?** The Calvin cycle requires ATP and NADPH, products of the light reactions. If a classmate asserted that the light reactions don't depend on the Calvin cycle and, with continual light, could just keep on producing ATP and NADPH, how would you respond?

For suggested answers, see Appendix A.

**CONCEPT 7.2**

# The light reactions convert solar energy to the chemical energy of ATP and NADPH

Chloroplasts are chemical factories powered by the sun. Their thylakoids transform light energy into the chemical energy of ATP and NADPH, which will be used to synthesize glucose and other molecules that can be used as energy sources. To better understand the conversion of light to chemical energy, we need to know about some important properties of light.

## The Nature of Sunlight

Light is a form of energy known as electromagnetic energy, also called electromagnetic radiation. Electromagnetic energy travels in rhythmic waves analogous to those created by dropping a pebble into a pond. Electromagnetic waves, however, are disturbances of electric and magnetic fields rather than disturbances of a material medium such as water.

The distance between the crests of electromagnetic waves is called the **wavelength**. Wavelengths range from less than a nanometer (for gamma rays) to more than a kilometer (for radio waves). This entire range of radiation is known as the **electromagnetic spectrum (Figure 7.7)**. The segment most important to life is the narrow band from about 380 nm to 750 nm in wavelength. This radiation is known as **visible light** because it can be detected as various colors by the human eye.

The model of light as waves explains many of light's properties, but in certain respects light behaves as though it consists of discrete particles, called **photons**. Photons are not tangible objects, but they act like objects in that each of them has a fixed quantity of energy. The amount of energy is inversely related to the wavelength of the light: the shorter the wavelength, the greater the energy of each photon of that light. Thus, a photon of violet light packs nearly twice as much energy as a photon of red light (see Figure 7.7).

Although the sun radiates the full spectrum of electromagnetic energy, the atmosphere acts like a selective window, allowing visible light to pass through while screening out a substantial fraction of other radiation. The part of the spectrum we can see—visible light—is also the radiation that drives photosynthesis.

▲ **Figure 7.7 The electromagnetic spectrum.** White light is a mixture of all wavelengths of visible light. A prism can sort white light into its component colors by bending light of different wavelengths at different angles. (Droplets of water in the atmosphere can act as prisms, causing a rainbow to form.) Visible light drives photosynthesis.

## Photosynthetic Pigments: The Light Receptors

When light meets matter, it may be reflected, transmitted, or absorbed. Substances that absorb visible light are known as *pigments*. Different pigments absorb light of different wavelengths, and the wavelengths that are absorbed disappear. If a pigment is illuminated with white light, the color we see is the color most reflected or transmitted by the pigment. (If a pigment absorbs all wavelengths, it appears black.) We see green when we look at a leaf because chlorophyll absorbs violet-blue and red light while transmitting and reflecting green light **(Figure 7.8)**. The ability of a pigment to absorb various wavelengths of light can be measured with an instrument called a **spectrophotometer**. This machine directs beams of light of different wavelengths through a solution of the pigment and measures the fraction of the light transmitted at each wavelength. A graph plotting a pigment's light absorption versus wavelength is called an **absorption spectrum** **(Figure 7.9)**.

The absorption spectra of chloroplast pigments provide clues to the relative effectiveness of different wavelengths for driving photosynthesis, since light can perform work in chloroplasts only if it is absorbed. **Figure 7.10a** shows the absorption spectra of three types of pigments in chloroplasts: **chlorophyll *a***, the key light-capturing pigment that participates directly in the light reactions; the accessory pigment **chlorophyll *b***; and a separate group of accessory pigments called carotenoids. The spectrum of chlorophyll *a* suggests that violet-blue and red light work best for photosynthesis,

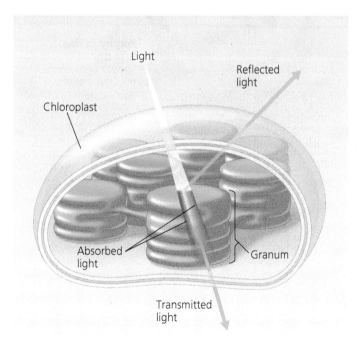

▲ **Figure 7.8 Why leaves are green: interaction of light with chloroplasts.** The chlorophyll molecules of chloroplasts absorb violet-blue and red light (the colors most effective in driving photosynthesis) and reflect or transmit green light. This is why leaves appear green.

▼ **Figure 7.9** **Research Method**

### Determining an Absorption Spectrum

**Application** An absorption spectrum is a visual representation of how well a particular pigment absorbs different wavelengths of visible light. Absorption spectra of various chloroplast pigments help scientists decipher the role of each pigment in a plant.

**Technique** A spectrophotometer measures the relative amounts of light of different wavelengths absorbed and transmitted by a pigment solution.

1. White light is separated into colors (wavelengths) by a prism.

2. One by one, the different colors of light are passed through the sample (chlorophyll in this example). Green light and blue light are shown here.

3. The transmitted light strikes a photoelectric tube, which converts the light energy to electricity.

4. The electric current is measured by a galvanometer. The meter indicates the fraction of light transmitted through the sample, from which we can determine the amount of light absorbed.

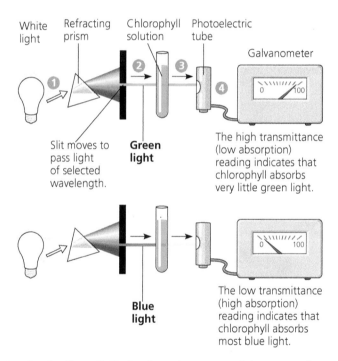

**Results** See Figure 7.10a for absorption spectra of three types of chloroplast pigments.

since they are absorbed, while green is the least effective color. This is confirmed by an **action spectrum** for photosynthesis **(Figure 7.10b)**, which profiles the relative effectiveness of different wavelengths of radiation in driving the process. An action spectrum is prepared by illuminating chloroplasts with light of different colors and then plotting wavelength against some measure of photosynthetic rate, such as $CO_2$ consumption or $O_2$ release. The action spectrum for photosynthesis was first demonstrated by Theodor W. Engelmann, a German

## Which wavelengths of light are most effective in driving photosynthesis?

**Experiment** Absorption and action spectra, along with a classic experiment by Theodor W. Engelmann, reveal which wavelengths of light are photosynthetically important.

**Results**

**(a) Absorption spectra.** The three curves show the wavelengths of light best absorbed by three types of chloroplast pigments.

**(b) Action spectrum.** This graph plots the rate of photosynthesis versus wavelength. The resulting action spectrum resembles the absorption spectrum for chlorophyll *a* but does not match exactly (see part a). This is partly due to the absorption of light by accessory pigments such as chlorophyll *b* and carotenoids.

**(c) Engelmann's experiment.** In 1883, Theodor W. Engelmann illuminated a filamentous alga with light that had been passed through a prism, exposing different segments of the alga to different wavelengths. He used aerobic bacteria, which concentrate near an oxygen source, to determine which segments of the alga were releasing the most $O_2$ and thus photosynthesizing most. Bacteria congregated in greatest numbers around the parts of the alga illuminated with violet-blue or red light.

**Conclusion** Light in the violet-blue and red portions of the spectrum is most effective in driving photosynthesis.

*Source:* T. W. Engelmann, *Bacterium photometricum*. Ein Beitrag zur vergleichenden Physiologie des Licht-und Farbensinnes, *Archiv. für Physiologie* 30:95–124 (1883).

(MB) An Experimental Inquiry Tutorial can be assigned in MasteringBiology.

**INTERPRET THE DATA** What wavelengths of light drive the highest rates of photosynthesis?

botanist, in 1883. Before equipment for measuring $O_2$ levels had even been invented, Engelmann performed a clever experiment in which he used bacteria to measure rates of photosynthesis in filamentous algae **(Figure 7.10c)**. His results are a striking match to the modern action spectrum shown in Figure 7.10b.

Notice by comparing Figures 7.10a and 7.10b that the action spectrum for photosynthesis is much broader than the absorption spectrum of chlorophyll *a*. The absorption spectrum of chlorophyll *a* alone underestimates the effectiveness of certain wavelengths in driving photosynthesis. This is partly because accessory pigments with different absorption spectra also present in chloroplasts—including chlorophyll *b* and carotenoids—broaden the spectrum of colors that can be used for photosynthesis. **Figure 7.11** shows the structure of chlorophyll *a* compared with that of chlorophyll *b*. A slight structural difference between them is enough to cause the two pigments to absorb at slightly different wavelengths in the red and blue parts of the spectrum (see Figure 7.10a). As a result, chlorophyll *a* appears blue green and chlorophyll *b* olive green under visible light.

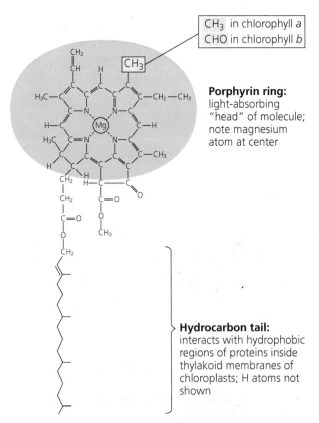

▲ **Figure 7.11 Structure of chlorophyll molecules in chloroplasts of plants.** Chlorophyll *a* and chlorophyll *b* differ only in one of the functional groups bonded to the porphyrin ring.

Other accessory pigments include **carotenoids**, hydrocarbons that are various shades of yellow and orange because they absorb violet and blue-green light (see Figure 7.10a). Carotenoids may broaden the spectrum of colors that can drive photosynthesis. However, a more important function of at least some carotenoids seems to be *photoprotection*: These compounds absorb and dissipate excessive light energy that would otherwise damage chlorophyll or interact with oxygen, forming reactive oxidative molecules that are dangerous to the cell. Interestingly, carotenoids similar to the photoprotective ones in chloroplasts have a photoprotective role in the human eye. (Remember being told to eat your carrots for improved night vision?) These and related molecules are, of course, found naturally in many vegetables and fruits. They are also often advertised in health food products as "phytochemicals" (from the Greek *phyton*, plant), some of which have antioxidant properties. Plants can synthesize all the antioxidants they require, but humans and other animals must obtain some of them from their diets.

## Excitation of Chlorophyll by Light

What exactly happens when chlorophyll and other pigments absorb light? The colors corresponding to the absorbed wavelengths disappear from the spectrum of the transmitted and reflected light, but energy cannot disappear. When a molecule absorbs a photon of light, one of the molecule's electrons is elevated to an orbital where it has more potential energy. When the electron is in its normal orbital, the pigment molecule is said to be in its ground state. Absorption of a photon boosts an electron to an orbital of higher energy, and the pigment molecule is then said to be in an excited state. The only photons absorbed are those whose energy is exactly equal to the energy difference between the ground state and an excited state, and this energy difference varies from one kind of molecule to another. Thus, a particular compound absorbs only photons corresponding to specific wavelengths, which is why each pigment has a unique absorption spectrum.

Once absorption of a photon raises an electron to an excited state, the electron cannot stay there long. The excited state, like all high-energy states, is unstable. Generally, when isolated pigment molecules absorb light, their excited electrons drop back down to the ground-state orbital in a billionth of a second, releasing their excess energy as heat. This conversion of light energy to heat is what makes the top of an automobile so hot on a sunny day. (White cars are coolest because their paint reflects all wavelengths of visible light.) In isolation, some pigments, including chlorophyll, emit light as well as heat after absorbing photons. As excited electrons fall back to the ground state, photons are given off, an afterglow called fluorescence. An illuminated solution of chlorophyll isolated from chloroplasts will fluoresce in the red part of the spectrum and also give off heat **(Figure 7.12)**. This is best seen by illuminating with ultraviolet light, which chlorophyll can also absorb (see Figures 7.7 and 7.10a). Viewed under visible light, the fluorescence would be harder to see against the green of the solution.

## A Photosystem: A Reaction-Center Complex Associated with Light-Harvesting Complexes

Chlorophyll molecules excited by the absorption of light energy produce very different results in an intact chloroplast than they do in isolation (see Figure 7.12). In their native environment of the thylakoid membrane, chlorophyll molecules are organized along with other small organic molecules and proteins into complexes called photosystems.

▶ **Figure 7.12 Excitation of isolated chlorophyll by light. (a)** Absorption of a photon causes a transition of the chlorophyll molecule from its ground state to its excited state. The photon boosts an electron to an orbital where it has more potential energy. If the illuminated molecule exists in isolation, its excited electron immediately drops back down to the ground-state orbital, and its excess energy is given off as heat and fluorescence (light). **(b)** A chlorophyll solution excited with ultraviolet light fluoresces with a red-orange glow.

**WHAT IF?** *If a leaf containing a similar concentration of chlorophyll as the solution was exposed to the same ultraviolet light, no fluorescence would be seen. Propose an explanation for the difference in fluorescence emission between the solution and the leaf.*

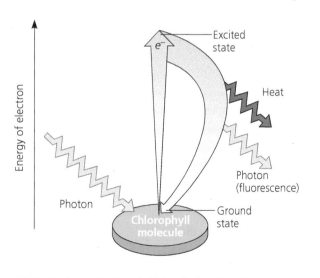

**(a) Excitation of isolated chlorophyll molecule**

**(b) Fluorescence**

A **photosystem** is composed of a **reaction-center complex** surrounded by several light-harvesting complexes **(Figure 7.13)**. The reaction-center complex is an organized association of proteins holding a special pair of chlorophyll *a* molecules. Each **light-harvesting complex** consists of various pigment molecules (which may include chlorophyll *a*, chlorophyll *b*, and multiple carotenoids) bound to proteins. The number and variety of pigment molecules enable a photosystem to harvest light over a larger surface area and a larger portion of the spectrum than could any single pigment molecule alone. Together, these light-harvesting complexes act as an antenna for the reaction-center complex. When a pigment molecule absorbs a photon, the energy is transferred from pigment molecule to pigment molecule within a light-harvesting complex, somewhat like a human "wave" at a sports arena, until it is passed into the reaction-center complex. The reaction-center complex also contains a molecule capable of accepting electrons and becoming reduced; this is called the **primary electron acceptor**. The pair of chlorophyll *a* molecules in the reaction-center complex are special because their molecular environment—their location and the other molecules with which they are associated—enables them to use the energy from light not only to boost one of their electrons to a higher energy level, but also to transfer it to a different molecule—the primary electron acceptor.

The solar-powered transfer of an electron from the reaction-center chlorophyll *a* pair to the primary electron acceptor is the first step of the light reactions. As soon as the chlorophyll electron is excited to a higher energy level, the primary electron acceptor captures it; this is a redox reaction. In the flask shown in Figure 7.12b, isolated chlorophyll fluoresces because there is no electron acceptor, so electrons of photoexcited chlorophyll drop right back to the ground state. In the structured environment of a chloroplast, however, an electron acceptor is readily available, and the potential energy represented by the excited electron is not dissipated as light and heat. Thus, each photosystem—a reaction-center complex surrounded by light-harvesting complexes—functions in the chloroplast as a unit. It converts light energy to chemical energy, which will ultimately be used for the synthesis of sugar.

The thylakoid membrane is populated by two types of photosystems that cooperate in the light reactions of photosynthesis. They are called **photosystem II (PS II)** and **photosystem I (PS I)**. (They were named in order of their discovery, but photosystem II functions first in the light reactions.) Each has a characteristic reaction-center complex—a particular kind of primary electron acceptor next to a special pair of chlorophyll *a* molecules associated with specific proteins. The reaction-center chlorophyll *a* of photosystem II is known as P680 because this pigment is best at absorbing

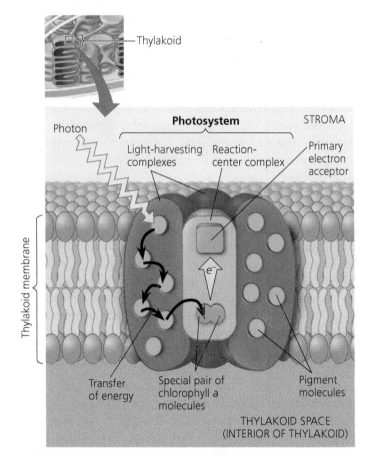

**(a) How a photosystem harvests light.** When a photon strikes a pigment molecule in a light-harvesting complex, the energy is passed from molecule to molecule until it reaches the reaction-center complex. Here, an excited electron from the special pair of chlorophyll *a* molecules is transferred to the primary electron acceptor.

**(b) Structure of a photosystem.** This computer model, based on X-ray crystallography, shows two photosystem complexes side by side, oriented opposite to each other. Chlorophyll molecules (small green ball-and-stick models) are interspersed with protein subunits (cylinders and ribbons). For simplicity, this photosystem will be shown as a single complex in the rest of the chapter.

▲ **Figure 7.13 The structure and function of a photosystem.**

light having a wavelength of 680 nm (in the red part of the spectrum). The chlorophyll *a* at the reaction-center complex of photosystem I is called P700 because it most effectively absorbs light of wavelength 700 nm (in the far-red part of the spectrum). These two pigments, P680 and P700, are nearly identical chlorophyll *a* molecules. However, their association with different proteins in the thylakoid membrane affects the electron distribution in the two pigments and accounts for the slight differences in their light-absorbing properties. Now let's see how the two photosystems work together in using light energy to generate ATP and NADPH, the two main products of the light reactions.

## Linear Electron Flow

Light drives the synthesis of ATP and NADPH by energizing the two photosystems embedded in the thylakoid membranes of chloroplasts. The key to this energy transformation is a flow of electrons through the photosystems and other molecular components built into the thylakoid membrane. This is called **linear electron flow**, and it occurs during the light reactions of photosynthesis, as shown in **Figure 7.14**. The numbered steps in the text correspond to the numbered steps in the figure.

① A photon of light strikes one of the pigment molecules in a light-harvesting complex of PS II, boosting one of its electrons to a higher energy level. As this electron falls back to its ground state, an electron in a nearby pigment molecule is simultaneously raised to an excited state. The process continues, with the energy being relayed to other pigment molecules until it reaches the P680 pair of chlorophyll *a* molecules in the PS II reaction-center complex. It excites an electron in this pair of chlorophylls to a higher energy state.

② This electron is transferred from the excited P680 to the primary electron acceptor. We can refer to the resulting form of P680, missing an electron, as P680+.

③ An enzyme catalyzes the splitting of a water molecule into two electrons, two hydrogen ions (H+), and an oxygen atom. The electrons are supplied one by one to the P680+ pair, each electron replacing one transferred to the primary electron acceptor. (P680+ is the strongest biological oxidizing agent known; its electron "hole" must be filled. This greatly facilitates the transfer of electrons from the split water molecule.) The H+ are released into the thylakoid

▼ Figure 7.14 **How linear electron flow during the light reactions generates ATP and NADPH.** The gold arrows trace the flow of light-driven electrons from water to NADPH. The black arrows trace the transfer of energy from pigment molecule to pigment molecule.

space. The oxygen atom immediately combines with an oxygen atom generated by the splitting of another water molecule, forming $O_2$.

④ Each photoexcited electron passes from the primary electron acceptor of PS II to PS I via an electron transport chain, the components of which are similar to those of the electron transport chain that functions in cellular respiration. The electron transport chain between PS II and PS I is made up of the electron carrier plastoquinone (Pq), a cytochrome complex, and a protein called plastocyanin (Pc).

⑤ The exergonic "fall" of electrons to a lower energy level provides energy for the synthesis of ATP. As electrons pass through the cytochrome complex, $H^+$ are pumped into the thylakoid space, contributing to the proton gradient that is subsequently used in chemiosmosis.

⑥ Meanwhile, light energy has been transferred via light-harvesting complex pigments to the PS I reaction-center complex, exciting an electron of the P700 pair of chlorophyll *a* molecules located there. The photoexcited electron is then transferred to PS I's primary electron acceptor, creating an electron "hole" in the P700—which we now can call $P700^+$. In other words, $P700^+$ can now act as an electron acceptor, accepting an electron that reaches the bottom of the electron transport chain from PS II.

⑦ Photoexcited electrons are passed in a series of redox reactions from the primary electron acceptor of PS I down a second electron transport chain through the protein ferredoxin (Fd). (This chain does not create a proton gradient and thus does not produce ATP.)

⑧ The enzyme $NADP^+$ reductase catalyzes the transfer of electrons from Fd to $NADP^+$. Two electrons are required for its reduction to NADPH. This molecule is at a higher energy level than water, so its electrons are more readily available for the reactions of the Calvin cycle. This process also removes an $H^+$ from the stroma.

▲ **Figure 7.15 A mechanical analogy for linear electron flow during the light reactions.**

The energy changes of electrons during their linear flow through the light reactions are shown in a mechanical analogy in **Figure 7.15**. Although the scheme shown in Figures 7.14 and 7.15 may seem complicated, do not lose track of the big picture: The light reactions use solar power to generate ATP and NADPH, which provide chemical energy and reducing power, respectively, to the carbohydrate-synthesizing reactions of the Calvin cycle.

## Cyclic Electron Flow

In certain cases, photoexcited electrons can take an alternative path called **cyclic electron flow**, which uses photosystem I but not photosystem II. You can see in **Figure 7.16** that cyclic flow is a short circuit: The electrons cycle back from ferredoxin (Fd) to the cytochrome complex and from there continue on to a P700 chlorophyll in the PS I reaction-center complex. There

◀ **Figure 7.16 Cyclic electron flow.** Photoexcited electrons from PS I are occasionally shunted back from ferredoxin (Fd) to chlorophyll via the cytochrome complex and plastocyanin (Pc). This electron shunt supplements the supply of ATP (via chemiosmosis) but produces no NADPH. The "shadow" of linear electron flow is included in the diagram for comparison with the cyclic route. The two Fd molecules in this diagram are actually one and the same—the final electron carrier in the electron transport chain of PS I—although it is depicted twice to clearly show its role in two parts of the process.

❓ *Look at Figure 7.15, and explain how you would alter it to show a mechanical analogy for cyclic electron flow.*

is no production of NADPH and no release of oxygen that results from this process. On the other hand, cyclic flow does generate ATP.

Rather than having both PSII and PSI, several of the currently existing groups of photosynthetic bacteria are known to have a single photosystem related to either PSII or PSI. For these species, which include the purple sulfur bacteria (see Figure 7.2e) and the green sulfur bacteria, cyclic electron flow is the one and only means of generating ATP during the process of photosynthesis. Evolutionary biologists hypothesize that these bacterial groups are descendants of ancestral bacteria in which photosynthesis first evolved, in a form similar to cyclic electron flow.

Cyclic electron flow can also occur in photosynthetic species that possess both photosystems; this includes some prokaryotes, such as the cyanobacteria shown in Figure 7.2d, as well as the eukaryotic photosynthetic species that have been tested thus far. Although the process is probably in part an "evolutionary leftover," research suggests it plays at least one beneficial role for these organisms. Mutant plants that are not able to carry out cyclic electron flow are capable of growing well in low light, but do not grow well where light is intense. This is evidence for the idea that cyclic electron flow may be photoprotective. Later you'll learn more about cyclic electron flow as it relates to a particular adaptation of photosynthesis ($C_4$ plants; see Concept 7.4).

Whether ATP synthesis is driven by linear or cyclic electron flow, the actual mechanism is the same. Before we move on to consider the Calvin cycle, let's review chemiosmosis, the process that uses membranes to couple redox reactions to ATP production.

## A Comparison of Chemiosmosis in Chloroplasts and Mitochondria

Chloroplasts and mitochondria generate ATP by the same basic mechanism: chemiosmosis. An electron transport chain pumps protons ($H^+$) across a membrane as electrons are passed through a series of carriers that are progressively more electronegative. Thus, electron transport chains transform redox energy to a proton-motive force, potential energy stored in the form of an $H^+$ gradient across a membrane. An ATP synthase complex in the same membrane couples the diffusion of hydrogen ions down their gradient to the phosphorylation of ADP, forming ATP.

Some of the electron carriers, including the iron-containing proteins called cytochromes, are very similar in chloroplasts and mitochondria. The ATP synthase complexes of the two organelles are also quite similar. But there are noteworthy differences between photophosphorylation in chloroplasts and oxidative phosphorylation in mitochondria. In chloroplasts, the high-energy electrons dropped down the transport chain come from water, while in mitochondria, they are extracted from organic molecules (which are thus oxidized). Chloroplasts do not need molecules from food to make ATP; their photosystems capture light energy and use it to drive the electrons from water to the top of the transport chain. In other words, mitochondria use chemiosmosis to transfer chemical energy from food molecules to ATP, whereas chloroplasts transform light energy into chemical energy in ATP.

Although the spatial organization of chemiosmosis differs slightly between chloroplasts and mitochondria, it is easy to see similarities in the two **(Figure 7.17)**. The inner membrane

▶ **Figure 7.17 Comparison of chemiosmosis in mitochondria and chloroplasts.** In both kinds of organelles, electron transport chains pump protons ($H^+$) across a membrane from a region of low $H^+$ concentration (light gray in this diagram) to one of high $H^+$ concentration (dark gray). The protons then diffuse back across the membrane through ATP synthase, driving the synthesis of ATP.

of the mitochondrion pumps protons from the mitochondrial matrix out to the intermembrane space, which then serves as a reservoir of hydrogen ions. The thylakoid membrane of the chloroplast pumps protons from the stroma into the thylakoid space (interior of the thylakoid), which functions as the $H^+$ reservoir. If you imagine the cristae of mitochondria pinching off from the inner membrane, this may help you see how the thylakoid space and the intermembrane space are comparable

spaces in the two organelles, while the mitochondrial matrix is analogous to the stroma of the chloroplast.

In the mitochondrion, protons diffuse down their concentration gradient from the intermembrane space through ATP synthase to the matrix, driving ATP synthesis. In the chloroplast, ATP is synthesized as the hydrogen ions diffuse from the thylakoid space back to the stroma through ATP synthase complexes, whose catalytic knobs are on the stroma side of the membrane **(Figure 7.18)**. Thus, ATP forms in the stroma, where it is used to help drive sugar synthesis during the Calvin cycle.

The proton ($H^+$) gradient, or pH gradient, across the thylakoid membrane is substantial. When chloroplasts

▲ **Figure 7.18 The light reactions and chemiosmosis: Current model of the organization of the thylakoid membrane.** The gold arrows track the linear electron flow outlined in Figure 7.14. At least three steps in the light reactions contribute to the $H^+$ gradient by increasing $H^+$ concentration in the thylakoid space: ❶ Water is split by photosystem II on the side of the membrane facing the thylakoid space; ❷ as plastoquinone (Pq) transfers electrons to the cytochrome complex, four protons are translocated across the membrane into the thylakoid space; and ❸ a hydrogen ion is removed from the stroma when it is taken up by $NADP^+$. Notice that in step 2, hydrogen ions are being pumped from the stroma into the thylakoid space, as in Figure 7.17. The diffusion of $H^+$ from the thylakoid space back to the stroma (along the $H^+$ concentration gradient) powers the ATP synthase. These light-driven reactions store chemical energy in NADPH and ATP, which shuttle the energy to the carbohydrate-producing Calvin cycle.

in an experimental setting are illuminated, the pH in the thylakoid space drops to about 5 (the $H^+$ concentration increases), and the pH in the stroma increases to about 8 (the $H^+$ concentration decreases). This gradient of three pH units corresponds to a thousandfold difference in $H^+$ concentration. If the lights are then turned off, the pH gradient is abolished, but it can quickly be restored by turning the lights back on. Experiments such as this provided strong evidence in support of the chemiosmotic model.

The currently-accepted model for the organization of the light-reaction "machinery" within the thylakoid membrane is based on several research studies. Each of the molecules and molecular complexes in the figure is present in numerous copies in each thylakoid. Notice that NADPH, like ATP, is produced on the side of the membrane facing the stroma, where the Calvin cycle reactions take place.

Let's summarize the light reactions. Electron flow pushes electrons from water, where they are at a low state of potential energy, ultimately to NADPH, where they are stored at a high state of potential energy. The light-driven electron flow also generates ATP. Thus, the equipment of the thylakoid membrane converts light energy to chemical energy stored in ATP and NADPH. (Oxygen is a by-product.) Let's now see how the Calvin cycle uses the products of the light reactions to synthesize sugar from $CO_2$.

## CONCEPT 7.3

# The Calvin cycle uses the chemical energy of ATP and NADPH to reduce $CO_2$ to sugar

The Calvin cycle is similar to the citric acid cycle in that a starting material is regenerated after some molecules enter the cycle and others exit the cycle. However, the citric acid cycle is catabolic, oxidizing acetyl CoA and using the energy to synthesize ATP. In contrast, the Calvin cycle is anabolic, building carbohydrates from smaller molecules and consuming energy. Carbon enters the Calvin cycle in the form of $CO_2$ and leaves in the form of sugar. The cycle spends ATP as an energy source and consumes NADPH as reducing power for adding high-energy electrons to make the sugar.

As we mentioned previously (in Concept 7.1), the carbohydrate produced directly from the Calvin cycle is actually not glucose, but a three-carbon sugar; the name of this sugar is **glyceraldehyde 3-phosphate (G3P)**. For the net synthesis of *one* molecule of G3P, the cycle must take place three times, fixing *three* molecules of $CO_2$—one per turn of the cycle. (Recall that the term carbon fixation refers to the initial incorporation of $CO_2$ into organic material.) As we trace the steps of the cycle, it's important to keep in mind that we are following three molecules of $CO_2$ through the reactions. **Figure 7.19** divides the Calvin cycle into three phases: carbon fixation, reduction, and regeneration of the $CO_2$ acceptor.

**Phase 1: Carbon fixation.** The Calvin cycle incorporates each $CO_2$ molecule, one at a time, by attaching it to a five-carbon sugar named ribulose bisphosphate (abbreviated RuBP). The enzyme that catalyzes this first step is RuBP carboxylase-oxygenase, or **rubisco**. (This is the most abundant protein in chloroplasts and is also thought to be the most abundant protein on Earth.) The product of the reaction is a six-carbon intermediate that is short-lived because it is so energetically unstable that it immediately splits in half, forming two molecules of 3-phosphoglycerate (for each $CO_2$ fixed).

**Phase 2: Reduction.** Each molecule of 3-phosphoglycerate receives an additional phosphate group from ATP, becoming 1,3-bisphosphoglycerate. Next, a pair of electrons donated from NADPH reduces 1,3-bisphosphoglycerate, which also loses a phosphate group in the process, becoming glyceraldehyde 3-phosphate (G3P). Specifically, the electrons from NADPH reduce a carboxyl group on 1,3-bisphosphoglycerate to the aldehyde group of G3P, which stores more potential energy. G3P is a sugar—the same three-carbon sugar formed in glycolysis by the splitting of glucose. Notice in Figure 7.19 that for every *three* molecules of $CO_2$ that enter the cycle, there are *six* molecules of G3P formed. But only one molecule of this three-carbon sugar can be counted as a net gain of carbohydrate because the rest are required to complete the cycle. The cycle began with 15 carbons' worth of carbohydrate in the form of three molecules of the five-carbon sugar RuBP. Now there are 18 carbons' worth of carbohydrate in the form of six molecules of G3P. One molecule exits the cycle to be used by the plant cell, but the other five molecules must be recycled to regenerate the three molecules of RuBP.

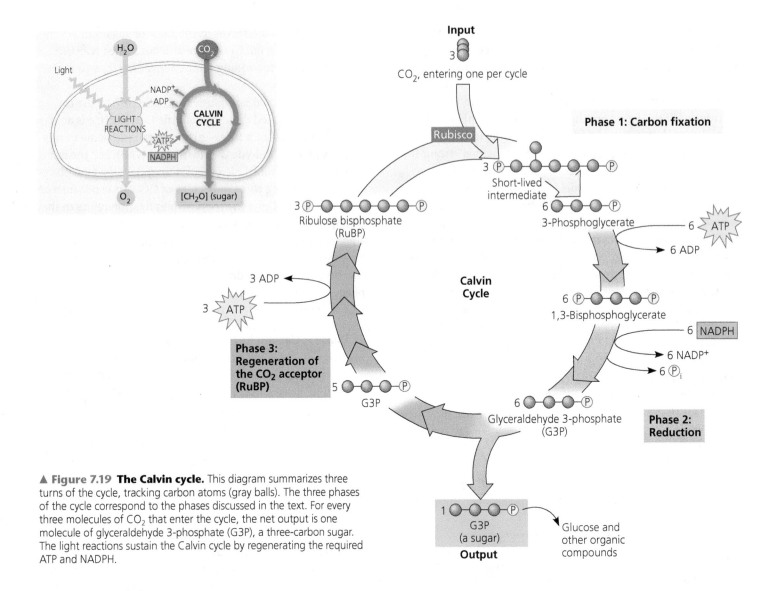

**▲ Figure 7.19 The Calvin cycle.** This diagram summarizes three turns of the cycle, tracking carbon atoms (gray balls). The three phases of the cycle correspond to the phases discussed in the text. For every three molecules of $CO_2$ that enter the cycle, the net output is one molecule of glyceraldehyde 3-phosphate (G3P), a three-carbon sugar. The light reactions sustain the Calvin cycle by regenerating the required ATP and NADPH.

**Phase 3: Regeneration of the $CO_2$ acceptor (RuBP).** In a complex series of reactions, the carbon skeletons of five molecules of G3P are rearranged by the last steps of the Calvin cycle into three molecules of RuBP. To accomplish this, the cycle spends three more molecules of ATP. The RuBP is now prepared to receive $CO_2$ again, and the cycle continues.

For the net synthesis of one G3P molecule, the Calvin cycle consumes a total of nine molecules of ATP and six molecules of NADPH. The light reactions regenerate the ATP and NADPH. The G3P spun off from the Calvin cycle becomes the starting material for metabolic pathways that synthesize other organic compounds, including glucose (formed by combining two molecules of G3P), the disaccharide sucrose, and other carbohydrates. Neither the light reactions nor the Calvin cycle alone can make sugar from $CO_2$. Photosynthesis is an emergent property of the intact chloroplast, which integrates the two stages of photosynthesis.

**CONCEPT CHECK 7.3**

1. To synthesize one glucose molecule, the Calvin cycle uses _____ molecules of $CO_2$, _____ molecules of ATP, and _____ molecules of NADPH.
2. How are the large numbers of ATP and NADPH molecules used during the Calvin cycle consistent with the high value of glucose as an energy source?
3. **WHAT IF?** Explain why a poison that inhibits an enzyme of the Calvin cycle will also inhibit the light reactions.
4. **DRAW IT** Redraw the cycle in Figure 7.19 using numerals to indicate the numbers of carbons instead of gray balls, multiplying at each step to ensure that you have accounted for all carbons. In what forms do the carbon atoms enter and leave the cycle?
5. **MAKE CONNECTIONS** Review Figure 7.19. Discuss the roles of intermediate and product played by glyceraldehyde 3-phosphate (G3P) in the two processes shown in these figures.

For suggested answers, see Appendix A.

## CONCEPT 7.4

# Alternative mechanisms of carbon fixation have evolved in hot, arid climates

**EVOLUTION** Ever since plants first moved onto land about 475 million years ago, they have been adapting to the problems of terrestrial life, particularly the problem of dehydration. We will consider anatomical adaptations that help plants conserve water, while in this chapter we are concerned with metabolic adaptations. The solutions often involve trade-offs. An important example is the compromise between photosynthesis and the prevention of excessive water loss from the plant. The $CO_2$ required for photosynthesis enters a leaf (and the resulting $O_2$ exits) via stomata, the pores on the leaf surface (see Figure 7.4). However, stomata are also the main avenues of transpiration, the evaporative loss of water from leaves. On a hot, dry day, most plants close their stomata, a response that conserves water. This response also reduces photosynthetic yield by limiting access to $CO_2$. With stomata even partially closed, $CO_2$ concentrations begin to decrease in the air spaces within the leaf, and the concentration of $O_2$ released from the light reactions begins to increase. These conditions within the leaf favor an apparently wasteful process called photorespiration.

*toxic 2phospho glycerate.*

### Photorespiration: An Evolutionary Relic?

In most plants, initial fixation of carbon occurs via rubisco, the Calvin cycle enzyme that adds $CO_2$ to ribulose bisphosphate. Such plants are called $C_3$ **plants** because the first organic product of carbon fixation is a three-carbon compound, 3-phosphoglycerate (see Figure 7.19). Rice, wheat, and soybeans are $C_3$ plants that are important in agriculture. When their stomata partially close on hot, dry days, $C_3$ plants produce less sugar because the declining level of $CO_2$ in the leaf starves the Calvin cycle. In addition, rubisco is capable of binding $O_2$ in place of $CO_2$. As $CO_2$ becomes scarce within the air spaces of the leaf and $O_2$ builds up, rubisco adds $O_2$ to the Calvin cycle instead of $CO_2$. The product splits, and a two-carbon compound leaves the chloroplast. Peroxisomes and mitochondria within the plant cell rearrange and split this compound, releasing $CO_2$. The process is called **photorespiration** because it occurs in the light (*photo*) and consumes $O_2$ while producing $CO_2$ (*respiration*). However, unlike normal cellular respiration, photorespiration uses ATP rather than generating it. And unlike photosynthesis, photorespiration produces no sugar. In fact, photorespiration *decreases* photosynthetic output by siphoning organic material from the Calvin cycle and releasing $CO_2$ that would

otherwise be fixed. This $CO_2$ can eventually be fixed if it is still in the leaf once the $CO_2$ concentration is high enough. In the meantime, though, the process is energetically costly, much like a hamster running on its wheel.

How can we explain the existence of a metabolic process that seems to be counterproductive for the plant? According to one hypothesis, photorespiration is evolutionary baggage—a metabolic relic from a much earlier time when the atmosphere had less $O_2$ and more $CO_2$ than it does today. In the ancient atmosphere that prevailed when rubisco first evolved, the inability of the enzyme's active site to exclude $O_2$ would have made little difference. The hypothesis suggests that modern rubisco retains some of its chance affinity for $O_2$, which is now so concentrated in the atmosphere that a certain amount of photorespiration is inevitable.

We now know that, at least in some cases, photorespiration plays a protective role in plants. Plants that are impaired in their ability to carry out photorespiration (due to defective genes) are more susceptible to damage induced by excess light. Researchers consider this clear evidence that photorespiration acts to neutralize the otherwise damaging products of the light reactions, which build up when a low $CO_2$ concentration limits the progress of the Calvin cycle. Whether there are other benefits of photorespiration is still unknown. In many types of plants—including a significant number of crop plants—photorespiration drains away as much as 50% of the carbon fixed by the Calvin cycle. As heterotrophs that depend on carbon fixation in chloroplasts for our food, we naturally view photorespiration as wasteful. Indeed, if photorespiration could be reduced in certain plant species without otherwise affecting photosynthetic productivity, crop yields and food supplies might increase.

In some plant species, alternate modes of carbon fixation have evolved that minimize photorespiration and optimize the Calvin cycle—even in hot, arid climates. The two most important of these photosynthetic adaptations are $C_4$ photosynthesis and crassulacean acid metabolism (CAM).

### $C_4$ Plants

The $C_4$ **plants** are so named because they preface the Calvin cycle with an alternate mode of carbon fixation that forms a four-carbon compound as its first product. The $C_4$ pathway is believed to have evolved independently at least 45 separate times and is used by several thousand species in at least 19 plant families. Among the $C_4$ plants important to agriculture are sugarcane and corn, members of the grass family.

The anatomy of a $C_4$ leaf is correlated with the mechanism of $C_4$ photosynthesis. In $C_4$ plants, there are two distinct types of photosynthetic cells: bundle-sheath cells and mesophyll cells. **Bundle-sheath cells** are arranged into tightly packed

**C₄ leaf anatomy**

**The C₄ pathway**

❶ In mesophyll cells, the enzyme PEP carboxylase adds carbon dioxide to PEP.

❷ A four-carbon compound (such as malate) conveys the atoms of the $CO_2$ into a bundle-sheath cell via plasmodesmata.

❸ In bundle-sheath cells, $CO_2$ is released and enters the Calvin cycle.

▲ **Figure 7.20 C₄ leaf anatomy and the C₄ pathway.** The structure and biochemical functions of the leaves of C₄ plants are an evolutionary adaptation to hot, dry climates. This adaptation maintains a $CO_2$ concentration in the bundle sheath that favors photosynthesis over photorespiration.

sheaths around the veins of the leaf (**Figure 7.20**). Between the bundle sheath and the leaf surface are the more loosely arranged mesophyll cells, which, in C₄ leaves, are closely associated and never more than two to three cells away from the bundle-sheath cells. The Calvin cycle is confined to the chloroplasts of the bundle-sheath cells. However, the Calvin cycle is preceded by incorporation of $CO_2$ into organic compounds in the mesophyll cells. See the numbered steps in Figure 7.20, which are also described here:

❶ The first step is carried out by an enzyme present only in mesophyll cells called **PEP carboxylase**. This enzyme adds $CO_2$ to phosphoenolpyruvate (PEP), forming the four-carbon product oxaloacetate. PEP carboxylase has a much higher affinity for $CO_2$ than does rubisco and no affinity for $O_2$. Therefore, PEP carboxylase can fix carbon efficiently when rubisco cannot—that is, when it is hot and dry and stomata are partially closed, causing $CO_2$ concentration in the leaf to be lower and $O_2$ concentration to be relatively higher.

❷ After the C₄ plant fixes carbon from $CO_2$, the mesophyll cells export their four-carbon products (malate in the example shown in Figure 7.20) to bundle-sheath cells through plasmodesmata.

❸ Within the bundle-sheath cells, the four-carbon compounds release $CO_2$, which is reassimilated into organic material by rubisco and the Calvin cycle. The same reaction regenerates pyruvate, which is transported to mesophyll cells. There, ATP is used to convert pyruvate to PEP, allowing the reaction cycle to continue. This ATP can be thought of, in a sense, as the "price" of concentrating $CO_2$ in the

bundle-sheath cells. To generate this extra ATP, bundle-sheath cells carry out cyclic electron flow, the process described earlier in this chapter (see Figure 7.16). In fact, these cells contain PS I but no PS II, so cyclic electron flow is their only photosynthetic mode of generating ATP.

In effect, the mesophyll cells of a C₄ plant pump $CO_2$ into the bundle sheath, keeping the $CO_2$ concentration in the bundle-sheath cells high enough for rubisco to bind $CO_2$ rather than $O_2$. The cyclic series of reactions involving PEP carboxylase and the regeneration of PEP can be thought of as a $CO_2$-concentrating pump that is powered by ATP. In this way, C₄ photosynthesis spends ATP energy to minimize photorespiration and enhance sugar production. This adaptation is especially advantageous in hot regions with intense sunlight, where stomata partially close during the day, and it is in such environments that C₄ plants evolved and thrive today.

The concentration of $CO_2$ in the atmosphere has drastically increased since the Industrial Revolution began in the 1800s, and it continues to rise today due to human activities such as the burning of fossil fuels. The resulting global climate change, including an increase in average temperatures around the planet, may have far-reaching effects on plant species. Scientists are concerned that increasing $CO_2$ concentration and temperature may affect C₃ and C₄ plants differently, thus changing the relative abundance of these species in a given plant community.

Which type of plant would stand to gain more from increasing $CO_2$ levels? Recall that in C₃ plants, the binding of $O_2$

rather than $CO_2$ by rubisco leads to photorespiration, lowering the efficiency of photosynthesis. $C_4$ plants overcome this problem by concentrating $CO_2$ in the bundle-sheath cells at the cost of ATP. Rising $CO_2$ levels should benefit $C_3$ plants by lowering the amount of photorespiration that occurs. At the same time, rising temperatures have the opposite effect, increasing photorespiration. (Other factors such as water availability may also come into play.) In contrast, many $C_4$ plants could be largely unaffected by increasing $CO_2$ levels or temperature. Researchers have investigated aspects of this question in several studies; you can work with data from one such experiment in the Scientific Skills Exercise. In different regions, the particular combination of $CO_2$ concentration and

temperature is likely to alter the balance of $C_3$ and $C_4$ plants in varying ways. The effects of such a widespread and variable change in community structure are unpredictable and thus a cause of legitimate concern.

## CAM Plants

A second photosynthetic adaptation to arid conditions has evolved in many succulent (water-storing) plants, numerous cacti, pineapples, and representatives of several other plant families. These plants open their stomata during the night and close them during the day, just the reverse of how other plants behave. Closing stomata during the day helps desert plants

### Scientific Skills Exercise

## Making Scatter Plots with Regression Lines

**Does Atmospheric CO2 Concentration Affect the Productivity of Agricultural Crops?** Atmospheric concentration of $CO_2$ has been rising globally, and scientists wondered whether this would affect $C_3$ and $C_4$ plants differently. In this exercise, you will make a scatter plot to examine the relationship between $CO_2$ concentration and growth of corn (maize), a $C_4$ crop plant, and velvetleaf, a $C_3$ weed found in cornfields.

**How the Experiment Was Done** Researchers grew corn and velvetleaf plants under controlled conditions for 45 days, where all plants received the same amounts of water and light. The plants were divided into three groups, and each was exposed to a different concentration of $CO_2$ in the air: 350, 600, or 1,000 ppm (parts per million).

**Data from the Experiment** The table shows the dry mass (in grams) of corn and velvetleaf plants grown at the three concentrations of $CO_2$. The dry mass values are averages of the leaves, stems, and roots of eight plants.

▶ Corn plant surrounded by invasive velvetleaf plants

|  | 350 ppm $CO_2$ | 600 ppm $CO_2$ | 1,000 ppm $CO_2$ |
|---|---|---|---|
| Average dry mass of one corn plant (g) | 91 | 89 | 80 |
| Average dry mass of one velvetleaf plant (g) | 35 | 48 | 54 |

**Interpret the Data**

1. To explore the relationship between the two variables, it is useful to graph the data in a scatter plot, and then draw a regression line. (a) First, place labels for the dependent and independent variables on the appropriate axes. Explain your choices. (b) Now plot the data points for corn and velvetleaf using different symbols for each set of data, and add a key for the two symbols. (For additional information about graphs, see the Scientific Skills Review in Appendix F and in the Study Area in MasteringBiology.)

2. Draw a "best-fit" line for each set of points. A best-fit line does not necessarily pass through all or even most points. Instead, it is a straight line that passes as close as possible to all data points from that set. Draw a best-fit line for each set of data. Because placement of the line is a matter of judgment, two individuals may draw two slightly different lines for a given set of points. The line that actually fits best, a regression line, can be identified by squaring the distances of all points to any candidate line, then selecting the line that minimizes the sum of the squares. (See the graph in the Scientific Skills Exercise for an example of a linear regression line.) Excel or

other software programs, including those on a graphing calculator, can plot a regression line once data points are entered. Using either Excel or a graphing calculator, enter the data points for each data set and have the program draw the two regression lines. Compare them to the lines you drew.

3. Describe the trends shown by the regression lines in your scatter plot. (a) Compare the relationship between increasing concentration of $CO_2$ and the dry mass of corn to that of velvetleaf. (b) Considering that velvetleaf is a weed invasive to cornfields, predict how increased $CO_2$ concentration may affect interactions between the two species.

4. Based on the data in the scatter plot, estimate the percentage change in dry mass of corn and velvetleaf plants if atmospheric $CO_2$ concentration increased from 390 ppm (current levels) to 800 ppm. (a) What is the estimated dry mass of corn and velvetleaf plants at 390 ppm? 800 ppm? (b) To calculate the percentage change in mass for each plant, subtract the mass at 390 ppm from the mass at 800 ppm (change in mass), divide by the mass at 390 ppm (initial mass), and multiply by 100. What is the estimated percentage change in dry mass for corn? For velvetleaf? (c) Do these results support the conclusion from other experiments that $C_3$ plants grow better than $C_4$ plants under increased $CO_2$ concentration? Why or why not?

(MB) A version of this Scientific Skills Exercise can be assigned in MasteringBiology.

**Data from** D. T. Patterson and E. P. Flint, Potential effects of global atmospheric $CO_2$ enrichment on the growth and competitiveness of $C_3$ and $C_4$ weed and crop plants, *Weed Science* 28(1):71–75 (1980).

conserve water, but it also prevents $CO_2$ from entering the leaves. During the night, when their stomata are open, these plants take up $CO_2$ and incorporate it into a variety of organic acids. This mode of carbon fixation is called **crassulacean acid metabolism**, or **CAM**, after the plant family Crassulaceae, the succulents in which the process was first discovered. The mesophyll cells of **CAM plants** store the organic acids they make during the night in their vacuoles until morning, when the stomata close. During the day, when the light reactions can supply ATP and NADPH for the Calvin cycle, $CO_2$ is released from the organic acids made the night before to become incorporated into sugar in the chloroplasts.

Notice in **Figure 7.21** that the CAM pathway is similar to the $C_4$ pathway in that carbon dioxide is first incorporated into organic intermediates before it enters the Calvin cycle. The difference is that in $C_4$ plants, the initial steps of carbon fixation are separated structurally from the Calvin cycle, whereas in CAM plants, the two steps occur at separate times but within the same cell. (Keep in mind that CAM, $C_4$, and $C_3$ plants all eventually use the Calvin cycle to make sugar from carbon dioxide.)

**CONCEPT CHECK 7.4**

1. Describe how photorespiration lowers photosynthetic output for plants.
2. The presence of only PS I, not PS II, in the bundle-sheath cells of $C_4$ plants has an effect on $O_2$ concentration. What is that effect, and how might that benefit the plant?
3. **MAKE CONNECTIONS** Ocean acidification and changes in the distribution of $C_3$ and $C_4$ plants may seem to be two very different problems, but what do they have in common? Explain.
4. **WHAT IF?** How would you expect the relative abundance of $C_3$ versus $C_4$ and CAM species to change in a geographic region whose climate becomes much hotter and drier, with no change in $CO_2$ concentration?

For suggested answers, see Appendix A.

## The Importance of Photosynthesis: *A Review*

In this chapter, we have followed photosynthesis from photons to food. The light reactions capture solar energy and use it to make ATP and transfer electrons from water to $NADP^+$, forming NADPH. The Calvin cycle uses the ATP and NADPH to produce sugar from carbon dioxide. The energy that enters the chloroplasts as sunlight becomes stored as chemical energy in organic compounds. The entire process is reviewed visually in **Figure 7.22**, where photosynthesis is also put in its natural context.

As for the fates of photosynthetic products, enzymes in the chloroplast and cytosol convert the G3P made in the Calvin cycle to many other organic compounds. In fact, the sugar made in the chloroplasts supplies the entire plant with chemical energy and carbon skeletons for the synthesis of all the major organic molecules of plant cells. About 50% of the organic material made by photosynthesis is consumed as fuel for cellular respiration in plant cell mitochondria.

Technically, green cells are the only autotrophic parts of the plant. The rest of the plant depends on organic molecules exported from leaves via veins (see Figure 7.22, top). In most plants, carbohydrate is transported out of the leaves to the rest of the plant in the form of sucrose, a disaccharide. After arriving at nonphotosynthetic cells, the sucrose provides raw material for cellular respiration and a multitude of anabolic pathways that synthesize proteins, lipids, and other products. A considerable amount of sugar in the form of glucose is linked together to make the polysaccharide cellulose, especially in plant cells that are still growing and maturing. Cellulose, the main ingredient of cell walls, is the most abundant organic molecule in the plant—and probably on the surface of the planet.

Sugarcane

Pineapple

$C_4$

CAM

**(a) Spatial separation of steps.** In $C_4$ plants, carbon fixation and the Calvin cycle occur in different types of cells.

**(b) Temporal separation of steps.** In CAM plants, carbon fixation and the Calvin cycle occur in the same cell at different times.

▲ **Figure 7.21 $C_4$ and CAM photosynthesis compared.** Both adaptations are characterized by ❶ preliminary incorporation of $CO_2$ into organic acids, followed by ❷ transfer of $CO_2$ to the Calvin cycle. The $C_4$ and CAM pathways are two evolutionary solutions to the problem of maintaining photosynthesis with stomata partially or completely closed on hot, dry days.

Most plants and other photosynthesizers make more organic material each day than they need to use as respiratory fuel and precursors for biosynthesis. They stockpile the extra sugar by synthesizing starch, storing some in the chloroplasts themselves and some in storage cells of roots, tubers, seeds, and fruits. In accounting for the consumption of the food molecules produced by photosynthesis, let's not forget that most plants lose leaves, roots, stems, fruits, and sometimes their entire bodies to heterotrophs, including humans.

On a global scale, photosynthesis is the process responsible for the presence of oxygen in our atmosphere. Furthermore, while each chloroplast is minuscule, their collective productivity in terms of food production is prodigious: Photosynthesis makes an estimated 150 billion metric tons

of carbohydrate per year (a metric ton is 1,000 kg, about 1.1 tons). That's organic matter equivalent in mass to a stack of about 60 trillion biology textbooks—17 stacks of books reaching from Earth to the sun! No chemical process is more important than photosynthesis to the welfare of life on Earth.

In Chapters 4 through 7, you have learned about many activities of cells. **Figure 7.23** integrates these processes in the context of a working plant cell. As you study the figure, reflect on how each process fits into the big picture: As the most basic unit of living organisms, a cell performs all functions characteristic of life.

▼ **Figure 7.22 A review of photosynthesis.** This diagram shows the main reactants and products of photosynthesis as they move through the tissues of a tree (left) and a chloroplast (right).

**MAKE CONNECTIONS** *Can plants use the sugar they produce during photosynthesis to directly power the work of the cell? Explain.*

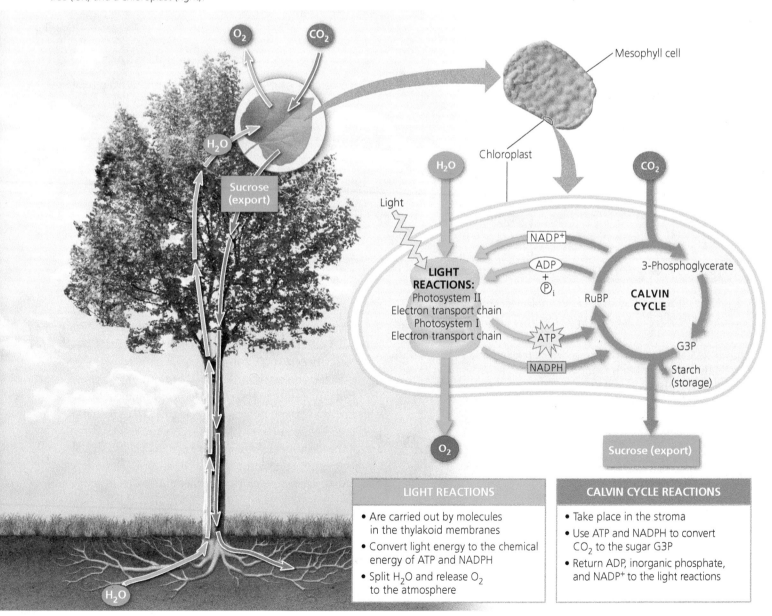

| LIGHT REACTIONS | CALVIN CYCLE REACTIONS |
|---|---|
| • Are carried out by molecules in the thylakoid membranes | • Take place in the stroma |
| • Convert light energy to the chemical energy of ATP and NADPH | • Use ATP and NADPH to convert $CO_2$ to the sugar G3P |
| • Split $H_2O$ and release $O_2$ to the atmosphere | • Return ADP, inorganic phosphate, and $NADP^+$ to the light reactions |

# MAKE CONNECTIONS

## The Working Cell

This figure illustrates how a generalized plant cell functions, integrating the cellular activities you learned about in Chapter 7.

Nucleus

DNA

mRNA

Nuclear pore

Protein

Ribosome    mRNA

Protein in vesicle

Rough endoplasmic reticulum (ER)

Golgi apparatus

Vesicle forming

Protein

Plasma membrane

Cell wall

### Flow of Genetic Information in the Cell: DNA → RNA → Protein

1. In the nucleus, DNA serves as a template for the synthesis of mRNA, which moves to the cytoplasm.

2. mRNA attaches to a ribosome, which remains free in the cytosol or binds to the rough ER. Proteins are synthesized.

3. Proteins and membrane produced by the rough ER flow in vesicles to the Golgi apparatus, where they are processed.

4. Transport vesicles carrying proteins pinch off from the Golgi apparatus.

5. Some vesicles merge with the plasma membrane, releasing proteins by exocytosis.

6. Proteins synthesized on free ribosomes stay in the cell and perform specific functions; examples include the enzymes that catalyze the reactions of cellular respiration and photosynthesis. *See Figure 7.19.*

## Energy Transformations in the Cell: Photosynthesis and Cellular Respiration (Chapter 7)

**7** In chloroplasts, the process of photosynthesis uses the energy of light to convert $CO_2$ and $H_2O$ to organic molecules, with $O_2$ as a by-product. *See Figure 7.22.*

**8** In mitochondria, organic molecules are broken down by cellular respiration, capturing energy in molecules of ATP, which are used to power the work of the cell, such as protein synthesis and active transport. $CO_2$ and $H_2O$ are by-products.

Vacuole

## Movement Across Cell Membranes (Chapter 4)

**9** Water diffuses into and out of the cell directly through the plasma membrane and by facilitated diffusion through aquaporins.

**10** By passive transport, the $CO_2$ used in photosynthesis diffuses into the cell and the $O_2$ formed as a by-product of photosynthesis diffuses out of the cell. Both solutes move down their concentration gradients. *See Figure 7.22.*

**11** In active transport, energy (usually supplied by ATP) is used to transport a solute against its concentration gradient.

Exocytosis (shown in step 5) and endocytosis move larger materials out of and into the cell.

**7** Photosynthesis in chloroplast

$CO_2$

$H_2O$

Organic molecules

$O_2$

**8** Cellular respiration in mitochondrion

ATP

ATP

Transport pump

ATP

ATP

**11**

**10**

**9**

$O_2$

$CO_2$

$H_2O$

**MAKE CONNECTIONS** The first enzyme that functions in glycolysis is hexokinase. In this plant cell, describe the entire process by which this enzyme is produced and where it functions, specifying the locations for each step.

**ANIMATION** *BioFlix* Visit the Study Area in **MasteringBiology** for BioFlix® 3-D Animations in Chapters 4 and 7. BioFlix Tutorials can also be assigned in MasteringBiology.

# 7 Chapter Review

## SUMMARY OF KEY CONCEPTS

CONCEPT 7.1

### Photosynthesis converts light energy to the chemical energy of food (pp. 131–134)

- In **autotrophic** eukaryotes, photosynthesis occurs in chloroplasts, organelles containing **thylakoids**. Stacks of thylakoids form grana. **Photosynthesis** is summarized as

$$6\ CO_2 + 12\ H_2O + \text{Light energy} \rightarrow C_6H_{12}O_6 + 6\ O_2 + 6\ H_2O.$$

Chloroplasts split water into hydrogen and oxygen, incorporating the electrons of hydrogen into sugar molecules. Photosynthesis is a redox process: $H_2O$ is oxidized, and $CO_2$ is reduced. The **light reactions** in the thylakoid membranes split water, releasing $O_2$, producing ATP, and forming **NADPH**. The **Calvin cycle** in the **stroma** forms sugar from $CO_2$, using ATP for energy and NADPH for reducing power.

> **?** *Compare the roles of $CO_2$ and $H_2O$ in respiration and photosynthesis.*

CONCEPT 7.2

### The light reactions convert solar energy to the chemical energy of ATP and NADPH (pp. 134–143)

- Light is a form of electromagnetic energy. The colors we see as **visible light** include those **wavelengths** that drive photosynthesis. A pigment absorbs light of specific wavelengths; **chlorophyll *a*** is the main photosynthetic pigment in plants. Other accessory pigments absorb different wavelengths of light and pass the energy on to chlorophyll *a*.
- A pigment goes from a ground state to an excited state when a **photon** of light boosts one of the pigment's electrons to a higher-energy orbital. This excited state is unstable. Electrons from isolated pigments tend to fall back to the ground state, giving off heat and/or light.
- A **photosystem** is composed of a **reaction-center complex** surrounded by **light-harvesting complexes** that funnel the energy of photons to the reaction-center complex. When a special pair of reaction-center chlorophyll *a* molecules absorbs energy, one of its electrons is boosted to a higher energy level and transferred to the **primary electron acceptor**. Photosystem II contains P680 chlorophyll *a* molecules in the reaction-center complex; **photosystem I** contains P700 molecules.

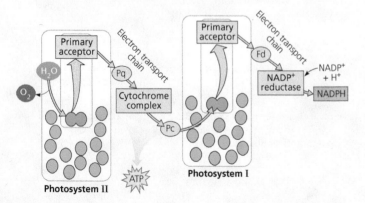

- **Linear electron flow** during the light reactions uses both photosystems and produces NADPH, ATP, and oxygen:
- **Cyclic electron flow** employs only one photosystem, producing ATP but no NADPH or $O_2$.
- During chemiosmosis in both mitochondria and chloroplasts, electron transport chains generate an $H^+$ gradient across a membrane. ATP synthase uses this proton-motive force to make ATP.

> **?** *The absorption spectrum of chlorophyll a differs from the action spectrum of photosynthesis. Explain this observation.*

CONCEPT 7.3

### The Calvin cycle uses the chemical energy of ATP and NADPH to reduce $CO_2$ to sugar (pp. 143–144)

- The Calvin cycle occurs in the stroma, using electrons from NADPH and energy from ATP. One molecule of **G3P** exits the cycle per three $CO_2$ molecules fixed and is converted to glucose and other organic molecules.

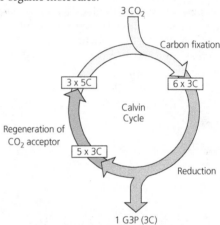

> **DRAW IT** *On the diagram above, draw where ATP and NADPH are used and where rubisco functions. Describe these steps.*

CONCEPT 7.4

### Alternative mechanisms of carbon fixation have evolved in hot, arid climates (pp. 145–151)

- On dry, hot days, **$C_3$ plants** close their stomata, conserving water. Oxygen from the light reactions builds up. In **photorespiration**, $O_2$ substitutes for $CO_2$ in the active site of rubisco. This process consumes organic fuel and releases $CO_2$ without producing ATP or carbohydrate. Photorespiration may be an evolutionary relic, and it may play a photoprotective role.
- **$C_4$ plants** minimize the cost of photorespiration by incorporating $CO_2$ into four-carbon compounds in mesophyll cells. These compounds are exported to **bundle-sheath cells**, where they release carbon dioxide for use in the Calvin cycle.
- **CAM plants** open their stomata at night, incorporating $CO_2$ into organic acids, which are stored in mesophyll cells. During the day, the stomata close, and the $CO_2$ is released from the organic acids for use in the Calvin cycle.
- Organic compounds produced by photosynthesis provide the energy and building material for Earth's ecosystems.

> **?** *Why are $C_4$ and CAM photosynthesis more energetically expensive than $C_3$ photosynthesis? What climate conditions would favor $C_4$ and CAM plants?*

# TEST YOUR UNDERSTANDING

## Level 1: Knowledge/Comprehension

**1.** The light reactions of photosynthesis supply the Calvin cycle with
- **a.** light energy.
- **b.** $CO_2$ and ATP.
- **c.** $H_2O$ and NADPH.
- **d.** ATP and NADPH.

**2.** Which of the following sequences correctly represents the flow of electrons during photosynthesis?
- **a.** NADPH $\rightarrow O_2 \rightarrow CO_2$
- **b.** $H_2O \rightarrow$ NADPH $\rightarrow$ Calvin cycle
- **c.** $H_2O \rightarrow$ photosystem I $\rightarrow$ photosystem II
- **d.** NADPH $\rightarrow$ electron transport chain $\rightarrow O_2$

**3.** How is photosynthesis similar in $C_4$ plants and CAM plants?
- **a.** In both cases, only photosystem I is used.
- **b.** Both types of plants make sugar without the Calvin cycle.
- **c.** In both cases, rubisco is not used to fix carbon initially.
- **d.** Both types of plants make most of their sugar in the dark.

**4.** Which of the following statements is a correct distinction between autotrophs and heterotrophs?
- **a.** Autotrophs, but not heterotrophs, can nourish themselves beginning with $CO_2$ and other nutrients that are inorganic.
- **b.** Only heterotrophs require chemical compounds from the environment.
- **c.** Cellular respiration is unique to heterotrophs.
- **d.** Only heterotrophs have mitochondria.

**5.** Which of the following does *not* occur during the Calvin cycle?
- **a.** carbon fixation
- **b.** oxidation of NADPH
- **c.** release of oxygen
- **d.** regeneration of the $CO_2$ acceptor

## Level 2: Application/Analysis

**6.** In mechanism, photophosphorylation is most similar to
- **a.** substrate-level phosphorylation in glycolysis.
- **b.** oxidative phosphorylation in cellular respiration.
- **c.** carbon fixation.
- **d.** reduction of $NADP^+$.

**7.** Which process is most directly driven by light energy?
- **a.** creation of a pH gradient by pumping protons across the thylakoid membrane
- **b.** reduction of $NADP^+$ molecules
- **c.** removal of electrons from chlorophyll molecules
- **d.** ATP synthesis

## Level 3: Synthesis/Evaluation

**8. SCIENCE, TECHNOLOGY, AND SOCIETY**
Scientific evidence indicates that the $CO_2$ added to the air by the burning of wood and fossil fuels is contributing to global warming, a rise in global temperature. Tropical rain forests are estimated to be responsible for approximately 20% of global photosynthesis, yet the consumption of large amounts of $CO_2$ by living trees is thought to make little or no *net* contribution to reduction of global warming. Why might this be? (*Hint*: What processes in both living and dead trees produce $CO_2$?)

**9. EVOLUTION CONNECTION**
Photorespiration can decrease soybeans' photosynthetic output by about 50%. Would you expect this figure to be higher or lower in wild relatives of soybeans? Why?

**10. SCIENTIFIC INQUIRY**
**MAKE CONNECTIONS** The following diagram represents an experiment with isolated thylakoids. The thylakoids were first made acidic by soaking them in a solution at pH 4. After the thylakoid space reached pH 4, the thylakoids were transferred to a basic solution at pH 8. The thylakoids then made ATP in the dark.

Draw an enlargement of part of the thylakoid membrane in the beaker with the solution at pH 8. Draw ATP synthase. Label the areas of high $H^+$ concentration and low $H^+$ concentration. Show the direction protons flow through the enzyme, and show the reaction where ATP is synthesized. Would ATP end up in the thylakoid or outside of it? Explain why the thylakoids in the experiment were able to make ATP in the dark.

**11. WRITE ABOUT A THEME: ENERGY AND MATTER**
Life is solar powered. Almost all the producers of the biosphere depend on energy from the sun to produce the organic molecules that supply the energy and carbon skeletons needed for life. In a short essay (100–150 words), describe how the process of photosynthesis in the chloroplasts of plants transforms the energy of sunlight into the chemical energy of sugar molecules.

**12.**  **SYNTHESIZE YOUR KNOWLEDGE**

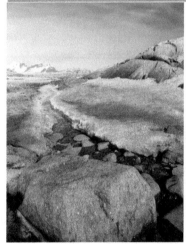

The photo shows "watermelon snow" in Antarctica, caused by a species of photosynthetic green algae that thrives in subzero temperatures (*Chlamydomonas nivalis*). These algae are also found in high altitude year-round snowfields. In both locations, UV light levels tend to be high. Based on what you learned in this chapter, propose an explanation for why this photosynthetic alga appears reddish-pink.

*For selected answers, see Appendix A.*

## MasteringBiology®

**Students** Go to **MasteringBiology** for assignments, the eText, and the Study Area with practice tests, animations, and activities.

**Instructors** Go to **MasteringBiology** for automatically graded tutorials and questions that you can assign to your students, plus Instructor Resources.

# 8 Cell Communication

**OVERVIEW**

## Cellular Messaging

▼ **Figure 8.1** How does cell signaling trigger the desperate flight of this impala?

▼ Epinephrine

The impala in **Figure 8.1** flees for its life, racing to escape the predatory cheetah nipping at its heels. The impala is breathing rapidly, its heart pounding and its legs pumping furiously. These physiological functions are all part of the impala's "fight-or-flight" response, driven by hormones released from its adrenal glands at times of stress—in this case, upon sensing the cheetah. What systems of cell-to-cell communication allow the trillions of cells in the impala to "talk" to each other, coordinating their activities?

Cells can signal to each other and interpret the signals they receive from other cells and the environment. The signals may include light and touch, but are most often chemicals. The flight response shown here is triggered by a signaling molecule called epinephrine (also called adrenaline; see the model to the left). Studying cell communication, biologists have discovered ample evidence for the evolutionary relatedness of all life. The same small set of cell-signaling mechanisms shows up again and again in diverse species, in processes ranging from bacterial signaling to embryonic development to cancer. In this chapter, we focus on the main mechanisms by which cells receive, process, and respond to chemical signals sent from other cells. We will also consider *apoptosis*, a type of programmed cell death that integrates input from multiple signaling pathways.

## CONCEPT 8.1

## External signals are converted to responses within the cell

What does a "talking" cell say to a "listening" cell, and how does the latter cell respond to the message? Let's approach these questions by first looking at communication among microorganisms.

### Evolution of Cell Signaling

**EVOLUTION** One topic of cell "conversation" is sex. Cells of the yeast *Saccharomyces cerevisiae*—which are used to make bread, wine, and beer—identify their mates by chemical signaling. There are two sexes, or mating types, called **a** and **α** (**Figure 8.2**). Each type secretes a specific factor that binds to receptors only on the other type of cell. When exposed to each other's mating factors, a pair of cells of opposite type change shape, grow toward each other, and fuse (mate). The new **a/α** cell contains all the genes of both original cells, a combination of genetic resources that provides advantages to the cell's descendants, which arise by subsequent cell divisions.

Once received by the yeast cell surface receptor, a mating signal is changed, or *transduced*, into a form that brings about the cellular response of mating. This occurs in a series of steps called a *signal transduction pathway*. Many such pathways exist in both yeast and animal cells. In fact, the molecular details of signal transduction in yeasts and mammals are strikingly similar, even though their last common ancestor lived over a billion years ago. This suggests that early versions of cell-signaling mechanisms evolved well before the first multicellular creatures appeared on Earth.

Scientists think that signaling mechanisms first evolved in ancient prokaryotes and single-celled eukaryotes and then were adopted for new uses by their multicellular descendants. Cell signaling is critical in the microbial world (**Figure 8.3**). Bacterial cells secrete molecules that can be detected by other bacterial cells. Sensing the concentration of such signaling molecules allows bacteria to monitor the local density of cells, a phenomenon called *quorum sensing*.

Quorum sensing allows bacterial populations to coordinate their behaviors in activities that require a given number of cells acting synchronously. One example is formation of a *biofilm*, an aggregation of bacterial cells adhered to a surface. The cells in the biofilm generally derive nutrition from the surface they are on. You have probably encountered biofilms many times, perhaps without realizing it. The slimy coating on a fallen log or on leaves lying on a forest path, and even the film on your teeth each morning, are examples of bacterial biofilms. (In fact, tooth-brushing disrupts biofilms that would otherwise cause cavities.) The formation of biofilms requires a sophisticated communication system, the basis of which is cell signaling.

## Local and Long-Distance Signaling

Like bacteria or yeast cells, cells in a multicellular organism usually communicate via signaling molecules targeted for cells that may or may not be immediately adjacent. As we saw in Chapter 4, eukaryotic cells may communicate by direct

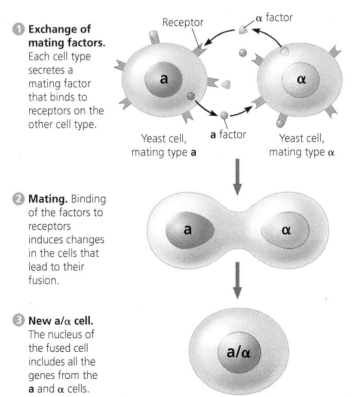

**1** Exchange of mating factors. Each cell type secretes a mating factor that binds to receptors on the other cell type.

**2** Mating. Binding of the factors to receptors induces changes in the cells that lead to their fusion.

**3** New a/α cell. The nucleus of the fused cell includes all the genes from the **a** and α cells.

▲ **Figure 8.2 Communication between mating yeast cells.** *Saccharomyces cerevisiae* cells use chemical signaling to identify cells of opposite mating type and initiate the mating process. The two mating types and their corresponding chemical signaling molecules, or mating factors, are called **a** and *α*.

**1** Individual rod-shaped cells

0.5 mm

**2** Aggregation in progress

2.5 mm

**3** Spore-forming structure (fruiting body)

Fruiting bodies

▲ **Figure 8.3 Communication among bacteria.** Soil-dwelling bacteria called myxobacteria ("slime bacteria") use chemical signals to share information about nutrient availability. When food is scarce, starving cells secrete a molecule that stimulates neighboring cells to aggregate. The cells form a structure, called a fruiting body, that produces thick-walled spores capable of surviving until the environment improves. The bacteria shown here are *Myxococcus xanthus* (steps 1–3, SEMs; lower photo, LM).

contact, one type of local signaling (Figure 8.4). Both animals and plants have cell junctions that, where present, directly connect the cytoplasms of adjacent cells (Figure 8.4a). In these cases, signaling substances dissolved in the cytosol can pass freely between adjacent cells. Moreover, animal cells may communicate via direct contact between membrane-bound cell-surface molecules in a process called cell-cell recognition (Figure 8.4b). This sort of local signaling is especially important in embryonic development and the immune response.

In many other cases of local signaling, messenger molecules are secreted by the signaling cell. Some of these travel only short distances; such local regulators influence cells in the vicinity. One class of local regulators in animals, *growth factors*, are compounds that stimulate nearby target cells to grow and divide. Numerous cells can simultaneously receive and respond to the molecules of growth factor produced by a single cell in their vicinity. This type of local signaling in animals is called *paracrine signaling* (Figure 8.5a).

Another, more specialized type of local signaling called *synaptic signaling* occurs in the animal nervous system (Figure 8.5b). An electrical signal along a nerve cell triggers the secretion of neurotransmitter molecules. These molecules act as chemical signals, diffusing across the synapse—the narrow space between the nerve cell and its target cell—triggering a response in the target cell.

Beyond communication through plasmodesmata (plant cell junctions), local signaling in plants is not as well understood. Because of their cell walls, plants use mechanisms different from those operating locally in animals.

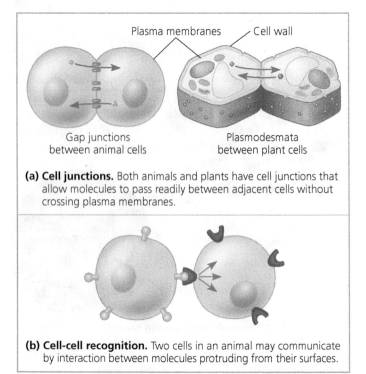

**(a) Cell junctions.** Both animals and plants have cell junctions that allow molecules to pass readily between adjacent cells without crossing plasma membranes.

**(b) Cell-cell recognition.** Two cells in an animal may communicate by interaction between molecules protruding from their surfaces.

▲ **Figure 8.4 Communication by direct contact between cells.**

Both animals and plants use chemicals called **hormones** for long-distance signaling. In hormonal signaling in animals, also known as *endocrine signaling*, specialized cells release hormone molecules, which travel via the circulatory system to other parts of the body, where they reach target cells that can recognize and respond to the hormones (Figure 8.5c). Plant hormones (often called *plant growth regulators*) sometimes travel in vessels but more often reach their targets by moving through cells or by diffusing through the air as a gas. Hormones vary widely in size and type, as do local regulators. For instance, the plant hormone ethylene, a gas that promotes fruit ripening and helps regulate growth, is a hydrocarbon of only six atoms ($C_2H_4$), small enough to pass through cell walls. In contrast, the mammalian hormone insulin, which regulates sugar levels in the blood, is a protein with thousands of atoms.

What happens when a cell encounters a secreted signaling molecule? The ability of a cell to respond is determined by whether it has a specific receptor molecule that can bind to the signaling molecule. The information conveyed by this binding, the signal, must then be changed into another form—transduced—inside the cell before the cell can respond. The remainder of the chapter discusses this process, primarily as it occurs in animal cells.

## The Three Stages of Cell Signaling: *A Preview*

Our current understanding of how chemical messengers act via signal transduction pathways had its origins in the pioneering work of Earl W. Sutherland, whose research led to a Nobel Prize in 1971. Sutherland and his colleagues at Vanderbilt University were investigating how the animal hormone epinephrine (adrenaline) stimulates the breakdown of the storage polysaccharide glycogen within liver cells and skeletal muscle cells. Glycogen breakdown releases the sugar glucose 1-phosphate, which the cell converts to glucose 6-phosphate. The liver or muscle cell can then use this compound, an early intermediate in glycolysis, for energy production. Alternatively, the compound can be stripped of phosphate and released from the cell into the blood as glucose, which can fuel cells throughout the body. Thus, one effect of epinephrine is the mobilization of fuel reserves, which can be used by the animal to either defend itself (fight) or escape whatever elicited a scare (flight). (The impala in Figure 8.1 is obviously engaged in the latter.)

Sutherland's research team discovered that epinephrine stimulates glycogen breakdown by somehow activating a cytosolic enzyme, glycogen phosphorylase. However, when epinephrine was added to a test-tube mixture containing the enzyme and its substrate, glycogen, no breakdown occurred. Glycogen phosphorylase could be activated by epinephrine only when the hormone was added to *intact* cells in a solution. This result told Sutherland two things. First, epinephrine does

**Local signaling**

Target cells

Secreting cell

Secretory vesicles

Local regulator

**(a) Paracrine signaling.** A secreting cell acts on nearby target cells by secreting molecules of a local regulator (a growth factor, for example).

Electrical signal triggers release of neurotransmitter.

Neurotransmitter diffuses across synapse.

Target cell

**(b) Synaptic signaling.** A nerve cell releases neurotransmitter molecules into a synapse, stimulating the target cell, such as a muscle or nerve cell.

**Long-distance signaling**

Endocrine cell

Target cell specifically binds hormone.

Hormone travels in bloodstream.

Blood vessel

**(c) Endocrine (hormonal) signaling.** Specialized endocrine cells secrete hormones into body fluids, often blood. Hormones reach virtually all body cells, but are bound only by some cells.

▲ Figure 8.5 **Local and long-distance cell signaling by secreted molecules in animals.** In both local and long-distance signaling, only specific target cells that can recognize a given signaling molecule will respond to it.

not interact directly with the enzyme responsible for glycogen breakdown; an intermediate step or series of steps must be occurring inside the cell. Second, the plasma membrane itself is necessary for transmission of the signal to take place.

Sutherland's early work suggested that the process going on at the receiving end of a cellular conversation can be dissected into three stages: reception, transduction, and response **(Figure 8.6)**:

❶ **Reception.** Reception is the target cell's detection of a signaling molecule coming from outside the cell. A chemical signal is "detected" when the signaling molecule binds to a receptor protein located at the cell's surface (or inside the cell, to be discussed later).

❷ **Transduction.** The binding of the signaling molecule changes the receptor protein in some way, initiating the

process of transduction. The transduction stage converts the signal to a form that can bring about a specific cellular response. In Sutherland's system, the binding of epinephrine to a receptor protein in a liver cell's plasma membrane leads to activation of glycogen phosphorylase. Transduction sometimes occurs in a single step but more often requires a sequence of changes in a series of different molecules— a **signal transduction pathway**. The molecules in the pathway are often called relay molecules.

❸ **Response.** In the third stage of cell signaling, the transduced signal finally triggers a specific cellular response. The response may be almost any imaginable cellular activity—such as catalysis by an enzyme (for example, glycogen phosphorylase), rearrangement of the cytoskeleton, or activation of specific genes in the nucleus. The cell-signaling process helps ensure that crucial

▶ Figure 8.6 **Overview of cell signaling.** From the perspective of the cell receiving the message, cell signaling can be divided into three stages: signal reception, signal transduction, and cellular response. When reception occurs at the plasma membrane, as shown here, the transduction stage is usually a pathway of several steps, with each specific relay molecule in the pathway bringing about a change in the next molecule. The final molecule in the pathway triggers the cell's response.

**?** *How does the epinephrine in Sutherland's experiment fit into this diagram of cell signaling?*

EXTRACELLULAR FLUID

CYTOPLASM

Plasma membrane

❶ **Reception**

❷ **Transduction**

❸ **Response**

Receptor

1 → 2 → 3

Three relay molecules in a signal transduction pathway

Activation of cellular response

Signaling molecule

activities like these occur in the right cells, at the right time, and in proper coordination with the activities of other cells of the organism. We'll now explore the mechanisms of cell signaling in more detail, including a discussion of regulation and termination of the process.

▲ **Figure 8.7 The structure of a G protein-coupled receptor (GPCR).** Shown here is a model of the human $\beta_2$-adrenergic receptor in the presence of a molecule mimicking the natural ligand (green in the model) and cholesterol (orange). Two receptor molecules (blue) are shown as ribbon models in a side view within the plasma membrane.

# Reception: A signaling molecule binds to a receptor protein, causing it to change shape

A radio station broadcasts its signal indiscriminately, but it can be picked up only by radios tuned to the right frequency: Reception of the signal depends on the receiver. Similarly, the signals emitted by an **a** yeast cell are "heard" only by its prospective mates, **α** cells. In the case of the epinephrine circulating throughout the bloodstream of the impala in Figure 8.1, the hormone encounters many types of cells, but only certain target cells detect and react to the hormone molecule. A receptor protein on or in the target cell allows the cell to "hear" the signal and respond to it. The signaling molecule is complementary in shape to a specific site on the receptor and attaches there, like a key in a lock. The signaling molecule acts as a **ligand**, the term for a molecule that specifically binds to another molecule, often a larger one. Ligand binding generally causes a receptor protein to undergo a change in shape. For many receptors, this shape change directly activates the receptor, enabling it to interact with other cellular molecules. For other kinds of receptors, the immediate effect of ligand binding is to cause the aggregation of two or more receptor molecules, which leads to further molecular events inside the cell. Most signal receptors are plasma membrane proteins, but others are located inside the cell. We discuss both of these types next.

## Receptors in the Plasma Membrane

Cell-surface receptor proteins play crucial roles in the biological systems of animals. The largest family of human cell surface receptors are the nearly 1,000 G protein-coupled receptors (GPCRs); an example is shown in (**Figure 8.7**).

Most water-soluble signaling molecules bind to specific sites on transmembrane receptor proteins that transmit information from the extracellular environment to the inside of the cell. We can see how cell-surface transmembrane receptors work by looking at three major types: G protein-coupled receptors (GPCRs), receptor tyrosine kinases, and ion channel receptors. These receptors are discussed and illustrated in **Figure 8.8**; study this figure before going on.

Given the many important functions of cell-surface receptors, it is not surprising that their malfunctions are associated with many human diseases, including cancer, heart disease, and asthma. To better understand and treat these conditions, a major focus of both university research teams and the pharmaceutical industry has been to analyze the structure of these receptors.

Although cell-surface receptors represent 30% of all human proteins, determining their structures has proved challenging: They make up only 1% of the proteins whose structures have been determined by X-ray crystallography. For one thing, cell-surface receptors tend to be flexible and inherently unstable, thus difficult to crystallize. It took years of persistent efforts for researchers to determine the first few of these structures, such as the GPCR shown in Figure 8.7. In that case, the β-adrenergic receptor was stable enough to be crystallized while it was among membrane molecules, in the presence of its ligand.

Abnormal functioning of receptor tyrosine kinases (RTKs) is associated with many types of cancers. For example, breast cancer patients have a poor prognosis if their tumor cells harbor excessive levels of a receptor tyrosine kinase called HER2 (see Concept 9.3). Using molecular biological techniques, researchers have developed a protein called

# ▼ Figure 8.8
**Exploring Cell-Surface Transmembrane Receptors**

## G Protein-Coupled Receptors

Signaling molecule binding site

Segment that interacts with G proteins

**G protein-coupled receptor**

A **G protein-coupled receptor** (GPCR) is a cell-surface transmembrane receptor that works with the help of a **G protein**, a protein that binds the energy-rich molecule GTP. Many different signaling molecules—including yeast mating factors, epinephrine (adrenaline) and many other hormones, as well as neurotransmitters—use GPCRs. These receptors vary in the binding sites for their signaling molecules (often referred to as their ligands) and also for different types of G proteins inside the cell. Nevertheless, GPCR proteins are all remarkably similar in structure. In fact, they make up a large family of eukaryotic receptor proteins with a secondary structure in which the single polypeptide, represented here in a ribbon model, has seven transmembrane α helices, outlined with cylinders and depicted in a row for clarity. Specific loops between the helices (here, the loops on the right) form binding sites for signaling molecules (outside the cell) and G proteins (on the cytoplasmic side).

GPCR-based signaling systems are extremely widespread and diverse in their functions, including roles in embryonic development and sensory reception. In humans, for example, vision, smell, and taste depend on GPCRs. Similarities in structure in G proteins and GPCRs in diverse organisms suggest that G proteins and their associated receptors evolved very early among eukaryotes.

Malfunctions of the associated G proteins themselves are involved in many human diseases, including bacterial infections. The bacteria that cause cholera, pertussis (whooping cough), and botulism, among others, make their victims ill by producing toxins that interfere with G protein function. Pharmacologists now realize that up to 60% of all medicines used today exert their effects by influencing G protein pathways.

**❶** Loosely attached to the cytoplasmic side of the membrane, the G protein functions as a molecular switch that is either on or off, depending on which of two guanine nucleotides is attached, GDP or GTP—hence the term *G protein*. (GTP, or guanosine triphosphate, is similar to ATP.) When GDP is bound to the G protein, as shown above, the G protein is inactive. The receptor and G protein work together with another protein, usually an enzyme.

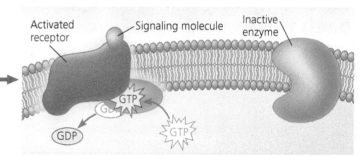

**❷** When the appropriate signaling molecule binds to the extracellular side of the receptor, the receptor is activated and changes shape. Its cytoplasmic side then binds an inactive G protein, causing a GTP to displace the GDP. This activates the G protein.

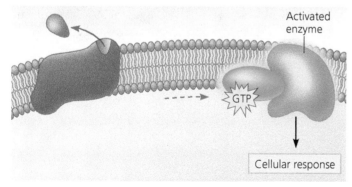

**❸** The activated G protein dissociates from the receptor, diffuses along the membrane, and then binds to an enzyme, altering the enzyme's shape and activity. Once activated, the enzyme can trigger the next step leading to a cellular response. Binding of signaling molecules is reversible: Like other ligands, they bind and dissociate many times. The ligand concentration outside the cell determines how often a ligand is bound and causes signaling.

**❹** The changes in the enzyme and G protein are only temporary because the G protein also functions as a GTPase enzyme—in other words, it then hydrolyzes its bound GTP to GDP and $P_i$. Now inactive again, the G protein leaves the enzyme, which returns to its original state. The G protein is now available for reuse. The GTPase function of the G protein allows the pathway to shut down rapidly when the signaling molecule is no longer present.

© Pearson Education, Inc.

*CONTINUED ON NEXT PAGE*

## Receptor Tyrosine Kinases

**Receptor tyrosine kinases (RTKs)** belong to a major class of plasma membrane receptors characterized by having enzymatic activity. A kinase is any enzyme that catalyzes the transfer of phosphate groups. The part of the receptor protein extending into the cytoplasm functions more specifically as a tyrosine kinase, an enzyme that catalyzes the transfer of a phosphate group from ATP to the amino acid tyrosine on a substrate protein. Thus, RTKs are membrane receptors that attach phosphates to tyrosines.

One RTK may activate ten or more different transduction pathways and cellular responses. Often, more than one signal transduction pathway can be triggered at once, helping the cell regulate and coordinate many aspects of cell growth and cell reproduction. The ability of a single ligand-binding event to trigger so many pathways is a key difference between RTKs and GPCRs, which activate a single transduction pathway. Abnormal RTKs that function even in the absence of signaling molecules are associated with many kinds of cancer.

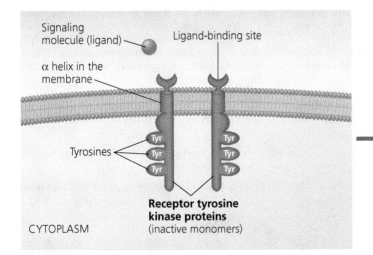

① Many receptor tyrosine kinases have the structure depicted schematically here. Before the signaling molecule binds, the receptors exist as individual units referred to as monomers. Notice that each has an extracellular ligand-binding site, an α helix spanning the membrane, and an intracellular tail containing multiple tyrosines.

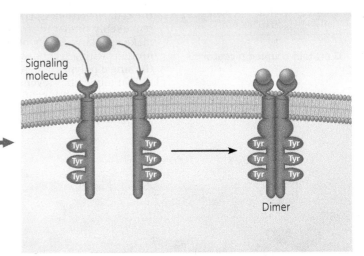

② The binding of a signaling molecule (such as a growth factor) causes two receptor monomers to associate closely with each other, forming a complex known as a dimer in a process called dimerization (In some cases, larger clusters form. The details of monomer association are a focus of current research.)

③ Dimerization activates the tyrosine kinase region of each monomer; each tyrosine kinase adds a phosphate from an ATP molecule to a tyrosine on the tail of the other monomer.

④ Now that the receptor is fully activated, it is recognized by specific relay proteins inside the cell. Each such protein binds to a specific phosphorylated tyrosine, undergoing a resulting structural change that activates the bound protein. Each activated protein triggers a transduction pathway, leading to a cellular response.

## Ion Channel Receptors

A **ligand-gated ion channel** is a type of membrane receptor containing a region that can act as a "gate" when the receptor changes shape. When a signaling molecule binds as a ligand to the receptor protein, the gate opens or closes, allowing or blocking the flow of specific ions, such as $Na^+$ or $Ca^{2+}$, through a channel in the receptor. Like the other receptors we have discussed, these proteins bind the ligand at a specific site on their extracellular sides.

1 Here we show a ligand-gated ion channel receptor in which the gate remains closed until a ligand binds to the receptor.

2 When the ligand binds to the receptor and the gate opens, specific ions can flow through the channel and rapidly change the concentration of that particular ion inside the cell. This change may directly affect the activity of the cell in some way.

3 When the ligand dissociates from this receptor, the gate closes and ions no longer enter the cell.

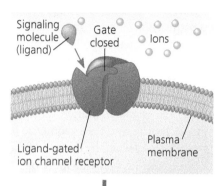

Ligand-gated ion channels are very important in the nervous system. For example, the neurotransmitter molecules released at a synapse between two nerve cells (see Figure 8.5b) bind as ligands to ion channels on the receiving cell, causing the channels to open. Ions flow in (or, in some cases, out), triggering an electrical signal that propagates down the length of the receiving cell. Some gated ion channels are controlled by electrical signals instead of ligands; these voltage-gated ion channels are also crucial to the functioning of the nervous. Some ion channels are present on membranes of organelles, such as the ER.

**MAKE CONNECTIONS** *Is the flow of ions through a ligand-gated channel an example of active or passive transport? (Review Concepts 7.3 and 7.4.)*

Herceptin that binds to HER2 on cells and inhibits cell division, thus thwarting further tumor development. In some clinical studies, treatment with Herceptin improved patient survival rates by more than one-third. One goal of ongoing research into these cell-surface receptors and other cell-signaling proteins is development of additional successful treatments.

### Intracellular Receptors

Intracellular receptor proteins are found in either the cytoplasm or nucleus of target cells. To reach such a receptor, a signaling molecule passes through the target cell's plasma membrane. A number of important signaling molecules can do this because they are either hydrophobic enough or small enough to cross the hydrophobic interior of the membrane. These hydrophobic chemical messengers include the steroid hormones and thyroid hormones of animals. Another chemical signaling molecule with an intracellular receptor is nitric oxide (NO), a gas; its very small molecules readily pass between the membrane phospholipids.

Once a hormone has entered a cell, it may bind to an intracellular receptor in the cytoplasm or the nucleus. The binding changes the receptor into a hormone-receptor complex that is able to cause a response—in many cases, the turning on or off of particular genes.

The behavior of aldosterone is a representative example of how steroid hormones work. This hormone is secreted by cells of the adrenal gland, a gland that sits above the kidney. Aldosterone then travels through the blood and enters cells all over the body. However, a response occurs only in kidney cells, which contain receptor molecules for this hormone. In these cells, the hormone binds to the receptor protein, activating it. With aldosterone attached, the active form of the receptor protein then enters the nucleus and turns on specific genes that control water and sodium flow in kidney cells, ultimately affecting blood volume **(Figure 8.9)**.

How does the activated hormone-receptor complex turn on genes? Recall that the genes in a cell's DNA function by being transcribed and processed into messenger RNA (mRNA), which leaves the nucleus and is translated into a specific protein by ribosomes in the cytoplasm. Special proteins called *transcription factors* control which genes are turned on—that is, which genes are transcribed into mRNA—in a particular cell at a particular time. When the aldosterone receptor is activated, it acts as a transcription factor that turns on specific genes.

By acting as a transcription factor, the aldosterone receptor itself carries out the transduction part of the signaling pathway. Most other intracellular receptors function in the same way, although many of them, such as the thyroid hormone receptor, are already in the nucleus before the signaling molecule reaches them. Interestingly, many of these intracellular

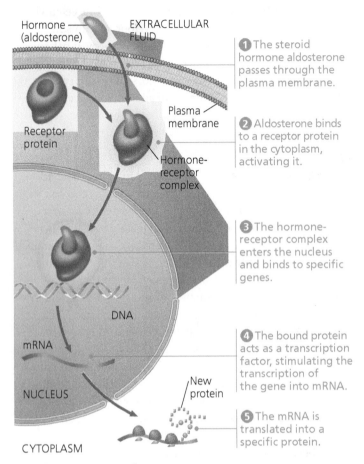

**①** The steroid hormone aldosterone passes through the plasma membrane.

**②** Aldosterone binds to a receptor protein in the cytoplasm, activating it.

**③** The hormone-receptor complex enters the nucleus and binds to specific genes.

**④** The bound protein acts as a transcription factor, stimulating the transcription of the gene into mRNA.

**⑤** The mRNA is translated into a specific protein.

▲ **Figure 8.9  Steroid hormone interacting with an intracellular receptor.**

**?**  *Why is a cell-surface receptor protein not required for this steroid hormone to enter the cell?*

receptor proteins are structurally similar, suggesting an evolutionary kinship.

**CONCEPT CHECK 8.2**

1. Nerve growth factor (NGF) is a water-soluble signaling molecule. Would you expect the receptor for NGF to be intracellular or in the plasma membrane? Why?

2. **WHAT IF?**  What would the effect be if a cell made defective receptor tyrosine kinase proteins that were unable to dimerize?

3. **MAKE CONNECTIONS**  How is ligand binding similar to the process of allosteric regulation of enzymes?

4. **WHAT IF?**  The model shown in Figure 8.7 represents the receptor in an inactive state, not bound to a G protein. Can you suggest an approach for crystallizing the protein that would reveal the structure of the receptor while it is actively signaling?

For suggested answers, see Appendix A.

# Transduction: Cascades of molecular interactions relay signals from receptors to target molecules in the cell

When receptors for signaling molecules are plasma membrane proteins, like most of those we have discussed, the transduction stage of cell signaling is usually a multistep pathway involving many molecules. Steps often include activation of proteins by addition or removal of phosphate groups or release of other small molecules or ions that act as messengers. One benefit of multiple steps is the possibility of greatly amplifying a signal. If each molecule in a pathway transmits the signal to numerous molecules at the next step in the series, the result is a geometric increase in the number of activated molecules by the end of the pathway. Moreover, multistep pathways provide more opportunities for coordination and control than do simpler systems. This allows regulation of the response, as we'll discuss later in the chapter.

## Signal Transduction Pathways

The binding of a specific signaling molecule to a receptor in the plasma membrane triggers the first step in the chain of molecular interactions—the signal transduction pathway—that leads to a particular response within the cell. Like falling dominoes, the signal-activated receptor activates another molecule, which activates yet another molecule, and so on, until the protein that produces the final cellular response is activated. The molecules that relay a signal from receptor to response, which we call relay molecules in this book, are often proteins. The interaction of proteins is a major theme of cell signaling. Indeed, protein interaction is a unifying theme of all cellular activities.

Keep in mind that the original signaling molecule is not physically passed along a signaling pathway; in most cases, it never even enters the cell. When we say that the signal is relayed along a pathway, we mean that certain information is passed on. At each step, the signal is transduced into a different form, commonly a shape change in the next protein. Very often, the shape change is brought about by phosphorylation.

## Protein Phosphorylation and Dephosphorylation

Previous chapters introduced the concept of activating a protein by adding one or more phosphate groups to it. In Figure 8.8, you have already seen how phosphorylation is involved in the activation of receptor tyrosine kinases. In fact, the phosphorylation and dephosphorylation of proteins is a widespread cellular mechanism for regulating protein activity. An enzyme that transfers phosphate groups from ATP to a protein is generally known as a **protein kinase**. Recall that a receptor tyrosine kinase is a specific kind of protein kinase that phosphorylates tyrosines on the other receptor tyrosine kinase in a dimer. Most cytoplasmic protein kinases, however, act on proteins different from themselves. Another distinction is that most cytoplasmic protein kinases phosphorylate either of two other amino acids, serine or threonine, rather than tyrosine. Serine/threonine kinases are widely involved in signaling pathways in animals, plants, and fungi.

Many of the relay molecules in signal transduction pathways are protein kinases, and they often act on other protein kinases in the pathway. **Figure 8.10** depicts a hypothetical pathway containing three different protein kinases that create a **phosphorylation cascade**. The sequence of steps shown in the figure is similar to many known pathways, including those triggered in yeast by mating factors and in animal cells by many growth factors. The signal is transmitted by a cascade of protein phosphorylations, each causing a shape change because of the interaction of the newly added phosphate groups with charged or polar amino acids on the protein being phosphorylated. The change in shape alters the function of the protein, most often activating it. In some cases, though, phosphorylation *decreases* the activity of the protein.

The importance of protein kinases can hardly be overstated. About 2% of our own genes are thought to code for protein kinases. A single cell may have hundreds of different kinds, each specific for a different substrate protein. Together, they probably regulate the activity of a large proportion of the thousands of proteins in a cell. Among these are most of the proteins that, in turn, regulate cell division. Abnormal activity of such a kinase can cause abnormal cell division and contribute to the development of cancer.

Equally important in the phosphorylation cascade are the **protein phosphatases**, enzymes that can rapidly remove phosphate groups from proteins, a process called

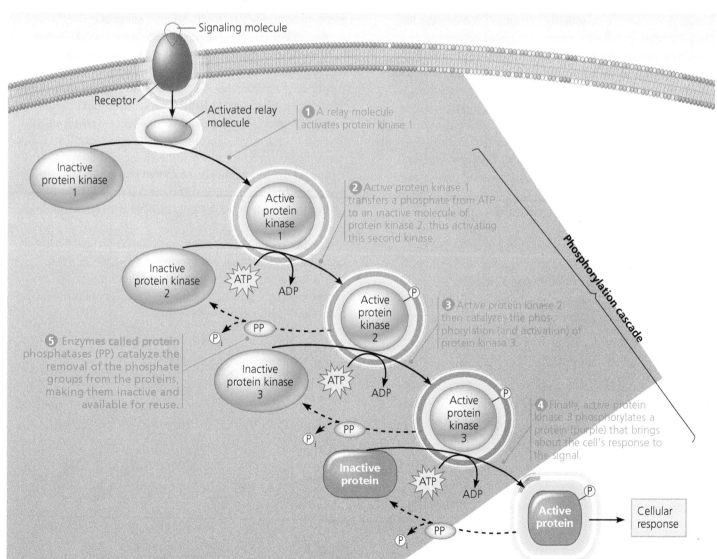

▲ **Figure 8.10 A phosphorylation cascade.** In a phosphorylation cascade, a series of different proteins in a pathway are phosphorylated in turn, each protein adding a phosphate group to the next one in line. Here, phosphorylation activates each protein, and dephosphorylation returns it to its inactive form. The active and inactive forms of each protein are represented by different shapes to remind you that activation is usually associated with a change in molecular shape.

**WHAT IF?** *What would happen if a mutation in protein kinase 3 made it incapable of being phosphorylated?*

dephosphorylation. By dephosphorylating and thus inactivating protein kinases, phosphatases provide the mechanism for turning off the signal transduction pathway when the initial signal is no longer present. Phosphatases also make the protein kinases available for reuse, enabling the cell to respond again to an extracellular signal. The phosphorylation-dephosphorylation system acts as a molecular switch in the cell, turning activities on or off, or up or down, as required. At any given moment, the activity of a protein regulated by phosphorylation depends on the balance in the cell between active kinase molecules and active phosphatase molecules.

## Small Molecules and Ions as Second Messengers

Not all components of signal transduction pathways are proteins. Many signaling pathways also involve small, nonprotein, water-soluble molecules or ions called **second messengers**. (This term is used because the pathway's "first messenger" is considered to be the extracellular signaling molecule—the ligand—that binds to the membrane receptor.) Because second messengers are small and also water-soluble, they can readily spread throughout the cell by diffusion. For example, as we'll see shortly, a second messenger called cyclic AMP carries the signal initiated by epinephrine from the plasma membrane of a liver or muscle cell into the cell's interior, where the signal eventually brings about glycogen breakdown. Second messengers participate in pathways that are initiated by both G protein-coupled receptors and receptor tyrosine kinases. The two most widely used second messengers are cyclic AMP and calcium ions, $Ca^{2+}$. A large variety of relay proteins are sensitive to the cytosolic concentration of one or the other of these second messengers.

### Cyclic AMP

As discussed previously, Earl Sutherland established that epinephrine somehow causes glycogen breakdown without passing through the plasma membrane. This discovery prompted

him to search for a second messenger that transmits the signal from the plasma membrane to the metabolic machinery in the cytoplasm.

Sutherland found that the binding of epinephrine to the plasma membrane of a liver cell elevates the cytosolic concentration of a compound called cyclic adenosine monophosphate, abbreviated as either **cyclic AMP** or **cAMP** (Figure 8.11). An enzyme embedded in the plasma membrane, **adenylyl cyclase**, converts ATP to cAMP in response to an extracellular signal—in this case, provided by epinephrine. But epinephrine doesn't stimulate adenylyl cyclase directly. When epinephrine outside the cell binds to a specific receptor protein, the protein activates adenylyl cyclase, which in turn can catalyze the synthesis of many molecules of cAMP. In this way, the normal cellular concentration of cAMP can be boosted 20-fold in a matter of seconds. The cAMP broadcasts the signal to the cytoplasm. It does not persist for long in the absence of the hormone because another enzyme, called phosphodiesterase, converts cAMP to AMP. Another surge of epinephrine is needed to boost the cytosolic concentration of cAMP again.

Subsequent research has revealed that epinephrine is only one of many hormones and other signaling molecules that trigger the formation of cAMP. It has also brought to light the other components of cAMP pathways, including G proteins, G protein-coupled receptors, and protein kinases (Figure 8.12). The immediate effect of an elevation in cAMP levels is usually the activation of a serine/threonine kinase called *protein kinase A*. The activated protein kinase A then phosphorylates various other proteins, depending on the cell type. (The complete pathway for epinephrine's stimulation of glycogen breakdown is shown later, in Figure 8.16.)

Further regulation of cell metabolism is provided by other G protein systems that *inhibit* adenylyl cyclase. In these systems, a different signaling molecule activates a different receptor, which in turn activates an *inhibitory* G protein that blocks activation of adenylyl cyclase.

▲ **Figure 8.11 Cyclic AMP.** The second messenger cyclic AMP (cAMP) is made from ATP by adenylyl cyclase, an enzyme embedded in the plasma membrane. Note that the phosphate group in cAMP is attached to both the 5′ and the 3′ carbons; this cyclic arrangement is the basis for the molecule's name. Cyclic AMP is inactivated by phosphodiesterase, an enzyme that converts it to AMP.

**WHAT IF?** *What would happen if a molecule that inactivated phosphodiesterase were introduced into the cell?*

Now that we know about the role of cAMP in G protein signaling pathways, we can explain in molecular detail how certain microbes cause disease. Consider cholera, a disease that is frequently epidemic in places where the water supply is contaminated with human feces. People acquire the cholera bacterium, *Vibrio cholerae*, by drinking contaminated water. The bacteria form a biofilm on the lining of the small intestine and produce a toxin. The cholera toxin is an enzyme that chemically modifies a G protein involved in regulating salt and water secretion. Because the modified G protein is unable to hydrolyze GTP to GDP, it remains stuck in its active form, continuously stimulating adenylyl cyclase to make cAMP. The resulting high concentration of cAMP causes the intestinal cells to secrete large amounts of salts into the intestines, with water following by osmosis. An infected person quickly develops profuse diarrhea and if left untreated can soon die from the loss of water and salts.

Our understanding of signaling pathways involving cyclic AMP or related messengers has allowed us to develop treatments for certain conditions in humans. In one pathway, *cyclic GMP*, or *cGMP*, acts as a signaling molecule whose effects include relaxation of smooth muscle cells in artery walls. A compound that inhibits the hydrolysis of cGMP to GMP, thus prolonging the signal, was originally prescribed for chest pains because it increased blood flow to the heart muscle. Under the trade name Viagra, this compound is now widely used as a treatment for erectile dysfunction in human males. Because Viagra leads to dilation of blood vessels, it also allows increased blood flow to the penis, optimizing physiological conditions for penile erections.

## Calcium Ions and Inositol Trisphosphate (IP$_3$)

Many of the signaling molecules that function in animals—including neurotransmitters, growth factors, and some hormones—induce responses in their target cells via signal transduction pathways that increase the cytosolic concentration of calcium ions (Ca$^{2+}$). Calcium is even more widely used than cAMP as a second messenger. Increasing the cytosolic concentration of Ca$^{2+}$ causes many responses in animal cells, including muscle cell contraction, secretion of certain substances, and cell division. In plant cells, a wide range of hormonal and environmental stimuli can cause brief increases in cytosolic Ca$^{2+}$ concentration, triggering various signaling pathways, such as the pathway for greening in response to light. Cells use Ca$^{2+}$ as a second messenger in pathways triggered by both G protein-coupled receptors and receptor tyrosine kinases.

Although cells always contain some Ca$^{2+}$, this ion can function as a second messenger because its concentration in the cytosol is normally much lower than the concentration outside the cell **(Figure 8.13)**. In fact, the level of Ca$^{2+}$ in the

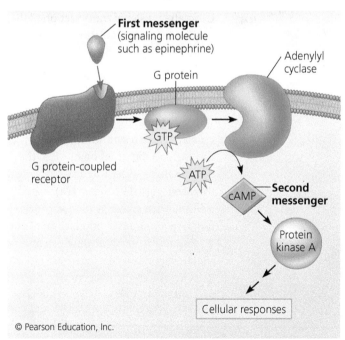

▲ **Figure 8.12 cAMP as a second messenger in a G protein signaling pathway.** The first messenger activates a G protein coupled receptor, which activates a specific G protein. In turn, the G protein activates adenylyl cyclase, which catalyzes the conversion of ATP to cAMP. The cAMP then acts as a second messenger and activates another protein, usually protein kinase A, leading to cellular responses.

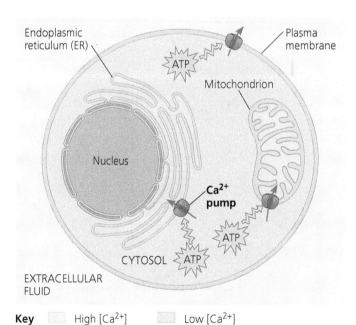

Key ☐ High [Ca$^{2+}$] ☐ Low [Ca$^{2+}$]

▲ **Figure 8.13 The maintenance of calcium ion concentrations in an animal cell.** The Ca$^{2+}$ concentration in the cytosol is usually much lower (beige) than in the extracellular fluid and ER (blue). Protein pumps in the plasma membrane and the ER membrane, driven by ATP, move Ca$^{2+}$ from the cytosol into the extracellular fluid and into the lumen of the ER. Mitochondrial pumps, driven by chemiosmosis (see Concept 9.4), move Ca$^{2+}$ into mitochondria when the calcium level in the cytosol rises significantly.

blood and extracellular fluid of an animal is often more than 10,000 times higher than that in the cytosol. Calcium ions are actively transported out of the cell and are actively imported from the cytosol into the endoplasmic reticulum (and, under some conditions, into mitochondria and chloroplasts) by various protein pumps. As a result, the calcium concentration in the ER is usually much higher than that in the cytosol. Because the cytosolic calcium level is low, a small change in absolute numbers of ions represents a relatively large percentage change in calcium concentration.

In response to a signal relayed by a signal transduction pathway, the cytosolic calcium level may rise, usually by a mechanism that releases $Ca^{2+}$ from the cell's ER. The pathways leading to calcium release involve two other second messengers, **inositol trisphosphate ($IP_3$)** and **diacylglycerol (DAG)**. These two messengers are produced by cleavage of a certain kind of phospholipid in the plasma membrane. **Figure 8.14** shows the complete picture of how a signal causes $IP_3$ to stimulate the release of calcium from the ER. Because $IP_3$ acts before calcium in these pathways, calcium could be considered a "*third* messenger." However, scientists use the term *second messenger* for all small, nonprotein components of signal transduction pathways.

**CONCEPT CHECK 8.3**

1. What is a protein kinase, and what is its role in a signal transduction pathway?
2. When a signal transduction pathway involves a phosphorylation cascade, how does the cell's response get turned off?
3. What is the actual "signal" that is being transduced in any signal transduction pathway, such as those shown in Figures 8.6 and 8.10? In what way is this information being passed from the exterior to the interior of the cell?
4. **WHAT IF?** Upon activation of phospholipase C by the binding of a ligand to a receptor, what effect does the $IP_3$-gated calcium channel have on $Ca^{2+}$ concentration in the cytosol?

For suggested answers, see Appendix A.

**CONCEPT 8.4**

# Response: Cell signaling leads to regulation of transcription or cytoplasmic activities

We now take a closer look at the cell's subsequent response to an extracellular signal—what some researchers call the "output response." What is the nature of the final step in a signaling pathway?

① A signaling molecule binds to a receptor, leading to activation of phospholipase C.

② Phospholipase C cleaves a plasma membrane phospholipid called $PIP_2$ into DAG and $IP_3$.

③ DAG functions as a second messenger in other pathways.

④ $IP_3$ quickly diffuses through the cytosol and binds to an $IP_3$-gated calcium channel in the ER membrane, causing it to open.

⑤ Calcium ions flow out of the ER (down their concentration gradient), raising the $Ca^{2+}$ level in the cytosol.

⑥ The calcium ions activate the next protein in one or more signaling pathways.

▲ **Figure 8.14 Calcium and $IP_3$ in signaling pathways.** Calcium ions ($Ca^{2+}$) and inositol trisphosphate ($IP_3$) function as second messengers in many signal transduction pathways. In this figure, the process is initiated by the binding of a signaling molecule to a G protein-coupled receptor. A receptor tyrosine kinase could also initiate this pathway by activating phospholipase C.

## Nuclear and Cytoplasmic Responses

Ultimately, a signal transduction pathway leads to the regulation of one or more cellular activities. The response at the end of the pathway may occur in the nucleus of the cell or in the cytoplasm.

Many signaling pathways ultimately regulate protein synthesis, usually by turning specific genes on or off in the nucleus. Like an activated steroid receptor (see Figure 8.9), the final activated molecule in a signaling pathway may function as a transcription factor. **Figure 8.15** shows an example in which a signaling pathway activates a transcription factor that turns a gene on: The response to this growth factor signal is transcription, the synthesis of one or more specific mRNAs, which will be translated in the cytoplasm into specific proteins. In other cases, the transcription factor might regulate a gene by turning it off. Often a transcription factor regulates several different genes.

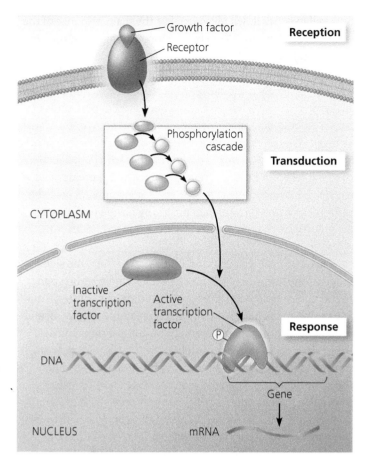

▲ **Figure 8.15 Nuclear responses to a signal: the activation of a specific gene by a growth factor.** This diagram is a simplified representation of a typical signaling pathway that leads to regulation of gene activity in the cell nucleus. The initial signaling molecule, a growth factor, triggers a phosphorylation cascade, as in Figure 8.10. (The ATP molecules and phosphate groups are not shown here.) Once phosphorylated, the last kinase in the sequence enters the nucleus and activates a gene-regulating protein, a transcription factor. This protein stimulates transcription of a specific gene (or genes). The resulting mRNAs then direct the synthesis of a particular protein in the cytoplasm.

Sometimes a signaling pathway may regulate the *activity* of proteins rather than causing their *synthesis* by activating gene expression. This directly affects proteins that function outside the nucleus. For example, a signal may cause the opening or closing of an ion channel in the plasma membrane or a change in cell metabolism. As we have seen, the response of liver cells to the hormone epinephrine helps regulate cellular energy metabolism by affecting the activity of an enzyme. The final step in the signaling pathway that begins with epinephrine binding activates the enzyme that catalyzes the breakdown of glycogen. **Figure 8.16** shows the complete pathway leading to the release of glucose 1-phosphate molecules from glycogen. Notice that as each molecule is activated, the response is amplified, a subject we'll return to shortly.

Signal receptors, relay molecules, and second messengers participate in a variety of pathways, leading to both nuclear and cytoplasmic responses. Some of these pathways lead to

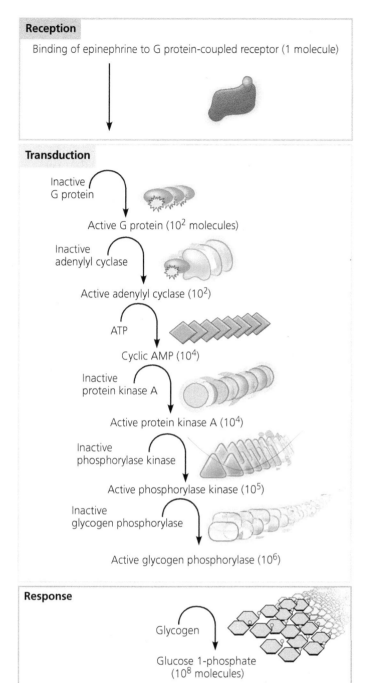

▲ **Figure 8.16 Cytoplasmic response to a signal: the stimulation of glycogen breakdown by epinephrine (adrenaline).** In this signaling system, the hormone epinephrine acts through a G protein-coupled receptor to activate a succession of relay molecules, including cAMP and two protein kinases (see also Figure 8.12). The final protein activated is the enzyme glycogen phosphorylase, which uses inorganic phosphate to release glucose monomers from glycogen in the form of glucose 1-phosphate molecules. This pathway amplifies the hormonal signal: One receptor protein can activate approximately 100 molecules of G protein, and each enzyme in the pathway, once activated, can act on many molecules of its substrate, the next molecule in the cascade. The number of activated molecules given for each step is approximate.

**?** *In the figure, how many glucose molecules are released in response to one signaling molecule? Calculate the factor by which the response is amplified in going from each step to the next.*

cell division. The molecular messengers that initiate cell division pathways include growth factors and certain plant and animal hormones. Malfunctioning of growth factor pathways like the one in Figure 8.15 can contribute to the development of cancer.

## Regulation of the Response

Whether the response occurs in the nucleus or in the cytoplasm, it is not simply turned "on" or "off." Rather, the extent and specificity of the response are regulated in multiple ways. Here we'll consider four aspects of this regulation. First, as mentioned earlier, signaling pathways generally amplify the cell's response to a single signaling event. The degree of amplification depends on the function of the specific molecules in the pathway. Second, the many steps in a multistep pathway provide control points at which the cell's response can be further regulated, contributing to the specificity of the response and allowing coordination with other signaling pathways. Third, the overall efficiency of the response is enhanced by the presence of proteins known as scaffolding proteins. Finally, a crucial point in regulating the response is the termination of the signal.

### Signal Amplification

Elaborate enzyme cascades amplify the cell's response to a signal. At each catalytic step in the cascade, the number of activated products can be much greater than in the preceding step. For example, in the epinephrine-triggered pathway in Figure 8.16, each adenylyl cyclase molecule catalyzes the formation of 100 or so cAMP molecules, each molecule of protein kinase A phosphorylates about 10 molecules of the next kinase in the pathway, and so on. The amplification effect stems from the fact that these proteins persist in the active form long enough to process multiple molecules of substrate before they become inactive again. As a result of the signal's amplification, a small number of epinephrine molecules binding to receptors on the surface of a liver cell or muscle cell can lead to the release of hundreds of millions of glucose molecules from glycogen.

### The Specificity of Cell Signaling and Coordination of the Response

Consider two different cells in your body—a liver cell and a heart muscle cell, for example. Both are in contact with your bloodstream and are therefore constantly exposed to many different hormone molecules, as well as to local regulators secreted by nearby cells. Yet the liver cell responds to some signals but ignores others, and the same is true for the heart cell. And some kinds of signals trigger responses in both cells—but different responses. For instance, epinephrine stimulates the

liver cell to break down glycogen, but the main response of the heart cell to epinephrine is contraction, leading to a more rapid heartbeat. How do we account for this difference?

The explanation for the specificity exhibited in cellular responses to signals is the same as the basic explanation for virtually all differences between cells: Because different kinds of cells turn on different sets of genes, *different kinds of cells have different collections of proteins* (Figure 8.17). The response of a particular cell to a signal depends on its particular collection of signal receptor proteins, relay proteins, and proteins needed to carry out the response. A liver cell, for example, is poised to respond appropriately to epinephrine by having the proteins listed in Figure 8.16 as well as those needed to manufacture glycogen.

Thus, two cells that respond differently to the same signal differ in one or more of the proteins that handle and respond to the signal. Notice in Figure 8.17 that different pathways may have some molecules in common. For example, cells A, B, and C all use the same receptor protein for the red signaling molecule; differences in other proteins account for their differing responses. In cell D, a different receptor protein is used for the same signaling molecule, leading to yet another response. In cell B, a pathway that is triggered by a single kind of signal diverges to produce two responses; such branched pathways often involve receptor tyrosine kinases (which can activate multiple relay proteins) or second messengers (which can regulate numerous proteins). In cell C, two pathways triggered by separate signals converge to modulate a single response. Branching of pathways and "cross-talk" (interaction) between pathways are important in regulating and coordinating a cell's responses to information coming in from different sources in the body. (You'll learn more about this coordination in Concept 8.5.) Moreover, the use of some of the same proteins in more than one pathway allows the cell to economize on the number of different proteins it must make.

An example of a signal that leads to a complex, coordinated cellular response can be found in the processes leading to the mating of yeast cells described earlier (see Figure 8.2). In the **Scientific Skills Exercise**, you can work with data from experiments investigating the cellular response of a yeast cell to the signal initiated by a mating factor from a cell of the opposite mating type.

### Signaling Efficiency: Scaffolding Proteins and Signaling Complexes

The illustrations of signaling pathways in Figure 8.17 (as well as diagrams of other pathways in this chapter) are greatly simplified. The diagrams show only a few relay molecules and, for clarity's sake, display these molecules spread out in the cytosol. If this were true in the cell, signaling pathways would operate very inefficiently because most relay molecules are proteins, and proteins are too large to diffuse quickly through

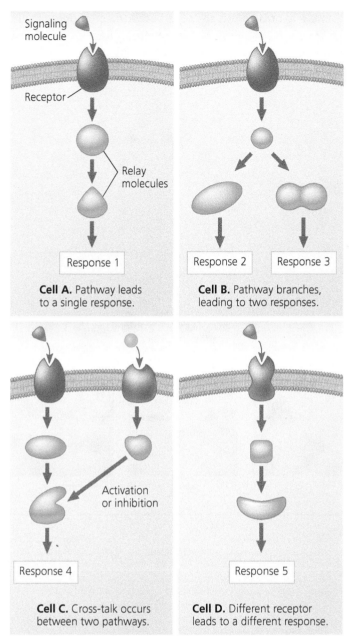

**Signaling molecule**

**Receptor**

**Relay molecules**

Response 1

**Cell A.** Pathway leads to a single response.

Response 2 | Response 3

**Cell B.** Pathway branches, leading to two responses.

Activation or inhibition

Response 4

**Cell C.** Cross-talk occurs between two pathways.

Response 5

**Cell D.** Different receptor leads to a different response.

▲ **Figure 8.17 The specificity of cell signaling.** The particular proteins a cell possesses determine what signaling molecules it responds to and the nature of the response. The four cells in these diagrams respond to the same signaling molecule (red) in different ways because each has a different set of proteins (purple and teal). Note, however, that the same kinds of molecules can participate in more than one pathway.

**MAKE CONNECTIONS** *Study the signaling pathway shown in Figure 8.14, and explain how the situation pictured for cell B above could apply to that pathway.*

the viscous cytosol. How does a particular protein kinase, for instance, find its substrate?

In many cases, the efficiency of signal transduction is apparently increased by the presence of **scaffolding proteins**, large relay proteins to which several other relay proteins are simultaneously attached. For example, one scaffolding protein isolated from mouse brain cells holds three protein kinases

and carries these kinases with it when it binds to an appropriately activated membrane receptor; it thus facilitates a specific phosphorylation cascade **(Figure 8.18)**. Researchers have found scaffolding proteins in brain cells that *permanently* hold together networks of signaling pathway proteins at synapses. This hardwiring enhances the speed and accuracy of signal transfer between cells, because the rate of protein-protein interaction is not limited by diffusion. Furthermore, in some cases the scaffolding proteins themselves may directly activate relay proteins.

When signaling pathways were first discovered, they were thought to be linear, independent pathways. Our understanding of cellular communication has benefited from the realization that signaling pathway components interact with each other in various ways. As seen in Figure 8.17, some proteins may participate in more than one pathway, either in different cell types or in the same cell at different times or under different conditions. These observations underscore the importance of transient—or, in some cases, permanent—protein complexes in the process of cell signaling.

The importance of the relay proteins that serve as points of branching or intersection in signaling pathways is highlighted by the problems arising when these proteins are defective or missing. For instance, in an inherited disorder called Wiskott-Aldrich syndrome (WAS), the absence of a single relay protein leads to such diverse effects as abnormal bleeding, eczema, and a predisposition to infections and leukemia. These symptoms are thought to arise primarily from the absence of the protein in cells of the immune system. By studying normal cells, scientists found that the WAS protein is located just beneath the immune cell surface. The protein interacts both with microfilaments of the cytoskeleton and with several different components of signaling pathways that relay information from the cell surface, including pathways regulating immune cell proliferation. This multifunctional relay protein is thus both a

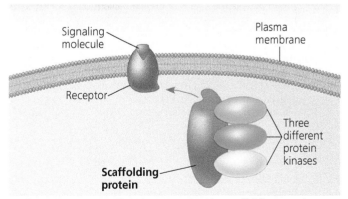

**Signaling molecule**

**Plasma membrane**

**Receptor**

**Three different protein kinases**

**Scaffolding protein**

▲ **Figure 8.18 A scaffolding protein.** The scaffolding protein shown here simultaneously binds to a specific activated membrane receptor and three different protein kinases. This physical arrangement facilitates signal transduction by these molecules.

# Using Experiments to Test a Model

1. Mating factor activates receptor.

Mating factor

G protein-coupled receptor

2. G protein binds GTP and becomes activated.

GDP

GTP

Phosphorylation cascade

Fus3

Fus3 (P)

3. Phosphorylation cascade activates Fus3, which moves to plasma membrane.

Shmoo projection forming

Formin (P)

Actin subunit

Fus3 (P)

Formin

Formin (P)

4. Fus3 phosphorylates formin, activating it.

Microfilament

5. Formin initiates growth of microfilaments that form the shmoo projections.

**Are Both Fus3 Kinase and Formin Required for Directional Cell Growth During Mating in Yeast?** When a yeast cell binds mating factor molecules from a cell of the opposite mating type, a signaling pathway causes it to grow a projection toward the potential mate. The cell with the projection is called a "shmoo" (because it resembles a 1950s cartoon character by that name). Researchers sought to determine how mating factor signaling leads to growth of this cell projection on one side of the cell—in other words, to asymmetric cell growth. Previous work had shown that activation of Fus3, one of the kinases in the signaling cascade, caused it to move to the membrane near where the mating factor bound its receptor. The researchers' first experiment identified one of the phosphorylation targets of Fus3 kinase as formin, a protein directing microfilament construction. Based on this information, the researchers developed the working model shown here for the signaling pathway that leads to the formation of shmoo projections in yeast cells.

**How the Experiment Was Done** To determine if Fus3 and formin were required for shmoo formation, the researchers generated two mutant yeast strains: one that lacked the gene for making Fus3 kinase (a strain called ΔFus3) and one that lacked the gene for making formin (Δformin). To observe the effects of these mutations on schmoo formation after cells' exposure to mating factor, the symmetry of growth was investigated. First, the existing cell walls of each strain were stained with a green fluorescent dye. These green-stained cells were then exposed to mating factor and stained with a red fluorescent dye that labels only new cell wall growth. Growth of the cell on all sides (symmetric growth) is indicated by a uniform yellow color, resulting from merged green and red stains. (This occurs normally in wild-type cells that have not been exposed to mating factor, which are not shown.)

**Data from the Experiment** The micrographs above, right, were taken of wild-type, ΔFus3, and Δformin cells after they were stained green, exposed to mating factor, and then stained red. The wild-type cells expressed both Fus3 and formin.

**Interpret the Data**

1. A model helps scientists form a testable hypothesis. The diagram shows the working model of shmoo formation developed by the researchers. (a) What hypothesis from the model was being tested with the ΔFus3 strain? (b) With the Δformin strain? (c) What is the purpose of including wild-type yeast cells in the experiment?

Wild type          ΔFus3          Δformin

2. When designing an experiment, scientists make predictions about what results will occur if their hypothesis is correct. (a) If the hypothesis about the role of Fus3 kinase activity in shmoo production is correct, what result should be observed in the ΔFus3 strain? If it is incorrect, what result is expected? (b) If the hypothesis about the role of formin in shmoo production is correct, what result should be observed in the Δformin strain? If it is incorrect, what result is expected?

3. For each micrograph, describe the shape of the cells and the pattern of cell wall staining. Explain the significance of your observations. Which strain(s) of yeast cells formed shmoos?

4. (a) Do the data support the hypothesis about the role of Fus3 kinase in shmoo production? (b) Do the data support the hypothesis about the role of formin in shmoo production? (c) Do the data support the working model (the working hypothesis) in the diagram?

5. Fus3 kinase and formin proteins are generally distributed evenly throughout a yeast cell. Based on the model in the diagram, explain why the projection would emerge on the same side of the cell that bound the mating factor.

6. What do you predict would happen if the yeast had a mutation that prevented the G protein from binding GTP?

**MB** A version of this Scientific Skills Exercise can be assigned in MasteringBiology.

**Data from** D. Matheos et al., Pheromone-induced polarization is dependent on the Fus3p MAPK acting through the formin Bni1p, *Journal of Cell Biology* 165:99–109 (2004).

branch point and an important intersection point in a complex signal transduction network that controls immune cell behavior. When the WAS protein is absent, the cytoskeleton is not properly organized and signaling pathways are disrupted, leading to the WAS symptoms.

### Termination of the Signal

To keep Figure 8.17 simple, we did not indicate the *inactivation* mechanisms that are an essential aspect of any cell-signaling pathway. For a cell of a multicellular organism to remain capable of responding to incoming signals, each molecular change in its signaling pathways must last only a short time. As we saw in the cholera example, if a signaling pathway component becomes locked into one state, whether active or inactive, consequences for the organism can be dire.

The ability of a cell to receive new signals depends on reversibility of the changes produced by prior signals. The binding of signaling molecules to receptors is reversible. As the external concentration of signaling molecules falls, fewer receptors are bound at any given moment, and the unbound receptors revert to their inactive form. The cellular response occurs only when the concentration of receptors with bound signaling molecules is above a certain threshold. When the number of active receptors falls below that threshold, the cellular response ceases. Then, by a variety of means, the relay molecules return to their inactive forms: The GTPase activity intrinsic to a G protein hydrolyzes its bound GTP; the enzyme phosphodiesterase converts cAMP to AMP; protein phosphatases inactivate phosphorylated kinases and other proteins; and so forth. As a result, the cell is soon ready to respond to a fresh signal.

In this section, we explored the complexity of signaling initiation and termination in a single pathway, and we saw the potential for pathways to intersect with each other. In the next section, we'll consider one especially important network of interacting pathways in the cell.

---

**CONCEPT CHECK 8.4**

1. How can a target cell's response to a single hormone molecule result in a response that affects a million other molecules?

2. **WHAT IF?** If two cells have different scaffolding proteins, explain how they might behave differently in response to the same signaling molecule.

3. **MAKE CONNECTIONS** Some human diseases are associated with malfunctioning protein phosphatases. How would such proteins affect signaling pathways? (Review the discussion of protein phosphatases in Concept 8.3, and see Figure 8.10.)

For suggested answers, see Appendix A.

---

# Apoptosis integrates multiple cell-signaling pathways

To be or not to be? One of the most elaborate networks of signaling pathways in the cell seems to ask and answer this question, originally posed by Hamlet. Cells that are infected, are damaged, or have reached the end of their functional life span often undergo "programmed cell death" **(Figure 8.19)**. The best-understood type of this controlled cell suicide is **apoptosis** (from the Greek, meaning "falling off," and used in a classic Greek poem to refer to leaves falling from a tree). During this process, cellular agents chop up the DNA and fragment the organelles and other cytoplasmic components. The cell shrinks and becomes lobed (a change called "blebbing"), and the cell's parts are packaged up in vesicles that are engulfed and digested by specialized scavenger cells, leaving no trace. Apoptosis protects neighboring cells from damage that they would otherwise suffer if a dying cell merely leaked out all its contents, including its many digestive enzymes.

The signal that triggers apoptosis can come from either outside or inside the cell. Outside the cell, signaling molecules released from other cells can initiate a signal transduction pathway that activates the genes and proteins responsible for carrying out cell death. Within a cell whose DNA has been irretrievably damaged, a series of protein-protein interactions can pass along a signal that similarly triggers cell death. Considering some examples of apoptosis can help us to see how signaling pathways are integrated in cells.

## Apoptosis in the Soil Worm *Caenorhabditis elegans*

The molecular mechanisms of apoptosis were worked out by researchers studying embryonic development of a small soil worm, a nematode called *Caenorhabditis elegans*. Because the

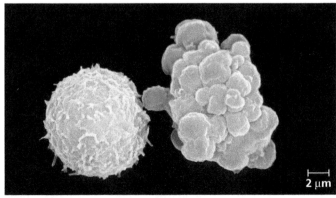

▲ **Figure 8.19 Apoptosis of a human white blood cell.** On the left is a normal white blood cell, while on the right is a white blood cell undergoing apoptosis. The apoptotic cell is shrinking and forming lobes ("blebs"), which eventually are shed as membrane-bounded cell fragments (colorized SEMs).

adult worm has only about 1,000 cells, the researchers were able to work out the entire ancestry of each cell. The timely suicide of cells occurs exactly 131 times during normal development of *C. elegans*, at precisely the same points in the cell lineage of each worm. In worms and other species, apoptosis is triggered by signals that activate a cascade of "suicide" proteins in the cells destined to die.

Genetic research on *C. elegans* initially revealed two key apoptosis genes, called *ced-3* and *ced-4* (*ced* stands for "cell death"), which encode proteins essential for apoptosis. The proteins are called Ced-3 and Ced-4, respectively. These and most other proteins involved in apoptosis are continually present in cells, but in inactive form; thus, regulation in this case occurs at the level of protein activity rather than through gene activity and protein synthesis. In *C. elegans*, a protein in the outer mitochondrial membrane, called Ced-9 (the product of the *ced-9* gene), serves as a master regulator of apoptosis, acting as a brake in the absence of a signal promoting apoptosis **(Figure 8.20)**. When a death signal is received by the cell, signal transduction involves a change in Ced-9 that disables the brake, and the apoptotic pathway activates proteases and nucleases, enzymes that cut up the proteins and DNA of the cell. The main proteases of apoptosis are called *caspases*; in the nematode, the chief caspase is the Ced-3 protein.

## Apoptotic Pathways and the Signals That Trigger Them

In humans and other mammals, several different pathways, involving about 15 different caspases, can carry out apoptosis. The pathway that is used depends on the type of cell and on the particular signal that initiates apoptosis. One major pathway involves certain mitochondrial proteins that are triggered to form molecular pores in the mitochondrial outer membrane, causing it to leak and release other proteins that promote apoptosis. Perhaps surprisingly, these latter include cytochrome *c*, which functions in mitochondrial electron transport in healthy cells but acts as a cell death factor when released from mitochondria. The process of mitochondrial apoptosis in mammals uses proteins similar to the nematode proteins Ced-3, Ced-4, and Ced-9. These can be thought of as relay proteins capable of transducing the apoptotic signal.

At key gateways into the apoptotic program, relay proteins integrate signals from several different sources and can send a cell down an apoptotic pathway. Often, the signal originates outside the cell, like the death-signaling molecule depicted in Figure 8.20b, which presumably was released by a neighboring cell. When a death-signaling ligand occupies a cell-surface receptor, this binding leads to activation of caspases and other enzymes that carry out apoptosis, without involving the mitochondrial pathway. This process of signal reception, transduction, and response is similar to what we have discussed throughout this chapter. In a twist on the classic scenario, two other types of alarm signals that can lead to apoptosis originate

**(a) No death signal.** As long as Ced-9, located in the outer mitochondrial membrane, is active, apoptosis is inhibited, and the cell remains alive.

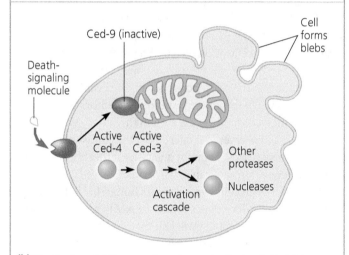

**(b) Death signal.** When a cell receives a death signal, Ced-9 is inactivated, relieving its inhibition of Ced-3 and Ced-4. Active Ced-3, a protease, triggers a cascade of reactions leading to activation of nucleases and other proteases. The action of these enzymes causes the changes seen in apoptotic cells and eventual cell death.

▲ **Figure 8.20 Molecular basis of apoptosis in *C. elegans.*** Three proteins, Ced-3, Ced-4, and Ced-9, are critical to apoptosis and its regulation in the nematode. Apoptosis is more complicated in mammals but involves proteins similar to those in the nematode.

from *inside* the cell rather than from a cell-surface receptor. One signal comes from the nucleus, generated when the DNA has suffered irreparable damage, and a second comes from the endoplasmic reticulum when excessive protein misfolding occurs. Mammalian cells make life-or-death "decisions" by somehow integrating the death signals and life signals they receive from these external and internal sources.

A built-in cell suicide mechanism is essential to development and maintenance in all animals. The similarities between apoptosis genes in nematodes and those in mammals, as well as the observation that apoptosis occurs in multicellular fungi and even in single-celled yeasts, indicate that the

Interdigital tissue | Cells undergoing apoptosis | 1 mm | Space between digits

▲ **Figure 8.21 Effect of apoptosis during paw development in the mouse.** In mice, humans, other mammals, and land birds, the embryonic region that develops into feet or hands initially has a solid, platelike structure.

Apoptosis eliminates the cells in the interdigital regions, thus forming the digits. The embryonic mouse paws shown in these fluorescence light micrographs are stained so that cells undergoing apoptosis appear a bright yellowish green.

Apoptosis of cells begins at the margin of each interdigital region (left), peaks as the tissue in these regions is reduced (middle), and is no longer visible when the interdigital tissue has been eliminated (right).

basic mechanism evolved early in the evolution of eukaryotes. In vertebrates, apoptosis is essential for normal development of the nervous system, for normal operation of the immune system, and for normal morphogenesis of hands and feet in humans and paws in other mammals (**Figure 8.21**). The level of apoptosis between the developing digits is lower in the webbed feet of ducks and other water birds than in the nonwebbed feet of land birds, such as chickens. In the case of humans, the failure of appropriate apoptosis can result in webbed fingers and toes.

Significant evidence points to the involvement of apoptosis in certain degenerative diseases of the nervous system, such as Parkinson's disease and Alzheimer's disease. In Alzheimer's disease, an accumulation of aggregated proteins in neuronal cells activates an enzyme that triggers apoptosis, resulting in the loss of brain function seen in these patients. Furthermore, cancer can result from a failure of cell suicide; some cases of human melanoma, for example, have been linked to faulty

forms of the human version of the *C. elegans* Ced-4 protein. It is not surprising, therefore, that the signaling pathways feeding into apoptosis are quite elaborate. After all, the life-or-death question is the most fundamental one imaginable for a cell.

This chapter has introduced you to many of the general mechanisms of cell communication, such as ligand binding, protein-protein interactions and shape changes, cascades of interactions, and protein phosphorylation. Throughout your study of biology, you will encounter numerous examples of cell signaling.

**CONCEPT CHECK 8.5**

1. Give an example of apoptosis during embryonic development, and explain its function in the developing embryo.
2. **WHAT IF?** What types of protein defects could result in apoptosis occurring when it should not? What types could result in apoptosis not occurring when it should?

For suggested answers, see Appendix A.

---

# 8 Chapter Review

## SUMMARY OF KEY CONCEPTS

**CONCEPT** 8.1

### External signals are converted to responses within the cell (pp. 154–158)

- **Signal transduction pathways** are crucial for many processes. Signaling during yeast cell mating has much in common with processes in multicellular organisms, suggesting an early evolutionary origin of signaling mechanisms. Bacterial cells can sense the local density of bacterial cells (quorum sensing).
- Local signaling by animal cells involves direct contact or the secretion of local regulators. For long-distance signaling, animal and plant cells use **hormones**; animals also pass signals electrically.

- Like other hormones that bind to membrane receptors, epinephrine triggers a three-stage cell-signaling pathway:

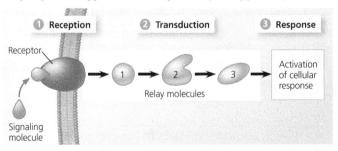

**?** *What determines whether a cell responds to a hormone such as epinephrine? What determines how a cell responds to such a hormone?*

## CONCEPT 8.2

### Reception: A signaling molecule binds to a receptor protein, causing it to change shape (pp. 158–162)

- The binding between signaling molecule (**ligand**) and receptor is highly specific. A specific shape change in a receptor is often the initial transduction of the signal.
- There are three major types of cell-surface transmembrane receptors: (1) **G protein-coupled receptors (GPCRs)** work with cytoplasmic **G proteins**. Ligand binding activates the receptor, which then activates a specific G protein, which activates yet another protein, thus propagating the signal. (2) **Receptor tyrosine kinases (RTKs)** react to the binding of signaling molecules by forming dimers and then adding phosphate groups to tyrosines on the cytoplasmic part of the other monomer making up the dimer. Relay proteins in the cell can then be activated by binding to different phosphorylated tyrosines, allowing this receptor to trigger several pathways at once. (3) **Ligand-gated ion channels** open or close in response to binding by specific signaling molecules, regulating the flow of specific ions across the membrane.
- The activity of all three types of receptors is crucial; abnormal GPCRs and RTKs are associated with many human diseases.
- Intracellular receptors are cytoplasmic or nuclear proteins. Signaling molecules that are hydrophobic or small enough to cross the plasma membrane bind to these receptors inside the cell.

**?** *How are the structures of a GPCR and an RTK similar? How does initiation of signal transduction differ for these two types of receptors?*

## CONCEPT 8.3

### Transduction: Cascades of molecular interactions relay signals from receptors to target molecules in the cell (pp. 162–166)

- At each step in a signal transduction pathway, the signal is transduced into a different form, which commonly involves a shape change in a protein. Many signal transduction pathways include **phosphorylation cascades**, in which a series of **protein kinases** each add a phosphate group to the next one in line, activating it. Enzymes called **protein phosphatases** remove the phosphate groups. The balance between phosphorylation and dephosphorylation regulates the activity of proteins involved in the sequential steps of a signal transduction pathway.
- **Second messengers**, such as the small molecule **cyclic AMP (cAMP)** and the ion $Ca^{2+}$, diffuse readily through the cytosol and thus help broadcast signals quickly. Many G proteins activate **adenylyl cyclase**, which makes cAMP from ATP. Cells use $Ca^{2+}$ as a second messenger in both GPCR and RTK pathways. The tyrosine kinase pathways can also involve two other second messengers, **diacylglycerol (DAG)** and **inositol trisphosphate (IP₃)**. $IP_3$ can trigger a subsequent increase in $Ca^{2+}$ levels.

**?** *What is the difference between a protein kinase and a second messenger? Can both operate in the same signal transduction pathway?*

## CONCEPT 8.4

### Response: Cell signaling leads to regulation of transcription or cytoplasmic activities (pp. 166–171)

- Some pathways lead to a nuclear response: Specific genes are turned on or off by activated transcription factors. In others, the response involves cytoplasmic regulation.

- Cellular responses are not simply on or off; they are regulated at many steps. Each protein in a signaling pathway amplifies the signal by activating multiple copies of the next component; for long pathways, the total amplification may be over a millionfold. The combination of proteins in a cell confers specificity in the signals it detects and the responses it carries out. **Scaffolding proteins** increase signaling efficiency. Pathway branching further helps the cell coordinate signals and responses. Signal response is terminated quickly by the reversal of ligand binding.

**?** *What mechanisms in the cell terminate its response to a signal and maintain its ability to respond to new signals?*

## CONCEPT 8.5

### Apoptosis integrates multiple cell-signaling pathways (pp. 171–173)

- **Apoptosis** is a type of programmed cell death in which cell components are disposed of in an orderly fashion. Studies of the soil worm *Caenorhabditis elegans* clarified molecular details of the relevant signaling pathways. A death signal leads to activation of caspases and nucleases, the main enzymes involved in apoptosis.
- Several apoptotic signaling pathways exist in the cells of humans and other mammals, triggered in different ways. Signals eliciting apoptosis can originate from outside or inside the cell.

**?** *What is an explanation for the similarities between genes in yeasts, nematodes, and mammals that control apoptosis?*

## TEST YOUR UNDERSTANDING

### Level 1: Knowledge/Comprehension

1. Binding of a signaling molecule to which type of receptor leads directly to a change in the distribution of ions on opposite sides of the membrane?
   a. intracellular receptor
   b. G protein-coupled receptor
   c. phosphorylated receptor tyrosine kinase dimer
   d. ligand-gated ion channel

2. The activation of receptor tyrosine kinases is characterized by
   a. dimerization and phosphorylation.
   b. dimerization and $IP_3$ binding.
   c. a phosphorylation cascade.
   d. GTP hydrolysis.

3. Lipid-soluble signaling molecules, such as aldosterone, cross the membranes of all cells but affect only target cells because
   a. only target cells retain the appropriate DNA segments.
   b. intracellular receptors are present only in target cells.
   c. only target cells have enzymes that break down aldosterone.
   d. only in target cells is aldosterone able to initiate the phosphorylation cascade that turns genes on.

4. Consider this pathway: epinephrine → G protein-coupled receptor → G protein → adenylyl cyclase → cAMP. Identify the second messenger.
   a. cAMP
   b. G protein
   c. GTP
   d. adenylyl cyclase

5. Apoptosis involves all but which of the following?
   a. fragmentation of the DNA
   b. cell-signaling pathways
   c. lysis of the cell
   d. digestion of cellular contents by scavenger cells

## Level 2: Application/Analysis

**6.** Which observation suggested to Sutherland the involvement of a second messenger in epinephrine's effect on liver cells?
- **a.** Enzymatic activity was proportional to the amount of calcium added to a cell-free extract.
- **b.** Receptor studies indicated that epinephrine was a ligand.
- **c.** Glycogen breakdown was observed only when epinephrine was administered to intact cells.
- **d.** Glycogen breakdown was observed when epinephrine and glycogen phosphorylase were combined.

**7.** Protein phosphorylation is commonly involved with all of the following *except*
- **a.** activation of receptor tyrosine kinases.
- **b.** activation of protein kinase molecules.
- **c.** activation of G protein-coupled receptors.
- **d.** regulation of transcription by signaling molecules.

## Level 3: Synthesis/Evaluation

**8.** **DRAW IT** Draw the following apoptotic pathway, which operates in human immune cells. A death signal is received when a molecule called Fas binds its cell-surface receptor. The binding of many Fas molecules to receptors causes receptor clustering. The intracellular regions of the receptors, when together, bind proteins called adaptor proteins. These in turn bind to inactive molecules of caspase-8, which become activated and then activate caspase-3. Once activated, caspase-3 initiates apoptosis.

**9. EVOLUTION CONNECTION**
What evolutionary mechanisms might account for the origin and persistence of cell-to-cell signaling systems in prokaryotes?

**10. SCIENTIFIC INQUIRY**
Epinephrine initiates a signal transduction pathway that produces cyclic AMP (cAMP) and leads to the breakdown of glycogen to glucose, a major energy source for cells. But glycogen breakdown is only part of the fight-or-flight response that epinephrine brings about; the overall effect on the body includes an increase in heart rate and alertness, as well as a burst of energy. Given that caffeine blocks the activity of cAMP phosphodiesterase, propose a mechanism by which caffeine ingestion leads to heightened alertness and sleeplessness.

**11. SCIENCE, TECHNOLOGY, AND SOCIETY**
The aging process is thought to be initiated at the cellular level. Among the changes that can occur after a certain number of cell divisions is the loss of a cell's ability to respond to growth factors and other signals. Much research into aging is aimed at understanding such losses, with the ultimate goal of extending the human life span. Not everyone, however, agrees that this is a desirable goal. If life expectancy were greatly increased, what might be the social and ecological consequences?

**12. WRITE ABOUT A THEME: ORGANIZATION**
The properties of life emerge at the biological level of the cell. The highly regulated process of apoptosis is not simply the destruction of a cell; it is also an emergent property. Write a short essay (about 100–150 words) that briefly explains the role of apoptosis in the development and proper functioning of an animal, and describe how this form of programmed cell death is a process that emerges from the orderly integration of signaling pathways.

**13. SYNTHESIZE YOUR KNOWLEDGE**

There are five basic tastes—sour, salty, sweet, bitter, and "umami." Salt is detected when the concentration of salt outside of a taste bud cell is higher than that inside of it, and ion channels allow the passive leakage of $Na^+$ into the cell. The resulting change in membrane potential (see Concept 4.4) sends the "salty" signal to the brain. Umami is a savory taste generated by glutamate (glutamic acid, found in monosodium glutamate, or MSG), which is used as a flavor enhancer in foods such as taco-flavored tortilla chips. The glutamate receptor is a GPCR, which, when bound, initiates a signaling pathway that ends with a cellular response, perceived by you as "taste." If you eat a regular potato chip and then rinse your mouth, you will no longer taste salt. But if you eat a flavored tortilla chip and then rinse, the taste persists. (Try it!) Propose a possible explanation for this difference.

*For selected answers, see Appendix A.*

## MasteringBiology®

**Students** Go to **MasteringBiology** for assignments, the eText, and the Study Area with practice tests, animations, and activities.

**Instructors** Go to **MasteringBiology** for automatically graded tutorials and questions that you can assign to your students, plus Instructor Resources.

# The Cell Cycle

9

**KEY CONCEPTS**

9.1 Most cell division results in genetically identical daughter cells

9.2 The mitotic phase alternates with interphase in the cell cycle

9.3 The eukaryotic cell cycle is regulated by a molecular control system

OVERVIEW

## The Key Roles of Cell Division

The ability of organisms to produce more of their own kind is the one characteristic that best distinguishes living things from nonliving matter. This unique capacity to procreate, like all biological functions, has a cellular basis. Rudolf Virchow, a German physician, put it this way in 1855: "Where a cell exists, there must have been a preexisting cell, just as the animal arises only from an animal and the plant only from a plant." He summarized this concept with the Latin axiom *"Omnis cellula e cellula,"* meaning "Every cell from a cell." The continuity of life is based on the reproduction of cells, or **cell division**. The series of confocal fluorescence micrographs in **Figure 9.1**, starting at the upper left, follows the events of cell division as the cells of a two-celled embryo become four.

Cell division plays several important roles in life. When a prokaryotic cell divides, it is actually reproducing, since the process gives rise to a new organism (another cell). The same is true of any unicellular eukaryote, such as the amoeba shown in **Figure 9.2a**. As for multicellular eukaryotes, cell division enables each of these organisms to develop from a single cell—the fertilized egg. A two-celled embryo, the first stage in this process, is shown in **Figure 9.2b**. And cell division continues to function in renewal and repair in fully grown multicellular eukaryotes, replacing cells that die from normal wear and tear or accidents. For example, dividing cells in your bone marrow continuously make new blood cells **(Figure 9.2c)**.

The cell division process is an integral part of the **cell cycle**, the life of a cell from the time it is first formed during division of a parent cell until its own division into two daughter cells. (Our use of the words *daughter* or *sister* in relation to cells is not meant to imply gender.) Passing identical genetic material to cellular offspring is a crucial function of cell division. In this chapter, you will learn how this process occurs.

▼ **Figure 9.1** How do dividing cells distribute chromosomes to daughter cells?

▶ Chromosomes (blue) are moved by cell machinery (red) during division of a rat kangaroo cell.

◄ **(a) Reproduction.** An amoeba, a single-celled eukaryote, is dividing into two cells. Each new cell will be an individual organism (LM).

▶ **(b) Growth and development.** This micrograph shows a sand dollar embryo shortly after the fertilized egg divided, forming two cells (LM).

◄ **(c) Tissue renewal.** These dividing bone marrow cells will give rise to new blood cells (LM).

▲ **Figure 9.2** **The functions of cell division.**

After studying the cellular mechanics of cell division in eukaryotes and bacteria, you will learn about the molecular control system that regulates progress through the eukaryotic cell cycle and what happens when the control system malfunctions. Because a breakdown in cell cycle control plays a major role in cancer development, this aspect of cell biology is an active area of research.

**CONCEPT** 9.1

# Most cell division results in genetically identical daughter cells

The reproduction of a cell, with all of its complexity, cannot occur by a mere pinching in half; a cell is not like a soap bubble that simply enlarges and splits in two. In both prokaryotes and eukaryotes, most cell division involves the distribution of identical genetic material—DNA—to two daughter cells. (The exception is meiosis, the special type of eukaryotic cell division that can produce sperm and eggs.) What is most remarkable about cell division is the fidelity with which the DNA is passed from one generation of cells to the next. A dividing cell replicates its DNA, allocates the two copies to opposite ends of the cell, and only then splits into daughter cells.

## Cellular Organization of the Genetic Material

A cell's endowment of DNA, its genetic information, is called its **genome**. Although a prokaryotic genome is often a single DNA molecule, eukaryotic genomes usually consist of a

number of DNA molecules. The overall length of DNA in a eukaryotic cell is enormous. A typical human cell, for example, has about 2 m of DNA—a length about 250,000 times greater than the cell's diameter. Before the cell can divide to form genetically identical daughter cells, all of this DNA must be copied, or replicated, and then the two copies must be separated so that each daughter cell ends up with a complete genome.

The replication and distribution of so much DNA is manageable because the DNA molecules are packaged into structures called **chromosomes**, so named because they take up certain dyes used in microscopy (from the Greek *chroma*, color, and *soma*, body; **Figure 9.3**). Each eukaryotic chromosome consists of one very long, linear DNA molecule associated with many proteins. The DNA molecule carries several hundred to a few thousand genes, the units of information that specify an organism's inherited traits. The associated proteins maintain the structure of the chromosome and help control the activity of the genes. Together, the entire complex of DNA and proteins that is the building material of chromosomes is referred to as **chromatin**. As you will soon see, the chromatin of a chromosome varies in its degree of condensation during the process of cell division.

Every eukaryotic species has a characteristic number of chromosomes in each cell's nucleus. For example, the nuclei of human **somatic cells** (all body cells except the reproductive cells) each contain 46 chromosomes, made up of two sets of 23, one set inherited from each parent. Reproductive cells, or **gametes**—sperm and eggs—have one set, or half as many chromosomes as somatic cells; in our example, human gametes have one set of 23 chromosomes. The number of chromosomes in somatic cells varies widely among species: 18 in cabbage plants, 48 in chimpanzees, 56 in elephants, 90 in hedgehogs, and 148 in one species of alga. We'll now consider how these chromosomes behave during cell division.

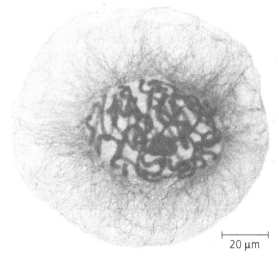

▲ **Figure 9.3** **Eukaryotic chromosomes.** Chromosomes (stained purple) are visible within the nucleus of this cell from an African blood lily. The thinner red threads in the surrounding cytoplasm are the cytoskeleton. The cell is preparing to divide (LM).

## Distribution of Chromosomes During Eukaryotic Cell Division

When a cell is not dividing, and even as it replicates its DNA in preparation for cell division, each chromosome is in the form of a long, thin chromatin fiber. After DNA replication, however, the chromosomes condense as a part of cell division: Each chromatin fiber becomes densely coiled and folded, making the chromosomes much shorter and so thick that we can see them with a light microscope.

Each duplicated chromosome has two **sister chromatids**, which are joined copies of the original chromosome (**Figure 9.4**). The two chromatids, each containing an identical DNA molecule, are initially attached all along their lengths by protein complexes called *cohesins*; this attachment is known as *sister chromatid cohesion*. Each sister chromatid has a **centromere**, a region of the chromosomal DNA where the chromatid is attached most closely to its sister chromatid. This attachment is mediated by proteins bound to the centromeric DNA; other bound proteins condense the DNA, giving the du-plicated chromosome a narrow "waist." The portion of a chro-matid to either side of the centromere is referred to as an *arm* of the chromatid. (An unduplicated chromosome has a single centromere, distinguished by the proteins that bind there, and two arms.)

Later in the cell division process, the two sister chromatids of each duplicated chromosome separate and move into two new nuclei, one forming at each end of the cell. Once the sister chromatids separate, they are no longer called sister chromatids but are considered individual chromo-somes; this step essentially doubles the number of chromosomes in the cell. Thus, each new nucleus receives a collection of chromosomes identical to that of the par-ent cell (**Figure 9.5**). **Mitosis**, the division of the genetic material in the nucleus, is usually followed immediately by **cytoki-nesis**, the division of the cytoplasm. One cell has become two, each the genetic equivalent of the parent cell.

From a fertilized egg, mitosis and cyto-kinesis produced the 200 trillion somatic cells that now make up your body, and the same processes continue to generate new cells to replace dead and damaged ones. In contrast, you produce gametes—eggs or sperm—by a variation of cell division called *meiosis*, which yields daughter cells with only one set of chromosomes, half as many chromosomes as the parent cell. Meiosis in humans occurs only in special

Sister chromatids

Centromere   0.5 μm

▲ **Figure 9.4 A highly condensed, duplicated human chromosome (SEM).**

**DRAW IT** *Circle one sister chromatid of the chromosome in this micrograph.*

cells in the ovaries or testes (the gonads). Generating gametes, meiosis reduces the chromosome number from 46 (two sets) to 23 (one set). Fertilization fuses two gametes together and returns the chromosome number to 46 (two sets). Mitosis then conserves that number in every somatic cell nucleus of the new human individual. In Chapter 10, we will examine the role of meiosis in reproduction and inheritance in more detail. In the remainder of this chapter, we focus on mitosis and the rest of the cell cycle in eukaryotes.

1 One of the multiple chromosomes in a eukaryotic cell is represented here, not yet duplicated. Normally it would be a long, thin chromatin fiber containing one DNA molecule and associated proteins; here its condensed form is shown for illustration purposes only.

Chromosomes    Chromosomal DNA molecules

Centromere

Chromosome arm

Chromosome duplication (including DNA replication) and condensation

2 Once duplicated, a chromosome consists of two sister chroma-tids connected along their entire lengths by sister chromatid cohesion. Each chromatid contains a copy of the DNA molecule.

Sister chromatids

Separation of sister chromatids into two chromosomes

3 Molecular and mechanical processes separate the sister chromatids into two chromosomes and distribute them to two daughter cells.

▲ **Figure 9.5 Chromosome duplication and distribution during cell division.**

**?** How many chromatid arms does the chromosome in 2 have?

CONCEPT CHECK 9.1

1. How many chromosomes are drawn in each part of Figure 9.5? (Ignore the micrograph in part 2.)
2. **WHAT IF?** A chicken has 78 chromosomes in its somatic cells. How many chromosomes did the chicken inherit from each parent? How many chromosomes are in each of the chicken's gametes? How many chromosomes will be in each somatic cell of the chicken's offspring?

For suggested answers, see Appendix A.

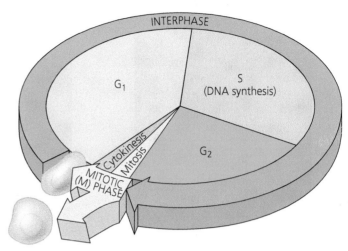

▲ Figure 9.6 **The cell cycle.** In a dividing cell, the mitotic (M) phase alternates with interphase, a growth period. The first part of interphase ($G_1$) is followed by the S phase, when the chromosomes duplicate; $G_2$ is the last part of interphase. In the M phase, mitosis distributes the daughter chromosomes to daughter nuclei, and cytokinesis divides the cytoplasm, producing two daughter cells.

 ## 9.2

# The mitotic phase alternates with interphase in the cell cycle

In 1882, a German anatomist named Walther Flemming developed dyes that allowed him to observe, for the first time, the behavior of chromosomes during mitosis and cytokinesis. (In fact, Flemming coined the terms *mitosis* and *chromatin*.) During the period between one cell division and the next, it appeared to Flemming that the cell was simply growing larger. But we now know that many critical events occur during this stage in the life of a cell.

## Phases of the Cell Cycle

Mitosis is just one part of the cell cycle **(Figure 9.6)**. In fact, the **mitotic (M) phase**, which includes both mitosis and cytokinesis, is usually the shortest part of the cell cycle. The mitotic phase alternates with a much longer stage called **interphase**, which often accounts for about 90% of the cycle. Interphase can be divided into subphases: the **$G_1$ phase** ("first gap"), the **S phase** ("synthesis"), and the **$G_2$ phase** ("second gap"). The G phases were misnamed as "gaps" when they were first observed because the cells appeared inactive, but we now know that intense metabolic activity and growth occur throughout interphase. During all three subphases of interphase, in fact, a cell grows by producing proteins and cytoplasmic organelles such as mitochondria and endoplasmic reticulum. Duplication of the chromosomes, crucial for eventual division of the cell, occurs entirely during the S phase. Thus, a cell grows ($G_1$), continues to grow as it copies its chromosomes (S), grows more as it completes preparations for cell division ($G_2$), and divides (M). The daughter cells may then repeat the cycle.

A particular human cell might undergo one division in 24 hours. Of this time, the M phase would occupy less than 1 hour, while the S phase might occupy about 10–12 hours, or about half the cycle. The rest of the time would be apportioned between the $G_1$ and $G_2$ phases. The $G_2$ phase usually takes 4–6

hours; in our example, $G_1$ would occupy about 5–6 hours. $G_1$ is the most variable in length in different types of cells. Some cells in a multicellular organism divide very infrequently or not at all. These cells spend their time in $G_1$ (or a related phase called $G_0$) doing their job in the organism—a nerve cell carries impulses, for example.

Mitosis is conventionally broken down into five stages: **prophase**, **prometaphase**, **metaphase**, **anaphase**, and **telophase**. Overlapping with the latter stages of mitosis, cytokinesis completes the mitotic phase. **Figure 9.7** describes these stages in an animal cell. Study this figure thoroughly before progressing to the next two sections, which examine mitosis and cytokinesis more closely.

## The Mitotic Spindle: *A Closer Look*

Many of the events of mitosis depend on the **mitotic spindle**, which begins to form in the cytoplasm during prophase. This structure consists of fibers made of microtubules and associated proteins. While the mitotic spindle assembles, the other microtubules of the cytoskeleton partially disassemble, providing the material used to construct the spindle. The spindle microtubules elongate (polymerize) by incorporating more subunits of the protein tubulin and shorten (depolymerize) by losing subunits.

In animal cells, the assembly of spindle microtubules starts at the **centrosome**, a subcellular region containing material that functions throughout the cell cycle to organize the cell's microtubules. (It is also a type of *microtubule-organizing center*.) A pair of centrioles is located at the

## G₂ of Interphase

Centrosomes (with centriole pairs)

Chromosomes (duplicated, uncondensed)

Nucleolus

Nuclear envelope

Plasma membrane

## Prophase

Early mitotic spindle

Aster

Centromere

Two sister chromatids of one chromosome

## Prometaphase

Fragments of nuclear envelope

Nonkinetochore microtubules

Kinetochore

Kinetochore microtubule

### G₂ of Interphase

- A nuclear envelope encloses the nucleus.
- The nucleus contains one or more nucleoli (singular, *nucleolus*).
- Two centrosomes have formed by duplication of a single centrosome. Centrosomes are regions in animal cells that organize the microtubules of the spindle. Each centrosome contains two centrioles.
- Chromosomes, duplicated during S phase, cannot be seen individually because they have not yet condensed.

The fluorescence micrographs show dividing lung cells from a newt; this species has 22 chromosomes. Chromosomes appear blue, microtubules green, and intermediate filaments red. For simplicity, the drawings show only 6 chromosomes.

### Prophase

- The chromatin fibers become more tightly coiled, condensing into discrete chromosomes observable with a light microscope.
- The nucleoli disappear.
- Each duplicated chromosome appears as two identical sister chromatids joined at their centromeres and, in some species, all along their arms by cohesins (sister chromatid cohesion).
- The mitotic spindle (named for its shape) begins to form. It is composed of the centrosomes and the microtubules that extend from them. The radial arrays of shorter microtubules that extend from the centrosomes are called asters ("stars").
- The centrosomes move away from each other, propelled partly by the lengthening microtubules between them.

*fragmentation of nuclear envelope*
*Golgi apparatus and ER*

### Prometaphase

- The nuclear envelope fragments.
- The microtubules extending from each centrosome can now invade the nuclear area.
- The chromosomes have become even more condensed.
- Each of the two chromatids of each chromosome now has a kinetochore, a specialized protein structure at the centromere.
- Some of the microtubules attach to the kinetochores, becoming "kinetochore microtubules," which jerk the chromosomes back and forth.
- Nonkinetochore microtubules interact with those from the opposite pole of the spindle.

? *How many molecules of DNA are in the prometaphase drawing? How many molecules per chromosome? How many double helices are there per chromosome? Per chromatid?*

10 μm

| Metaphase | Anaphase | Telophase and Cytokinesis |

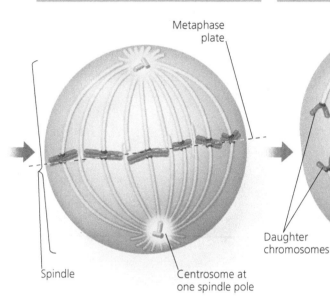

Metaphase plate

Spindle

Centrosome at one spindle pole

Daughter chromosomes

Cleavage furrow

Nucleolus forming

Nuclear envelope forming

### Metaphase

- The centrosomes are now at opposite poles of the cell.
- The chromosomes have all arrived at the *metaphase plate*, a plane that is equidistant between the spindle's two poles. The chromosomes' centromeres lie at the metaphase plate.
- For each chromosome, the kinetochores of the sister chromatids are attached to kinetochore microtubules coming from opposite poles.

### Anaphase

- Anaphase is the shortest stage of mitosis, often lasting only a few minutes.
- Anaphase begins when the cohesin proteins are cleaved. This allows the two sister chromatids of each pair to part suddenly. Each chromatid thus becomes a full-fledged chromosome.
- The two liberated daughter chromosomes begin moving toward opposite ends of the cell as their kinetochore microtubules shorten. Because these microtubules are attached at the centromere region, the chromosomes move centromere first (at about 1 μm/min).
- The cell elongates as the nonkinetochore microtubules lengthen.
- By the end of anaphase, the two ends of the cell have equivalent—and complete—collections of chromosomes.

### Telophase

- Two daughter nuclei form in the cell. Nuclear envelopes arise from the fragments of the parent cell's nuclear envelope and other portions of the endomembrane system.
- Nucleoli reappear.
- The chromosomes become less condensed.
- Any remaining spindle microtubules are depolymerized.
- Mitosis, the division of one nucleus into two genetically identical nuclei, is now complete.

### Cytokinesis

- The division of the cytoplasm is usually well under way by late telophase, so the two daughter cells appear shortly after the end of mitosis.
- In animal cells, cytokinesis involves the formation of a cleavage furrow, which pinches the cell in two.

ANIMATION

***BioFlix*** Visit the Study Area in **MasteringBiology** for the BioFlix® 3-D Animation on Mitosis. BioFlix Tutorials can also be assigned in MasteringBiology.

center of the centrosome, but they are not essential for cell division: If the centrioles are destroyed with a laser microbeam, a spindle nevertheless forms during mitosis. In fact, centrioles are not even present in plant cells, which do form mitotic spindles.

During interphase in animal cells, the single centrosome duplicates, forming two centrosomes, which remain near the nucleus. The two centrosomes move apart during prophase and prometaphase of mitosis as spindle microtubules grow out from them. By the end of prometaphase, the two centrosomes, one at each pole of the spindle, are at opposite ends of the cell. An **aster**, a radial array of short microtubules, extends from each centrosome. The spindle includes the centrosomes, the spindle microtubules, and the asters.

Each of the two sister chromatids of a duplicated chromosome has a **kinetochore**, a structure made up of proteins that have assembled on specific sections of DNA at each centromere. The chromosome's two kinetochores face in opposite directions. During prometaphase, some of the spindle microtubules attach to the kinetochores; these are called kinetochore microtubules. (The number of microtubules attached to a kinetochore varies among species, from one microtubule in yeast cells to 40 or so in some mammalian cells.) When one of a chromosome's kinetochores is "captured" by microtubules, the chromosome begins to move toward the pole from which those microtubules extend. However, this movement is checked as soon as microtubules from the opposite pole attach to the kinetochore on the other chromatid. What happens next is like a tug-of-war that ends in a draw. The chromosome moves first in one direction, then in the other, back and forth, finally settling midway between the two ends of the cell. At metaphase, the centromeres of all the duplicated chromosomes are on a plane midway between the spindle's two poles. This plane is called the **metaphase plate**, which is an imaginary plate rather than an actual cellular structure (**Figure 9.8**). Meanwhile, microtubules that do not attach to kinetochores have been elongating, and by metaphase they overlap and interact with other nonkinetochore microtubules from the opposite pole of the spindle. By metaphase, the microtubules of the asters have also grown and are in contact with the plasma membrane. The spindle is now complete.

The structure of the spindle correlates well with its function during anaphase. Anaphase begins suddenly when the cohesins holding together the sister chromatids of each chromosome are cleaved by an enzyme called *separase*. Once separated, the chromatids become full-fledged chromosomes that move toward opposite ends of the cell.

How do the kinetochore microtubules function in this poleward movement of chromosomes? Apparently, two mechanisms are in play, both involving motor proteins. (To

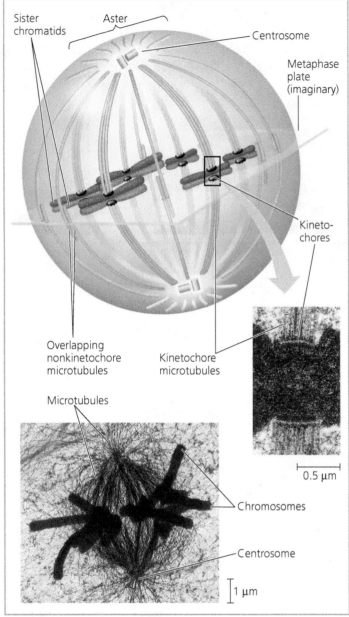

▲ Figure 9.8 **The mitotic spindle at metaphase.** The kinetochores of each chromosome's two sister chromatids face in opposite directions. Here, each kinetochore is attached to a cluster of kinetochore microtubules extending from the nearest centrosome. Nonkinetochore microtubules overlap at the metaphase plate (TEMs).

**DRAW IT** *On the lower micrograph, draw a line indicating the position of the metaphase plate. Circle an aster. Draw arrows indicating the directions of chromosome movement once anaphase begins.*

review how motor proteins move an object along a microtubule.) Results of a cleverly designed experiment suggested that motor proteins on the kinetochores "walk" the chromosomes along the microtubules, which depolymerize at their kinetochore ends after the motor proteins have passed (**Figure 9.9**). (This is referred to as the "Pac-man" mechanism because of its resemblance to the arcade game character that moves by eating all the dots in its path.) However, other researchers, working with different cell types or cells from other species, have shown that chromosomes are "reeled in" by motor proteins at the spindle poles and that the microtubules depolymerize after they pass by these motor proteins. The general consensus now is that both mechanisms are used and that their relative contributions vary among cell types.

In a dividing animal cell, the nonkinetochore microtubules are responsible for elongating the whole cell during anaphase. Nonkinetochore microtubules from opposite poles overlap each other extensively during metaphase (see Figure 9.8). During anaphase, the region of overlap is reduced as motor proteins attached to the microtubules walk them away from one another, using energy from ATP. As the microtubules push apart from each other, their spindle poles are pushed apart, elongating the cell. At the same time, the microtubules lengthen somewhat by the addition of tubulin subunits to their overlapping ends. As a result, the microtubules continue to overlap.

At the end of anaphase, duplicate groups of chromosomes have arrived at opposite ends of the elongated parent cell. Nuclei re-form during telophase. Cytokinesis generally begins during anaphase or telophase, and the spindle eventually disassembles by depolymerization of microtubules.

## Cytokinesis: *A Closer Look*

In animal cells, cytokinesis occurs by a process known as **cleavage**. The first sign of cleavage is the appearance of a **cleavage furrow**, a shallow groove in the cell surface near the old metaphase plate **(Figure 9.10a)**. On the cytoplasmic side of the furrow is a contractile ring of actin microfilaments associated with molecules of the protein myosin. The actin microfilaments interact with the myosin molecules, causing the ring to contract. The contraction of the dividing cell's ring of microfilaments is like the pulling of a drawstring. The cleavage furrow deepens until the parent cell is pinched in two, producing two completely separated cells, each with its own nucleus and its own share of cytosol, organelles, and other subcellular structures.

Cytokinesis in plant cells, which have cell walls, is markedly different. There is no cleavage furrow. Instead, during telophase, vesicles derived from the Golgi apparatus move along microtubules to the middle of the cell, where they coalesce, producing a **cell plate** **(Figure 9.10b)**. Cell wall materials carried in the vesicles collect inside the cell plate as it grows. The cell plate enlarges until its surrounding membrane fuses with the plasma membrane along the perimeter of the cell. Two daughter cells result, each with its own plasma membrane. Meanwhile, a new cell wall arising from the contents of the cell plate has formed between the daughter cells.

### ▼ Figure 9.9 Inquiry

## At which end do kinetochore microtubules shorten during anaphase?

**Experiment** Gary Borisy and colleagues at the University of Wisconsin wanted to determine whether kinetochore microtubules depolymerize at the kinetochore end or the pole end as chromosomes move toward the poles during mitosis. First they labeled the microtubules of a pig kidney cell in early anaphase with a yellow fluorescent dye.

Then they marked a region of the kinetochore microtubules between one spindle pole and the chromosomes by using a laser to eliminate the fluorescence from that region, while leaving the microtubules intact (see below). As anaphase proceeded, they monitored the changes in microtubule length on either side of the mark.

**Results** As the chromosomes moved poleward, the microtubule segments on the kinetochore side of the mark shortened, while those on the spindle pole side stayed the same length.

**Conclusion** During anaphase in this cell type, chromosome movement is correlated with kinetochore microtubules shortening at their kinetochore ends and not at their spindle pole ends. This experiment supports the hypothesis that during anaphase, a chromosome is walked along a microtubule as the microtubule depolymerizes at its kinetochore end, releasing tubulin subunits.

**Source** G. J. Gorbsky, P. J. Sammak, and G. G. Borisy, Chromosomes move poleward in anaphase along stationary microtubules that coordinately disassemble from their kinetochore ends, *Journal of Cell Biology* 104:9–18 (1987).

**WHAT IF?** If this experiment had been done on a cell type in which "reeling in" at the poles was the main cause of chromosome movement, how would the mark have moved relative to the poles? How would the microtubule lengths have changed?

## ▼ Figure 9.10 Cytokinesis in animal and plant cells.

### (a) Cleavage of an animal cell (SEM)

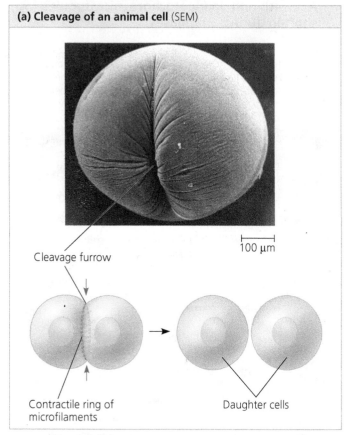

100 µm

Cleavage furrow

Contractile ring of microfilaments

Daughter cells

### (b) Cell plate formation in a plant cell (TEM)

1 µm

Vesicles forming cell plate

Wall of parent cell

Cell plate

New cell wall

Daughter cells

**Figure 9.11** is a series of micrographs of a dividing plant cell. Examining this figure will help you review mitosis and cytokinesis.

## Binary Fission in Bacteria

Prokaryotes (bacteria and archaea) can undergo a type of reproduction in which the cell grows to roughly double its size and then divides to form two cells. The term **binary fission**, meaning "division in half," refers to this process and to the asexual reproduction of single-celled eukaryotes, such as the amoeba in Figure 9.2a. However, the process in eukaryotes involves mitosis, while that in prokaryotes does not.

In bacteria, most genes are carried on a single bacterial chromosome that consists of a circular DNA molecule and associated proteins. Although bacteria are smaller and simpler than eukaryotic cells, the challenge of replicating their genomes in an orderly fashion and distributing the copies equally to two daughter cells is still formidable. The chromosome of the bacterium *Escherichia coli*, for example, when it is fully stretched out, is about 500 times as long as the cell. For such a long chromosome to fit within the cell requires that it be highly coiled and folded.

In *E. coli*, the process of cell division is initiated when the DNA of the bacterial chromosome begins to replicate at a specific place on the chromosome called the **origin of replication**, producing two origins. As the chromosome continues to replicate, one origin moves rapidly toward the opposite end of the cell **(Figure 9.12)**. While the chromosome is replicating, the cell elongates. When replication is complete and the bacterium has reached about twice its initial size, its plasma membrane pinches inward, dividing the parent *E. coli* cell into two daughter cells. In this way, each cell inherits a complete genome.

Using the techniques of modern DNA technology to tag the origins of replication with molecules that glow green in fluorescence microscopy, researchers have directly observed the movement of bacterial chromosomes. This movement is reminiscent of the poleward movements of the centromere regions of eukaryotic chromosomes during anaphase of mitosis, but bacteria don't have visible mitotic spindles or even microtubules. In most bacterial species studied, the two origins of replication end up at opposite ends of the cell or in some other very specific location, possibly anchored there by one or more proteins. How bacterial chromosomes move and how their specific location is established and maintained are active areas of research. Several proteins have been identified that play important roles. Polymerization of one protein resembling eukaryotic actin apparently functions in bacterial chromosome movement during cell division, and another protein that is related to tubulin helps pinch the plasma membrane inward, separating the two bacterial daughter cells.

Nucleus Nucleolus | Chromosomes condensing | Chromosomes

Cell plate

10 µm

**① Prophase.** The chromosomes are condensing and the nucleolus is beginning to disappear. Although not yet visible in the micrograph, the mitotic spindle is starting to form.

**② Prometaphase.** Discrete chromosomes are now visible; each consists of two aligned, identical sister chromatids. Later in prometaphase, the nuclear envelope will fragment.

**③ Metaphase.** The spindle is complete, and the chromosomes, attached to microtubules at their kinetochores, are all at the metaphase plate.

**④ Anaphase.** The chromatids of each chromosome have separated, and the daughter chromosomes are moving to the ends of the cell as their kinetochore microtubules shorten.

**⑤ Telophase.** Daughter nuclei are forming. Meanwhile, cytokinesis has started: The cell plate, which will divide the cytoplasm in two, is growing toward the perimeter of the parent cell.

▲ **Figure 9.11 Mitosis in a plant cell.** These light micrographs show mitosis in cells of an onion root.

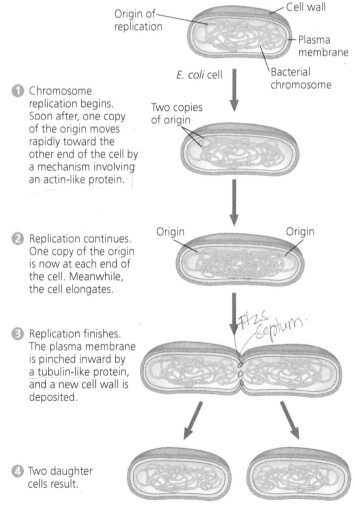

① Chromosome replication begins. Soon after, one copy of the origin moves rapidly toward the other end of the cell by a mechanism involving an actin-like protein.

② Replication continues. One copy of the origin is now at each end of the cell. Meanwhile, the cell elongates.

③ Replication finishes. The plasma membrane is pinched inward by a tubulin-like protein, and a new cell wall is deposited.

④ Two daughter cells result.

▲ **Figure 9.12 Bacterial cell division by binary fission.** The bacterium *E. coli*, shown here, has a single, circular chromosome.

## The Evolution of Mitosis

**EVOLUTION** Given that prokaryotes preceded eukaryotes on Earth by more than a billion years, we might hypothesize that mitosis evolved from simpler prokaryotic mechanisms of cell reproduction. The fact that some of the proteins involved in bacterial binary fission are related to eukaryotic proteins that function in mitosis supports that hypothesis.

As eukaryotes with nuclear envelopes and larger genomes evolved, the ancestral process of binary fission, seen today in bacteria, somehow gave rise to mitosis. Variations on cell division exist in different groups of organisms. These variant processes may be similar to mechanisms used by ancestral species and thus may resemble steps in the evolution of mitosis from a binary fission-like process presumably carried out by very early bacteria. Possible intermediate stages are suggested by two unusual types of nuclear division found today in certain unicellular eukaryotes—dinoflagellates, diatoms, and some yeasts **(Figure 9.13)**. These two modes of nuclear division are thought to be cases where ancestral mechanisms have remained relatively unchanged over evolutionary time. In both types, the nuclear envelope remains intact, in contrast to what happens in most eukaryotic cells.

Bacterial chromosome

**(a) Bacteria.** During binary fission in bacteria, the origins of the daughter chromosomes move to opposite ends of the cell. The mechanism involves polymerization of actin-like molecules, and possibly proteins that may anchor the daughter chromosomes to specific sites on the plasma membrane.

Chromosomes

Microtubules

Intact nuclear envelope

**(b) Dinoflagellates.** In unicellular protists called dinoflagellates, the chromosomes attach to the nuclear envelope, which remains intact during cell division. Microtubules pass through the nucleus inside cytoplasmic tunnels, reinforcing the spatial orientation of the nucleus, which then divides in a process reminiscent of bacterial binary fission.

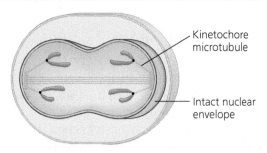

Kinetochore microtubule

Intact nuclear envelope

**(c) Diatoms and some yeasts.** In these two other groups of unicellular eukaryotes, the nuclear envelope also remains intact during cell division. In these organisms, the microtubules form a spindle *within* the nucleus. Microtubules separate the chromosomes, and the nucleus splits into two daughter nuclei.

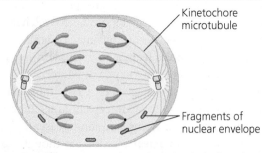

Kinetochore microtubule

Fragments of nuclear envelope

**(d) Most eukaryotes.** In most other eukaryotes, including plants and animals, the spindle forms outside the nucleus, and the nuclear envelope breaks down during mitosis. Microtubules separate the chromosomes, and two nuclear envelopes then form.

▲ **Figure 9.13 Mechanisms of cell division in several groups of organisms.** Some unicellular eukaryotes existing today have mechanisms of cell division that may resemble intermediate steps in the evolution of mitosis. Except for (a), these schematic diagrams do not show cell walls.

---

1. How many chromosomes are drawn in Figure 9.8? Are they duplicated? How many chromatids are shown?
2. Compare cytokinesis in animal cells and plant cells.
3. During which stages of the cell cycle does a chromosome consist of two identical chromatids?
4. Compare the roles of tubulin and actin during eukaryotic cell division with the roles of tubulin-like and actin-like proteins during bacterial binary fission.
5. A kinetochore has been compared to a coupling device that connects a motor to the cargo that it moves. Explain.
6. **MAKE CONNECTIONS** What other functions do actin and tubulin carry out? Name the proteins they interact with to do so.

For suggested answers, see Appendix A.

CONCEPT 9.3

# The eukaryotic cell cycle is regulated by a molecular control system

The timing and rate of cell division in different parts of a plant or animal are crucial to normal growth, development, and maintenance. The frequency of cell division varies with the type of cell. For example, human skin cells divide frequently throughout life, whereas liver cells maintain the ability to divide but keep it in reserve until an appropriate need arises—say, to repair a wound. Some of the most specialized cells, such as fully formed nerve cells and muscle cells, do not divide at all in a mature human. These cell cycle differences result from regulation at the molecular level. The mechanisms of this regulation are of great interest, not only to understand the life cycles of normal cells but also to learn how cancer cells manage to escape the usual controls.

## The Cell Cycle Control System

What controls the cell cycle? In the early 1970s, a variety of experiments led to the hypothesis that the cell cycle is driven by specific signaling molecules present in the cytoplasm. Some of the first strong evidence for this hypothesis came from experiments with mammalian cells grown in culture. In these experiments, two cells in different phases of the cell cycle were fused to form a single cell with two nuclei (**Figure 9.14**). If one of the original cells was in the S phase and the other was in $G_1$, the $G_1$ nucleus immediately entered the S phase, as though stimulated by signaling molecules present in the cytoplasm of the first cell. Similarly, if a cell undergoing mitosis (M phase) was fused with another cell in any stage of its cell cycle, even $G_1$, the second nucleus immediately entered mitosis, with condensation of the chromatin and formation of a mitotic spindle.

## Do molecular signals in the cytoplasm regulate the cell cycle?

**Experiment** Researchers at the University of Colorado wondered whether a cell's progression through the cell cycle is controlled by cytoplasmic molecules. To investigate this, they selected cultured mammalian cells that were at different phases of the cell cycle and induced them to fuse. Two such experiments are shown here.

| Experiment 1 | Experiment 2 |
|---|---|

When a cell in the S phase was fused with a cell in $G_1$, the $G_1$ nucleus immediately entered the S phase—DNA was synthesized.

When a cell in the M phase was fused with a cell in $G_1$, the $G_1$ nucleus immediately began mitosis—a spindle formed and the chromosomes condensed, even though the chromosomes had not been duplicated.

**Conclusion** The results of fusing a $G_1$ cell with a cell in the S or M phase of the cell cycle suggest that molecules present in the cytoplasm during the S or M phase control the progression to those phases.

**Source** R. T. Johnson and P. N. Rao, Mammalian cell fusion: Induction of premature chromosome condensation in interphase nuclei, *Nature* 226:717–722 (1970).

**WHAT IF?** If the progression of phases did not depend on cytoplasmic molecules and, instead, each phase automatically began when the previous one was complete, how would the results have differed?

The experiment shown in Figure 9.14 and other experiments on animal cells and yeasts demonstrated that the sequential events of the cell cycle are directed by a distinct **cell cycle control system**, a cyclically operating set of molecules in the cell that both triggers and coordinates key events in the cell cycle. The cell cycle control system has been compared to the control device of an automatic washing machine **(Figure 9.15)**. Like the washer's timing device, the cell cycle control system proceeds on its own, according to a built-in clock. However, just as a washer's cycle is subject to both internal control (such as the sensor that detects when the tub is filled with water) and external adjustment (such as starting

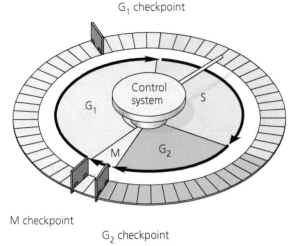

▲ **Figure 9.15 Mechanical analogy for the cell cycle control system.** In this diagram of the cell cycle, the flat "stepping stones" around the perimeter represent sequential events. Like the control device of an automatic washer, the cell cycle control system proceeds on its own, driven by a built-in clock. However, the system is subject to internal and external regulation at various checkpoints; three important checkpoints are shown (red).

or stopping the machine), the cell cycle is regulated at certain checkpoints by both internal and external signals that stop or restart the machine. A **checkpoint** is a control point in the cell cycle where stop and go-ahead signals can regulate the cycle. Three important checkpoints are found in the $G_1$, $G_2$, and M phases (the red gates in Figure 9.15).

To understand how cell cycle checkpoints work, we first need to see what kinds of molecules make up the cell cycle control system (the molecular basis for the cell cycle clock) and how a cell progresses through the cycle. Then we will consider the internal and external checkpoint signals that can make the clock either pause or continue.

### The Cell Cycle Clock: Cyclins and Cyclin-Dependent Kinases

Rhythmic fluctuations in the abundance and activity of cell cycle control molecules pace the sequential events of the cell cycle. These regulatory molecules are mainly proteins of two types: protein kinases and cyclins. Protein kinases are enzymes that activate or inactivate other proteins by phosphorylating them (see Chapter 8).

Many of the kinases that drive the cell cycle are actually present at a constant concentration in the growing cell, but much of the time they are in an inactive form. To be active, such a kinase must be attached to a **cyclin**, a protein that gets its name from its cyclically fluctuating concentration in the cell. Because of this requirement, these kinases are called **cyclin-dependent kinases**, or **Cdks**. The activity of a Cdk rises and falls with changes in the concentration of its cyclin partner. **Figure 9.16a** shows the fluctuating activity of **MPF**,

(a) **Fluctuation of MPF activity and cyclin concentration during the cell cycle**

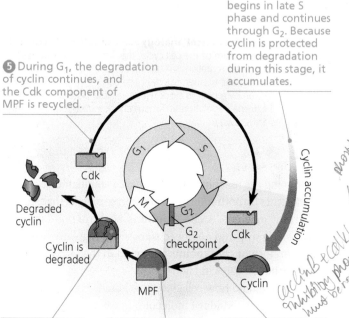

**1** Synthesis of cyclin begins in late S phase and continues through G₂. Because cyclin is protected from degradation during this stage, it accumulates.

**5** During G₁, the degradation of cyclin continues, and the Cdk component of MPF is recycled.

**4** During anaphase, the cyclin component of MPF is degraded, terminating the M phase. The cell enters the G₁ phase.

**3** MPF promotes mitosis by phosphorylating various proteins. MPF's activity peaks during metaphase.

**2** Cyclin combines with Cdk, producing MPF. When enough MPF molecules accumulate, the cell passes the G₂ checkpoint and begins mitosis.

(b) **Molecular mechanisms that help regulate the cell cycle**

▲ **Figure 9.16 Molecular control of the cell cycle at the G₂ checkpoint.** The steps of the cell cycle are timed by rhythmic fluctuations in the activity of cyclin-dependent kinases (Cdks). Here we focus on a cyclin-Cdk complex in animal cells called MPF, which acts at the G₂ checkpoint as a go-ahead signal, triggering the events of mitosis.

**?** *Explain how the events in the diagram in (b) are related to the "Time" axis of the graph in (a), beginning at the left end.*

the cyclin-Cdk complex that was discovered first (in frog eggs). Note that the peaks of MPF activity correspond to the peaks of cyclin concentration. The cyclin level rises during the S and G₂ phases and then falls abruptly during M phase.

The initials MPF stand for "maturation-promoting factor," but we can think of MPF as "M-phase-promoting factor"

because it triggers the cell's passage into the M phase, past the G₂ checkpoint **(Figure 9.16b)**. When cyclins that accumulate during G₂ associate with Cdk molecules, the resulting MPF complex phosphorylates a variety of proteins, initiating mitosis. MPF acts both directly as a kinase and indirectly by activating other kinases. For example, MPF causes phosphorylation of various proteins of the nuclear lamina, which promotes fragmentation of the nuclear envelope during prometaphase of mitosis. There is also evidence that MPF contributes to molecular events required for chromosome condensation and spindle formation during prophase.

During anaphase, MPF helps switch itself off by initiating a process that leads to the destruction of its own cyclin. The noncyclin part of MPF, the Cdk, persists in the cell, inactive until it becomes part of MPF again by associating with new cyclin molecules synthesized during the S and G₂ phases of the next round of the cycle.

The fluctuating activities of different cyclin-Cdk complexes are of major importance in controlling all the stages of the cell cycle and give the go-ahead signals at some checkpoints as well. As mentioned above, MPF controls the cell's passage through the G₂ checkpoint. Cell behavior at the G₁ checkpoint is also regulated by the activity of cyclin-Cdk protein complexes. Animal cells appear to have at least three Cdk proteins and several different cyclins that operate at this checkpoint. Next, let's consider checkpoints in more detail.

## Stop and Go Signs: Internal and External Signals at the Checkpoints

Animal cells generally have built-in stop signals that halt the cell cycle at checkpoints until overridden by go-ahead signals. (The signals are transmitted within the cell by the kinds of signal transduction pathways discussed in Chapter 8.) Many signals registered at checkpoints come from cellular surveillance mechanisms inside the cell. These signals report whether crucial cellular processes that should have occurred by that point have in fact been completed correctly and thus whether or not the cell cycle should proceed. Checkpoints also register signals from outside the cell. Three important checkpoints are those in G₁, G₂, and M phases, shown in Figure 9.15.

For many cells, the G₁ checkpoint—dubbed the "restriction point" in mammalian cells—seems to be the most important. If a cell receives a go-ahead signal at the G₁ checkpoint, it will usually complete the G₁, S, G₂, and M phases and divide. If it does not receive a go-ahead signal at that point, it may exit the cycle, switching into a nondividing state called the **G₀ phase (Figure 9.17a)**. Most cells of the human body are actually in the G₀ phase. As mentioned earlier, mature nerve cells and muscle cells never divide. Other cells, such as liver cells, can be "called back" from the G₀ phase to the cell cycle by external cues, such as growth factors released during injury.

**WHAT IF?** *What might be the result if the cell ignored either checkpoint and progressed through the cell cycle?*

$G_1$ checkpoint

$G_0$

$G_1$

In the absence of a go-ahead signal, a cell exits the cell cycle and enters $G_0$, a nondividing state.

**(a) $G_1$ checkpoint**

$G_1$

If a cell receives a go-ahead signal, the cell continues on in the cell cycle.

$G_1$

M

$G_2$

M checkpoint

Prometaphase

A cell in mitosis receives a stop signal when any of its chromosomes are not attached to spindle fibers.

**(b) M checkpoint**

$G_1$

M

$G_2$

Anaphase

$G_2$ checkpoint

Metaphase

When all chromosomes are attached to spindle fibers from both poles, a go-ahead signal allows the cell to proceed into anaphase.

Biologists are currently working out the pathways that link signals originating inside and outside the cell with the responses by cyclin-dependent kinases and other proteins. An example of an internal signal occurs at the third important checkpoint, the M phase checkpoint **(Figure 9.17b)**. Anaphase, the separation of sister chromatids, does not begin until all the chromosomes are properly attached to the spindle at the metaphase plate. Researchers have learned that as long as some kinetochores are unattached to spindle microtubules, the sister chromatids remain together, delaying anaphase. Only when the kinetochores of all the chromosomes are properly attached to the spindle does the appropriate regulatory protein complex become activated. (In this case, the regulatory molecule is not a cyclin-Cdk complex but, instead, a different complex made up of several proteins.) Once activated, the complex sets off a chain of molecular events that activates the enzyme separase, which cleaves the cohesins, allowing the sister chromatids to separate. This mechanism ensures that daughter cells do not end up with missing or extra chromosomes.

Studies using animal cells in culture have led to the identification of many external factors, both chemical and physical, that can influence cell division. For example, cells fail to divide if an essential nutrient is lacking in the culture medium. (This is analogous to trying to run a washing machine without the water supply hooked up; an internal sensor won't allow the

machine to continue past the point where water is needed.) And even if all other conditions are favorable, most types of mammalian cells divide in culture only if the growth medium includes specific growth factors. As mentioned in Chapter 8, a **growth factor** is a protein released by certain cells that stimulates other cells to divide. Different cell types respond specifically to different growth factors or combinations of growth factors.

Consider, for example, *platelet-derived growth factor (PDGF)*, which is made by blood cell fragments called platelets. The experiment illustrated in **Figure 9.18** demonstrates that PDGF is required for the division of cultured fibroblasts, a type of connective tissue cell. Fibroblasts have PDGF receptors on their plasma membranes. The binding of PDGF molecules to these receptors (which are receptor tyrosine kinases; see Figure 8.8) triggers a signal transduction pathway that allows the cells to pass the $G_1$ checkpoint and divide. PDGF stimulates fibroblast division not only in the artificial conditions of cell culture, but also in an animal's body. When an injury occurs, platelets release PDGF in the vicinity. The resulting proliferation of fibroblasts helps heal the wound.

① A sample of human connective tissue is cut up into small pieces.

Scalpels

Petri dish

② Enzymes are used to digest the extracellular matrix in the tissue pieces, resulting in a suspension of free fibroblasts.

③ Cells are transferred to culture vessels containing a basic growth medium consisting of glucose, amino acids, salts, and antibiotics (to prevent bacterial growth).

④ PDGF is added to half the vessels. The culture vessels are incubated at 37°C for 24 hours.

**Without PDGF**

In the basic growth medium without PDGF (the control), the cells fail to divide.

**With PDGF**

In the basic growth medium plus PDGF, the cells proliferate. The SEM shows cultured fibroblasts.

**MAKE CONNECTIONS**
*PDGF signals cells by binding to a cell-surface receptor tyrosine kinase. If you added a chemical that blocked phosphorylation, how would the results differ? (See Figure 8.8.)*

10 μm

Cells anchor to dish surface and divide (anchorage dependence).

When cells have formed a complete single layer, they stop dividing (density-dependent inhibition).

If some cells are scraped away, the remaining cells divide to fill the gap and then stop once they contact each other (density-dependent inhibition).

20 μm

**(a) Normal mammalian cells.** Contact with neighboring cells and the availability of nutrients, growth factors, and a substratum for attachment limit cell density to a single layer.

20 μm

**(b) Cancer cells.** Cancer cells usually continue to divide well beyond a single layer, forming a clump of overlapping cells. They do not exhibit anchorage dependence or density-dependent inhibition.

▲ Figure 9.19 **Density-dependent inhibition and anchorage dependence of cell division.** Individual cells are shown disproportionately large in the drawings.

The effect of an external physical factor on cell division is clearly seen in **density-dependent inhibition**, a phenomenon in which crowded cells stop dividing (**Figure 9.19a**). As first observed many years ago, cultured cells normally divide until they form a single layer of cells on the inner surface of the culture flask, at which point the cells stop dividing. If some cells are removed, those bordering the open space begin dividing again and continue until the vacancy is filled. Follow-up studies revealed that the binding of a cell-surface protein to its counterpart on an adjoining cell sends a cell division-inhibiting signal forward in the cell cycle, even in the presence of growth factors.

Most animal cells also exhibit **anchorage dependence** (see Figure 9.19a). To divide, they must be attached to a substratum, such as the inside of a culture flask or the extracellular matrix of a tissue. Experiments suggest that like cell density, anchorage is signaled to the cell cycle control system via pathways involving plasma membrane proteins and elements of the cytoskeleton linked to them.

Density-dependent inhibition and anchorage dependence appear to function not only in cell culture but also in the body's tissues, checking the growth of cells at some optimal density and location during embryonic development and throughout an organism's life. Cancer cells, which we discuss next, exhibit neither density-dependent inhibition nor anchorage dependence (**Figure 9.19b**).

## Loss of Cell Cycle Controls in Cancer Cells

Cancer cells do not heed the normal signals that regulate the cell cycle. In culture, they do not stop dividing when growth factors are depleted. A logical hypothesis is that cancer cells do not need growth factors in their culture medium to grow and divide. They may make a required growth factor themselves, or they may have an abnormality in the signaling pathway that conveys the growth factor's signal to the cell cycle control system even in the absence of that factor. Another possibility is an abnormal cell cycle control system. In these scenarios, the underlying basis of the abnormality is almost always a change in one or more genes (for example, a mutation) that alters the function of their protein products, resulting in faulty cell cycle control.

There are other important differences between normal cells and cancer cells that reflect derangements of the cell cycle. If and when they stop dividing, cancer cells do so at random points in the cycle, rather than at the normal checkpoints. Moreover, cancer cells can go on dividing indefinitely in culture if they are given a continual supply of nutrients; in essence, they are "immortal." A striking example is a cell line that has been reproducing in culture since 1951. Cells of this line are called HeLa cells because their original source was a tumor removed from a woman named *Henrietta Lacks*. Cells in culture that acquire the ability to divide indefinitely are said to have undergone **transformation**, the process that causes them to behave like cancer cells. By contrast, nearly all normal, nontransformed mammalian cells growing in culture divide only about 20 to 50 times before they stop dividing, age, and die. Finally, cancer cells evade the normal controls that trigger a cell to undergo apoptosis when something is wrong—for example, when an irreparable mistake has occurred during DNA replication preceding mitosis.

The abnormal behavior of cancer cells can be catastrophic when it occurs in the body. The problem begins when a single cell in a tissue undergoes the first changes of the multistep process that converts a normal cell to a cancer cell. Such a cell often has altered proteins on its surface, and the body's immune system normally recognizes the cell as "nonself"—an insurgent—and destroys it. However, if the cell evades destruction, it may proliferate and form a tumor, a mass of abnormal cells within otherwise normal tissue. The abnormal cells may remain at the original site if they have too few genetic and cellular changes to survive at another site. In that case, the tumor is called a **benign tumor**. Most benign tumors do not cause serious problems and can be removed by surgery. In contrast, a **malignant tumor** includes cells whose genetic and cellular changes enable them to spread to new tissues and impair the functions of one or more organs; these cells are also considered *transformed* cells. An individual with a malignant tumor is said to have cancer; **Figure 9.20** shows the development of breast cancer, as well as a typical breast cancer cell.

The changes that have occurred in cells of malignant tumors show up in many ways besides excessive proliferation. These cells may have unusual numbers of chromosomes, though whether this is a cause or an effect of transformation is a topic of debate. Their metabolism may be altered, and they may cease to function in any constructive way. Abnormal changes on the cell surface cause cancer cells to lose attachments to neighboring cells and the extracellular matrix, allowing them to spread into nearby tissues. Cancer cells may also secrete signaling molecules that cause blood vessels to grow toward the tumor. A few tumor cells may separate from the original tumor, enter blood vessels and lymph vessels, and travel to other parts of the body. There, they may proliferate and form a new tumor. This spread of cancer cells to locations distant from their original site is called **metastasis** (see Figure 9.20).

A tumor that appears to be localized may be treated with high-energy radiation, which damages DNA in cancer cells

▼ **Figure 9.20 The growth and metastasis of a malignant breast tumor.** A series of genetic and cellular changes contribute to a tumor becoming malignant (cancerous). The cells of malignant tumors grow in an uncontrolled way and can spread to neighboring tissues and, via lymph and blood vessels, to other parts of the body. The spread of cancer cells beyond their original site is called metastasis.

Breast cancer cell (colorized SEM)

1 A tumor grows from a single cancer cell.

2 Cancer cells invade neighboring tissue.

3 Cancer cells spread through lymph and blood vessels to other parts of the body.

4 A small percentage of cancer cells may metastasize to another part of the body.

much more than it does in normal cells, apparently because the majority of cancer cells have lost the ability to repair such damage. To treat known or suspected metastatic tumors, chemotherapy is used, in which drugs that are toxic to actively dividing cells are administered through the circulatory system. As you might expect, chemotherapeutic drugs interfere with specific steps in the cell cycle. For example, the drug Taxol freezes the mitotic spindle by preventing microtubule depolymerization, which stops actively dividing cells from proceeding past metaphase and leads to their destruction. The side effects of chemotherapy are due to the effects of the drugs on normal cells that divide often, due to the function of that cell type in the organism. For example, nausea results

from chemotherapy's effects on intestinal cells, hair loss from effects on hair follicle cells, and susceptibility to infection from effects on immune system cells. You'll work with data from an experiment involving a potential chemotherapeutic agent in the Scientific Skills Exercise.

Over the past several decades, researchers have produced a flood of valuable information about cell-signaling pathways and how their malfunction contributes to the development of cancer through effects on the cell cycle. Coupled with new molecular techniques, such as the ability to rapidly sequence the DNA of cells in a particular tumor, medical treatments for cancer are beginning to become more "personalized" to a particular patient's tumor.

## Scientific Skills Exercise

# *Interpreting Histograms*

**At What Phase Is the Cell Cycle Arrested by an Inhibitor?** Many medical treatments are aimed at stopping cancer cell proliferation by blocking the cell cycle of cancerous tumor cells. One potential treatment is a cell cycle inhibitor derived from human umbilical cord stem cells. In this exercise, you will compare two histograms to determine where in the cell cycle the inhibitor blocks the division of cancer cells.

**How the Experiment Was Done** In the treated sample, human glioblastoma (brain cancer) cells were grown in tissue culture in the presence of the inhibitor, while control sample cells were grown in its absence. After 72 hours of growth, the two cell samples were harvested. To get a "snapshot" of the phase of the cell cycle each cell was in at that time, the samples were treated with a fluorescent chemical that binds to DNA and then run through a flow cytometer, an instrument that records the fluorescence level of each cell. Computer software then graphed the number of cells in each sample with a particular fluorescence level, as shown below.

**Data from the Experiment**

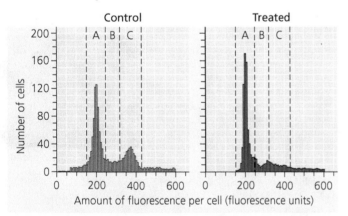

The data are plotted in a type of graph called a histogram (above), which groups values for a numeric variable on the *x*-axis into intervals. A histogram allows you to see how all the experimental subjects (cells, in this case) are distributed along a continuous variable (amount of fluorescence). In these histograms, the bars are so narrow that the data appear to follow a curve for which you can

detect peaks and dips. Each narrow bar represents the number of cells observed to have a level of fluorescence in the range of that interval. This in turn indicates the relative amount of DNA in those cells. Overall, comparing the two histograms allows you to see how the DNA content of this cell population is altered by the treatment.

**Interpret the Data**

1. Familiarize yourself with the data shown in the histograms. (a) Which axis indirectly shows the relative amount of DNA per cell? Explain your answer. (b) In the control sample, compare the first peak in the histogram (in region A) to the second peak (in region C). Which peak shows the population of cells with the higher amount of DNA per cell? Explain. (For additional information about graphs, see the Scientific Skills Review in Appendix F and in the Study Area in MasteringBiology.)

2. (a) In the control sample histogram, identify the phase of the cell cycle ($G_1$, S, or $G_2$) of the population of cells in each region delineated by vertical lines. Label the histogram with these phases and explain your answer. (b) Does the S phase population of cells show a distinct peak in the histogram? Why or why not?

3. The histogram representing the treated sample shows the effect of growing the cancer cells alongside human umbilical cord stem cells that produce the potential inhibitor. (a) Label the histogram with the cell cycle phases. Which phase of the cell cycle has the greatest number of cells in the treated sample? Explain. (b) Compare the distribution of cells among $G_1$, S, and $G_2$ phases in the control and treated samples. What does this tell you about the cells in the treated sample? (c) Based on what you learned in Concept 9.3, propose a mechanism by which the stem cell-derived inhibitor might arrest the cancer cell cycle at this stage. (More than one answer is possible.)

**Data from** K. K. Velpula et al., Regulation of glioblastoma progression by cord blood stem cells is mediated by downregulation of cyclin D1, *PLoS ONE* 6(3): e18017 (2011).

(MB) A version of this Scientific Skills Exercise can be assigned in MasteringBiology.

For example, the cells of roughly 20% of breast cancer tumors show abnormally high amounts of a cell-surface receptor tyrosine kinase called HER2, and many show an increase in the number of estrogen receptor (ER) molecules, intracellular receptors that can trigger cell division. Based on lab findings, a physician can prescribe chemotherapy with a molecule that blocks the function of the specific protein (Herceptin for HER2 and tamoxifen for ERs). Treatment using these agents, when appropriate, has led to increased survival rates and fewer cancer recurrences.

**CONCEPT CHECK 9.3**

1. In Figure 9.14, why do the nuclei resulting from experiment 2 contain different amounts of DNA?
2. How does MPF allow a cell to pass the $G_2$ phase checkpoint and enter mitosis? (See Figure 9.16.)
3. **MAKE CONNECTIONS** Explain in general how receptor tyrosine kinases and intracellular receptors might function in triggering cell division. (Review Figures 8.8 and 8.9 and Chapter 8.)

For suggested answers, see Appendix A.

# 9 Chapter Review

## SUMMARY OF KEY CONCEPTS

- Unicellular organisms reproduce by **cell division**; multicellular organisms depend on cell division for their development from a fertilized egg and for growth and repair. Cell division is part of the **cell cycle**, an ordered sequence of events in the life of a cell.

**CONCEPT** 9.1

### Most cell division results in genetically identical daughter cells (pp. 177–179)

- The genetic material (DNA) of a cell—its **genome**—is partitioned among **chromosomes**. Each eukaryotic chromosome consists of one DNA molecule associated with many proteins. Together, the complex of DNA and associated proteins is called **chromatin**. The chromatin of a chromosome exists in different states of condensation at different times. In animals, **gametes** have one set of chromosomes and **somatic cells** have two sets.
- Cells replicate their genetic material before they divide, each daughter cell receiving a copy of the DNA. Prior to cell division, chromosomes are duplicated. Each one then consists of two identical **sister chromatids** joined along their lengths by sister chromatid cohesion and held most tightly together at a constricted region at the **centromeres**. When this cohesion is broken, the chromatids separate during cell division, becoming the chromosomes of the daughter cells. Eukaryotic cell division consists of **mitosis** (division of the nucleus) and **cytokinesis** (division of the cytoplasm).

    ? *Differentiate between these terms: chromosome, chromatin, and chromatid.*

**CONCEPT** 9.2

### The mitotic phase alternates with interphase in the cell cycle (pp. 179–186)

- Between divisions, a cell is in **interphase**: the $G_1$, **S**, and $G_2$ phases. The cell grows throughout interphase, with DNA being replicated only during the synthesis (S) phase. Mitosis and cytokinesis make up the **mitotic (M) phase** of the cell cycle.
- The **mitotic spindle**, made up of microtubules, controls chromosome movement during mitosis. In animal cells, it arises from the **centrosomes** and includes spindle microtubules and **asters**. Some spindle microtubules attach to the **kinetochores** of chromosomes and move the chromosomes to the **metaphase plate**. After sister chromatids separate, motor proteins move them along kinetochore microtubules toward opposite ends of the cell.

The cell elongates when motor proteins push nonkinetochore microtubules from opposite poles away from each other.

- Mitosis is usually followed by cytokinesis. Animal cells carry out cytokinesis by **cleavage**, and plant cells form a **cell plate**.

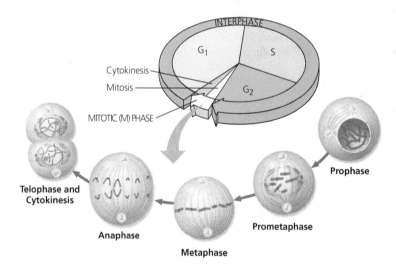

- During **binary fission** in bacteria, the chromosome replicates and the daughter chromosomes actively move apart. Some of the proteins involved in bacterial binary fission are related to eukaryotic actin and tubulin.
- Since prokaryotes preceded eukaryotes by more than a billion years, it is likely that mitosis evolved from prokaryotic cell division. Certain unicellular eukaryotes exhibit mechanisms of cell division that may be similar to those of ancestors of existing eukaryotes. Such mechanisms might represent intermediate steps in the evolution of mitosis.

    ? *In which of the three subphases of interphase and the stages of mitosis do chromosomes exist as single DNA molecules?*

**CONCEPT** 9.3

### The eukaryotic cell cycle is regulated by a molecular control system (pp. 186–192)

- Signaling molecules present in the cytoplasm regulate progress through the cell cycle.

- The **cell cycle control system** is molecularly based. Cyclic changes in regulatory proteins work as a cell cycle clock. The key molecules are **cyclins** and **cyclin-dependent kinases (Cdks)**. The clock has specific **checkpoints** where the cell cycle stops until a go-ahead signal is received; important checkpoints occur in G$_1$, G$_2$, and M phases. Cell culture has enabled researchers to study the molecular details of cell division. Both internal signals and external signals control the cell cycle checkpoints via signal transduction pathways. Most cells exhibit **density-dependent inhibition** of cell division as well as **anchorage dependence**.
- Cancer cells elude normal cell cycle regulation and divide unchecked, forming tumors. **Malignant tumors** invade nearby tissues and can undergo **metastasis**, exporting cancer cells to other sites, where they may form secondary tumors. Recent cell cycle and cell signaling research, and new techniques for sequencing DNA, have led to improved cancer treatments.

? *Explain the significance of the G$_1$, G$_2$, and M checkpoints and the go-ahead signals involved in the cell cycle control system.*

# TEST YOUR UNDERSTANDING

## Level 1: KNOWLEDGE/COMPREHENSION

1. Through a microscope, you can see a cell plate beginning to develop across the middle of a cell and nuclei forming on either side of the cell plate. This cell is most likely
   a. an animal cell in the process of cytokinesis.
   b. a plant cell in the process of cytokinesis.
   c. a bacterial cell dividing.
   d. a plant cell in metaphase.

2. Vinblastine is a standard chemotherapeutic drug used to treat cancer. Because it interferes with the assembly of microtubules, its effectiveness must be related to
   a. disruption of mitotic spindle formation.
   b. suppression of cyclin production.
   c. myosin denaturation and inhibition of cleavage furrow formation.
   d. inhibition of DNA synthesis.

3. One difference between cancer cells and normal cells is that cancer cells
   a. are unable to synthesize DNA.
   b. are arrested at the S phase of the cell cycle.
   c. continue to divide even when they are tightly packed together.
   d. cannot function properly because they are affected by density-dependent inhibition.

4. The decline of MPF activity at the end of mitosis is due to
   a. the destruction of the protein kinase Cdk.
   b. decreased synthesis of Cdk.
   c. the degradation of cyclin.
   d. the accumulation of cyclin.

5. In the cells of some organisms, mitosis occurs without cytokinesis. This will result in
   a. cells with more than one nucleus.
   b. cells that are unusually small.
   c. cells lacking nuclei.
   d. cell cycles lacking an S phase.

6. Which of the following does *not* occur during mitosis?
   a. condensation of the chromosomes
   b. replication of the DNA
   c. separation of sister chromatids
   d. spindle formation

## Level 2: APPLICATION/ANALYSIS

7. A particular cell has half as much DNA as some other cells in a mitotically active tissue. The cell in question is most likely in
   a. G$_1$.
   b. G$_2$.
   c. prophase.
   d. metaphase.

8. The drug cytochalasin B blocks the function of actin. Which of the following aspects of the animal cell cycle would be most disrupted by cytochalasin B?
   a. spindle formation
   b. spindle attachment to kinetochores
   c. cell elongation during anaphase
   d. cleavage furrow formation and cytokinesis

9. In the light micrograph below of dividing cells near the tip of an onion root, identify a cell in each of the following stages: prophase, prometaphase, metaphase, anaphase, and telophase. Describe the major events occurring at each stage.

10. **DRAW IT** Draw one eukaryotic chromosome as it would appear during interphase, during each of the stages of mitosis, and during cytokinesis. Also draw and label the nuclear envelope and any microtubules attached to the chromosome(s).

## Level 3: SYNTHESIS/EVALUATION

11. **EVOLUTION CONNECTION**
    The result of mitosis is that the daughter cells end up with the same number of chromosomes that the parent cell had. Another way to maintain the number of chromosomes would be to carry out cell division first and then duplicate the chromosomes in each daughter cell. Do you think this would be an equally good way of organizing the cell cycle? Why do you suppose that evolution has not led to this alternative?

12. **SCIENTIFIC INQUIRY**
    Although both ends of a microtubule can gain or lose subunits, one end (called the plus end) polymerizes and depolymerizes at a higher rate than the other end (the minus end). For spindle microtubules, the plus ends are in the center of the spindle, and the minus ends are at the poles. Motor proteins that move along microtubules specialize in walking either toward the plus end or toward the minus end; the two types are called plus end–directed and minus end–directed motor proteins, respectively. Given what you know about chromosome movement and spindle changes during anaphase, predict which type of motor proteins would be present on (a) kinetochore microtubules and (b) nonkinetochore microtubules.

**13. WRITE ABOUT A THEME: INFORMATION**
Continuity of life is based on heritable information in the form of DNA. In a short essay (100–150 words), explain how the process of mitosis faithfully parcels out exact copies of this heritable information in the production of genetically identical daughter cells.

**14.** SYNTHESIZE YOUR KNOWLEDGE

Shown here are two HeLa cancer cells that are just completing cytokinesis. Explain how the cell division of cancer cells like these is misregulated. What genetic and other changes might have caused these cells to escape normal cell cycle regulation?

*For selected answers, see Appendix A.*

## MasteringBiology®

**Students** Go to **MasteringBiology** for assignments, the eText, and the Study Area with practice tests, animations, and activities.

**Instructors** Go to **MasteringBiology** for automatically graded tutorials and questions that you can assign to your students, plus Instructor Resources.

# 10

# Meiosis and Sexual Life Cycles

▼ **Figure 10.1** What accounts for family resemblance?

OVERVIEW

## Variations on a Theme

We all know that offspring resemble their parents more than they do unrelated individuals. If you examine the family members shown in **Figure 10.1**, you can pick out some similar features among them. The transmission of traits from one generation to the next is called inheritance, or **heredity** (from the Latin *heres*, heir). However, sons and daughters are not identical copies of either parent or of their siblings. Along with inherited similarity, there is also **variation**. What are the biological mechanisms leading to the "family resemblance" evident among the family members in the photo above? The answer to this question eluded biologists until the advance of genetics in the 20th century.

**Genetics** is the scientific study of heredity and hereditary variation. In this unit, you'll learn about genetics at multiple levels, from organisms to cells to molecules. We begin by examining how chromosomes pass from parents to offspring in sexually reproducing organisms. The processes of meiosis (a special type of cell division) and fertilization (the fusion of sperm and egg, as seen in the photo at the left) maintain a species' chromosome count during the sexual life cycle. We will describe the cellular mechanics of meiosis and explain how this process differs from mitosis. Finally, we will consider how both meiosis and fertilization contribute to genetic variation, such as that seen in Figure 10.1.

# Offspring acquire genes from parents by inheriting chromosomes

Family friends may tell you that you have your mother's freckles or your father's eyes. Of course, parents do not, in any literal sense, give their children freckles, eyes, hair, or any other traits. What, then, *is* actually inherited?

## Inheritance of Genes

Parents endow their offspring with coded information in the form of hereditary units called **genes**. The genes we inherit from our mothers and fathers are our genetic link to our parents, and they account for family resemblances such as shared eye color or freckles. Our genes program the specific traits that emerge as we develop from fertilized eggs into adults.

The genetic program is written in the language of DNA, the polymer of four different nucleotides. Inherited information is passed on in the form of each gene's specific sequence of DNA nucleotides, much as printed information is communicated in the form of meaningful sequences of letters. In both cases, the language is symbolic. Just as your brain translates the word *apple* into a mental image of the fruit, cells translate genes into freckles and other features. Most genes program cells to synthesize specific enzymes and other proteins, whose cumulative action produces an organism's inherited traits. The programming of these traits in the form of DNA is one of the unifying themes of biology.

The transmission of hereditary traits has its molecular basis in the replication of DNA, which produces copies of genes that can be passed from parents to offspring. In animals and plants, reproductive cells called **gametes** are the vehicles that transmit genes from one generation to the next. During fertilization, male and female gametes (sperm and eggs) unite, passing on genes of both parents to their offspring.

Except for small amounts of DNA in mitochondria and chloroplasts, the DNA of a eukaryotic cell is packaged into chromosomes within the nucleus. Every species has a characteristic number of chromosomes. For example, humans have 46 chromosomes in their **somatic cells**—all cells of the body except the gametes and their precursors. Each chromosome consists of a single long DNA molecule elaborately coiled in association with various proteins. One chromosome includes several hundred to a few thousand genes, each of which is a specific sequence of nucleotides within the DNA molecule. A gene's specific location along the length of a chromosome is called the gene's **locus** (plural, *loci*; from the Latin, meaning "place"). Our genetic endowment (our genome) consists of the genes and other DNA that make up the chromosomes we inherited from our parents.

## Comparison of Asexual and Sexual Reproduction

Only organisms that reproduce asexually have offspring that are exact genetic copies of themselves. In **asexual reproduction**, a single individual is the sole parent and passes copies of all its genes to its offspring without the fusion of gametes. For example, single-celled eukaryotic organisms can reproduce asexually by mitotic cell division, in which DNA is copied and allocated equally to two daughter cells. The genomes of the offspring are virtually exact copies of the parent's genome. Some multicellular organisms are also capable of reproducing asexually **(Figure 10.2)**. Because the cells of the offspring are derived by mitosis in the parent, the "chip off the old block" is usually genetically identical to its parent. An individual that reproduces asexually gives rise to a **clone**, a group of genetically identical individuals. Genetic differences occasionally arise in asexually reproducing organisms as a result of changes in the DNA called mutations.

In **sexual reproduction**, two parents give rise to offspring that have unique combinations of genes inherited from the two parents. In contrast to a clone, offspring of sexual reproduction vary genetically from their siblings and both parents: They are variations on a common theme of family resemblance, not exact replicas. Genetic variation like that shown in Figure 10.1 is an important consequence of sexual reproduction. What mechanisms generate this genetic variation? The key is the behavior of chromosomes during the sexual life cycle.

0.5 mm

Parent

Bud

**(a) Hydra**                    **(b) Redwoods**

▲ **Figure 10.2 Asexual reproduction in two multicellular organisms. (a)** This relatively simple animal, a hydra, reproduces by budding. The bud, a localized mass of mitotically dividing cells, develops into a small hydra, which detaches from the parent (LM). **(b)** All the trees in this circle of redwoods arose asexually from a single parent tree, whose stump is in the center of the circle.

1. **MAKE CONNECTIONS** Using what you know of gene expression in a cell, explain what causes the traits of parents (such as hair color) to show up in their offspring.

2. How do asexually reproducing eukaryotic organisms produce offspring that are genetically identical to each other and to their parents?

3. **WHAT IF?** A horticulturalist breeds orchids, trying to obtain a plant with a unique combination of desirable traits. After many years, she finally succeeds. To produce more plants like this one, should she cross-breed it with another plant or clone it? Why?

For suggested answers, see Appendix A.

---

**CONCEPT** 10.2

# Fertilization and meiosis alternate in sexual life cycles

A **life cycle** is the generation-to-generation sequence of stages in the reproductive history of an organism, from conception to production of its own offspring. In this section, we use humans as an example to track the behavior of chromosomes through the sexual life cycle. We begin by considering the chromosome count in human somatic cells and gametes. We will then explore how the behavior of chromosomes relates to the human life cycle and other types of sexual life cycles.

## Sets of Chromosomes in Human Cells

In humans, each somatic cell has 46 chromosomes. During mitosis, the chromosomes become condensed enough to be visible under a light microscope. At this point, they can be distinguished from one another by their size, the positions of their centromeres, and the pattern of colored bands produced by certain chromatin-binding stains.

Careful examination of a micrograph of the 46 human chromosomes from a single cell in mitosis reveals that there are two chromosomes of each of 23 types. This becomes clear when images of the chromosomes are arranged in pairs, starting with the longest chromosomes. The resulting ordered display is called a **karyotype** (Figure 10.3). The two chromosomes of a pair have the same length, centromere position, and staining pattern: These are called **homologous chromosomes**, or **homologs**. Both chromosomes of each pair carry genes controlling the same inherited characters. For example, if a gene for eye color is situated at a particular locus on a certain chromosome, then the homolog of that chromosome will also have a version of the same gene specifying eye color at the equivalent locus.

The two distinct chromosomes referred to as X and Y are an important exception to the general pattern of homologous

---

▼ **Figure 10.3** **Research Method**

### Preparing a Karyotype

**Application** A karyotype is a display of condensed chromosomes arranged in pairs. Karyotyping can be used to screen for defective chromosomes or abnormal numbers of chromosomes associated with certain congenital disorders, such as Down syndrome.

**Technique** Karyotypes are prepared from isolated somatic cells, which are treated with a drug to stimulate mitosis and then grown in culture for several days. Cells arrested in metaphase, when chromosomes are most highly condensed, are stained and then viewed with a microscope equipped with a digital camera. An image of the chromosomes is displayed on a computer monitor, and digital software is used to arrange them in pairs according to their appearance.

**Results** This karyotype shows the chromosomes from a normal human male, digitally colored to emphasize their banding patterns. The size of the chromosome, position of the centromere, and pattern of stained bands help identify specific chromosomes. Although difficult to discern in the karyotype, each metaphase chromosome consists of two closely attached sister chromatids (see the diagram of a pair of homologous duplicated chromosomes).

---

chromosomes in human somatic cells. Human females have a homologous pair of X chromosomes (XX), but males have one X and one Y chromosome (XY). Only small parts of the X and Y are homologous. Most of the genes carried on the X chromosome do not have counterparts on the tiny Y, and the Y chromosome has genes lacking on the X. Because they determine an individual's sex, the X and Y chromosomes are called **sex chromosomes**. The other chromosomes are called **autosomes**. *- somatic cells.*

The pairs of homologous chromosomes in each human somatic cell is a consequence of our sexual origins. We inherit one chromosome of a pair from each parent. Thus, the 46 chromosomes in our somatic cells are actually two sets of 23 chromosomes—a maternal set (from our mother) and a paternal set (from our father). The number of chromosomes in a single set is represented by $n$. Any cell with two chromosome sets is called a **diploid cell** and has a diploid number of chromosomes, abbreviated $2n$. For humans, the diploid number is 46 ($2n = 46$), the number of chromosomes in our somatic cells. In a cell in which DNA synthesis has occurred, all the chromosomes are duplicated, and therefore each consists of two identical sister chromatids, associated closely at the centromere and along the arms. (Even though the chromosomes are duplicated, we still say the cell is diploid ($2n$) because it has only two sets of information.) **Figure 10.4** helps clarify the various terms that we use to describe duplicated chromosomes in a diploid cell.

Unlike somatic cells, gametes contain a single set of chromosomes. Such cells are called **haploid cells**, and each has a

haploid number of chromosomes ($n$). For humans, the haploid number is 23 ($n = 23$). The set of 23 consists of the 22 autosomes plus a single sex chromosome. An unfertilized egg contains an X chromosome, but a sperm may contain an X or a Y chromosome.

Each sexually reproducing species has a characteristic diploid and haploid number. For example, the fruit fly *Drosophila melanogaster* has a diploid number ($2n$) of 8 and a haploid number ($n$) of 4, while for dogs, $2n$ is 78 and $n$ is 39. Now let's consider chromosome behavior during sexual life cycles. We'll use the human life cycle as an example.

## Behavior of Chromosome Sets in the Human Life Cycle

The human life cycle begins when a haploid sperm from the father fuses with a haploid egg from the mother **(Figure 10.5)**. This union of gametes, culminating in fusion of their nuclei, is called **fertilization**. The resulting fertilized egg, or **zygote**, is

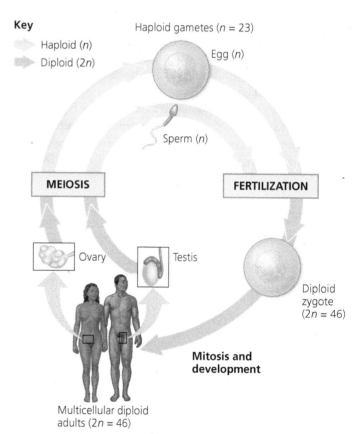

▲ **Figure 10.5 The human life cycle.** In each generation, the number of chromosome sets doubles at fertilization but is halved during meiosis. For humans, the number of chromosomes in a haploid cell is 23, consisting of one set ($n = 23$); the number of chromosomes in the diploid zygote and all somatic cells arising from it is 46, consisting of two sets ($2n = 46$).

This figure introduces a color code that will be used for other life cycles later in this book. The aqua arrows identify haploid stages of a life cycle, and the tan arrows identify diploid stages.

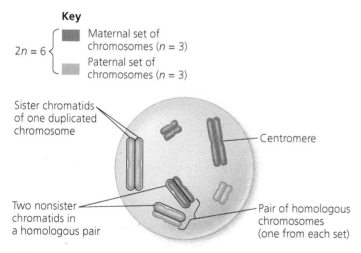

▲ **Figure 10.4 Describing chromosomes.** A cell from an organism with a diploid number of 6 ($2n = 6$) is depicted here following chromosome duplication and condensation. Each of the six duplicated chromosomes consists of two sister chromatids associated closely along their lengths. Each homologous pair is composed of one chromosome from the maternal set (red) and one from the paternal set (blue). Each set is made up of three chromosomes in this example (long, medium, and short). Together, one maternal and one paternal chromatid in a pair of homologous chromosomes are called nonsister chromatids.

**?** *How many sets of chromosomes are present in this diagram? How many pairs of homologous chromosomes are present?*

diploid because it contains two haploid sets of chromosomes bearing genes representing the maternal and paternal family lines. As a human develops into a sexually mature adult, mitosis of the zygote and its descendant cells generates all the somatic cells of the body. Both chromosome sets in the zygote and all the genes they carry are passed with precision to the somatic cells.

The only cells of the human body not produced by mitosis are the gametes, which develop from specialized cells called *germ cells* in the gonads—ovaries in females and testes in males. Imagine what would happen if human gametes were made by mitosis: They would be diploid like the somatic cells. At the next round of fertilization, when two gametes fused, the normal chromosome number of 46 would double to 92, and each subsequent generation would double the number of chromosomes yet again. This does not happen, however, because in sexually reproducing organisms, gamete formation involves a type of cell division called **meiosis**. This type of cell division reduces the number of sets of chromosomes from two to one in the gametes, counterbalancing the doubling that occurs at fertilization. As a result of meiosis, each human sperm and egg is haploid ($n = 23$). Fertilization restores the diploid condition by combining two haploid sets of chromosomes, and the human life cycle is repeated, generation after generation (see Figure 10.5).

In general, the steps of the human life cycle are typical of many sexually reproducing animals. Indeed, the processes of fertilization and meiosis are the hallmarks of sexual reproduction in plants, fungi, and protists as well as in animals. Fertilization and meiosis alternate in sexual life cycles, maintaining a constant number of chromosomes in each species from one generation to the next.

## The Variety of Sexual Life Cycles

Although the alternation of meiosis and fertilization is common to all organisms that reproduce sexually, the timing of these two events in the life cycle varies, depending on the species. These variations can be grouped into three main types of life cycles. In the type that occurs in humans and most other animals, gametes are the only haploid cells **(Figure 10.6a)**. Meiosis occurs in germ cells during the production of gametes, which undergo no further cell division prior to fertilization. After fertilization, the diploid zygote divides by mitosis, producing a multicellular organism that is diploid.

Plants and some species of algae exhibit a second type of life cycle called **alternation of generations (Figure 10.6b)**. This type includes both diploid and haploid stages that are multicellular. The multicellular diploid stage is called the *sporophyte*. Meiosis in the sporophyte produces haploid cells called *spores*. Unlike a gamete, a haploid spore doesn't fuse with another cell but divides mitotically, generating a multicellular haploid stage called the *gametophyte*. Cells of the gametophyte give rise to gametes by mitosis. Fusion of two haploid gametes at fertilization results in a diploid zygote, which develops into the next sporophyte generation. Therefore, in this type of life cycle, the sporophyte generation produces a gametophyte as its offspring, and the gametophyte generation produces the next sporophyte generation (see Figure 10.6b). The term *alternation of generations* fits well as a name for this type of life cycle.

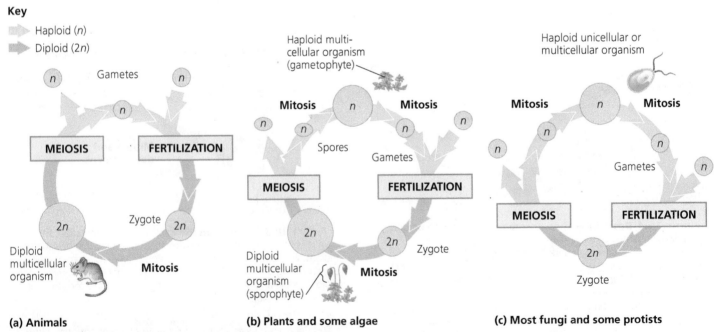

**(a) Animals**

**(b) Plants and some algae**

**(c) Most fungi and some protists**

▲ **Figure 10.6 Three types of sexual life cycles.** The common feature of all three cycles is the alternation of meiosis and fertilization, key events that contribute to genetic variation among offspring. The cycles differ in the timing of these two key events.

A third type of life cycle occurs in most fungi and some protists, including some algae (**Figure 10.6c**). After gametes fuse and form a diploid zygote, meiosis occurs without a multicellular diploid offspring developing. Meiosis produces not gametes but haploid cells that then divide by mitosis and give rise to either unicellular descendants or a haploid multicellular adult organism. Subsequently, the haploid organism carries out further mitoses, producing the cells that develop into gametes. The only diploid stage found in these species is the single-celled zygote.

Note that *either* haploid or diploid cells can divide by mitosis, depending on the type of life cycle. Only diploid cells, however, can undergo meiosis because haploid cells have only a single set of chromosomes that cannot be further reduced. Though the three types of sexual life cycles differ in the timing of meiosis and fertilization, they share a fundamental result: genetic variation among offspring.

**CONCEPT CHECK 10.2**

1. **MAKE CONNECTIONS** In Figure 10.4, how many DNA molecules (double helices) are present? What is the haploid number of this cell? Is a set of chromosomes haploid or diploid?

2. In the karyotype shown in Figure 10.3, how many pairs of chromosomes are present? How many sets?

3. **WHAT IF?** A certain eukaryote lives as a unicellular organism, but during environmental stress, it produces gametes. The gametes fuse, and the resulting zygote undergoes meiosis, generating new single cells. What type of organism could this be?

For suggested answers, see Appendix A.

CONCEPT 10.3

# Meiosis reduces the number of chromosome sets from diploid to haploid

Many of the steps of meiosis closely resemble corresponding steps in mitosis. Meiosis, like mitosis, is preceded by the duplication of chromosomes. However, this single duplication is followed by not one but two consecutive cell divisions, called **meiosis I** and **meiosis II**. These two divisions result in four daughter cells (rather than the two daughter cells of mitosis), each with only half as many chromosomes as the parent cell—one set, rather than two.

## The Stages of Meiosis

The overview of meiosis in **Figure 10.7** shows, for a single pair of homologous chromosomes in a diploid cell, that both members of the pair are duplicated and the copies sorted into four haploid daughter cells. Recall that sister chromatids are two copies of *one* chromosome, closely associated all along

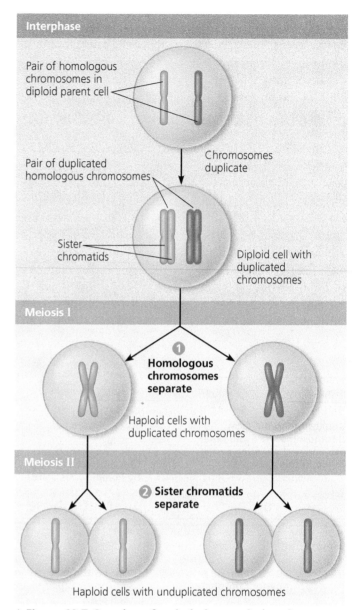

▲ **Figure 10.7 Overview of meiosis: how meiosis reduces chromosome number.** After the chromosomes duplicate in interphase, the diploid cell divides *twice*, yielding four haploid daughter cells. This overview tracks just one pair of homologous chromosomes, which for the sake of simplicity are drawn in the condensed state throughout.

**DRAW IT** *Redraw the cells in this figure using a simple double helix to represent each DNA molecule.*

their lengths; this association is called *sister chromatid cohesion*. Together, the sister chromatids make up one duplicated chromosome (see Figure 10.4). In contrast, the two chromosomes of a homologous pair are individual chromosomes that were inherited from different parents. Homologs appear alike in the microscope, but they may have different versions of genes, each called an *allele*, at corresponding loci. Homologs are not associated with each other in any obvious way except during meiosis.

**Figure 10.8** describes in detail the stages of the two divisions of meiosis for an animal cell whose diploid number is 6. Study this figure thoroughly before going on.

▼ **Figure 10.8**

# Exploring Meiosis in an Animal Cell

## MEIOSIS I: Separates homologous chromosomes

| Prophase I | Metaphase I | Anaphase I | Telophase I and Cytokinesis |
|---|---|---|---|

Centrosome (with centriole pair)

Sister chromatids

Chiasmata

Spindle

Homologous chromosomes

Fragments of nuclear envelope

**Duplicated homologous chromosomes (red and blue) pair and exchange segments; 2n = 6 in this example.**

Centromere (with kinetochore)

Metaphase plate

Microtubules attached to kinetochore

**Chromosomes line up by homologous pairs.**

Sister chromatids remain attached

Homologous chromosomes separate

**Each pair of homologous chromosomes separates.**

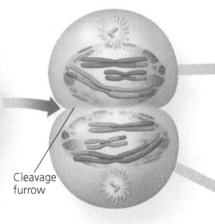

Cleavage furrow

**Two haploid cells form; each chromosome still consists of two sister chromatids.**

## Prophase I

- Centrosome movement, spindle formation, and nuclear envelope breakdown occur as in mitosis. Chromosomes condense progressively throughout prophase I.

- During early prophase I, before the stage shown above, each chromosome pairs with its homolog, aligned gene by gene, and **crossing over** occurs: The DNA molecules of non-sister chromatids are broken (by proteins) and are rejoined to each other.

- At the stage shown above, each homologous pair has one or more X-shaped regions called **chiasmata** (singular, *chiasma*), where crossovers have occurred.

- Later in prophase I, after the stage shown above, microtubules from one pole or the other will attach to the two kinetochores, one at the centromere of each homolog. (The two kinetochores of a homolog, not yet visible above, act as a single kinetochore.) The homologous pairs will then move toward the metaphase plate.

## Metaphase I

- Pairs of homologous chromosomes are now arranged at the metaphase plate, with one chromosome in each pair facing each pole.

- Both chromatids of one homolog are attached to kinetochore microtubules from one pole; those of the other homolog are attached to microtubules from the opposite pole.

## Anaphase I

- Breakdown of proteins that are responsible for sister chromatid cohesion along chromatid arms allows homologs to separate. *separase*

- The homologs move toward opposite poles, guided by the spindle apparatus.

- Sister chromatid cohesion persists at the centromere, causing chromatids to move as a unit toward the same pole.

## Telophase I and Cytokinesis

- When telophase I begins, each half of the cell has a complete haploid set of duplicated chromosomes. Each chromosome is composed of two sister chromatids; one or both chromatids include regions of nonsister chromatid DNA.

- Cytokinesis (division of the cytoplasm) usually occurs simultaneously with telophase I, forming two haploid daughter cells.

- In animal cells like these, a cleavage furrow forms. (In plant cells, a cell plate forms.)

- In some species, chromosomes decondense and nuclear envelopes form.

- No chromosome duplication occurs between meiosis I and meiosis II.

## MEIOSIS II: Separates sister chromatids

| Prophase II | Metaphase II | Anaphase II | Telophase II and Cytokinesis |
|---|---|---|---|

**During another round of cell division, the sister chromatids finally separate; four haploid daughter cells result, containing unduplicated chromosomes.**

Sister chromatids separate

Haploid daughter cells forming

### Prophase II

- A spindle apparatus forms.

- In late prophase II (not shown here), chromosomes, each still composed of two chromatids associated at the centromere, move toward the metaphase II plate.

### Metaphase II

- The chromosomes are positioned at the metaphase plate as in mitosis.

- Because of crossing over in meiosis I, the two sister chromatids of each chromo-some are *not* genetically identical.

- The kinetochores of sister chromatids are attached to microtubules extending from opposite poles.

### Anaphase II

- Breakdown of proteins holding the sister chromatids together at the centromere allows the chromatids to separate. The chromatids move toward opposite poles as individual chromosomes.

### Telophase II and Cytokinesis

- Nuclei form, the chromo-somes begin decondensing, and cytokinesis occurs.

- The meiotic division of one parent cell produces four daughter cells, each with a haploid set of (unduplicated) chromosomes.

- The four daughter cells are genetically distinct from one another and from the parent cell.

**MAKE CONNECTIONS** *Look at Figure 9.7 and imagine the two daughter cells undergoing another round of mitosis, yielding four cells. Compare the number of chromosomes in each of those four cells, after mitosis, with the number in each cell in Figure 10.8, after meiosis. What is it about the process of meiosis that accounts for this difference, even though meiosis also includes two cell divisions?*

**ANIMATION** **BioFlix** Visit the Study Area in **MasteringBiology** for the BioFlix® 3-D Animation on Meiosis. BioFlix Tutorials can also be assigned in MasteringBiology.

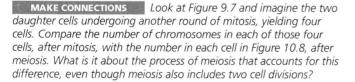

## Crossing Over and Synapsis During Prophase I

Prophase I of meiosis is a very busy time. The prophase I cell shown in Figure 10.8 is at a point fairly late in prophase I, when homologous pairing, crossing over, and chromosome condensation have already taken place. The sequence of events leading up to that point is shown in more detail in **Figure 10.9**.

After interphase, the chromosomes have been duplicated and the sister chromatids are held together by proteins called *cohesins*. Early in prophase I, the two members of a homologous pair associate loosely along their length. Each gene on one homolog is aligned precisely with the corresponding gene on the other homolog. The DNA of two nonsister chromatids—one maternal and one paternal—is broken by specific proteins at precisely corresponding points. Next, the formation of a zipper-like structure called the **synaptonemal complex** holds one homolog tightly to the other. During this association, called **synapsis**, the DNA breaks are closed up so that each broken end is joined to the corresponding segment of the *nonsister* chromatid. Thus, a paternal chromatid is joined to a piece of maternal chromatid beyond the crossover point, and vice versa.

These points of crossing over become visible as chiasmata (singular, *chiasma*) after the synaptonemal complex disassembles and the homologs move slightly apart from each other. The homologs remain attached because sister chromatids are still held together by sister chromatid cohesion, even though some of the DNA may no longer be attached to its original chromosome. At least one crossover per chromosome must occur in order for the homologous pair to stay together as it moves to the metaphase I plate.

## A Comparison of Mitosis and Meiosis

**Figure 10.10** summarizes the key differences between meiosis and mitosis in diploid cells. Basically, meiosis reduces the number of chromosome sets from two (diploid) to one (haploid), whereas mitosis conserves the number of chromosome sets. Therefore, meiosis produces cells that differ genetically from their parent cell and from each other, whereas mitosis produces daughter cells that are genetically identical to their parent cell and to each other.

Three events unique to meiosis occur during meiosis I:

1. **Synapsis and crossing over.** During prophase I, duplicated homologs pair up and crossing over occurs, as described above. Synapsis and crossing over normally do not occur during prophase of mitosis.

2. **Homologous pairs at the metaphase plate.** At metaphase I of meiosis, chromosomes are positioned at the metaphase plate as pairs of homologs, rather than individual chromosomes, as in metaphase of mitosis.

**1** After interphase, the chromosomes have been duplicated and sister chromatids are held together by proteins called cohesins (purple). Each pair of homologs associate along their length. The DNA molecules of two nonsister chromatids are broken at precisely corresponding points. The chromatin of the chromosomes is beginning to condense.

**2** A zipperlike protein complex, the synaptonemal complex (green), begins to form, attaching one homolog to the other. The chromatin continues to condense.

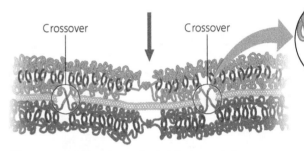

**3** The synaptonemal complex is fully formed; the two homologs are said to be in synapsis. During synapsis, the DNA breaks are closed up when each broken end is joined to the corresponding segment of the nonsister chromatid, producing crossovers.

**4** After the synaptonemal complex disassembles, the homologs move slightly apart from each other but remain attached because of sister chromatid cohesion, even though some of the DNA may no longer be attached to its original chromosome. The points of attachment where crossovers have occurred show up as chiasmata. The chromosomes continue to condense as they move toward the metaphase plate.

▲ **Figure 10.9 Crossing over and synapsis in prophase I: a closer look.** For simplicity, the four chromatids of the homologous pair shown here are depicted side by side, but in reality, the blue chromosome would be right on top of the red one (see the top cell in Figure 10.12).

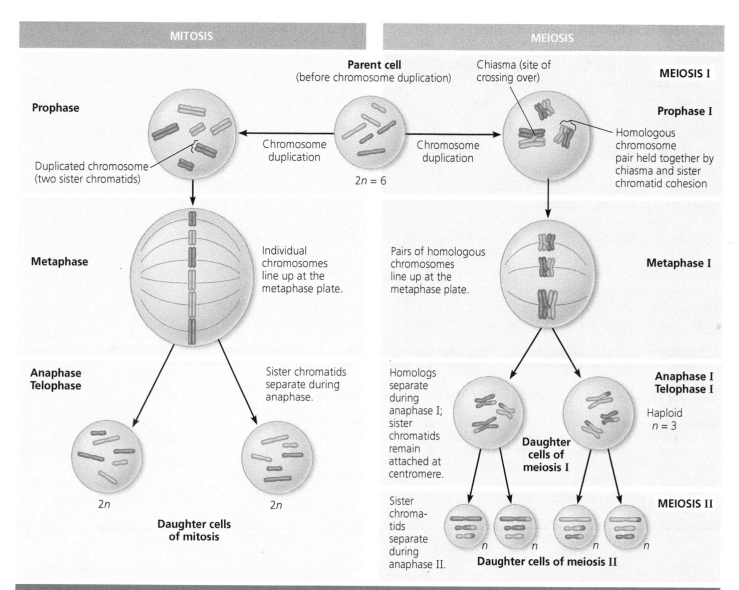

| | MITOSIS | MEIOSIS |
|---|---|---|

**Parent cell** (before chromosome duplication)

**Prophase**

Chromosome duplication

$2n = 6$

Chromosome duplication

Chiasma (site of crossing over)

**MEIOSIS I**

**Prophase I**

Duplicated chromosome (two sister chromatids)

Homologous chromosome pair held together by chiasma and sister chromatid cohesion

**Metaphase**

Individual chromosomes line up at the metaphase plate.

Pairs of homologous chromosomes line up at the metaphase plate.

**Metaphase I**

**Anaphase Telophase**

Sister chromatids separate during anaphase.

Homologs separate during anaphase I; sister chromatids remain attached at centromere.

**Anaphase I Telophase I**

Haploid $n = 3$

**Daughter cells of meiosis I**

$2n$          $2n$

**Daughter cells of mitosis**

Sister chromatids separate during anaphase II.

**MEIOSIS II**

$n$     $n$     $n$     $n$

**Daughter cells of meiosis II**

## SUMMARY

| Property | Mitosis (occurs in both diploid and haploid cells) | Meiosis (can only occur in diploid cells) |
|---|---|---|
| DNA replication | Occurs during interphase before mitosis begins | Occurs during interphase before meiosis I begins |
| Number of divisions | One, including prophase, prometaphase, metaphase, anaphase, and telophase | Two, each including prophase, metaphase, anaphase, and telophase |
| Synapsis of homologous chromosomes | Does not occur | Occurs during prophase I along with crossing over between nonsister chromatids; resulting chiasmata hold pairs together due to sister chromatid cohesion |
| Number of daughter cells and genetic composition | Two, each genetically identical to the parent cell, with the same number of chromosomes | Four, each haploid ($n$); genetically different from the parent cell and from each other |
| Role in the animal or plant body | Enables multicellular animal or plant (gametophyte or sporophyte) to arise from a single cell; produces cells for growth, repair, and, in some species, asexual reproduction; produces gametes in the gametophyte plant | Produces gametes (in animals) or spores (in the sporophyte plant); reduces number of chromosome sets by half and introduces genetic variability among the gametes or spores |

▲ **Figure 10.10 A comparison of mitosis and meiosis.**

**DRAW IT** *Could any other combinations of chromosomes be generated during meiosis II from the specific cells shown in telophase I? Explain. (Hint: Draw the cells as they would appear in metaphase II.)*

3. **Separation of homologs.** At anaphase I of meiosis, the duplicated chromosomes of each homologous pair move toward opposite poles, but the sister chromatids of each duplicated chromosome remain attached. In anaphase of mitosis, by contrast, sister chromatids separate.

Sister chromatids stay together due to sister chromatid cohesion, mediated by cohesin proteins. In mitosis, this attachment lasts until the end of metaphase, when enzymes cleave the cohesins, freeing the sister chromatids to move to opposite poles of the cell. In meiosis, sister chromatid cohesion is released in two steps, one at the start of anaphase I and one at anaphase II. In metaphase I, homologs are held together by cohesion between sister chromatid arms in regions beyond points of crossing over, where stretches of sister chromatids now belong to different chromosomes. The combination of crossing over and sister chromatid cohesion along the arms results in the formation of a chiasma. Chiasmata hold homologs together as the spindle forms for the first meiotic division. At the onset of anaphase I, the release of cohesion along sister chromatid arms allows homologs to separate. At anaphase II, the release of sister chromatid cohesion at the centromeres allows the sister chromatids to separate. Thus, sister chromatid cohesion and crossing over, acting together, play an essential role in the lining up of chromosomes by homologous pairs at metaphase I.

Meiosis I is called the *reductional division* because it reduces the number of chromosome sets from two (diploid) to one (haploid). During meiosis II (the *equational division*), sister chromatids separate, producing haploid daughter cells. The mechanism for separating sister chromatids is virtually identical in meiosis II and mitosis. The molecular basis of chromosome behavior during meiosis continues to be a focus of intense research. In the Scientific Skills Exercise, you can work with data tracking the amount of DNA in cells as they progress through meiosis.

---

## Scientific Skills Exercise

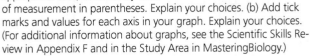

# Making a Line Graph and Converting Between Units of Data

**How Does DNA Content Change as Budding Yeast Cells Proceed Through Meiosis?** When nutrients are low, cells of the budding yeast (Saccharomyces cerevisiae) exit the mitotic cell cycle and enter meiosis. In this exercise, you will track the DNA content of a population of yeast cells as they progress through meiosis.

**How the Experiment Was Done** Researchers grew a culture of yeast cells in a nutrient-rich medium and then transferred them to a nutrient-poor medium to induce meiosis. At different times after induction, the DNA content per cell was measured in a sample of the cells, and the average DNA content per cell was recorded in femtograms (fg; 1 femtogram = 1 * 10-15 gram).

**Data from the Experiment**

| Time After Induction (hours) | Average Amount of DNA per Cell (fg) |
|---|---|
| 0.0 | 24.0 |
| 1.0 | 24.0 |
| 2.0 | 40.0 |
| 3.0 | 47.0 |
| 4.0 | 47.5 |
| 5.0 | 48.0 |
| 6.0 | 48.0 |
| 7.0 | 47.5 |
| 7.5 | 25.0 |
| 8.0 | 24.0 |
| 9.0 | 23.5 |
| 9.5 | 14.0 |
| 10.0 | 13.0 |
| 11.0 | 12.5 |
| 12.0 | 12.0 |
| 13.0 | 12.5 |
| 14.0 | 12.0 |

**Interpret the Data**

1. First, set up your graph. (a) Place the labels for the independent variable and the dependent variable on the appropriate axes, followed by units of measurement in parentheses. Explain your choices. (b) Add tick marks and values for each axis in your graph. Explain your choices. (For additional information about graphs, see the Scientific Skills Review in Appendix F and in the Study Area in MasteringBiology.)

2. Because the variable on the x-axis varies continuously, it makes sense to plot the data on a line graph. (a) Plot each data point from the table onto the graph. (b) Connect the data points with line segments.

3. Most of the yeast cells in the culture were in G1 of the cell cycle before being moved to the nutrient-poor medium. (a) How many femtograms of DNA are there in each yeast cell in G1? Estimate this value from the data in your graph. (b) How many femtograms of DNA should be present in each cell in G2? At the end of meiosis I (MI)? At the end of meiosis II (MII)? (See Figure 10.7.) (c) Using these values as a guideline, distinguish the different phases by inserting vertical dashed lines in the graph between phases and label each phase (G1, S, G2, MI, MII). You can figure out where to put the dividing lines based on what you know about the DNA content of each phase (see Figure 10.7). (d) Think carefully about the point where the line at the highest value begins to slope downward. What specific point of meiosis does this "corner" represent? What stage(s) correspond to the downward sloping line?

4. Given the fact that 1 fg of DNA = 9.78 * 105 base pairs (on average), you can convert the amount of DNA per cell to the length of DNA in numbers of base pairs. (a) Calculate the number of base pairs of DNA in the haploid yeast genome. Express your answer in millions of base pairs (Mb), a standard unit for expressing genome size. Show your work. (b) How many base pairs per minute were synthesized during the S phase of these yeast cells?

**Further Reading** G. Simchen, Commitment to meiosis: what determines the mode of division in budding yeast? *BioEssays* 31:169–177 (2009).

(MB) A version of this Scientific Skills Exercise can be assigned in MasteringBiology.

1. **MAKE CONNECTIONS** Compare the chromosomes in a cell at metaphase of mitosis with those in a cell at metaphase II. (See Figure 10.8.)

2. **WHAT IF?** After the synaptonemal complex disappears, how would the two homologs be associated if crossing over did not occur? What effect might this ultimately have on gamete formation?

For suggested answers, see Appendix A.

# CONCEPT 10.4

# Genetic variation produced in sexual life cycles contributes to evolution

How do we account for the genetic variation of the family members in Figure 10.1? As you will learn, mutations are the original source of genetic diversity. These changes in an organism's DNA create the different versions of genes known as alleles. Once these differences arise, reshuffling of the alleles during sexual reproduction produces the variation that results in each member of a sexually reproducing population having a unique combination of traits.

## Origins of Genetic Variation Among Offspring

In species that reproduce sexually, the behavior of chromosomes during meiosis and fertilization is responsible for most of the variation that arises in each generation. Three mechanisms contribute to the genetic variation arising from sexual reproduction: independent assortment of chromosomes, crossing over, and random fertilization.

### Independent Assortment of Chromosomes

One aspect of sexual reproduction that generates genetic variation is the random orientation of pairs of homologous chromosomes at metaphase of meiosis I. At metaphase I, the homologous pairs, each consisting of one maternal and one paternal chromosome, are situated at the metaphase plate. (Note that the terms *maternal* and *paternal* refer, respectively, to the mother and father of the individual whose cells are undergoing meiosis.) Each pair may orient with either its maternal or paternal homolog closer to a given pole—its orientation is as random as the flip of a coin. Thus, there is a 50% chance that a particular daughter cell of meiosis I will get the maternal chromosome of a certain homologous pair and a 50% chance that it will get the paternal chromosome.

Because each pair of homologous chromosomes is positioned independently of the other pairs at metaphase I, the first meiotic division results in each pair sorting its maternal and paternal homologs into daughter cells independently of every other pair. This is called *independent assortment*. Each daughter cell represents one outcome of all possible combinations of maternal and paternal chromosomes. As shown in **Figure 10.11**, the number of combinations possible for daughter cells formed by meiosis of a diploid cell with two pairs of homologous chromosomes ($n = 2$) is four: two possible arrangements for the first pair times two possible arrangements for the second pair. Note that only two of the four combinations of daughter cells shown in the figure would result from meiosis of a *single* diploid cell, because a single parent cell would have one or the other possible chromosomal arrangement at metaphase I, but not both. However, the population of daughter cells resulting from meiosis of a large number of diploid cells contains all four types in approximately equal numbers. In the case of $n = 3$, eight combinations of chromosomes are possible for daughter cells. More generally, the number of possible combinations when chromosomes sort independently during meiosis is $2^n$, where $n$ is the haploid number of the organism.

In the case of humans ($n = 23$), the number of possible combinations of maternal and paternal chromosomes in the resulting gametes is $2^{23}$, or about 8.4 million. Each gamete that you produce in your lifetime contains one of roughly 8.4 million possible combinations of chromosomes.

## Crossing Over

As a consequence of the independent assortment of chromosomes during meiosis, each of us produces a collection of gametes differing greatly in their combinations of the chromosomes we inherited from our two parents. Figure 10.11 suggests that each chromosome in a gamete is exclusively

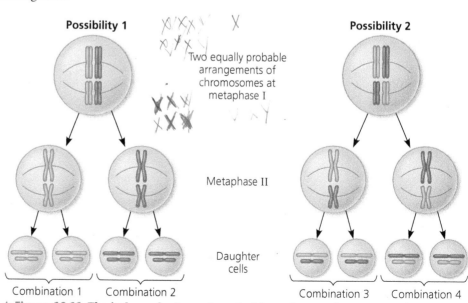

**Possibility 1**       Two equally probable arrangements of chromosomes at metaphase I       **Possibility 2**

Metaphase II

Daughter cells

Combination 1    Combination 2      Combination 3    Combination 4

▲ **Figure 10.11** **The independent assortment of homologous chromosomes in meiosis.**

maternal or paternal in origin. In fact, this is *not* the case, because crossing over produces **recombinant chromosomes**, individual chromosomes that carry genes (DNA) derived from two different parents (**Figure 10.12**). In meiosis in humans, an average of one to three crossover events occur per chromosome pair, depending on the size of the chromosomes and the position of their centromeres.

As you learned in Figure 10.9, crossing over produces chromosomes with new combinations of maternal and paternal alleles. At metaphase II, chromosomes that contain one or more recombinant chromatids can be oriented in two alternative, nonequivalent ways with respect to other chromosomes, because their sister chromatids are no longer identical (see Figure 10.12). The different possible arrangements of nonidentical sister chromatids during meiosis II further increase the number of genetic types of daughter cells that can result from meiosis.

### Random Fertilization

The random nature of fertilization adds to the genetic variation arising from meiosis. In humans, each male and female gamete represents one of about 8.4 million ($2^{23}$) possible chromosome combinations due to independent assortment. The fusion of a male gamete with a female gamete during fertilization will produce a zygote with any of about 70 trillion ($2^{23} \times 2^{23}$) diploid combinations. If we factor in the variation brought about by crossing over, the number of possibilities is truly astronomical. It may sound trite, but you really *are* unique.

## The Evolutionary Significance of Genetic Variation Within Populations

**EVOLUTION**   Now that you've learned how new combinations of genes arise among offspring in a sexually reproducing population, let's see how the genetic variation in a population relates to evolution. Darwin recognized that a population evolves through the differential reproductive success of its variant members. On average, those individuals best suited to the local environment leave the most offspring, thereby transmitting their genes. Thus, natural selection results in the accumulation of genetic variations favored by the environment. As the environment changes, the population may survive if, in each generation, at least some of its members can cope effectively with the new conditions. Mutations are the original source of different alleles, which are then mixed and matched during meiosis. New and different combinations of alleles may work better than those that previously prevailed.

In a stable environment, though, sexual reproduction seems as if it would be less advantageous than asexual reproduction, which ensures perpetuation of successful combinations of alleles. Furthermore, sexual reproduction is more expensive energetically than asexual reproduction. In spite of these apparent disadvantages, sexual reproduction is almost universal among animals. Why is this?

The ability of sexual reproduction to generate genetic diversity is the most commonly proposed explanation for the

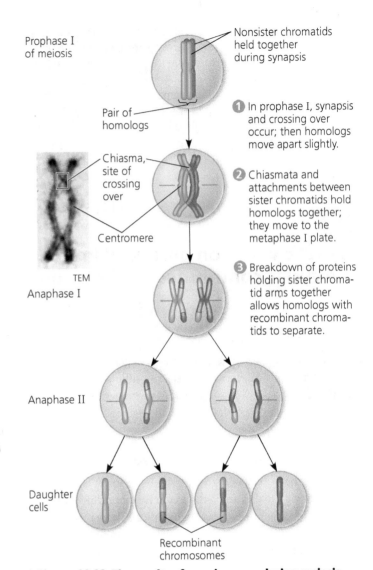

1 In prophase I, synapsis and crossing over occur; then homologs move apart slightly.

2 Chiasmata and attachments between sister chromatids hold homologs together; they move to the metaphase I plate.

3 Breakdown of proteins holding sister chromatid arms together allows homologs with recombinant chromatids to separate.

▲ **Figure 10.12 The results of crossing over during meiosis.**

evolutionary persistence of this process. Consider the rare case of the bdelloid rotifer **Figure 10.13**. This group has apparently not reproduced sexually throughout the 40 million years of its evolutionary history. Does this mean that genetic diversity is not advantageous in this species? It turns out that bdelloid rotifers are an exception that proves the rule: This group has mechanisms other than sexual reproduction for generating genetic diversity. For example, they live in environments that can dry up for long periods of time, during which they can enter a state of suspended animation. In this state, their cell membranes may crack in places, allowing entry of DNA from other rotifers and even other species. Evidence suggests that this DNA can become incorporated into the genome of the rotifer, leading to increased genetic diversity. This supports the idea that genetic diversity is advantageous, and that sexual reproduction has persisted because it generates such diversity.

In this chapter, we have seen how sexual reproduction greatly increases the genetic variation present in a population. Although Darwin realized that heritable variation is what makes evolution possible, he could not explain why offspring resemble—but are not identical to—their parents. Ironically, Gregor Mendel, a contemporary of Darwin, published a theory of inheritance that helps explain genetic variation, but his discoveries had no impact on biologists until 1900, more than 15 years after Darwin (1809–1882) and Mendel (1822–1884) had died. You'll learn how Mendel discovered the basic rules governing the inheritance of specific traits.

▲ **Figure 10.13 A bdelloid rotifer, an animal that reproduces only asexually.**

**CONCEPT CHECK 10.4**

1. What is the original source of variation among the different alleles of a gene?
2. The diploid number for fruit flies is 8, and the diploid number for grasshoppers is 46. If no crossing over took place, would the genetic variation among offspring from a given pair of parents be greater in fruit flies or grasshoppers? Explain.
2. **WHAT IF?** If maternal and paternal chromatids have the same two alleles for every gene, will crossing over lead to genetic variation?

For suggested answers, see Appendix A.

# 10 Chapter Review

## SUMMARY OF KEY CONCEPTS

**CONCEPT** 10.1

### Offspring acquire genes from parents by inheriting chromosomes (pp. 197–198)

- Each **gene** in an organism's DNA exists at a specific **locus** on a certain chromosome.
- In **asexual reproduction**, a single parent produces genetically identical offspring by mitosis. **Sexual reproduction** combines genes from two parents, leading to genetically diverse offspring.

? *Explain why human offspring resemble their parents but are not identical to them.*

**CONCEPT** 10.2

### Fertilization and meiosis alternate in sexual life cycles (pp. 198–201)

- Normal human **somatic cells** are **diploid**. They have 46 chromosomes made up of two sets of 23, one set from each parent. Human diploid cells have 22 **homologous** pairs of **autosomes**, and one pair of **sex chromosomes**; the latter determines whether the person is female (XX) or male (XY).
- In humans, ovaries and testes produce **haploid gametes** by **meiosis**, each gamete containing a single set of 23 chromosomes ($n = 23$). During **fertilization**, an egg and sperm unite, forming a diploid ($2n = 46$) single-celled **zygote**, which develops into a multicellular organism by mitosis.

- Sexual life cycles differ in the timing of meiosis relative to fertilization and in the point(s) of the cycle at which a multicellular organism is produced by mitosis.

? *Compare the life cycles of animals and plants, mentioning their similarities and differences.*

**CONCEPT** 10.3

### Meiosis reduces the number of chromosome sets from diploid to haploid (pp. 201–207)

- The two cell divisions of meiosis, **meiosis I** and **meiosis II**, produce four haploid daughter cells. The number of chromosome sets is reduced from two (diploid) to one (haploid) during meiosis I, the reductional division.
- Meiosis is distinguished from mitosis by three events of meiosis I:

**Prophase I:** Each homologous pair undergoes **synapsis** and **crossing over** between nonsister chromatids with the subsequent appearance of **chiasmata**.

**Metaphase I:** Chromosomes line up as homologous pairs on the metaphase plate.

**Anaphase I:** Homologs separate from each other; sister chromatids remain joined at the centromere.

Meiosis II separates the sister chromatids.

- Sister chromatid cohesion and crossing over allow chiasmata to hold homologs together until anaphase I. Cohesins are cleaved along the arms at anaphase I, allowing homologs to separate, and at the centromeres in anaphase II, releasing sister chromatids.

**?** *In prophase I, homologous chromosomes pair up and undergo synapsis and crossing over. Can this also occur during prophase II? Explain.*

**CONCEPT** 10.4

## Genetic variation produced in sexual life cycles contributes to evolution (pp. 207–209)

- Three events in sexual reproduction contribute to genetic variation in a population: independent assortment of chromosomes during meiosis I, crossing over during meiosis I, and random fertilization of egg cells by sperm. During crossing over, DNA of nonsister chromatids in a homologous pair is broken and rejoined.
- Genetic variation is the raw material for evolution by natural selection. Mutations are the original source of this variation; recombination of variant genes generates additional genetic diversity.

**?** *Explain how three processes unique to meiosis generate a great deal of genetic variation.*

# TEST YOUR UNDERSTANDING

## Level 1: Knowledge/Comprehension

1. A human cell containing 22 autosomes and a Y chromosome is
   **a.** a sperm.
   **b.** an egg.
   **c.** a zygote.
   **d.** a somatic cell of a male.

2. Homologous chromosomes move toward opposite poles of a dividing cell during
   **a.** mitosis.
   **b.** meiosis I.
   **c.** meiosis II.
   **d.** fertilization.

## Level 2: Application/Analysis

3. Meiosis II is similar to mitosis in that
   **a.** sister chromatids separate during anaphase.
   **b.** DNA replicates before the division.
   **c.** the daughter cells are diploid.
   **d.** homologous chromosomes synapse.

4. If the DNA content of a diploid cell in the $G_1$ phase of the cell cycle is $x$, then the DNA content of the same cell at metaphase of meiosis I would be
   **a.** $0.25x$.   **b.** $0.5x$.   **c.** $x$.   **d.** $2x$.

5. If we continued to follow the cell lineage from question 4, then the DNA content of a single cell at metaphase of meiosis II would be
   **a.** $0.25x$.   **b.** $0.5x$.   **c.** $x$.   **d.** $2x$.

6. **DRAW IT** The diagram at right shows a cell in meiosis.
   (a) Label the appropriate structures with these terms, drawing lines or brackets as needed: chromosome (label as duplicated or unduplicated), centromere, kinetochore, sister chromatids, nonsister chromatids, homologous pair, homologs, chiasma, sister chromatid cohesion, alleles (of the F and H genes).
   (b) Describe the makeup of a haploid set and a diploid set.
   (c) Identify the stage of meiosis shown.

## Level 3: Synthesis/Evaluation

7. How can you tell that the cell in question 6 is undergoing meiosis, not mitosis?

8. **EVOLUTION CONNECTION**
   Many species can reproduce either asexually or sexually. What might be the evolutionary significance of the switch from asexual to sexual reproduction that occurs in some organisms when the environment becomes unfavorable?

9. **SCIENTIFIC INQUIRY**
   The diagram in question 6 represents just a few of the chromosomes of a meiotic cell in a certain person. A previous study has shown that the freckles gene is located at the locus marked F, and the hair-color gene is located at the locus marked H, both on the long chromosome. The individual from whom this cell was taken has inherited different alleles for each gene ("freckles" and "black hair" from one parent, and "no freckles" and "blond hair" from the other). Predict allele combinations in the gametes resulting from this meiotic event. (It will help if you draw out the rest of meiosis, labeling alleles by name.) List other possible combinations of these alleles in this individual's gametes.

10. **WRITE ABOUT A THEME: INFORMATION**
    The continuity of life is based on heritable information in the form of DNA. In a short essay (100–150 words), explain how chromosome behavior during sexual reproduction in animals ensures perpetuation of parental traits in offspring and, at the same time, genetic variation among offspring.

**11.**

The Cavendish banana is the most popular fruit in the world, but is currently threatened by extinction due to a fungal agent (see the photo). This banana variety is "triploid" (3n, with three sets of chromosomes) and can only reproduce through cloning by cultivators. Given what you know about meiosis, explain how the banana's triploid number accounts for its seedless condition. Considering genetic diversity, discuss how the absence of sexual reproduction might contribute to the vulnerability of this domesticated species to infectious agents.

*For selected answers, see Appendix A.*

## MasteringBiology®

**Students** Go to **MasteringBiology** for assignments, the eText, and the Study Area with practice tests, animations, and activities.

**Instructors** Go to **MasteringBiology** for automatically graded tutorials and questions that you can assign to your students, plus Instructor Resources.

# 11

# Mendel and the Gene Idea

OVERVIEW

## Drawing from the Deck of Genes

▼ **Figure 11.1** What principles of inheritance did Gregor Mendel discover by breeding garden pea plants?

Scanning the crowd at a soccer match attests to the marvelous variety and diversity of humankind. Brown, blue, green, or gray eyes; black, brown, blond, or red hair—these are just a few examples of heritable variations that we may observe among individuals in a population. What are the genetic principles that account for the transmission of such traits from parents to offspring in humans and other organisms?

The explanation of heredity most widely in favor during the 1800s was the "blending" hypothesis, the idea that genetic material contributed by the two parents mixes in a manner analogous to the way blue and yellow paints blend to make green. This hypothesis predicts that over many generations, a freely mating population will give rise to a uniform population of individuals. However, our everyday observations and the results of breeding experiments with animals and plants contradict that prediction. The blending hypothesis also fails to explain other phenomena of inheritance, such as traits reappearing after skipping a generation.

An alternative to the blending model is a "particulate" hypothesis of inheritance: the gene idea. According to this model, parents pass on discrete heritable units—genes—that retain their separate identities in offspring. An organism's collection of genes is more like a deck of cards than a bucket of paint. Like playing cards, genes can be shuffled and passed along, generation after generation, in undiluted form.

Modern genetics had its genesis in an abbey garden, where a monk named Gregor Mendel documented a particulate mechanism for inheritance. **Figure 11.1** shows Mendel (back row, holding a sprig of fuchsia) with his fellow monks. Mendel developed his theory of inheritance several decades before chromosomes were observed under the microscope and well before the significance of their behavior was understood. In this chapter, we will step into Mendel's garden to re-create his experiments and explain how he arrived at his theory of inheritance. We'll also explore inheritance patterns more complex than those observed by Mendel in garden peas. Finally, we'll see how the Mendelian model applies to the inheritance of human variations, including hereditary disorders such as sickle-cell disease.

# CONCEPT 11.1

# Mendel used the scientific approach to identify two laws of inheritance

Mendel discovered the basic principles of heredity by breeding garden peas in carefully planned experiments. As we retrace his work, you'll recognize the key elements of the scientific process that were introduced in Chapter 1.

## Mendel's Experimental, Quantitative Approach

One reason Mendel probably chose to work with peas is that they are available in many varieties. For example, one variety has purple flowers, while another variety has white flowers. A heritable feature that varies among individuals, such as flower color, is called a **character**. Each variant for a character, such as purple or white color for flowers, is called a **trait**.

Mendel could strictly control mating between plants. Each pea flower has both pollen-producing organs (stamens) and an egg-bearing organ (carpel). In nature, pea plants usually self-fertilize: Pollen grains from the stamens land on the carpel of the same flower, and sperm released from the pollen grains fertilize eggs present in the carpel. To achieve cross-pollination (fertilization between different plants), Mendel removed the immature stamens of a plant before they produced pollen and then dusted pollen from another plant onto the altered flowers **(Figure 11.2)**. Each resulting zygote then developed into a plant embryo encased in a seed (a pea). Mendel could thus always be sure of the parentage of new seeds.

Mendel chose to track only those characters that occurred in two distinct, alternative forms: purple or white flower color. He also made sure that he started his experiments with varieties that, over many generations of self-pollination, had produced only the same variety as the parent plant. Such plants are said to be **true-breeding**. For example, a plant with purple flowers is true-breeding if the seeds produced by self-pollination in successive generations all give rise to plants that also have purple flowers.

In a typical breeding experiment, Mendel cross-pollinated two contrasting, true-breeding pea varieties—for example, purple-flowered plants and white-flowered plants (see Figure 11.2). This mating, or *crossing*, of two true-breeding varieties is called **hybridization**. The true-breeding parents are referred to as the **P generation** (parental generation), and their hybrid offspring are the **F₁ generation** (first filial generation, the word *filial* from the Latin word for "son"). Allowing these $F_1$ hybrids to self-pollinate (or to cross-pollinate with other $F_1$ hybrids) produces an **F₂ generation** (second filial generation). Mendel usually followed traits for at least the P, $F_1$, and $F_2$ generations. Had Mendel stopped his experiments with the $F_1$ generation, the basic patterns of inheritance would have escaped him.

## Crossing Pea Plants

**Application** By crossing (mating) two true-breeding varieties of an organism, scientists can study patterns of inheritance. In this example, Mendel crossed pea plants that varied in flower color.

**Technique**

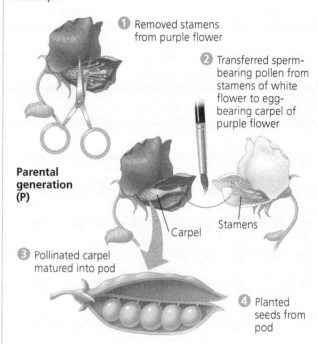

① Removed stamens from purple flower

② Transferred sperm-bearing pollen from stamens of white flower to egg-bearing carpel of purple flower

Parental generation (P)

Carpel

Stamens

③ Pollinated carpel matured into pod

④ Planted seeds from pod

**Results** When pollen from a white flower was transferred to a purple flower, the first-generation hybrids all had purple flowers. The result was the same for the reciprocal cross, which involved the transfer of pollen from purple flowers to white flowers.

First filial generation offspring (F₁)

⑤ Examined offspring: all purple flowers

Mendel's quantitative analysis of the $F_2$ plants from thousands of genetic crosses like these allowed him to deduce two fundamental principles of heredity, which have come to be called the law of segregation and the law of independent assortment.

## The Law of Segregation

If the blending model of inheritance were correct, the $F_1$ hybrids from a cross between purple-flowered and white-flowered pea plants would have pale purple flowers, a trait intermediate between those of the P generation. Notice in Figure 11.2 that the experiment produced a very different result: All the $F_1$ offspring had flowers just as purple as the purple-flowered parents. What happened to the white-flowered plants' genetic contribution to the hybrids? If it were lost, then the $F_1$ plants could produce only purple-flowered offspring in the $F_2$ generation. But when Mendel allowed the $F_1$ plants to self-pollinate and planted their seeds, the white-flower trait reappeared in the $F_2$ generation.

Mendel used very large sample sizes and kept accurate records of his results: 705 of the $F_2$ plants had purple flowers, and 224 had white flowers. These data fit a ratio of approximately three purple to one white (Figure 11.3). Mendel reasoned

that the heritable factor for white flowers did not disappear in the $F_1$ plants, but was somehow hidden, or masked, when the purple-flower factor was present. In Mendel's terminology, purple flower color is a *dominant* trait, and white flower color is a *recessive* trait. The reappearance of white-flowered plants in the $F_2$ generation was evidence that the heritable factor causing white flowers had not been diluted or destroyed by coexisting with the purple-flower factor in the $F_1$ hybrids.

Mendel observed the same pattern of inheritance in six other characters, each represented by two distinctly different traits (Table 11.1). For example, when Mendel crossed a true-breeding variety that produced smooth, round pea seeds with one that produced wrinkled seeds, all the $F_1$ hybrids produced round seeds; this is the dominant trait for seed shape. In the $F_2$ generation, approximately 75% of the seeds were round and 25% were wrinkled—a 3:1 ratio, as in Figure 11.3. Now let's see how Mendel deduced the law of segregation from his experimental results. In the discussion that follows, we will use modern terms instead of some of the terms used by Mendel. (For example, we'll use "gene" instead of Mendel's "heritable factor.")

---

### ▼ Figure 11.3 Inquiry

## When $F_1$ hybrid pea plants self- or cross-pollinate, which traits appear in the $F_2$ generation?

**Experiment** Around 1860, in a monastery garden in Brünn, Austria, Gregor Mendel used the character of flower color in pea plants to follow traits through two generations. He crossed true-breeding purple-flowered plants and white-flowered plants (crosses are symbolized by ×). The resulting $F_1$ hybrids were allowed to self-pollinate or were cross-pollinated with other $F_1$ hybrids. The $F_2$ generation plants were then observed for flower color.

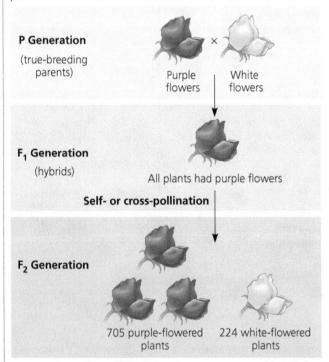

P Generation (true-breeding parents)

Purple flowers × White flowers

$F_1$ Generation (hybrids)

All plants had purple flowers

Self- or cross-pollination

$F_2$ Generation

705 purple-flowered plants    224 white-flowered plants

**Results** Both purple-flowered and white-flowered plants appeared in the $F_2$ generation, in a ratio of approximately 3:1.

**Conclusion** The "heritable factor" for the recessive trait (white flowers) had not been destroyed, deleted, or "blended" in the $F_1$ generation but was merely masked by the presence of the factor for purple flowers, which is the dominant trait.

**Source** G. Mendel, Experiments in plant hybridization, *Proceedings of the Natural History Society of Brünn* 4:3–47 (1866).

**WHAT IF?** If you mated two purple-flowered plants from the P generation, what ratio of traits would you expect to observe in the offspring? Explain.

---

**Table 11.1 The Results of Mendel's $F_1$ Crosses for Seven Characters in Pea Plants**

| Character | Dominant Trait | × | Recessive Trait | $F_2$ Generation Dominant: Recessive | Ratio |
|---|---|---|---|---|---|
| Flower color | Purple | × | White | 705:224 | 3.15:1 |
| Seed color | Yellow | × | Green | 6,022:2,001 | 3.01:1 |
| Seed shape | Round | × | Wrinkled | 5,474:1,850 | 2.96:1 |
| Pod shape | Inflated | × | Constricted | 882:299 | 2.95:1 |
| Pod color | Green | × | Yellow | 428:152 | 2.82:1 |
| Flower position | Axial | × | Terminal | 651:207 | 3.14:1 |
| Stem length | Tall | × | Dwarf | 787:277 | 2.84:1 |

---

Allele for purple flowers

Locus for flower-color gene

Pair of homologous chromosomes

Allele for white flowers

▲ **Figure 11.4 Alleles, alternative versions of a gene.** A somatic cell has two copies of each chromosome (forming a homologous pair) and thus two versions of each gene; the alleles may be identical or different. This figure depicts a pair of homologous chromosomes in an $F_1$ hybrid pea plant. The paternally inherited chromosome (blue), which was present in the sperm within a pollen grain, has an allele for purple flowers, and the maternally inherited chromosome (red), which was present in an egg within a carpel, has an allele for white flowers.

## Mendel's Model

Mendel developed a model to explain the 3:1 inheritance pattern that he consistently observed among the $F_2$ offspring in his pea experiments. We describe four related concepts making up this model, the fourth of which is the law of segregation.

First, *alternative versions of genes account for variations in inherited characters.* The gene for flower color in pea plants, for example, exists in two versions, one for purple flowers and the other for white flowers. These alternative versions of a gene are called **alleles (Figure 11.4).** Today, we can relate this concept to chromosomes and DNA: Each gene is a sequence of nucleotides at a specific place, or locus, along a particular chromosome. The DNA at that locus, however, can vary slightly in its nucleotide sequence and hence in its information content. The purple-flower allele and the white-flower allele are two DNA sequence variations possible at the flower-color locus on one of a pea plant's chromosomes.

▶ **Figure 11.5 Mendel's law of segregation.** This diagram shows the genetic makeup of the generations in Figure 11.3. It illustrates Mendel's model for inheritance of the alleles of a single gene. Each plant has two alleles for the gene controlling flower color, one allele inherited from each of the plant's parents. To construct a Punnett square that predicts the $F_2$ generation offspring, we list all the possible gametes from one parent (here, the $F_1$ female) along the left side of the square and all the possible gametes from the other parent (here, the $F_1$ male) along the top. The boxes represent the offspring resulting from all the possible unions of male and female gametes.

Second, *for each character, an organism inherits two copies (that is, two alleles) of a gene, one from each parent.* Remarkably, Mendel made this deduction without knowing about the role, or even the existence, of chromosomes. Each somatic cell in a diploid organism has two sets of chromosomes, one set inherited from each parent. Thus, a genetic locus is actually represented twice in a diploid cell, once on each homolog of a specific pair of chromosomes. The two alleles at a particular locus may be identical, as in the true-breeding plants of Mendel's P generation. Or the alleles may differ, as in the $F_1$ hybrids (see Figure 11.4).

Third, *if the two alleles at a locus differ, then one, the **dominant allele**, determines the organism's appearance; the other, the **recessive allele**, has no noticeable effect on the organism's appearance.* Accordingly, Mendel's $F_1$ plants had purple flowers because the allele for that trait is dominant and the allele for white flowers is recessive.

The fourth and final part of Mendel's model, the **law of segregation**, states that *the two alleles for a heritable character segregate (separate from each other) during gamete formation and end up in different gametes* **(Figure 11.5)**. Thus, an egg or a sperm gets only one of the two alleles that are present in the somatic cells of the organism making the gamete. In terms of

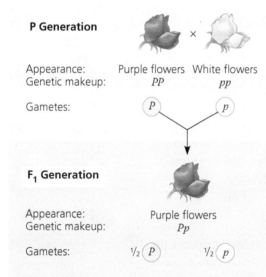

**P Generation**

Appearance: Purple flowers  White flowers
Genetic makeup: *PP*  *pp*

Gametes: *P*  *p*

Each true-breeding plant of the parental generation has two identical alleles, denoted as either *PP* or *pp*.

**Gametes (circles) each contain only one allele for the flower-color gene.** In this case, every gamete produced by a given parent has the same allele.

**F₁ Generation**

Appearance: Purple flowers
Genetic makeup: *Pp*

Gametes: ½ *P*  ½ *p*

**Union of parental gametes produces F₁ hybrids having a *Pp* combination.** Because the purple-flower allele is dominant, all these hybrids have purple flowers.

**When the hybrid plants produce gametes, the two alleles segregate.** Half of the gametes receive the *P* allele and the other half the *p* allele.

**F₂ Generation**

Sperm from F₁ (*Pp*) plant
*P*  *p*

Eggs from F₁ (*Pp*) plant
*P*  *p*

*PP*  *Pp*
*Pp*  *pp*

3 : 1

This box, a Punnett square, shows all possible combinations of alleles in offspring that result from an F₁ × F₁ (*Pp* × *Pp*) cross. Each square represents an equally probable product of fertilization. For example, the bottom left box shows the genetic combination resulting from a *p* egg fertilized by a *P* sperm.

**Random combination of the gametes results in the 3:1 ratio that Mendel observed in the F₂ generation.**

chromosomes, this segregation corresponds to the distribution of the two members of a pair of homologous chromosomes to different gametes in meiosis (see Figure 10.7). Note that if an organism has identical alleles for a particular character—that is, the organism is true-breeding for that character—then that allele is present in all gametes. But if different alleles are present, as in the $F_1$ hybrids, then 50% of the gametes receive the dominant allele and 50% receive the recessive allele.

Does Mendel's segregation model account for the 3:1 ratio he observed in the $F_2$ generation of his numerous crosses? For the flower-color character, the model predicts that the two different alleles present in an $F_1$ individual will segregate into gametes such that half the gametes will have the purple-flower allele and half will have the white-flower allele. During self-pollination, gametes of each class unite randomly. An egg with a purple-flower allele has an equal chance of being fertilized by a sperm with a purple-flower allele or one with a white-flower allele. Since the same is true for an egg with a white-flower allele, there are four equally likely combinations of sperm and egg. Figure 11.5 illustrates these combinations using a **Punnett square**, a handy diagrammatic device for predicting the allele composition of all offspring resulting from a cross between individuals of known genetic makeup. Notice that we use a capital letter to symbolize a dominant allele and a lower-case letter for a recessive allele. In our example, $P$ is the purple-flower allele, and $p$ is the white-flower allele; the gene itself is sometimes referred to as the $P/p$ gene.

In the $F_2$ offspring, what color will the flowers be? One-fourth of the plants have inherited two purple-flower alleles; these plants will have purple flowers. One-half of the $F_2$ offspring have inherited one purple-flower allele and one white-flower allele; these plants will also have purple flowers, the dominant trait. Finally, one-fourth of the $F_2$ plants have inherited two white-flower alleles and will express the recessive trait. Thus, Mendel's model accounts for the 3:1 ratio of traits that he observed in the $F_2$ generation.

## Useful Genetic Vocabulary

An organism that has a pair of identical alleles for a character is said to be **homozygous** for the gene controlling that character. In the parental generation in Figure 11.5, the purple pea plant is homozygous for the dominant allele ($PP$), while the white plant is homozygous for the recessive allele ($pp$). Homozygous plants "breed true" because all of their gametes contain the same allele—either $P$ or $p$ in this example. If we cross dominant homozygotes with recessive homozygotes, every offspring will have two different alleles—$Pp$ in the case of the $F_1$ hybrids of our flower-color experiment (see Figure 11.5). An organism that has two different alleles for a gene is said to be **heterozygous** for that gene. Unlike homozygotes, heterozygotes produce gametes with different alleles, so they are not true-breeding. For example, $P$- and $p$-containing gametes are both produced by our $F_1$ hybrids. Self-pollination of the $F_1$

hybrids thus produces both purple-flowered and white-flowered offspring.

Because of the different effects of dominant and recessive alleles, an organism's traits do not always reveal its genetic composition. Therefore, we distinguish between an organism's appearance or observable traits, called its **phenotype**, and its genetic makeup, its **genotype**. In the case of flower color in pea plants, $PP$ and $Pp$ plants have the same phenotype (purple) but different genotypes. **Figure 11.6** reviews these terms. Note that "phenotype" refers to physiological traits as well as traits that relate directly to appearance. For example, there is a pea variety that lacks the normal ability to self-pollinate. This physiological variation (non-self-pollination) is a phenotypic trait.

### The Testcross

Suppose we have a "mystery" pea plant that has purple flowers. We cannot tell from its flower color if this plant is homozygous ($PP$) or heterozygous ($Pp$) because both genotypes result in the same purple phenotype. To determine the genotype, we can cross this plant with a white-flowered plant ($pp$), which will make only gametes with the recessive allele ($p$). The allele in the gamete contributed by the mystery plant will therefore determine the appearance of the offspring **(Figure 11.7)**. If all the offspring of the cross have purple flowers, then the purple-flowered mystery plant must be homozygous for the dominant allele, because a $PP \times pp$ cross produces all $Pp$ offspring. But if both the purple and the white phenotypes appear among the offspring, then the purple-flowered parent must be heterozygous. The offspring of a $Pp \times pp$ cross will be expected to

▲ **Figure 11.6 Phenotype versus genotype.** Grouping $F_2$ offspring from a cross for flower color according to phenotype results in the typical 3:1 phenotypic ratio. In terms of genotype, however, there are actually two categories of purple-flowered plants, $PP$ (homozygous) and $Pp$ (heterozygous), giving a 1:2:1 genotypic ratio.

## The Testcross

**Application** An organism that exhibits a dominant trait, such as purple flowers in pea plants, can be either homozygous for the dominant allele or heterozygous. To determine the organism's genotype, geneticists can perform a testcross.

**Technique** In a testcross, the individual with the unknown genotype is crossed with a homozygous individual expressing the recessive trait (white flowers in this example), and Punnett squares are used to predict the possible outcomes.

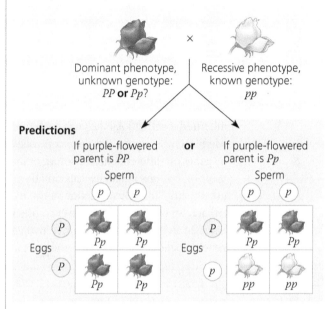

**Results** Matching the results to either prediction identifies the unknown parental genotype (either *PP* or *Pp* in this example). In this testcross, we transferred pollen from a white-flowered plant to the carpels of a purple-flowered plant; the opposite (reciprocal) cross would have led to the same results.

have a 1:1 phenotypic ratio. Breeding an organism of unknown genotype with a recessive homozygote is called a **testcross** because it can reveal the genotype of that organism. The testcross was devised by Mendel and continues to be an important tool of geneticists.

## The Law of Independent Assortment

Mendel derived the law of segregation from experiments in which he followed only a *single* character, such as flower color. All the F$_1$ progeny produced in his crosses of true-breeding parents were **monohybrids**, meaning that they were heterozygous for the one particular character being followed in the cross. We refer to a cross between such heterozygotes as a **monohybrid cross**.

Mendel identified his second law of inheritance by following *two* characters at the same time, such as seed color and seed shape. Seeds (peas) may be either yellow or green. They also may be either round (smooth) or wrinkled. From single-character crosses, Mendel knew that the allele for yellow seeds (*Y*) is dominant and the allele for green seeds (*y*) is recessive. For the seed-shape character, the allele for round (*R*) is dominant, and the allele for wrinkled (*r*) is recessive.

Imagine crossing two true-breeding pea varieties that differ in *both* of these characters—a cross between a plant with yellow-round seeds (*YYRR*) and a plant with green-wrinkled seeds (*yyrr*). The F$_1$ plants will be **dihybrids**, individuals heterozygous for the two characters being followed in the cross (*YyRr*). But are these two characters transmitted from parents to offspring as a package? That is, will the *Y* and *R* alleles always stay together, generation after generation? Or are seed color and seed shape inherited independently? **Figure 11.8** shows how a **dihybrid cross**, a cross between F$_1$ dihybrids, can determine which of these two hypotheses is correct.

The F$_1$ plants, of genotype *YyRr*, exhibit both dominant phenotypes, yellow seeds with round shapes, no matter which hypothesis is correct. The key step in the experiment is to see what happens when F$_1$ plants self-pollinate and produce F$_2$ offspring. If the hybrids must transmit their alleles in the same combinations in which the alleles were inherited from the P generation, then the F$_1$ hybrids will produce only two classes of gametes: *YR* and *yr*. This "dependent assortment" hypothesis predicts that the phenotypic ratio of the F$_2$ generation will be 3:1, just as in a monohybrid cross (see Figure 11.8, left side).

The alternative hypothesis is that the two pairs of alleles segregate independently of each other. In other words, genes are packaged into gametes in all possible allelic combinations, as long as each gamete has one allele for each gene. In our example, an F$_1$ plant will produce four classes of gametes in equal quantities: *YR*, *Yr*, *yR*, and *yr*. If sperm of the four classes fertilize eggs of the four classes, there will be 16 (4 × 4) equally probable ways in which the alleles can combine in the F$_2$ generation, as shown in Figure 11.8, right side. These combinations result in four phenotypic categories with a ratio of 9:3:3:1 (nine yellow-round to three green-round to three yellow-wrinkled to one green-wrinkled). When Mendel did the experiment and classified the F$_2$ offspring, his results were close to the predicted 9:3:3:1 phenotypic ratio, supporting the hypothesis that the alleles for one gene—controlling seed color or seed shape, in this example—segregate into gametes independently of the alleles of other genes.

Mendel tested his seven pea characters in various dihybrid combinations and always observed a 9:3:3:1 phenotypic ratio in the F$_2$ generation. Does this override the 3:1 phenotypic ratio seen for the monohybrid cross shown in Figure 11.5? To investigate this question, let's consider one of the two dihybrid characters by itself: Looking only at pea color, we see that there are 416 yellow and 140 green peas—a 2.97:1 ratio, or roughly

## Do the alleles for one character segregate into gametes dependently or independently of the alleles for a different character?

**Experiment** Gregor Mendel followed the characters of seed color and seed shape through the $F_2$ generation. He crossed two true-breeding plants, one with yellow-round seeds and one with green-wrinkled seeds, producing dihybrid $F_1$ plants. Self-pollination of the $F_1$ dihybrids produced the $F_2$ generation. The two hypotheses (dependent and independent "assortment" of the two genes) predict different phenotypic ratios.

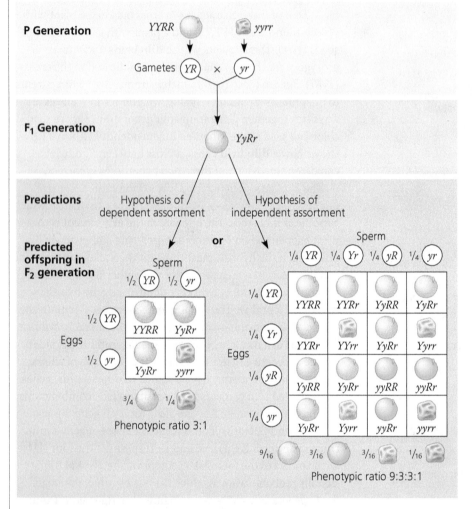

**Results**

315 ◯   108 ◯   101 ▨   32 ▨   Phenotypic ratio approximately 9:3:3:1

**Conclusion** Only the hypothesis of independent assortment predicts two of the observed phenotypes: green-round seeds and yellow-wrinkled seeds (see the right-hand Punnett square). The alleles for each gene segregate independently, and the two genes are said to assort independently.

**Source** G. Mendel, Experiments in plant hybridization, *Proceedings of the Natural History Society of Brünn* 4:3–47 (1866).

**WHAT IF?** Suppose Mendel had transferred pollen from an $F_1$ plant to the carpel of a plant that was homozygous recessive for both genes. Set up the cross and draw Punnett squares that predict the offspring for both hypotheses. Would this cross have supported the hypothesis of independent assortment equally well?

3:1. In the dihybrid cross, the pea color alleles segregate as if this were a monohybrid cross. The results of Mendel's dihybrid experiments are the basis for what we now call the **law of independent assortment**, which states that *two or more genes assort independently—that is, each pair of alleles segregates independently of each other pair during gamete formation.*

This law applies only to genes (allele pairs) located on different chromosomes—that is, on chromosomes that are not homologous—or very far apart on the same chromosome. (The latter case will be explained in Chapter 12, along with the more complex inheritance patterns of genes located near each other, which tend to be inherited together.) All the pea characters Mendel chose for analysis were controlled by genes on different chromosomes or far apart on one chromosome; this situation greatly simplified interpretation of his multicharacter pea crosses. All the examples we consider in the rest of this chapter involve genes located on different chromosomes.

### CONCEPT CHECK 11.1

1. In the dihybrid cross shown in Figure 11.8, calculate the phenotypic ratio in the $F_2$ generation, considering only the character of pea shape.

2. **DRAW IT** Pea plants heterozygous for flower position and stem length (*AaTt*) are allowed to self-pollinate, and 400 of the resulting seeds are planted. Draw a Punnett square for this cross. How many offspring would be predicted to have terminal flowers and be dwarf? (See Table 11.1.)

3. List all gametes that could be made by a pea plant heterozygous for seed color, seed shape, and pod shape (*YyRrIi;* see Table 11.1). How large a Punnett square would you need to draw to predict the offspring of a self-pollination of this "trihybrid"?

4. **MAKE CONNECTIONS** In some pea plant crosses, the plants are self-pollinated. Explain whether self-pollination is considered asexual or sexual reproduction.

*For suggested answers, see Appendix A.*

# The laws of probability govern Mendelian inheritance

Mendel's laws of segregation and independent assortment reflect the same rules of probability that apply to tossing coins, rolling dice, and drawing cards from a deck. The probability scale ranges from 0 to 1. An event that is certain to occur has a probability of 1, while an event that is certain *not* to occur has a probability of 0. With a coin that has heads on both sides, the probability of tossing heads is 1, and the probability of tossing tails is 0. With a normal coin, the chance of tossing heads is 1/2, and the chance of tossing tails is 1/2. The probability of drawing the ace of spades from a 52-card deck is 1/52. The probabilities of all possible outcomes for an event must add up to 1. With a deck of cards, the chance of picking a card other than the ace of spades is 51/52.

Tossing a coin illustrates an important lesson about probability. For every toss, the probability of heads is 1/2. The outcome of any particular toss is unaffected by what has happened on previous trials. We refer to phenomena such as coin tosses as independent events. Each toss of a coin, whether done sequentially with one coin or simultaneously with many, is independent of every other toss. And like two separate coin tosses, the alleles of one gene segregate into gametes independently of another gene's alleles (the law of independent assortment). Two basic rules of probability, described below, can help us predict the outcome of the fusion of such gametes in simple monohybrid crosses and more complicated crosses.

## The Multiplication and Addition Rules Applied to Monohybrid Crosses

How do we determine the probability that two or more independent events will occur together in some specific combination? For example, what is the chance that two coins tossed simultaneously will both land heads up? The **multiplication rule** states that to determine this probability, we multiply the probability of one event (one coin coming up heads) by the probability of the other event (the other coin coming up heads). By the multiplication rule, then, the probability that both coins will land heads up is $1/2 \times 1/2 = 1/4$.

We can apply the same reasoning to an $F_1$ monohybrid cross. With seed shape in pea plants as the heritable character, the genotype of $F_1$ plants is *Rr*. Segregation in a heterozygous plant is like flipping a coin in terms of calculating the probability of each outcome: Each egg produced has a 1/2 chance of carrying the dominant allele (*R*) and a 1/2 chance of carrying the recessive allele (*r*). The same odds apply to each sperm cell produced. For a particular $F_2$ plant to have wrinkled seeds, the recessive trait, both the egg and the sperm that come together must carry the *r* allele. The probability that an *r* allele will be

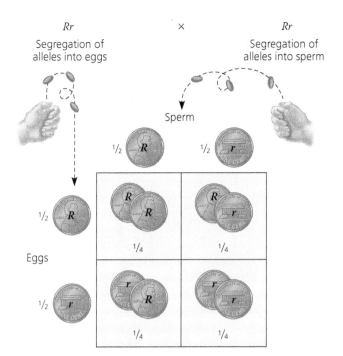

▲ **Figure 11.9 Segregation of alleles and fertilization as chance events.** When a heterozygote (*Rr*) forms gametes, whether a particular gamete ends up with an *R* or an *r* is like the toss of a coin. We can determine the probability for any genotype among the offspring of two heterozygotes by multiplying together the individual probabilities of an egg and sperm having a particular allele (*R* or *r* in this example).

present in both gametes at fertilization is found by multiplying 1/2 (the probability that the egg will have an *r*) × 1/2 (the probability that the sperm will have an *r*). Thus, the multiplication rule tells us that the probability of an $F_2$ plant having wrinkled seeds (*rr*) is 1/4 **(Figure 11.9)**. Likewise, the probability of an $F_2$ plant carrying both dominant alleles for seed shape (*RR*) is 1/4.

To figure out the probability that an $F_2$ plant from a monohybrid cross will be heterozygous rather than homozygous, we need to invoke a second rule. Notice in Figure 11.9 that the dominant allele can come from the egg and the recessive allele from the sperm, or vice versa. That is, $F_1$ gametes can combine to produce *Rr* offspring in two *mutually exclusive* ways: For any particular heterozygous $F_2$ plant, the dominant allele can come from the egg *or* the sperm, but not from both. According to the **addition rule**, the probability that any one of two or more mutually exclusive events will occur is calculated by adding their individual probabilities. As we have just seen, the multiplication rule gives us the individual probabilities that we will now add together. The probability for one possible way of obtaining an $F_2$ heterozygote—the dominant allele from the egg and the recessive allele from the sperm—is 1/4. The probability for the other possible way—the recessive allele from the egg and the dominant allele from the sperm—is also 1/4 (see Figure 11.9). Using the rule of addition, then, we can calculate the probability of an $F_2$ heterozygote as $1/4 + 1/4 = 1/2$.

## Solving Complex Genetics Problems with the Rules of Probability

We can also apply the rules of probability to predict the outcome of crosses involving multiple characters. Recall that each allelic pair segregates independently during gamete formation (the law of independent assortment). Thus, a dihybrid or other multi-character cross is equivalent to two or more independent mono-hybrid crosses occurring simultaneously. By applying what we have learned about monohybrid crosses, we can determine the probability of specific genotypes occurring in the $F_2$ generation without having to construct unwieldy Punnett squares.

Consider the dihybrid cross between $YyRr$ heterozygotes shown in Figure 11.8. We will focus first on the seed-color character. For a monohybrid cross of $Yy$ plants, we can use a simple Punnett square to determine that the probabilities of the off-spring genotypes are 1/4 for $YY$, 1/2 for $Yy$, and 1/4 for $yy$. We can draw a second Punnett square to determine that the same probabilities apply to the offspring genotypes for seed shape: 1/4 $RR$, 1/2 $Rr$, and 1/4 $rr$. Knowing these probabilities, we can simply use the multiplication rule to determine the probability of each of the genotypes in the $F_2$ generation. To give two examples, the calculations for finding the probabilities of two of the possible $F_2$ genotypes ($YYRR$ and $YyRR$) are shown below:

Probability of $YYRR$ = ¼ (probability of $YY$) × ¼ ($RR$) = ¹⁄₁₆

Probability of $YyRR$ =                   ½ ($Yy$) × ¼ ($RR$) = ⅛

The $YYRR$ genotype corresponds to the upper left box in the larger Punnett square in Figure 11.8 (one box = 1/16). Looking closely at the larger Punnett square in Figure 11.8, you will see that 2 of the 16 boxes (1/8) correspond to the $YyRR$ genotype.

Now let's see how we can combine the multiplication and addition rules to solve even more complex problems in Mendelian genetics. Imagine a cross of two pea varieties in which we track the inheritance of three characters. Let's cross a tri-hybrid with purple flowers and yellow, round seeds (heterozy-gous for all three genes) with a plant with purple flowers and green, wrinkled seeds (heterozygous for flower color but ho-mozygous recessive for the other two characters). Using Men-delian symbols, our cross is $PpYyRr \times Ppyyrr$. What fraction of offspring from this cross is predicted to exhibit the recessive phenotypes for *at least two* of the three characters?

To answer this question, we can start by listing all geno-types we could get that fulfill this condition: $ppyyRr$, $ppYyrr$, $Ppyyrr$, $PPyyrr$, and $ppyyrr$. (Because the condition is *at least two* recessive traits, it includes the last genotype, which shows all three recessive traits.) Next, we calculate the probability for each of these genotypes resulting from our $PpYyRr \times Ppyyrr$ cross by multiplying together the individual probabilities for the allele pairs, just as we did in our dihybrid example. Note that in a cross involving heterozygous and homozygous allele pairs (for example, $Yy \times yy$), the probability of heterozygous

offspring is 1/2 and the probability of homozygous offspring is 1/2. Finally, we use the addition rule to add the probabilities for all the different genotypes that fulfill the condition of at least two recessive traits, as shown below:

| | | |
|---|---|---|
| $ppyyRr$ | ¼ (probability of $pp$) × ½ ($yy$) × ½ ($Rr$) | = ¹⁄₁₆ |
| $ppYyrr$ | ¼ × ½ × ½ | = ¹⁄₁₆ |
| $Ppyyrr$ | ½ × ½ × ½ | = ²⁄₁₆ |
| $PPyyrr$ | ¼ × ½ × ½ | = ¹⁄₁₆ |
| $ppyyrr$ | ¼ × ½ × ½ | = ¹⁄₁₆ |
| Chance of *at least two* recessive traits | | = ⁶⁄₁₆ or ³⁄₈ |

In time, you'll be able to solve genetics problems faster by us-ing the rules of probability than by filling in Punnett squares.

We cannot predict with certainty the exact numbers of progeny of different genotypes resulting from a genetic cross. But the rules of probability give us the *chance* of various out-comes. Usually, the larger the sample size, the closer the results will conform to our predictions. The reason Mendel counted so many offspring from his crosses is that he understood this statistical feature of inheritance and had a keen sense of the rules of chance.

**CONCEPT CHECK 11.2**

1. For any gene with a dominant allele $A$ and recessive allele $a$, what proportions of the offspring from an $AA \times Aa$ cross are expected to be homozygous dominant, homozygous reces-sive, and heterozygous?

2. Two organisms, with genotypes $BbDD$ and $BBDd$, are mated. Assuming independent assortment of the $B/b$ and $D/d$ genes, write the genotypes of all possible offspring from this cross and use the rules of probability to calculate the chance of each genotype occurring.

3. **WHAT IF?** Three characters (flower color, seed color, and pod shape) are considered in a cross between two pea plants ($PpYyIi \times ppYyii$). What fraction of offspring are predicted to be homozygous recessive for at least two of the three characters?

For suggested answers, see Appendix A.

CONCEPT 11.3

# Inheritance patterns are often more complex than predicted by simple Mendelian genetics

In the 20th century, geneticists extended Mendelian prin-ciples not only to diverse organisms, but also to patterns of inheritance more complex than those described by Mendel. For the work that led to his two laws of inheritance, Mendel chose pea plant characters that turn out to have a relatively simple genetic basis: Each character is determined by one gene, for which there are only two alleles, one completely dominant and the other completely recessive. (There is one exception: Mendel's pod-shape character is actually determined by two genes.) Not all heritable characters are determined so simply, and the relationship between genotype and phenotype is rarely so straightforward. Mendel himself realized that he could not explain the more complicated patterns he observed in crosses involving other pea characters or other plant species. This does not diminish the utility of Mendelian genetics, however, because the basic principles of segregation and independent assortment apply even to more complex patterns of inheritance. In this section, we'll extend Mendelian genetics to hereditary patterns that were not reported by Mendel.

## Extending Mendelian Genetics for a Single Gene

The inheritance of characters determined by a single gene deviates from simple Mendelian patterns when alleles are not completely dominant or recessive, when a particular gene has more than two alleles, or when a single gene produces multiple phenotypes. We'll describe examples of each of these situations in this section.

### Degrees of Dominance

Alleles can show different degrees of dominance and recessiveness in relation to each other. In Mendel's classic pea crosses, the $F_1$ offspring always looked like one of the two parental varieties because one allele in a pair showed **complete dominance** over the other. In such situations, the phenotypes of the heterozygote and the dominant homozygote are indistinguishable.

For some genes, however, neither allele is completely dominant, and the $F_1$ hybrids have a phenotype somewhere between those of the two parental varieties. This phenomenon, called **incomplete dominance**, is seen when red snapdragons are crossed with white snapdragons: All the $F_1$ hybrids have pink flowers **(Figure 11.10)**. This third, intermediate phenotype results from flowers of the heterozygotes having less red pigment than the red homozygotes. (This is unlike the case of Mendel's pea plants, where the $Pp$ heterozygotes make enough pigment for the flowers to be purple, indistinguishable from those of $PP$ plants.)

At first glance, incomplete dominance of either allele seems to provide evidence for the blending hypothesis of inheritance, which would predict that the red or white trait could never be retrieved from the pink hybrids. In fact, interbreeding $F_1$ hybrids produces $F_2$ offspring with a phenotypic ratio of one red to two pink to one white. (Because heterozygotes have a separate phenotype, the genotypic and phenotypic ratios for the $F_2$ generation are the same, 1:2:1.) The segregation of the red-flower and white-flower alleles in the gametes produced by the pink-flowered plants confirms that the alleles for flower color are heritable factors that maintain their identity in the hybrids; that is, inheritance is particulate.

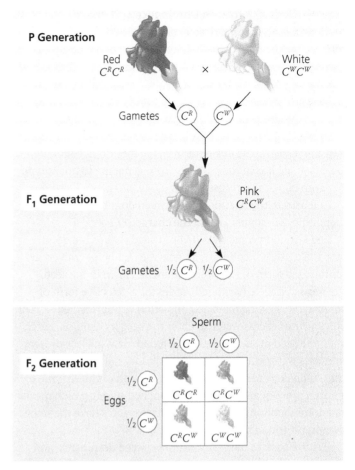

▲ **Figure 11.10 Incomplete dominance in snapdragon color.** When red snapdragons are crossed with white ones, the $F_1$ hybrids have pink flowers. Segregation of alleles into gametes of the $F_1$ plants results in an $F_2$ generation with a 1:2:1 ratio for both genotype and phenotype. Neither allele is dominant, so rather than using upper- and lowercase letters, we use the letter $C$ with a superscript to indicate an allele for flower color: $C^R$ for red and $C^W$ for white.

**?** *Suppose a classmate argues that this figure supports the blending hypothesis for inheritance. What might your classmate say, and how would you respond?*

Another variation on dominance relationships between alleles is called **codominance**; in this variation, the two alleles each affect the phenotype in separate, distinguishable ways. For example, the human MN blood group is determined by codominant alleles for two specific molecules located on the surface of red blood cells, the M and N molecules. A single gene locus, at which two allelic variations are possible, determines the phenotype of this blood group. Individuals homozygous for the $M$ allele ($MM$) have red blood cells with only M molecules; individuals homozygous for the $N$ allele ($NN$) have red blood cells with only N molecules. But *both* M and N molecules are present on the red blood cells of individuals heterozygous for the $M$ and $N$ alleles ($MN$). Note that the MN phenotype is *not* intermediate between the M and N phenotypes, which distinguishes codominance from incomplete dominance. Rather, *both* M and N phenotypes are exhibited by heterozygotes, since both molecules are present.

**The Relationship Between Dominance and Phenotype**

We've now seen that the relative effects of two alleles range from complete dominance of one allele, through incomplete dominance of either allele, to codominance of both alleles. It is important to understand that an allele is called *dominant* because it is seen in the phenotype, not because it somehow subdues a recessive allele. Alleles are simply variations in a gene's nucleotide sequence. When a dominant allele coexists with a recessive allele in a heterozygote, they do not actually interact at all. It is in the pathway from genotype to phenotype that dominance and recessiveness come into play.

To illustrate the relationship between dominance and phenotype, we can use one of the characters Mendel studied—round versus wrinkled pea seed shape. The dominant allele (round) codes for an enzyme that helps convert an unbranched form of starch to a branched form in the seed. The recessive allele (wrinkled) codes for a defective form of this enzyme, leading to an accumulation of unbranched starch, which causes excess water to enter the seed by osmosis. Later, when the seed dries, it wrinkles. If a dominant allele is present, no excess water enters the seed and it does not wrinkle when it dries. One dominant allele results in enough of the enzyme to synthesize adequate amounts of branched starch, which means that dominant homozygotes and heterozygotes have the same phenotype: round seeds.

A closer look at the relationship between dominance and phenotype reveals an intriguing fact: For any character, the observed dominant/recessive relationship of alleles depends on the level at which we examine the phenotype. **Tay-Sachs disease**, an inherited disorder in humans, provides an example. The brain cells of a child with Tay-Sachs disease cannot metabolize certain lipids because a crucial enzyme does not work properly. As these lipids accumulate in brain cells, the child begins to suffer seizures, blindness, and degeneration of motor and mental performance and dies within a few years.

Only children who inherit two copies of the Tay-Sachs allele (homozygotes) have the disease. Thus, at the *organismal* level, the Tay-Sachs allele qualifies as recessive. However, the activity level of the lipid-metabolizing enzyme in heterozygotes is intermediate between that in individuals homozygous for the normal allele and that in individuals with Tay-Sachs disease. The intermediate phenotype observed at the *biochemical* level is characteristic of incomplete dominance of either allele. Fortunately, the heterozygote condition does not lead to disease symptoms, apparently because half the normal enzyme activity is sufficient to prevent lipid accumulation in the brain. Extending our analysis to yet another level, we find that heterozygous individuals produce equal numbers of normal and dysfunctional enzyme molecules. Thus, at the *molecular* level, the normal allele and the Tay-Sachs allele are codominant. As you can see, whether alleles appear to be completely dominant, incompletely dominant, or codominant depends on the level at which the phenotype is analyzed.

**Frequency of Dominant Alleles** While you might assume that the dominant allele for a particular character would be more common in a population than the recessive one, this is not always so. For example, about one baby out of 400 in the United States is born with extra digits (fingers or toes), a condition known as polydactyly. Some cases are caused by the presence of a dominant allele. The low frequency of polydactyly indicates that the recessive allele, which results in five digits per appendage when homozygous, is far more prevalent than the dominant allele.

### Multiple Alleles

Only two alleles exist for each of the seven pea characters that Mendel studied, but most genes exist in more than two allelic forms. The ABO blood groups in humans, for instance, are determined by three alleles of a single gene: $I^A$, $I^B$, and $i$. Each person has two alleles of the three for the blood group gene, which determines his or her blood group (phenotype): A, B, AB, or O. These letters refer to two carbohydrates—A and B—that may be found on the surface of red blood cells. A person's blood cells may have carbohydrate A (type A blood), carbohydrate B (type B), both (type AB), or neither (type O), as shown schematically in **Figure 11.11**. Matching compatible blood groups is critical for safe blood transfusions.

**(a) The three alleles for the ABO blood groups and their carbohydrates.** Each allele codes for an enzyme that may add a specific carbohydrate (designated by the superscript on the allele and shown as a triangle or circle) to red blood cells.

| Allele | $I^A$ | $I^B$ | $i$ |
|---|---|---|---|
| Carbohydrate | A △ | B ○ | none |

**(b) Blood group genotypes and phenotypes.** There are six possible genotypes, resulting in four different phenotypes.

| Genotype | $I^A I^A$ or $I^A i$ | $I^B I^B$ or $I^B i$ | $I^A I^B$ | $ii$ |
|---|---|---|---|---|
| Red blood cell appearance | | | | |
| Phenotype (blood group) | A | B | AB | O |

▲ **Figure 11.11 Multiple alleles for the ABO blood groups.** The four blood groups result from different combinations of three alleles.

❓ *Based on the surface carbohydrate phenotypes in (b), what are the dominance relationships among the alleles?*

## Pleiotropy

So far, we have treated Mendelian inheritance as though each gene affects only one phenotypic character. Most genes, however, have multiple phenotypic effects, a property called **pleiotropy** (from the Greek *pleion*, more). In humans, for example, pleiotropic alleles are responsible for the multiple symptoms associated with certain hereditary diseases, such as cystic fibrosis and sickle-cell disease, discussed later in this chapter. In the garden pea, the gene that determines flower color also affects the color of the coating on the outer surface of the seed, which can be gray or white. Given the intricate molecular and cellular interactions responsible for an organism's development and physiology, it isn't surprising that a single gene can affect a number of characteristics in an organism.

## Extending Mendelian Genetics for Two or More Genes

Dominance relationships, multiple alleles, and pleiotropy all have to do with the effects of the alleles of a single gene. We now consider two situations in which two or more genes are involved in determining a particular phenotype. In the first case, one gene affects the phenotype of another because the two gene products interact, whereas in the second, multiple genes independently affect a single trait.

## Epistasis

In **epistasis** (from the Greek for "standing upon"), the phenotypic expression of a gene at one locus alters that of a gene at a second locus. An example will help clarify this concept. In Labrador retrievers (commonly called Labs), black coat color is dominant to brown. Let's designate *B* and *b* as the two alleles for this character. For a Lab to have brown fur, its genotype must be *bb*; these dogs are called chocolate Labs. But there is more to the story. A second gene determines whether or not pigment will be deposited in the hair. The dominant allele, symbolized by *E*, results in the deposition of either black or brown pigment, depending on the genotype at the first locus. But if the Lab is homozygous recessive for the second locus (*ee*), then the coat is yellow, regardless of the genotype at the black/brown locus. In this case, the gene for pigment deposition (*E/e*) is said to be epistatic to the gene that codes for black or brown pigment (*B/b*).

What happens if we mate black Labs that are heterozygous for both genes (*BbEe*)? Although the two genes affect the same phenotypic character (coat color), they follow the law of independent assortment. Thus, our breeding experiment represents an F₁ dihybrid cross, like those that produced a 9:3:3:1 ratio in Mendel's experiments. We can use a Punnett square to represent the genotypes of the F₂ offspring **(Figure 11.12)**. As a result of epistasis, the phenotypic ratio among the F₂ offspring is nine black to three chocolate (brown) to four yellow. Other types of epistatic interactions produce different ratios, but all are modified versions of 9:3:3:1.

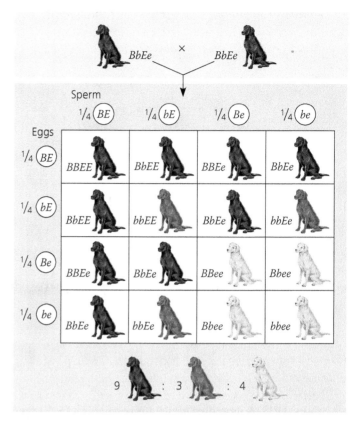

▲ **Figure 11.12 An example of epistasis.** This Punnett square illustrates the genotypes and phenotypes predicted for offspring of matings between two black Labrador retrievers of genotype *BbEe*. The *E/e* gene, which is epistatic to the *B/b* gene coding for hair pigment, controls whether or not pigment of any color will be deposited in the hair.

## Polygenic Inheritance

Mendel studied characters that could be classified on an either-or basis, such as purple versus white flower color. But for many characters, such as human skin color and height, an either-or classification is impossible because the characters vary in the population in gradations along a continuum. These are called **quantitative characters**. Quantitative variation usually indicates **polygenic inheritance**, the additive effect of two or more genes on a single phenotypic character. (In a way, this is the converse of pleiotropy, where a single gene affects several phenotypic characters.)

There is evidence, for instance, that skin pigmentation in humans is controlled by at least three separately inherited genes (probably more, but we will simplify). Let's consider three genes, with a dark-skin allele for each gene (*A*, *B*, or *C*) contributing one "unit" of darkness (also a simplification) to the phenotype and being incompletely dominant to the other, light-skin allele (*a*, *b*, or *c*). An *AABBCC* person would be very dark, while an *aabbcc* individual would be very light. An *AaBbCc* person would have skin of an intermediate shade. Because the alleles have a cumulative effect, the genotypes *AaBbCc* and *AABbcc* would make the same genetic contribution (three units) to skin darkness. There are seven skin-color phenotypes that could result from a mating between *AaBbCc* heterozygotes. In a large

Phenotypes:

| $1/64$ | $6/64$ | $15/64$ | $20/64$ | $15/64$ | $6/64$ | $1/64$ |
|---|---|---|---|---|---|---|

Number of dark-skin alleles:   0   1   2   3   4   5   6

▲ **Figure 11.13 A simplified model for polygenic inheritance of skin color.** In this model, three separately inherited genes affect skin color. The heterozygous individuals (*AaBbCc*) represented by the two rectangles at the top of this figure each carry three dark-skin alleles (black circles, representing *A*, *B*, or *C*) and three light-skin alleles (white circles, representing *a*, *b*, or *c*). The Punnett square shows all the possible genetic combinations in gametes and offspring of many hypothetical matings between these heterozygotes. The results are summarized by the phenotypic frequencies (fractions) under the Punnett square. (The phenotypic ratio is 1:6:15:20:15:6:1.)

number of such matings, the majority of offspring would be expected to have intermediate phenotypes (skin color in the middle range), as shown in **Figure 11.13**. You can graph the predictions from the Punnett square in the **Scientific Skills Exercise**. Environmental factors, such as exposure to the sun, also affect the skin-color phenotype.

## Nature and Nurture: The Environmental Impact on Phenotype

Another departure from simple Mendelian genetics arises when the phenotype for a character depends on environment as well as genotype. A single tree, locked into its inherited genotype, has leaves that vary in size, shape, and greenness, depending on their exposure to wind and sun. In humans, nutrition influences height, exercise alters build, sun-tanning darkens the skin, and experience improves performance on intelligence tests. Even identical twins, who are genetic equals, accumulate phenotypic differences as a result of their unique experiences.

Whether human characteristics are more influenced by genes or the environment— in everyday terms, nature versus nurture—is a very old and hotly contested debate that we will

not attempt to settle here. We can say, however, that a genotype generally is not associated with a rigidly defined phenotype, but rather with a range of phenotypic possibilities due to environmental influences. For some characters, such as the ABO blood group system, the range is extremely narrow; that is, a given genotype mandates a very specific phenotype. Other characteristics, such as a person's blood count of red and white cells, vary quite a bit, depending on such factors as the altitude, the customary level of physical activity, and the presence of infectious agents.

Generally, the phenotypic range is broadest for polygenic characters. Environment contributes to the quantitative nature of these characters, as we have seen in the continuous variation of skin color. Geneticists refer to such characters as **multifactorial**, meaning that many factors, both genetic and environmental, collectively influence phenotype.

## Integrating a Mendelian View of Heredity and Variation

We have now broadened our view of Mendelian inheritance by exploring the degrees of dominance as well as multiple alleles, pleiotropy, epistasis, polygenic inheritance, and the phenotypic impact of the environment. Stepping back to see the big picture, how can we integrate these refinements into a comprehensive theory of Mendelian genetics? The key is to make the transition from the reductionist emphasis on single genes and phenotypic characters to the emergent properties of the organism as a whole, one of the themes of this book.

The term *phenotype* can refer not only to specific characters, such as flower color and blood group, but also to an organism in its entirety—*all* aspects of its physical appearance, internal anatomy, physiology, and behavior. Similarly, the term *genotype* can refer to an organism's entire genetic makeup, not just its alleles for a single genetic locus. In most cases, a gene's impact on phenotype is affected by other genes and by the environment. In this integrated view of heredity and variation, an organism's phenotype reflects its overall genotype and unique environmental history.

Considering all that can occur in the pathway from genotype to phenotype, it is indeed impressive that Mendel could uncover the fundamental principles governing the transmission of individual genes from parents to offspring. Mendel's two laws, those of segregation and independent assortment, explain heritable variations in terms of alternative forms of genes (hereditary "particles," now known as the alleles of genes) that are passed along, generation after generation, according to simple rules of probability. This theory of inheritance is equally valid for peas, flies, fishes, birds, and human beings—indeed, for any organism with a sexual life cycle. Furthermore, by extending the principles of segregation and independent assortment to help explain such hereditary patterns as epistasis and quantitative characters, we begin to see how broadly Mendelian genetics applies. From Mendel's abbey

# Making a Histogram and Analyzing a Distribution Pattern

**What Is the Distribution of Phenotypes Among Offspring of Two Parents Who Are Both Heterozygous for Three Additive Genes?** Human skin color is a polygenic trait that is determined by the additive effects of several different genes. In this exercise, you will work with a simplified model of skin-color genetics where three genes are assumed to affect the darkness of skin color and where each gene has two alleles—dark or light. In this model, each dark allele contributes equally to the darkness of skin color, and each pair of alleles segregates independently of each other pair. Using a type of graph called a histogram, you will determine the distribution of phenotypes of offspring with different numbers of dark-skin alleles. (For additional information about graphs, see the Scientific Skills Review in Appendix F and in the Study Area in MasteringBiology.)

**How This Model Is Analyzed** To predict the phenotypes of the offspring of heterozygous parents, the ratios of the genes for this trait must be calculated. Figure 11.13 shows a simplified model for polygenic inheritance of skin color that includes three of the known genes. According to this model, three separately inherited genes affect the darkness of skin. The heterozygous individuals (*AaBbCc*) represented by the two rectangles at the top of this figure each carry three dark-skin alleles (black circles, which represent *A*, *B*, or *C*) and three light-skin alleles (white circles, which represent *a*, *b*, or *c*). The Punnett square shows all the possible genetic combinations in gametes and in offspring of a large number of hypothetical matings between these heterozygotes. The possible phenotypes are shown under the Punnett square.

**Predictions from the Punnett Square** If we assume that each square in the Punnett square represents one offspring of the heterozygous *AaBbCc* parents, then the squares below show the phenotypic frequencies of individuals with the same number of dark-skin alleles.

Phenotypes:

| Phenotypes: | $1/64$ | $6/64$ | $15/64$ | $20/64$ | $15/64$ | $6/64$ | $1/64$ |
|---|---|---|---|---|---|---|---|
| Number of dark-skin alleles: | 0 | 1 | 2 | 3 | 4 | 5 | 6 |

**Interpret the Data**

1. A histogram is a bar graph that shows the distribution of numeric data (here, the number of dark skin alleles). To make a histogram of the allele distribution, put skin color (as the number of dark-skin alleles) along the *x*-axis and number of offspring (out of 64) with each phenotype on the *y*-axis. There are no gaps in our allele data, so draw the bars side-to-side with no space in between.

2. You can see that the skin-color phenotypes are not distributed uniformly. (a) Which phenotype has the highest frequency? Draw a vertical dotted line through that bar. (b) Distributions of values like this one tend to show one of several common patterns. Sketch a rough curve that approximates the values and look at its shape. Is it symmetrically distributed around a central peak value (a "normal distribution," sometimes called a bell curve); is it skewed to one end of the *x*-axis or the other (a "skewed distribution"); or does it show two apparent groups of frequencies (a "bimodal distribution")? Explain the reason for the curve's shape. (It will help to read the text description that supports Figure 11.13.)

3. If one of the three genes were lethal when homozygous recessive, what would happen to the distribution of phenotype frequencies? To determine this, use *bb* as an example of a lethal genotype. Using Figure 11.13, identify offspring where the center circle (the *B/b* gene) in both the top and bottom rows of the square is white, representing the homozygous state *bb*. Because *bb* individuals would not survive, cross out those squares, then count the phenotype frequencies of the surviving offspring according to the number of dark-skin alleles (0–6) and graph the new data. What happens to the shape of the curve compared with the curve in question 2? What does this indicate about the distribution of phenotype frequencies?

**Further Reading** R.A. Sturm, A golden age of human pigmentation genetics, *Trends in Genetics* 22: 464–468 (2006). doi:10.1016/j.tig.2006.06.010

(MB) A version of this Scientific Skills Exercise can be assigned in MasteringBiology.

---

garden came a theory of particulate inheritance that anchors modern genetics. In the last section of this chapter, we'll apply Mendelian genetics to human inheritance, with emphasis on the transmission of hereditary diseases.

## CONCEPT CHECK 11.3

1. *Incomplete dominance* and *epistasis* are both terms that define genetic relationships. What is the most basic distinction between these terms?

2. If a man with type AB blood marries a woman with type O, what blood types would you expect in their children? What fraction would you expect of each type?

3. **WHAT IF?** A rooster with gray feathers and a hen of the same phenotype produce 15 gray, 6 black, and 8 white chicks. What is the simplest explanation for the inheritance of these colors in chickens? What phenotypes would you expect in the offspring of a cross between a gray rooster and a black hen?

For suggested answers, see Appendix A.

**CONCEPT 11.4**

# Many human traits follow Mendelian patterns of inheritance

Peas are convenient subjects for genetic research, but humans are not. The human generation span is long—about 20 years—and human parents produce many fewer offspring than peas and most other species. Even more important, it wouldn't be ethical to ask pairs of humans to breed so that the phenotypes of their offspring could be analyzed! In spite of these constraints, the study of human genetics continues, spurred on by our desire to understand our own inheritance. New molecular biological techniques have led to many breakthrough discoveries, but basic Mendelian genetics endures as the foundation of human genetics.

Unable to manipulate the matings of people, geneticists instead analyze results that have already occurred by collecting information about a family's history for a particular trait.

## Pedigree Analysis

Geneticists assemble information about members of a family into a tree diagram that describes the traits of parents and children across the generations, called a **pedigree**.

**Figure 11.14a** shows a three-generation pedigree that traces the occurrence of a pointed contour of the hairline on the forehead. This trait, called a widow's peak, is due to a dominant allele, *W*. Because the widow's-peak allele is dominant, all individuals who lack a widow's peak must be homozygous recessive (*ww*). The two grandparents with widow's peaks must have the *Ww* genotype, since some of their offspring are homozygous recessive. The offspring in the second generation who *do* have widow's peaks must also be heterozygous, because they are the products of *Ww* × *ww* matings. The third generation in this pedigree consists of two sisters. The one who has a widow's peak could be either homozygous (*WW*) or heterozygous (*Ww*), given what we know about the genotypes of her parents (both *Ww*).

**Figure 11.14b** is a pedigree of the same family, but this time we focus on a recessive trait, attached earlobes. We'll use *f* for the recessive allele and *F* for the dominant allele, which results in free earlobes. As you work your way through the pedigree, notice once again that you can apply what you have learned about Mendelian inheritance to understand the genotypes shown for the family members.

An important application of a pedigree is to help us calculate the probability that a future child will have a particular genotype and phenotype. Suppose that the couple represented in the second generation of Figure 11.14 decides to have one more child. What is the probability that the child will have a widow's peak? This is equivalent to a Mendelian $F_1$ monohybrid cross (*Ww* × *Ww*), and thus the probability that a child will inherit a dominant allele and have a widow's peak is 3/4 (1/4 *WW* + 1/2 *Ww*). What is the probability that the child will have attached earlobes? Again, we can treat this as a monohybrid cross (*Ff* × *Ff*), but this time we want to know the chance that the offspring will be homozygous recessive (*ff*). That probability is 1/4. Finally, what is the chance that the child will have a widow's peak *and* attached earlobes? Assuming that the genes for these two characters are on different chromosomes, the two pairs of alleles will assort independently in this dihybrid cross (*WwFf* × *WwFf*). Thus, we can use the multiplication rule: 3/4 (chance of widow's peak) × 1/4 (chance of attached earlobes) = 3/16 (chance of widow's peak and attached earlobes).

Pedigrees are a more serious matter when the alleles in question cause disabling or deadly diseases instead of innocuous human variations such as hairline or earlobe configuration. However, for disorders inherited as simple Mendelian traits, the same techniques of pedigree analysis apply.

## Recessively Inherited Disorders

Thousands of genetic disorders are known to be inherited as simple recessive traits. These disorders range in severity from

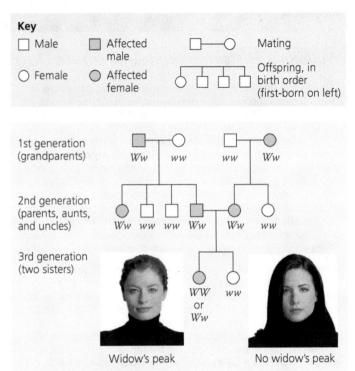

**(a) Is a widow's peak a dominant or recessive trait?**
**Tips for pedigree analysis:** Notice in the third generation that the second-born daughter lacks a widow's peak, although both of her parents had the trait. Such a pattern of inheritance supports the hypothesis that the trait is due to a dominant allele. If the trait were due to a *recessive* allele, and both parents had the recessive phenotype, then *all* of their offspring would also have the recessive phenotype.

**(b) Is an attached earlobe a dominant or recessive trait?**
**Tips for pedigree analysis:** Notice that the first-born daughter in the third generation has attached earlobes, although both of her parents lack that trait (they have free earlobes). Such a pattern is easily explained if the attached-lobe phenotype is due to a recessive allele. If it were due to a *dominant* allele, then at least one parent would also have had the trait.

▲ **Figure 11.14 Pedigree analysis.** Each of these pedigrees traces a trait through three generations of the same family. The two traits have different inheritance patterns, as seen by analysis of the pedigrees.

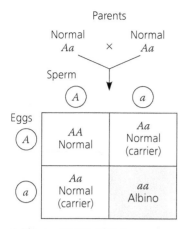

Parents

Normal          Normal
$Aa$      ×      $Aa$

Sperm

| | $A$ | $a$ |
|---|---|---|
| **Eggs** $A$ | $AA$ Normal | $Aa$ Normal (carrier) |
| $a$ | $Aa$ Normal (carrier) | $aa$ Albino |

▲ **Figure 11.15  Albinism: a recessive trait.** One of the two sisters shown here has normal coloration; the other is albino. Most recessive homozygotes are born to parents who are carriers of the disorder but themselves have a normal phenotype, the case shown in the Punnett square.

**?** *What is the probability that the sister with normal coloration is a carrier of the albinism allele?*

relatively mild, such as albinism (lack of pigmentation, which results in susceptibility to skin cancers and vision problems), to life-threatening, such as cystic fibrosis.

### The Behavior of Recessive Alleles

How can we account for the behavior of alleles that cause recessively inherited disorders? Recall that genes code for proteins of specific function. An allele that causes a genetic disorder (let's call it allele $a$) codes for either a malfunctioning protein or no protein at all. In the case of disorders classified as recessive, heterozygotes ($Aa$) are typically normal in phenotype because one copy of the normal allele ($A$) produces a sufficient amount of the specific protein. Thus, a recessively inherited disorder shows up only in the homozygous individuals ($aa$) who inherit one recessive allele from each parent. Although phenotypically normal with regard to the disorder, heterozygotes may transmit the recessive allele to their offspring and thus are called **carriers**. **Figure 11.15** illustrates these ideas using albinism as an example.

Most people who have recessive disorders are born to parents who are carriers of the disorder but have a normal phenotype, as is the case shown in the Punnett square in Figure 11.15. A mating between two carriers corresponds to a Mendelian $F_1$ monohybrid cross, so the predicted genotypic ratio for the offspring is 1 $AA$ : 2 $Aa$ : 1 $aa$. Thus, each child has a 1/4 chance of inheriting a double dose of the recessive allele; in the case of albinism, such a child will be albino. From the genotypic ratio, we also can see that out of three offspring with the *normal* phenotype (one $AA$ plus two $Aa$), two are predicted to be heterozygous carriers, a 2/3 chance. Recessive homozygotes could also result from $Aa \times aa$ and $aa \times aa$ matings, but if the disorder is lethal before reproductive age or results in sterility (neither of which is true for albinism), no $aa$ individuals will reproduce. Even if recessive homozygotes

are able to reproduce, such individuals will still account for a much smaller percentage of the population than heterozygous carriers.

In general, genetic disorders are not evenly distributed among all groups of people. For example, the incidence of Tay-Sachs disease, which we described earlier in this chapter, is disproportionately high among Ashkenazic Jews, Jewish people whose ancestors lived in central Europe. In that population, Tay-Sachs disease occurs in one out of 3,600 births, an incidence about 100 times greater than that among non-Jews or Mediterranean (Sephardic) Jews. This uneven distribution results from the different genetic histories of the world's peoples during less technological times, when populations were more geographically (and hence genetically) isolated.

When a disease-causing recessive allele is rare, it is relatively unlikely that two carriers of the same harmful allele will meet and mate. However, if the man and woman are close relatives (for example, siblings or first cousins), the probability of passing on recessive traits increases greatly. These are called consanguineous ("same blood") matings, and they are indicated in pedigrees by double lines. Because people with recent common ancestors are more likely to carry the same recessive alleles than are unrelated people, it is more likely that a mating of close relatives will produce offspring homozygous for recessive traits—including harmful ones. Such effects can be observed in many types of domesticated and zoo animals that have become inbred.

There is debate among geneticists about the extent to which human consanguinity increases the risk of inherited diseases. Many deleterious alleles have such severe effects that a homozygous embryo spontaneously aborts long before birth. Still, most societies and cultures have laws or taboos forbidding marriages between close relatives. These rules may have evolved out of empirical observation that in most populations, stillbirths and birth defects are more common when parents are closely related. Social and economic factors have also influenced the development of customs and laws against consanguineous marriages.

### Cystic Fibrosis

The most common lethal genetic disease in the United States is **cystic fibrosis**, which strikes one out of every 2,500 people of European descent but is much rarer in other groups. Among people of European descent, one out of 25 (4%) are carriers of the cystic fibrosis allele. The normal allele for this gene codes for a membrane protein that functions in the transport of chloride ions between certain cells and the extracellular fluid. These chloride transport channels are defective or absent in the plasma membranes of children who inherit two recessive alleles for cystic fibrosis. The result is an abnormally high concentration of extracellular chloride, which causes the mucus that coats certain cells to become thicker and stickier than normal. The mucus builds up in the pancreas, lungs, digestive tract, and other organs, leading to multiple (pleiotropic) effects, including poor absorption of nutrients from the intestines, chronic bronchitis, and recurrent bacterial infections.

Untreated, cystic fibrosis can cause death by the age of 5. Daily doses of antibiotics to stop infection, gentle pounding on the chest to clear mucus from clogged airways, and other therapies can prolong life. In the U.S., more than half of those with cystic fibrosis now survive into their 30s and beyond. Recent research on gene-based treatments also shows much promise.

### Sickle-Cell Disease: A Genetic Disorder with Evolutionary Implications

**EVOLUTION** The most common inherited disorder among people of African descent is **sickle-cell disease**, which affects one out of 400 African-Americans. Sickle-cell disease is caused by the substitution of a single amino acid in the hemoglobin protein of red blood cells; in homozygous individuals, all hemoglobin is of the sickle-cell (abnormal) variety. When the oxygen content of an affected individual's blood is low (at high altitudes or under physical stress, for instance), the sickle-cell hemoglobin molecules aggregate into long rods that deform the red cells into a sickle shape (see Figure 3.22). Sickled cells may clump and clog small blood vessels, often leading to other symptoms throughout the body, including physical weakness, pain, organ damage, and even paralysis. Regular blood transfusions can ward off brain damage in children with sickle-cell disease, and new drugs can help prevent or treat other problems, but there is no cure.

Although two sickle-cell alleles are necessary for an individual to manifest full-blown sickle-cell disease, the presence of one sickle-cell allele can affect the phenotype. Thus, at the organismal level, the normal allele is incompletely dominant to the sickle-cell allele. Heterozygotes (carriers), said to have *sickle-cell trait*, are usually healthy, but they may suffer some sickle-cell symptoms during prolonged periods of reduced blood oxygen. At the molecular level, the two alleles are codominant; both normal and abnormal (sickle-cell) hemoglobins are made in heterozygotes.

About one out of ten African-Americans have sickle-cell trait, an unusually high frequency of heterozygotes for an allele with severe detrimental effects in homozygotes. Why haven't evolutionary processes resulted in the disappearance of this allele from this population? One explanation is that having a single copy of the sickle-cell allele reduces the frequency and severity of malaria attacks, especially among young children. The malaria parasite spends part of its life cycle in red blood cells (see Figure 25.26), and the presence of even heterozygous amounts of sickle-cell hemoglobin results in lower parasite densities and hence reduced malaria symptoms. Thus, in tropical Africa, where infection with the malaria parasite is common, the sickle-cell allele confers an advantage to heterozygotes even though it is harmful in the homozygous state. The relatively high frequency of African-Americans with sickle-cell trait is a vestige of their African roots.

▲ **Figure 11.16 Achondroplasia: a dominant trait.** Dr. Michael C. Ain has achondroplasia, a form of dwarfism caused by a dominant allele. This has inspired his work: He is a specialist in the repair of bone defects caused by achondroplasia and other disorders. The dominant allele (*D*) might have arisen as a mutation in the egg or sperm of a parent or could have been inherited from an affected parent, as shown for an affected father in the Punnett square.

## Dominantly Inherited Disorders

Although many harmful alleles are recessive, a number of human disorders are due to dominant alleles. One example is *achondroplasia*, a form of dwarfism that occurs in one of every 25,000 people. Heterozygous individuals have the dwarf phenotype **(Figure 11.16)**. Therefore, all people who are not achondroplastic dwarfs—99.99% of the population—are homozygous for the recessive allele. Like the presence of extra fingers or toes mentioned earlier, achondroplasia is a trait for which the recessive allele is much more prevalent than the corresponding dominant allele.

Dominant alleles that cause a lethal disease are much less common than recessive alleles that have lethal effects. All lethal alleles arise by mutations (changes to the DNA) in cells that produce sperm or eggs; presumably, such mutations are equally likely to be recessive or dominant. A lethal recessive allele can be passed from one generation to the next by heterozygous carriers because the carriers themselves have normal phenotypes. A lethal dominant allele, however, often causes the death of afflicted individuals before they can mature and reproduce, so the allele is not passed on to future generations.

In cases of late-onset diseases, however, a lethal dominant allele may be passed on. If symptoms first appear after reproductive age, the individual may already have transmitted the allele to his or her children. For example, **Huntington's disease**, a degenerative disease of the nervous system, is caused by a lethal dominant allele that has no obvious phenotypic effect until the individual is about 35 to 45 years old. Once the deterioration of the nervous system begins, it is irreversible and inevitably fatal. As with other dominant traits, a child born to a parent with the Huntington's disease allele has a 50% chance of inheriting the allele and the disorder (see the Punnett square in Figure 11.16). In the United States, this devastating disease afflicts about one in 10,000 people.

At one time, the onset of symptoms was the only way to know if a person had inherited the Huntington's allele, but this is no longer the case. By analyzing DNA samples from a large family with a high incidence of the disorder, geneticists tracked the allele for Huntington's disease to a locus near the tip of chromosome 4, and the gene was sequenced in 1993. This information led to the development of a genetic test that could detect the presence of the Huntington's allele in an individual's genome. The availability of this test poses an agonizing dilemma for those with a family history of Huntington's disease. Some individuals may want to be tested for this disease, whereas others may decide it would be too stressful to find out.

## Multifactorial Disorders

The hereditary diseases we have discussed so far are sometimes described as simple Mendelian disorders because they result from an abnormality of one or both alleles at a single genetic locus. Many more people are susceptible to diseases that have a multifactorial basis—a genetic component plus a significant environmental influence. Heart disease, diabetes, cancer, alcoholism, certain mental illnesses such as schizophrenia and bipolar disorder, and many other diseases are multifactorial. In many cases, the hereditary component is polygenic. For example, many genes affect cardiovascular health, making some of us more prone than others to heart attacks and strokes. No matter what our genotype, however, our lifestyle has a tremendous effect on phenotype for cardiovascular health and other multifactorial characters. Exercise, a healthful diet, abstinence from smoking, and an ability to handle stressful situations all reduce our risk of heart disease and some types of cancer.

## Genetic Counseling Based on Mendelian Genetics

Avoiding simple Mendelian disorders is possible when the risk of a particular genetic disorder can be assessed before a child is conceived or during the early stages of the pregnancy. Many hospitals have genetic counselors who can provide information to prospective parents concerned about a family history for a specific disease.

Consider the case of a hypothetical couple, John and Carol. Each had a brother who died from the same recessively inherited lethal disease. Before conceiving their first child, John and Carol seek genetic counseling to determine the risk of having a child with the disease. From the information about their brothers, we know that both parents of John and both parents of Carol must have been carriers of the recessive allele. Thus, John and Carol are both products of $Aa \times Aa$ crosses, where $a$ symbolizes the allele that causes this particular disease. We also know that John and Carol are not homozygous recessive

(*aa*), because they do not have the disease. Therefore, their genotypes are either *AA* or *Aa*.

Given a genotypic ratio of 1 *AA* : 2 *Aa* : 1 *aa* for offspring of an $Aa \times Aa$ cross, John and Carol each have a 2/3 chance of being carriers (*Aa*). According to the rule of multiplication, the overall probability of their firstborn having the disorder is 2/3 (the chance that John is a carrier) times 2/3 (the chance that Carol is a carrier) times 1/4 (the chance of two carriers having a child with the disease), which equals 1/9. Suppose that Carol and John decide to have a child—after all, there is an 8/9 chance that their baby will not have the disorder. If, despite these odds, their child is born with the disease, then we would know that *both* John and Carol are, in fact, carriers (*Aa* genotype). If both John and Carol are carriers, there is a 1/4 chance that any subsequent child this couple has will have the disease. The probability is higher for subsequent children because the diagnosis of the disease in the first child established that both parents are carriers, not because the genotype of the first child affects in any way that of future children.

When we use Mendel's laws to predict possible outcomes of matings, it is important to remember that each child represents an independent event in the sense that its genotype is unaffected by the genotypes of older siblings. Suppose that John and Carol have three more children, and *all three* have the hypothetical hereditary disease. There is only one chance in 64 ($1/4 \times 1/4 \times 1/4$) that such an outcome will occur. Despite this run of misfortune, the chance that still another child of this couple will have the disease remains 1/4.

Genetic counseling like this relies on the Mendelian model of inheritance. We owe the "gene idea"—the concept of heritable factors transmitted according to simple rules of chance—to the elegant quantitative experiments of Gregor Mendel. The importance of his discoveries was overlooked by most biologists until early in the 20th century, decades after he reported his findings. In the next chapter, you'll learn how Mendel's laws have their physical basis in the behavior of chromosomes during sexual life cycles and how the synthesis of Mendelian genetics and a chromosome theory of inheritance catalyzed progress in genetics.

### CONCEPT CHECK 11.4

1. Beth and Tom each have a sibling with cystic fibrosis, but neither Beth nor Tom nor any of their parents have the disease. Calculate the probability that if this couple has a child, the child will have cystic fibrosis. What would be the probability if a test revealed that Tom is a carrier but Beth is not? Explain your answers.

2. **MAKE CONNECTIONS** In Table 11.1, note the phenotypic ratio of the dominant to recessive trait in the $F_2$ generation for the monohybrid cross involving flower color. Then determine the phenotypic ratio for the offspring of the second-generation couple in Figure 11.14b. What accounts for the difference in the two ratios?

For suggested answers, see Appendix A.

# 11 Chapter Review

## SUMMARY OF KEY CONCEPTS

### CONCEPT 11.1
#### Mendel used the scientific approach to identify two laws of inheritance (pp. 213–218)

- Gregor Mendel formulated a theory of inheritance based on experiments with garden peas, proposing that parents pass on to their offspring discrete genes that retain their identity through generations. This theory includes two "laws."

- The **law of segregation** states that genes have alternative forms, or **alleles**. In a diploid organism, the two alleles of a gene segregate (separate) during meiosis and gamete formation; each sperm or egg carries only one allele of each pair. This law explains the 3:1 ratio of $F_2$ phenotypes observed when **monohybrids** self-pollinate. Each organism inherits one allele for each gene from each parent. In **heterozygotes**, the two alleles are different, and expression of one (the **dominant allele**) masks the phenotypic effect of the other (the **recessive allele**). **Homozygotes** have identical alleles of a given gene and are **true-breeding**.

*pp* (homozygous)

*Pp* (heterozygous)

*Pp* (heterozygous)

*pp* (homozygous)

- The **law of independent assortment** states that the pair of alleles for a given gene segregates into gametes independently of the pair of alleles for any other gene. In a cross between **dihybrids** (individuals heterozygous for two genes), the offspring have four phenotypes in a 9:3:3:1 ratio.

**?** *When Mendel did crosses of true-breeding purple- and white-flowered pea plants, the white-flowered trait disappeared from the $F_1$ generation but reappeared in the $F_2$ generation. Use genetic terms to explain why that happened.*

### CONCEPT 11.2
#### The laws of probability govern Mendelian inheritance (pp. 219–220)

- The **multiplication rule** states that the probability of two or more events occurring together is equal to the product of the individual probabilities of the independent single events. The **addition rule** states that the probability of an event that can occur in two or more independent, mutually exclusive ways is the sum of the individual probabilities.

- The rules of probability can be used to solve complex genetics problems. A dihybrid or other multicharacter cross is equivalent to two or more independent monohybrid crosses occurring simultaneously. In calculating the chances of the various offspring genotypes from such crosses, each character is first considered separately and then the individual probabilities are multiplied.

**DRAW IT** *Redraw the Punnett square on the right side of Figure 11.8 as two smaller monohybrid Punnett squares, one for each gene. Below each square, list the fraction of each phenotype produced. Use the rule of multiplication to compute the overall fraction of each possible dihybrid phenotype. Write the phenotypic ratio.*

### CONCEPT 11.3
#### Inheritance patterns are often more complex than predicted by simple Mendelian genetics (pp. 220–224)

- Extensions of Mendelian genetics for a single gene:

| Relationship among alleles of a single gene | Description | Example |
|---|---|---|
| **Complete dominance of one allele** | Heterozygous phenotype same as that of homozygous dominant | *PP*    *Pp* |
| **Incomplete dominance of either allele** | Heterozygous phenotype intermediate between the two homozygous phenotypes | $C^R C^R$  $C^R C^W$  $C^W C^W$ |
| **Codominance** | Both phenotypes expressed in heterozygotes | $I^A I^B$ |
| **Multiple alleles** | In the whole population, some genes have more than two alleles | ABO blood group alleles $I^A, I^B, i$ |
| **Pleiotropy** | One gene is able to affect multiple phenotypic characters | Sickle-cell disease |

- Extensions of Mendelian genetics for two or more genes:

| Relationship among two or more genes | Description | Example |
|---|---|---|
| **Epistasis** | The phenotypic expression of one gene affects the expression of another gene | *BbEe* × *BbEe*  9 : 3 : 4 |
| **Polygenic inheritance** | A single phenotypic character is affected by two or more genes | *AaBbCc* × *AaBbCc* |

- The expression of a genotype can be affected by environmental influences. Polygenic characters that are also influenced by the environment are called **multifactorial** characters.

- An organism's overall phenotype reflects its complete genotype and unique environmental history. Even in more complex inheritance patterns, Mendel's fundamental laws still apply.

**?** *Which relationships (in the first column of the two tables above) are demonstrated by the inheritance patterns of the ABO blood group alleles? Explain why or why not, for each genetic relationship.*

## Many human traits follow Mendelian patterns of inheritance (pp. 225–229)

- Analysis of family **pedigrees** can be used to deduce the possible genotypes of individuals and make predictions about future offspring. Predictions are statistical probabilities rather than certainties.

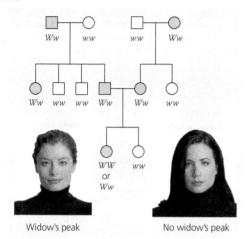

Widow's peak      No widow's peak

- Many genetic disorders are inherited as simple recessive traits, ranging from relatively mild disorders (albinism, for example) to life-threatening ones such as sickle-cell disease and cystic fibrosis. Most affected (homozygous recessive) individuals are children of phenotypically normal, heterozygous **carriers**.
- The sickle-cell allele has probably persisted for evolutionary reasons: Heterozygotes have an advantage because one copy of the sickle-cell allele reduces both the frequency and severity of malaria attacks.
- Lethal dominant alleles are eliminated from the population if affected people die before reproducing. Nonlethal dominant alleles and lethal alleles that are expressed relatively late in life are inherited in a Mendelian way.
- Many human diseases are multifactorial—that is, they have both genetic and environmental components and do not follow simple Mendelian inheritance patterns.
- Using family histories, genetic counselors help couples determine the probability of their children having genetic disorders.

> **?** *Both members of a couple know that they are carriers of the cystic fibrosis allele. None of their three children have cystic fibrosis, but any one of them might be a carrier. The couple would like to have a fourth child but are worried that he or she would very likely have the disease, since the first three do not. What would you tell the couple? Would it remove some more uncertainty in their prediction if they could find out from genetic tests whether the three children are carriers?*

## TIPS FOR GENETICS PROBLEMS

1. Write down symbols for the alleles. (These may be given in the problem.) When represented by single letters, the dominant allele is uppercase and the recessive allele is lowercase.

2. Write down the possible genotypes, as determined by the phenotype.
   a. If the phenotype is that of the dominant trait (for example, purple flowers), then the genotype is either homozygous dominant or heterozygous (*PP* or *Pp*, in this example).
   b. If the phenotype is that of the recessive trait, the genotype must be homozygous recessive (for example, *pp*).
   c. If the problem says "true-breeding," the genotype is homozygous.

3. Determine what the problem is asking. If asked to do a cross, write it out in the form [Genotype] × [Genotype], using the alleles you've decided on.

4. To figure out the outcome of a cross, set up a Punnett square.
   a. Put the gametes of one parent at the top and those of the other on the left. To determine the allele(s) in each gamete for a given genotype, set up a systematic way to list all the possibilities. (Remember, each gamete has one allele of each gene.) Note that there are $2^n$ possible types of gametes, where $n$ is the number of gene loci that are heterozygous. For example, an individual with genotype *AaBbCc* would produce $2^3 = 8$ types of gametes. Write the genotypes of the gametes in circles above the columns and to the left of the rows.
   b. Fill in the Punnett square as if each possible sperm were fertilizing each possible egg, making all of the possible offspring. In a cross of *AaBbCc* × *AaBbCc*, for example, the Punnett square would have 8 columns and 8 rows, so there are 64 different offspring; you would know the genotype of each and thus the phenotype. Count genotypes and phenotypes to obtain the genotypic and phenotypic ratios. Because the Punnett square is so large, this method is not the most efficient. Instead, see tip 5.

5. You can use the rules of probability if the Punnett square would be too big. (For example, see the question at the end of the summary for Concept 11.2 and question 7.) You can consider each gene separately (see the section Solving Complex Genetics Problems with the Rules of Probability in Concept 11.2).

6. If the problem gives you the phenotypic ratios of offspring, but not the genotypes of the parents in a given cross, the phenotypes can help you deduce the parents' unknown genotypes.
   a. For example, if 1/2 of the offspring have the recessive phenotype and 1/2 the dominant, you know that the cross was between a heterozygote and a homozygous recessive.
   b. If the ratio is 3:1, the cross was between two heterozygotes.
   c. If two genes are involved and you see a 9:3:3:1 ratio in the offspring, you know that each parent is heterozygous for both genes. *Caution*: Don't assume that the reported numbers will exactly equal the predicted ratios. For example, if there are 13 offspring with the dominant trait and 11 with the recessive, assume that the ratio is one dominant to one recessive.

7. For pedigree problems, use the tips in Figure 11.14 and below to determine what kind of trait is involved.
   a. If parents without the trait have offspring with the trait, the trait must be recessive and both of the parents must be carriers.
   b. If the trait is seen in every generation, it is most likely dominant (see the next possibility, though).
   c. If both parents have the trait, then in order for it to be recessive, all offspring must show the trait.
   d. To determine the likely genotype of a certain individual in a pedigree, first label the genotypes of all individuals in the pedigree as well as you can. If an individual has the dominant phenotype, the genotype must be *AA* or *Aa*; you can write this as *A-*; the recessive phenotype means the genotype must be *aa*. Try different possibilities to see how well each fits the results. Use Mendel's laws and the rules of probability to calculate the probability of each possible genotype being the correct one.

# TEST YOUR UNDERSTANDING

## Level 1: Knowledge/Comprehension

1. Match each term on the left with a statement on the right.

   **Term**
   — Gene
   — Allele
   — Character
   — Trait
   — Dominant allele
   — Recessive allele
   — Genotype
   — Phenotype
   — Homozygous
   — Heterozygous
   — Testcross
   — Monohybrid cross

   **Statement**
   a. Has no effect on phenotype in a heterozygote
   b. A variant for a character
   c. Having two identical alleles for a gene
   d. A cross between individuals heterozygous for a single character
   e. An alternative version of a gene
   f. Having two different alleles for a gene
   g. A heritable feature that varies among individuals
   h. An organism's appearance or observable traits
   i. A cross between an individual with an unknown genotype and a homozygous recessive individual
   j. Determines phenotype in a heterozygote
   k. The genetic makeup of an individual
   l. A heritable unit that determines a character; can exist in different forms

2. **DRAW IT** Two pea plants heterozygous for the characters of pod color and pod shape are crossed. Draw a Punnett square to determine the phenotypic ratios of the offspring.

3. A man with type A blood marries a woman with type B blood. Their child has type O blood. What are the genotypes of these three individuals? What genotypes, and in what frequencies, would you expect in future offspring from this marriage?

4. A man has six fingers on each hand and six toes on each foot. His wife and their daughter have the normal number of digits. Remember that extra digits is a dominant trait. What fraction of this couple's children would be expected to have extra digits?

5. **DRAW IT** A pea plant heterozygous for inflated pods ($Ii$) is crossed with a plant homozygous for constricted pods ($ii$). Draw a Punnett square for this cross. Assume that pollen comes from the $ii$ plant.

## Level 2: Application/Analysis

6. Flower position, stem length, and seed shape are three characters that Mendel studied. Each is controlled by an independently assorting gene and has dominant and recessive expression as follows:

   | Character | Dominant | Recessive |
   | --- | --- | --- |
   | Flower position | Axial ($A$) | Terminal ($a$) |
   | Stem length | Tall ($T$) | Dwarf ($t$) |
   | Seed shape | Round ($R$) | Wrinkled ($r$) |

   If a plant that is heterozygous for all three characters is allowed to self-fertilize, what proportion of the offspring would you expect to be as follows? (*Note*: Use the rules of probability instead of a huge Punnett square.)

   (a) homozygous for the three dominant traits
   (b) homozygous for the three recessive traits
   (c) heterozygous for all three characters
   (d) homozygous for axial and tall, while heterozygous for seed shape

7. A black guinea pig crossed with an albino guinea pig produces 12 black offspring. When the albino is crossed with a second black one, 7 blacks and 5 albinos are obtained. What is the best explanation for this genetic outcome? Write genotypes for the parents, gametes, and offspring.

8. In some plants, a true-breeding, red-flowered strain gives all pink flowers when crossed with a white-flowered strain: $C^R C^R$ (red) × $C^W C^W$ (white) → $C^R C^W$ (pink). If flower position (axial or terminal) is inherited as it is in peas (see Table 11.1), what will be the ratios of genotypes and phenotypes of the $F_1$ generation resulting from the following cross: axial-red (true-breeding) × terminal-white? What will be the ratios in the $F_2$ generation?

9. In sesame plants, the one-pod condition ($P$) is dominant to the three-pod condition ($p$), and normal leaf ($L$) is dominant to wrinkled leaf ($l$). Pod type and leaf type are inherited independently. Determine the genotypes for the two parents for all possible matings producing the following offspring:

   (a) 318 one-pod, normal leaf and 98 one-pod, wrinkled leaf
   (b) 323 three-pod, normal leaf and 106 three-pod, wrinkled leaf
   (c) 401 one-pod, normal leaf
   (d) 150 one-pod, normal leaf, 147 one-pod, wrinkled leaf, 51 three-pod, normal leaf, and 48 three-pod, wrinkled leaf
   (e) 223 one-pod, normal leaf, 72 one-pod, wrinkled leaf, 76 three-pod, normal leaf, and 27 three-pod, wrinkled leaf

10. Phenylketonuria (PKU) is an inherited disease caused by a recessive allele. If a woman and her husband, who are both carriers, have three children, what is the probability of each of the following?

    (a) All three children are of normal phenotype.
    (b) One or more of the three children have the disease.
    (c) All three children have the disease.
    (d) At least one child is phenotypically normal.

    (*Note*: It will help to remember that the probabilities of all possible outcomes always add up to 1.)

11. The genotype of $F_1$ individuals in a tetrahybrid cross is $AaBbCcDd$. Assuming independent assortment of these four genes, what are the probabilities that $F_2$ offspring will have the following genotypes?

    (a) $aabbccdd$
    (b) $AaBbCcDd$
    (c) $AABBCCDD$
    (d) $AaBBccDd$
    (e) $AaBBCCdd$

12. What is the probability that each of the following pairs of parents will produce the indicated offspring? (Assume independent assortment of all gene pairs.)

    (a) $AABBCC \times aabbcc \rightarrow AaBbCc$
    (b) $AABbCc \times AaBbCc \rightarrow AAbbCC$
    (c) $AaBbCc \times AaBbCc \rightarrow AaBbCc$
    (d) $aaBbCC \times AABbcc \rightarrow AaBbCc$

13. Karen and Steve each have a sibling with sickle-cell disease. Neither Karen nor Steve nor any of their parents have the disease, and none of them have been tested to see if they have the sickle-cell trait. Based on this incomplete information, calculate the probability that if this couple has a child, the child will have sickle-cell disease.

14. In tigers, a recessive allele that is pleiotropic causes an absence of fur pigmentation (a white tiger) and a cross-eyed condition. If two phenotypically normal tigers that are heterozygous at this locus are mated, what percentage of their offspring will be cross-eyed? What percentage of cross-eyed tigers will be white?

**15.** In 1981, a stray black cat with unusual rounded, curled-back ears was adopted by a family in California. Hundreds of descendants of the cat have since been born, and cat fanciers hope to develop the curl cat into a show breed. Suppose you owned the first curl cat and wanted to develop a true-breeding variety. How would you determine whether the curl allele is dominant or recessive? How would you obtain true-breeding curl cats? How could you be sure they are true-breeding?

**16.** Imagine that a newly discovered, recessively inherited disease is expressed only in individuals with type O blood, although the disease and blood group are independently inherited. A normal man with type A blood and a normal woman with type B blood have already had one child with the disease. The woman is now pregnant for a second time. What is the probability that the second child will also have the disease? Assume that both parents are heterozygous for the gene that causes the disease.

**17.** In maize (corn) plants, a dominant allele *I* inhibits kernel color, while the recessive allele *i* permits color when homozygous. At a different locus, the dominant allele *P* causes purple kernel color, while the homozygous recessive genotype *pp* causes red kernels. If plants heterozygous at both loci are crossed, what will be the genotypic and phenotypic ratios of the offspring?

**18.** The pedigree below traces the inheritance of alkaptonuria, a biochemical disorder. Affected individuals, indicated here by the colored circles and squares, are unable to metabolize a substance called alkapton, which colors the urine and stains body tissues. Does alkaptonuria appear to be caused by a dominant allele or by a recessive allele? Fill in the genotypes of the individuals whose genotypes can be deduced. What genotypes are possible for each of the other individuals?

**19.** Imagine that you are a genetic counselor, and a couple planning to start a family comes to you for information. Charles was married once before, and he and his first wife had a child with cystic fibrosis. The brother of his current wife, Elaine, died of cystic fibrosis. What is the probability that Charles and Elaine will have a baby with cystic fibrosis? (Neither Charles, Elaine, nor their parents have cystic fibrosis.)

**20.** In mice, black fur (*B*) is dominant to white (*b*). At a different locus, a dominant allele (*A*) produces a band of yellow just below the tip of each hair in mice with black fur. This gives a frosted appearance known as agouti. Expression of the recessive allele (*a*) results in a solid coat color. If mice that are heterozygous at both loci are crossed, what are the expected genotypic and phenotypic ratios of their offspring?

### Level 3: Synthesis/Evaluation

**21. SCIENTIFIC INQUIRY**
You are handed a mystery pea plant with tall stems and axial flowers and asked to determine its genotype as quickly as possible. You know that the allele for tall stems (*T*) is dominant to that for dwarf stems (*t*) and that the allele for axial flowers (*A*) is dominant to that for terminal flowers (*a*).

(a) What are *all* the possible genotypes for your mystery plant?
(b) Describe the *one* cross you would do, out in your garden, to determine the exact genotype of your mystery plant.
(c) While waiting for the results of your cross, you predict the results for each possible genotype listed in part a. How do you do this? Why is this not called "performing a cross"?
(d) Explain how the results of your cross and your predictions will help you learn the genotype of your mystery plant.

**22. SCIENCE, TECHNOLOGY, AND SOCIETY**
Imagine that one of your parents has Huntington's disease. What is the probability that you, too, will someday manifest the disease? There is no cure for Huntington's. Would you want to be tested for the Huntington's allele? Why or why not?

**23. FOCUS ON EVOLUTION**
Over the past half century, there has been a trend in the United States and other developed countries for people to marry and start families later in life than did their parents and grandparents. What effects might this trend have on the incidence (frequency) of late-acting dominant lethal alleles in the population?

**24. FOCUS ON INFORMATION**
The continuity of life is based on heritable information in the form of DNA. In a short essay (100–150 words), explain how the passage of genes from parents to offspring, in the form of particular alleles, ensures perpetuation of parental traits in offspring and, at the same time, genetic variation among offspring. Use genetic terms in your explanation.

*For selected answers, see Appendix A.*

## MasteringBiology®

**Students** Go to **MasteringBiology** for assignments, the eText, and the Study Area with practice tests, animations, and activities.

**Instructors** Go to **MasteringBiology** for automatically graded tutorials and questions that you can assign to your students, plus Instructor Resources.

# 12

# The Chromosomal Basis of Inheritance

▼ **Figure 12.1** Where are Mendel's hereditary factors located in the cell?

## OVERVIEW

## Locating Genes Along Chromosomes

Gregor Mendel's "hereditary factors" were purely an abstract concept when he proposed their existence in 1860. At that time, no cellular structures were known that could house these imaginary units. Even after chromosomes were first observed, many biologists remained skeptical about Mendel's laws of segregation and independent assortment until there was sufficient evidence that these principles of heredity had a physical basis in chromosomal behavior.

Today, we know that genes—Mendel's "factors"—are located along chromosomes. We can see the location of a particular gene by tagging chromosomes with a fluorescent dye that highlights that gene. For example, the two yellow spots in **Figure 12.1** mark the locus of a specific gene on the sister chromatids of human chromosome 6. This chapter will extend what you learned in the past two chapters. We'll describe the chromosomal basis for the transmission of genes from parents to offspring, along with some important exceptions to the standard mode of inheritance.

## CONCEPT 12.1

## Mendelian inheritance has its physical basis in the behavior of chromosomes

Using improved techniques of microscopy, cytologists worked out the process of mitosis in 1875 and meiosis in the 1890s. Cytology and genetics converged when biologists began to see parallels between the behavior of chromosomes and the behavior of Mendel's proposed hereditary factors during sexual life cycles: Chromosomes and genes are both present in pairs in diploid cells; homologous chromosomes separate and alleles segregate during the process of meiosis; and fertilization restores the paired condition for both chromosomes and genes. Around 1902, Walter S. Sutton, Theodor Boveri, and others independently noted these parallels, and the **chromosome theory of inheritance** began to take form. According to this theory, Mendelian genes have specific loci (positions) along chromosomes, and it is the chromosomes that undergo segregation and independent assortment.

**Figure 12.2** shows that the behavior of homologous chromosomes during meiosis can account for the segregation of the alleles at each genetic locus to

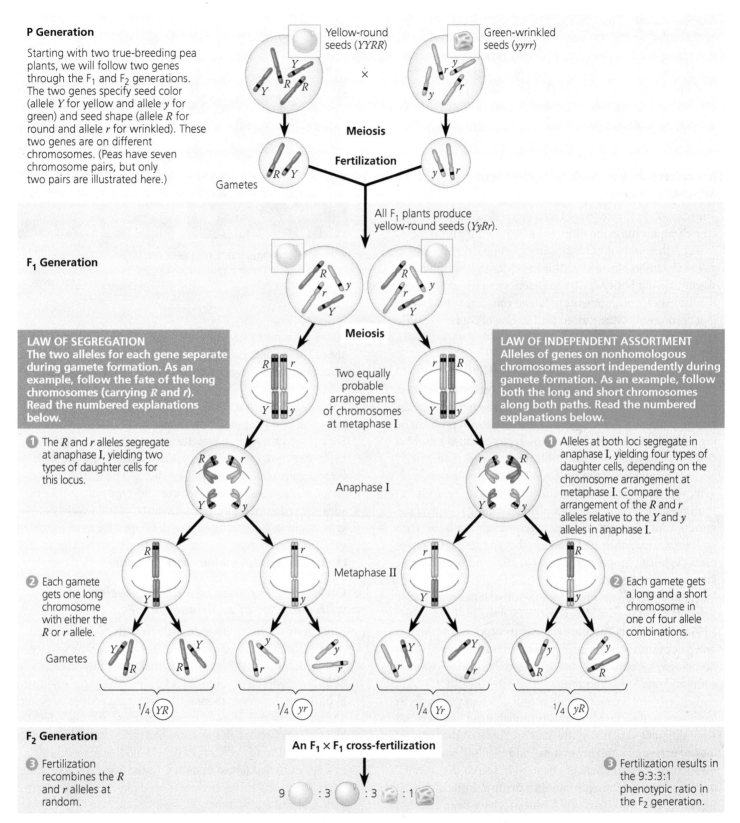

**P Generation**

Starting with two true-breeding pea plants, we will follow two genes through the $F_1$ and $F_2$ generations. The two genes specify seed color (allele $Y$ for yellow and allele $y$ for green) and seed shape (allele $R$ for round and allele $r$ for wrinkled). These two genes are on different chromosomes. (Peas have seven chromosome pairs, but only two pairs are illustrated here.)

Yellow-round seeds ($YYRR$)

Green-wrinkled seeds ($yyrr$)

×

**Meiosis**

**Fertilization**

Gametes

All $F_1$ plants produce yellow-round seeds ($YyRr$).

**$F_1$ Generation**

**LAW OF SEGREGATION**
The two alleles for each gene separate during gamete formation. As an example, follow the fate of the long chromosomes (carrying $R$ and $r$). Read the numbered explanations below.

**Meiosis**

Two equally probable arrangements of chromosomes at metaphase I

**LAW OF INDEPENDENT ASSORTMENT**
Alleles of genes on nonhomologous chromosomes assort independently during gamete formation. As an example, follow both the long and short chromosomes along both paths. Read the numbered explanations below.

① The $R$ and $r$ alleles segregate at anaphase I, yielding two types of daughter cells for this locus.

Anaphase I

① Alleles at both loci segregate in anaphase I, yielding four types of daughter cells, depending on the chromosome arrangement at metaphase I. Compare the arrangement of the $R$ and $r$ alleles relative to the $Y$ and $y$ alleles in anaphase I.

Metaphase II

② Each gamete gets one long chromosome with either the $R$ or $r$ allele.

② Each gamete gets a long and a short chromosome in one of four allele combinations.

Gametes

¼ $YR$   ¼ $yr$   ¼ $Yr$   ¼ $yR$

**$F_2$ Generation**

③ Fertilization recombines the $R$ and $r$ alleles at random.

**An $F_1 \times F_1$ cross-fertilization**

9 ○ : 3 ○ : 3 ▨ : 1 ▨

③ Fertilization results in the 9:3:3:1 phenotypic ratio in the $F_2$ generation.

▲ **Figure 12.2 The chromosomal basis of Mendel's laws.** Here we correlate a dihybrid cross that Mendel performed (see Figure 11.8) with the behavior of chromosomes during meiosis. The arrangement of chromosomes at metaphase I of meiosis and their movement during anaphase I account, respectively, for the independent assortment and segregation of the alleles for seed color and shape. Each cell that undergoes meiosis in an $F_1$ plant produces two kinds of gametes. If we count the results for all cells, however, each $F_1$ plant produces equal numbers of all four kinds of gametes because the alternative chromosome arrangements at metaphase I are equally likely.

**?** *If you crossed an $F_1$ plant with a plant that was homozygous recessive for both genes (yyrr), how would the phenotypic ratio of the offspring compare with the 9:3:3:1 ratio seen here?*

different gametes. The figure also shows that the behavior of nonhomologous chromosomes can account for the independent assortment of the alleles for two or more genes located on different chromosomes. By carefully studying this figure, which traces the same dihybrid pea cross you learned about in Figure 11.8, you can see how the behavior of chromosomes during meiosis in the $F_1$ generation and subsequent random fertilization give rise to the $F_2$ phenotypic ratio observed by Mendel.

## Morgan's Experimental Evidence: *Scientific Inquiry*

The first solid evidence associating a specific gene with a specific chromosome came early in the 20th century from the work of Thomas Hunt Morgan, an experimental embryologist at Columbia University. Although Morgan was initially skeptical about both Mendelian genetics and the chromosome theory, his early experiments provided convincing evidence that chromosomes are indeed the location of Mendel's heritable factors.

### Morgan's Choice of Experimental Organism

Many times in the history of biology, important discoveries have come to those insightful or lucky enough to choose an experimental organism suitable for the research problem being tackled. Mendel chose the garden pea because a number of distinct varieties were available. For his work, Morgan selected a species of fruit fly, *Drosophila melanogaster*, a common insect that feeds on the fungi growing on fruit. Fruit flies are prolific breeders; a single mating will produce hundreds of offspring, and a new generation can be bred every two weeks. Morgan's laboratory began using this convenient organism for genetic studies in 1907 and soon became known as "the fly room."

Another advantage of the fruit fly is that it has only four pairs of chromosomes, which are easily distinguishable with a light microscope. There are three pairs of autosomes and one pair of sex chromosomes. Female fruit flies have a pair of homologous X chromosomes, and males have one X chromosome and one Y chromosome.

While Mendel could readily obtain different pea varieties from seed suppliers, Morgan was probably the first person to want different varieties of the fruit fly. He faced the tedious task of carrying out many matings and then microscopically inspecting large numbers of offspring in search of naturally occurring variant individuals. After many months of this, he lamented, "Two years' work wasted. I have been breeding those flies for all that time and I've got nothing out of it." Morgan persisted, however, and was finally rewarded with the discovery of a single male fly with white eyes instead of the usual red. The phenotype for a character most commonly observed in natural populations, such as red eyes in *Drosophila*, is called the **wild type** (Figure 12.3). Traits that are alternatives to the wild type, such as white eyes in *Drosophila*,

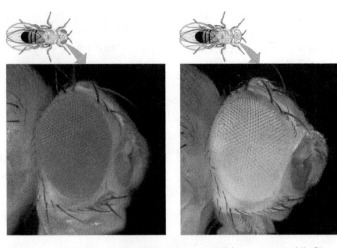

▲ **Figure 12.3 Morgan's first mutant.** Wild-type *Drosophila* flies have red eyes (left). Among his flies, Morgan discovered a mutant male with white eyes (right). This variation made it possible for Morgan to trace a gene for eye color to a specific chromosome (LMs).

are called *mutant phenotypes* because they are due to alleles assumed to have originated as changes, or mutations, in the wild-type allele.

Morgan and his students invented a notation for symbolizing alleles in *Drosophila* that is still widely used for fruit flies. For a given character in flies, the gene takes its symbol from the first mutant (non-wild type) discovered. Thus, the allele for white eyes in *Drosophila* is symbolized by *w*. The superscript $+$ identifies the allele for the wild-type trait: $w^+$ for the allele for red eyes, for example. Over the years, a variety of gene notation systems have been developed for different organisms. For example, human genes are usually written in all capitals, such as *HD* for the allele for Huntington's disease.

### Correlating Behavior of a Gene's Alleles with Behavior of a Chromosome Pair

Morgan mated his white-eyed male fly with a red-eyed female. All the $F_1$ offspring had red eyes, suggesting that the wild-type allele is dominant. When Morgan bred the $F_1$ flies to each other, he observed the classical 3:1 phenotypic ratio among the $F_2$ offspring. However, there was a surprising additional result: The white-eye trait showed up only in males. All the $F_2$ females had red eyes, while half the males had red eyes and half had white eyes. Therefore, Morgan concluded that somehow a fly's eye color was linked to its sex. (If the eye-color gene were unrelated to sex, half of the white-eyed flies would have been male and half female.)

Recall that a female fly has two X chromosomes (XX), while a male fly has an X and a Y (XY). The correlation between the trait of white eye color and the male sex of the affected $F_2$ flies suggested to Morgan that the gene involved in his white-eyed mutant was located exclusively on the X chromosome, with no corresponding allele present on the Y chromosome. His reasoning can be followed in **Figure 12.4**. For a male, a single

## In a cross between a wild-type female fruit fly and a mutant white-eyed male, what color eyes will the F₁ and F₂ offspring have?

**Experiment** Thomas Hunt Morgan wanted to analyze the behavior of two alleles of a fruit fly eye-color gene. In crosses similar to those done by Mendel with pea plants, Morgan and his colleagues mated a wild-type (red-eyed) female with a mutant white-eyed male.

Morgan then bred an F₁ red-eyed female to an F₁ red-eyed male to produce the F₂ generation.

**Results** The F₂ generation showed a typical Mendelian ratio of three red-eyed flies to one white-eyed fly. However, no females displayed the white-eye trait; all white-eyed flies were males.

**Conclusion** All F₁ offspring had red eyes, so the mutant white-eye trait ($w$) must be recessive to the wild-type red-eye trait ($w^+$). Since the recessive trait—white eyes—was expressed only in males in the F₂ generation, Morgan deduced that this eye-color gene is located on the X chromosome and that there is no corresponding locus on the Y chromosome.

**Source** T. H. Morgan, Sex-limited inheritance in *Drosophila, Science* 32:120–122 (1910).

(MB) A related Experimental Inquiry Tutorial can be assigned in MasteringBiology.

**WHAT IF?** Suppose this eye-color gene were located on an autosome. Predict the phenotypes (including gender) of the F₂ flies in this hypothetical cross. (*Hint*: Draw a Punnett square.)

---

copy of the mutant allele would confer white eyes; since a male has only one X chromosome, there can be no wild-type allele ($w^+$) present to mask the recessive allele. On the other hand, a female could have white eyes only if both her X chromosomes carried the recessive mutant allele ($w$). This was impossible for the F₂ females in Morgan's experiment because all the F₁ fathers had red eyes.

Morgan's finding of the correlation between a particular trait and an individual's sex provided support for the chromosome theory of inheritance: namely, that a specific gene is carried on a specific chromosome (in this case, an eye-color gene on the X chromosome). In addition, Morgan's work indicated that genes located on a sex chromosome exhibit unique inheritance patterns, which we'll discuss in the next section. Recognizing the importance of Morgan's early work, many bright students were attracted to his fly room.

**CONCEPT CHECK 12.1**

1. Which one of Mendel's laws relates to the inheritance of alleles for a single character? Which law relates to the inheritance of alleles for two characters in a dihybrid cross?
2. **MAKE CONNECTIONS** Review the description of meiosis (see Figure 10.8) and Mendel's laws of segregation and independent assortment (see Concept 11.1). What is the physical basis for each of Mendel's laws?
3. **WHAT IF?** Propose a possible reason that the first naturally occurring mutant fruit fly Morgan saw involved a gene on a sex chromosome.

For suggested answers, see Appendix A.

---

**CONCEPT** 12.2

# Sex-linked genes exhibit unique patterns of inheritance

As you just learned, Morgan's discovery of a trait (white eyes) that correlated with a fly's sex was a key episode in the development of the chromosome theory of inheritance. Because the identity of a fly's sex chromosomes could be inferred by observing the sex of the fly, the behavior of the two members of the pair of sex chromosomes could be correlated with the behavior of the two alleles of the eye-color gene. In this section, we'll take a closer look at the role of sex chromosomes in inheritance. We'll begin by reviewing the chromosomal basis of sex determination in humans and some other animals.

## The Chromosomal Basis of Sex

Whether we are male or female is one of our more obvious phenotypic characters. Although the anatomical and physiological differences between women and men are numerous, the chromosomal basis for determining sex is rather simple. In humans and other mammals, there are two varieties of sex chromosomes, designated X and Y. The Y chromosome is much smaller than the X chromosome (**Figure 12.5**). A person who inherits two X chromosomes, one from each parent, usually develops as a female. A male develops from a zygote containing one X chromosome and one Y chromosome (**Figure 12.6**). Short segments at either end of the Y chromosome are the only regions that are homologous with corresponding regions of the X. These homologous regions allow the X and Y chromosomes in males to pair and behave like homologous chromosomes during meiosis in the testes.

▲ **Figure 12.5 Human sex chromosomes.**

In mammalian testes and ovaries, the two sex chromosomes segregate during meiosis. Each egg receives one X chromosome. In contrast, sperm fall into two categories: Half the sperm cells a male produces receive an X chromosome, and half receive a Y chromosome. We can trace the sex of each offspring to the events of conception: If a sperm cell bearing an X chromosome happens to fertilize an egg, the zygote is XX, a female; if a sperm cell containing a Y chromosome fertilizes an egg, the zygote is XY, a male (see Figure 12.6). Thus, mammalian sex determination is a matter of chance—a fifty-fifty chance. In *Drosophila*, males are XY, but sex depends on the ratio between the number of X chromosomes and the number of autosome sets, not simply on the presence of the Y. There are other chromosomal systems as well, besides the X-Y system, for determining sex.

In humans, the anatomical signs of sex begin to emerge when the embryo is about 2 months old. Before then, the rudiments of the gonads are generic—they can develop into either testes or ovaries, depending on whether or not a Y chromosome is present. In 1990, a British research team identified a

gene on the Y chromosome required for the development of testes. They named the gene *SRY*, for sex-determining region of Y. In the absence of *SRY*, the gonads develop into ovaries. The biochemical, physiological, and anatomical features that distinguish males and females are complex, and many genes are involved in their development. In fact, *SRY* codes for a protein that regulates other genes.

Researchers have sequenced the human Y chromosome and have identified 78 genes that code for about 25 proteins (some genes are duplicates). About half of these genes are expressed only in the testis, and some are required for normal testicular functioning and the production of normal sperm. A gene located on either sex chromosome is called a **sex-linked gene**; those located on the Y chromosome are called *Y-linked genes*. The Y chromosome is passed along virtually intact from a father to all his sons. Because there are so few Y-linked genes, very few disorders are transferred from father to son on the Y chromosome. A rare example is that in the absence of certain Y-linked genes, an XY individual is male but does not produce normal sperm.

The human X chromosome contains approximately 1,100 genes, which are called **X-linked genes**. The fact that males and females inherit a different number of X chromosomes leads to a pattern of inheritance different from that produced by genes located on autosomes.

## Inheritance of X-Linked Genes

While most Y-linked genes help determine sex, the X chromosomes have genes for many characters unrelated to sex. X-linked genes in humans follow the same pattern of inheritance that Morgan observed for the eye-color locus he studied in *Drosophila* (see Figure 12.4). Fathers pass X-linked alleles to all of their daughters but to none of their sons. In contrast, mothers can pass X-linked alleles to both sons and daughters, as shown in **Figure 12.7** for the inheritance of a mild X-linked disorder, color blindness.

If an X-linked trait is due to a recessive allele, a female will express the phenotype only if she is homozygous for that allele. Because males have only one locus, the terms *homozygous* and *heterozygous* are meaningless when describing their X-linked genes; the term *hemizygous* is used in such cases. Any male receiving the recessive allele from his mother will express the trait. For this reason, far more males than females have X-linked recessive disorders. However, even though the chance of a female inheriting a double dose of the mutant allele is much less than the probability of a male inheriting a single dose, there *are* females with X-linked disorders. For instance, color blindness is almost always inherited as an X-linked trait. A color-blind daughter may be born to a color-blind father whose mate is a carrier (see Figure 12.7c). Because the X-linked allele for color blindness is relatively rare, however, the probability that such a man and woman will mate is low.

A number of human X-linked disorders are much more serious than color blindness. An example is **Duchenne muscular dystrophy**, which affects about one out of every 3,500 males

▲ **Figure 12.6 The mammalian X-Y chromosomal system of sex determination.** In mammals, the sex of an offspring depends on whether the sperm cell contains an X chromosome or a Y. Numerals indicate the number of autosomes.

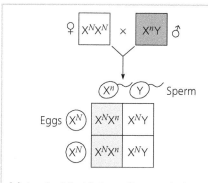

**(a)** A color-blind father will transmit the mutant allele to all daughters but to no sons. When the mother is a dominant homozygote, the daughters will have the normal phenotype but will be carriers of the mutation.

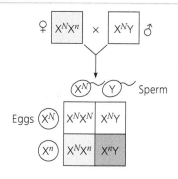

**(b)** If a carrier mates with a male who has normal color vision, there is a 50% chance that each daughter will be a carrier like her mother and a 50% chance that each son will have the disorder.

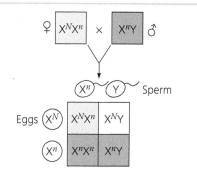

**(c)** If a carrier mates with a color-blind male, there is a 50% chance that each child born to them will have the disorder, regardless of sex. Daughters who have normal color vision will be carriers, whereas males who have normal color vision will be free of the recessive allele.

▲ **Figure 12.7 The transmission of X-linked recessive traits.** In this diagram, color blindness is used as an example. The superscript $N$ represents the dominant allele for normal color vision carried on the X chromosome, and the superscript $n$ represents the recessive allele, which has a mutation causing color blindness. White boxes indicate unaffected individuals, light orange boxes indicate carriers, and dark orange boxes indicate color-blind individuals.

**?** *If a color-blind woman married a man who had normal color vision, what would be the probable phenotypes of their children?*

born in the United States. The disease is characterized by a progressive weakening of the muscles and loss of coordination. Affected individuals rarely live past their early 20s. Researchers have traced the disorder to the absence of a key muscle protein called dystrophin and have mapped the gene for this protein to a specific locus on the X chromosome.

**Hemophilia** is an X-linked recessive disorder defined by the absence of one or more of the proteins required for blood clotting. When a person with hemophilia is injured, bleeding is prolonged because a firm clot is slow to form. Small cuts in the skin are usually not a problem, but bleeding in the muscles or joints can be painful and can lead to serious damage. In the 1800s, hemophilia was widespread among the royal families of Europe. Queen Victoria of England is known to have passed the allele to several of her descendants. Subsequent intermarriage with royal family members of other nations, such as Spain and Russia, further spread this X-linked trait, and its incidence is well documented in royal pedigrees. Today, people with hemophilia are treated as needed with intravenous injections of the protein that is missing.

## X Inactivation in Female Mammals

Female mammals, including humans, inherit two X chromosomes—twice the number inherited by males—so you may wonder if females make twice as much of the proteins encoded by X-linked genes. In fact, most of one X chromosome in each cell in female mammals becomes inactivated during early embryonic development. As a result, the cells of females and males have the same effective dose (one copy) of most X-linked genes. The inactive X in each cell of a female condenses into a compact object called a

**Barr body** (discovered by Canadian anatomist Murray Barr), which lies along the inside of the nuclear envelope. Most of the genes of the X chromosome that forms the Barr body are not expressed. In the ovaries, Barr-body chromosomes are reactivated in the cells that give rise to eggs, so every female gamete has an active X.

British geneticist Mary Lyon demonstrated that the selection of which X chromosome will form the Barr body occurs randomly and independently in each embryonic cell present at the time of X inactivation. As a consequence, females consist of a *mosaic* of two types of cells: those with the active X derived from the father and those with the active X derived from the mother. After an X chromosome is inactivated in a particular cell, all mitotic descendants of that cell have the same inactive X. Thus, if a female is heterozygous for a sex-linked trait, about half her cells will express one allele, while the others will express the alternate allele. **Figure 12.8** shows how this mosaicism results in the mottled coloration of a tortoiseshell cat. In humans, mosaicism can be observed in a recessive X-linked mutation that prevents the development of sweat glands. A woman who is heterozygous for this trait has patches of normal skin and patches of skin lacking sweat glands.

Inactivation of an X chromosome involves modification of the DNA and the histone proteins bound to it, including attachment of methyl groups ($-CH_3$) to one of the nitrogenous bases of DNA nucleotides. A particular region of each X chromosome contains several genes involved in the inactivation process. The two regions, one on each X chromosome, associate briefly with each other in each cell at an early stage of embryonic development. Then one of the genes, called *XIST* (for <u>X</u>-<u>i</u>nactive <u>s</u>pecific <u>t</u>ranscript), becomes active *only* on the

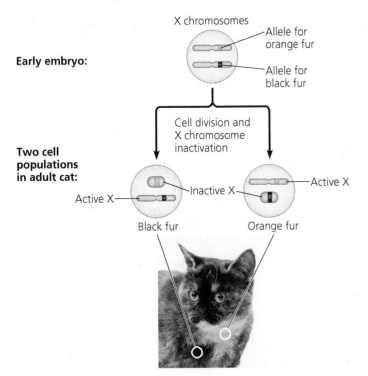

Early embryo:

X chromosomes — Allele for orange fur

Allele for black fur

Cell division and X chromosome inactivation

Two cell populations in adult cat:

Active X — Inactive X

Active X

Black fur    Orange fur

▲ **Figure 12.8 X inactivation and the tortoiseshell cat.** The tortoiseshell gene is on the X chromosome, and the tortoiseshell phenotype requires the presence of two different alleles, one for orange fur and one for black fur. Normally, only females can have both alleles, because only they have two X chromosomes. If a female cat is heterozygous for the tortoiseshell gene, she is tortoiseshell. Orange patches are formed by populations of cells in which the X chromosome with the orange allele is active; black patches have cells in which the X chromosome with the black allele is active. ("Calico" cats also have white areas, which are determined by yet another gene.)

chromosome that will become the Barr body. Multiple copies of the RNA product of this gene apparently attach to the X chromosome on which they are made, eventually almost covering it. Interaction of this RNA with the chromosome seems to initiate X inactivation, and the RNA products of other genes nearby on the X chromosome help to regulate the process.

**CONCEPT CHECK 12.2**

1. A white-eyed *Drosophila* female is mated with a red-eyed (wild-type) male, the reciprocal of the cross shown in Figure 12.4. What phenotypes and genotypes do you predict for the offspring?

2. Neither Tim nor Rhoda has Duchenne muscular dystrophy, but their firstborn son does have it. What is the probability that a second child of this couple will have the disease? What is the probability if the second child is a boy? A girl?

3. **MAKE CONNECTIONS** Consider what you learned about dominant and recessive alleles in Concept 11.1. If a disorder were caused by a dominant X-linked allele, how would the inheritance pattern differ from what we see for recessive X-linked disorders?

For suggested answers, see Appendix A.

# Linked genes tend to be inherited together because they are located near each other on the same chromosome

The number of genes in a cell is far greater than the number of chromosomes; in fact, each chromosome has hundreds or thousands of genes. (The small Y chromosome is an exception.) Genes located near each other on the same chromosome tend to be inherited together in genetic crosses; such genes are said to be genetically linked and are called **linked genes**. (Note the distinction between the terms *sex-linked gene*, referring to a single gene on a sex chromosome, and *linked genes*, referring to two or more genes on the same chromosome that tend to be inherited together.) When geneticists follow linked genes in breeding experiments, the results deviate from those expected from Mendel's law of independent assortment.

## How Linkage Affects Inheritance

To see how linkage between genes affects the inheritance of two different characters, let's examine another of Morgan's *Drosophila* experiments. In this case, the characters are body color and wing size, each with two different phenotypes. Wild-type flies have gray bodies and normal-sized wings. In addition to these flies, Morgan had managed to obtain, through breeding, doubly mutant flies with black bodies and wings much smaller than normal, called vestigial wings. The mutant alleles are recessive to the wild-type alleles, and neither gene is on a sex chromosome. In his investigation of these two genes, Morgan carried out the crosses shown in **Figure 12.9**. The first was a P generation cross to generate $F_1$ dihybrid flies, and the second was a testcross.

The resulting flies had a much higher proportion of the combinations of traits seen in the P generation flies (called parental phenotypes) than would be expected if the two genes assorted independently. Morgan thus concluded that body color and wing size are usually inherited together in specific (parental) combinations because the genes for these characters are near each other on the same chromosome:

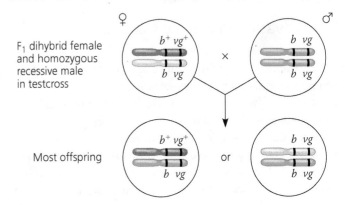

$F_1$ dihybrid female and homozygous recessive male in testcross

Most offspring

## How does linkage between two genes affect inheritance of characters?

**Experiment** Morgan wanted to know whether the genes for body color and wing size are genetically linked, and if so, how this affects their inheritance. The alleles for body color are $b^+$ (gray) and $b$ (black), and those for wing size are $vg^+$ (normal) and $vg$ (vestigial).

Morgan mated true-breeding P (parental) generation flies—wild-type flies with black, vestigial-winged flies—to produce heterozygous $F_1$ dihybrids ($b^+ b\ vg^+ vg$), all of which are wild-type in appearance.

He then mated wild-type $F_1$ dihybrid females with homozygous recessive males. This testcross will reveal the genotype of the eggs made by the dihybrid female.

The male's sperm contributes only recessive alleles, so the phenotype of the offspring reflects the genotype of the female's eggs.

Note: Although only females (with pointed abdomens) are shown, half the offspring in each class would be males (with rounded abdomens).

**P Generation** (homozygous)

Wild type (gray body, normal wings)
$b^+ b^+ vg^+ vg^+$

×

Double mutant (black body, vestigial wings)
$b\ b\ vg\ vg$

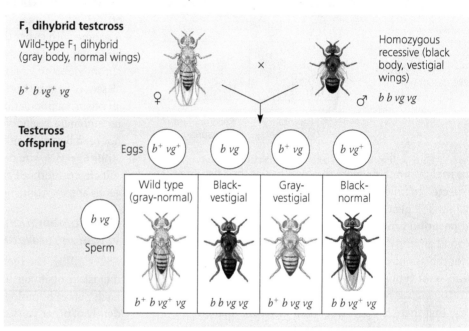

**$F_1$ dihybrid testcross**

Wild-type $F_1$ dihybrid (gray body, normal wings)
$b^+ b\ vg^+ vg$  ♀

×

Homozygous recessive (black body, vestigial wings)  ♂
$b\ b\ vg\ vg$

**Testcross offspring**

Eggs: $b^+ vg^+$ | $b\ vg$ | $b^+ vg$ | $b\ vg^+$

Sperm: $b\ vg$

| | Wild type (gray-normal) | Black-vestigial | Gray-vestigial | Black-normal |
|---|---|---|---|---|
| | $b^+ b\ vg^+ vg$ | $b\ b\ vg\ vg$ | $b^+ b\ vg\ vg$ | $b\ b\ vg^+ vg$ |

**PREDICTED RATIOS**

If genes are located on different chromosomes: 1 : 1 : 1 : 1

If genes are located on the same chromosome *and* parental alleles are always inherited together: 1 : 1 : 0 : 0

**Results** 965 : 944 : 206 : 185

**Conclusion** Since most offspring had a parental (P generation) phenotype, Morgan concluded that the genes for body color and wing size are genetically linked on the same chromosome. However, the production of a relatively small number of offspring with nonparental phenotypes indicated that some mechanism occasionally breaks the linkage between specific alleles of genes on the same chromosome.

**Source** T. H. Morgan and C. J. Lynch, The linkage of two factors in *Drosophila* that are not sex-linked, *Biological Bulletin* 23:174–182 (1912).

**WHAT IF?** *If the parental (P generation) flies had been true-breeding for gray body with vestigial wings and true-breeding for black body with normal wings, which phenotypic class(es) would be largest among the testcross offspring?*

However, as Figure 12.9 shows, both of the combinations of traits not seen in the P generation (called nonparental phenotypes) were also produced in Morgan's experiments, suggesting that the body-color and wing-size alleles are not always linked genetically. To understand this conclusion, we need to further explore **genetic recombination**, the production of offspring with combinations of traits that differ from those found in either P generation parent.

## Genetic Recombination and Linkage

Meiosis and random fertilization generate genetic variation among offspring of sexually reproducing organisms due to independent assortment of chromosomes and crossing over in meiosis I, and the possibility of any sperm fertilizing any egg. Here we'll examine the chromosomal basis of recombination in relation to the genetic findings of Mendel and Morgan.

## Recombination of Unlinked Genes: Independent Assortment of Chromosomes

Mendel learned from crosses in which he followed two characters that some offspring have combinations of traits that do not match those of either parent. For example, we can represent the cross between a pea plant with yellow-round seeds that is heterozygous for both seed color and seed shape (a dihybrid, *YyRr*) and a plant with green-wrinkled seeds (homozygous for both recessive alleles, *yyrr*) by the following Punnett square:

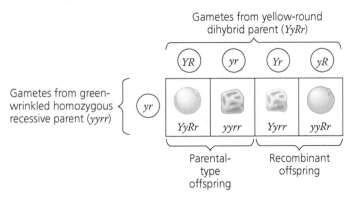

Notice in this Punnett square that one-half of the offspring are expected to inherit a phenotype that matches either of the parental (P generation) phenotypes. These offspring are called **parental types**. But two nonparental phenotypes are also found among the offspring. Because these offspring have new combinations of seed shape and color, they are called **recombinant types**, or **recombinants** for short. When 50% of all offspring are recombinants, as in this example, geneticists say that there is a 50% frequency of recombination. The predicted phenotypic ratios among the offspring are similar to what Mendel actually found in *YyRr* × *yyrr* crosses (a type of testcross because it reveals the genotype of the gametes made by the dihybrid *YyRr* plant).

A 50% frequency of recombination in such testcrosses is observed for any two genes that are located on different chromosomes and thus unlinked. The physical basis of recombination between unlinked genes is the random orientation of homologous chromosomes at metaphase I of meiosis, which leads to the independent assortment of the two unlinked genes (see the question in the Figure 12.2 legend).

## Recombination of Linked Genes: Crossing Over

Now let's return to Morgan's fly room to see how we can explain the results of the *Drosophila* testcross illustrated in Figure 12.9. Recall that most of the offspring from the testcross for body color and wing size had parental phenotypes. That suggested that the two genes were on the same chromosome, since the occurrence of parental types with a frequency greater than 50% indicates that the genes are linked. About 17% of offspring, however, were recombinants.

Faced with these results, Morgan proposed that some process must occasionally break the physical connection between specific genes on the same chromosome. Subsequent experiments demonstrated that this process, now called **crossing over**, accounts for the recombination of linked genes. In crossing over, which occurs while replicated homologous chromosomes are paired during prophase of meiosis I, a set of proteins orchestrates an exchange of corresponding segments of one maternal and one paternal chromatid. In effect, end portions of two nonsister chromatids trade places each time a crossover occurs.

**Figure 12.10** shows how crossing over in a dihybrid female fly resulted in recombinant eggs and ultimately recombinant offspring in Morgan's testcross. Most of the eggs had a chromosome with either the $b^+ vg^+$ or $b\, vg$ parental genotype for body color and wing size, but some eggs had a recombinant chromosome ($b^+ vg$ or $b\, vg^+$). Fertilization of these various classes of eggs by homozygous recessive sperm ($b\, vg$) produced an offspring population in which 17% exhibited a nonparental, recombinant phenotype, reflecting combinations of alleles not seen before in either P generation parent. In the **Scientific Skills Exercise**, you can use a statistical test to analyze the results from another $F_1$ dihybrid testcross to see whether the two genes are assorting independently or are linked.

## New Combinations of Alleles: Variation for Natural Selection

**EVOLUTION** The physical behavior of chromosomes during meiosis contributes to the generation of variation in offspring. Each pair of homologous chromosomes lines up independently of other pairs during metaphase I, and crossing over prior to that, during prophase I, can mix and match parts of maternal and paternal homologs. Mendel's elegant experiments show that the behavior of the abstract entities known as genes—or, more concretely, alleles of genes—also leads to variation in offspring (see Chapter 11). Now, putting these different ideas together, you can see that the recombinant chromosomes resulting from crossing over may bring alleles together in new combinations, and the subsequent events of meiosis distribute to gametes the recombinant chromosomes in a multitude of combinations, such as the new variants seen in Figures 12.9 and 12.10. Random fertilization then increases even further the number of variant allele combinations that can be created.

This abundance of genetic variation provides the raw material on which natural selection works. If the traits conferred by particular combinations of alleles are better suited for a given environment, organisms possessing those genotypes will be expected to thrive and leave more offspring, ensuring the continuation of their genetic complement. In the next generation, of course, the alleles will be shuffled anew. Ultimately, the interplay between environment and genotype will determine which genetic combinations persist over time.

▶ **Figure 12.10 Chromosomal basis for recombination of linked genes.** In these diagrams re-creating the testcross in Figure 12.9, we track chromosomes as well as genes. The maternal chromosomes are color-coded red and pink to distinguish one homolog from the other before any meiotic crossing over has taken place. Because crossing over between the $b^+/b$ and $vg^+/vg$ loci occurs in some, but not all, egg-producing cells, more eggs with parental-type chromosomes than with recombinant ones are produced in the mating females. Fertilization of the eggs by sperm of genotype $b\ vg$ gives rise to some recombinant offspring. The recombination frequency is the percentage of recombinant flies in the total pool of offspring.

**DRAW IT** *Suppose, as in the question at the bottom of Figure 12.9, the parental (P generation) flies were true-breeding for gray body with vestigial wings and black body with normal wings. Draw the chromosomes in each of the four possible kinds of eggs from an F₁ female, and label each chromosome as "parental" or "recombinant."*

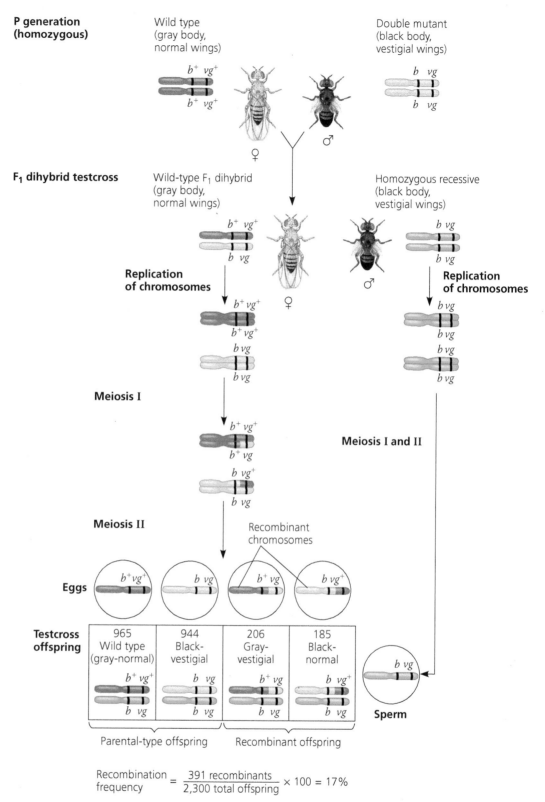

$$\text{Recombination frequency} = \frac{391\ \text{recombinants}}{2{,}300\ \text{total offspring}} \times 100 = 17\%$$

## Mapping the Distance Between Genes Using Recombination Data: *Scientific Inquiry*

The discovery of linked genes and recombination due to crossing over led one of Morgan's students, Alfred H. Sturtevant, to a method for constructing a **genetic map**, an ordered list of the genetic loci along a particular chromosome.

Sturtevant hypothesized that the percentage of recombinant offspring, the *recombination frequency*, calculated from experiments like that in Figures 12.9 and 12.10, depends on the distance between genes on a chromosome. He assumed that crossing over is a random event, with the chance of crossing over approximately equal at all points along a chromosome.

# Using the Chi-Square ($\chi^2$) Test

**Are Two Genes Linked or Unlinked?** Genes that are in close proximity on the same chromosome will result in the linked alleles being inherited together more often than not. But how can you tell if certain alleles are inherited together due to linkage or whether they just happen to assort together? In this exercise, you will use a simple statistical test, the chi-square ($\chi^2$) test, to analyze phenotypes of $F_1$ testcross progeny to see whether two genes are linked or unlinked.

**How These Experiments Are Done** If genes are unlinked and therefore assort independently, the phenotypic ratio of offspring from an $F_1$ testcross is expected to be 1:1:1:1 (see Figure 12.9). If the two genes are linked, however, the observed phenotypic ratio of the offspring will not match the expected ratio. Given random fluctuations in the data, how much must the observed numbers deviate from the expected numbers for us to conclude that the genes are not assorting independently but may instead be linked? To answer this question, scientists use a statistical test called a chi-square ($\chi^2$) test. This test compares an observed data set to an expected data set predicted by a hypothesis (here, that the genes are unlinked) and measures the discrepancy between the two, thus determining the "goodness of fit." If the discrepancy between the observed and expected data sets is so large that it is unlikely to have occurred by random fluctuation, we say there is statistically significant evidence against the hypothesis (or, more specifically, evidence for the genes being linked). If the discrepancy is small, then our observations are well explained by random variation alone. In this case, we say the observed data are consistent with our hypothesis, or that the discrepancy is statistically insignificant. Note, however, that consistency with our hypothesis is not the same as proof of our hypothesis. Also, the size of the experimental data set is important: With small data sets like this one, even if the genes are linked, discrepancies might be small by chance alone if the linkage is weak. (For simplicity, we overlook the effect of sample size here.)

**Data from the Simulated Experiment** In cosmos plants, purple stem ($A$) is dominant to green stem ($a$), and short petals ($B$) is dominant to long petals ($b$). In a simulated cross, $AABB$ plants were crossed with $aabb$ plants to generate $F_1$ dihybrids ($AaBb$), which were then test crossed ($AaBb \times aabb$). 900 offspring plants were scored for stem color and flower petal length.

| Offspring from testcross of $AaBb$ ($F_1$) × $aabb$ | Purple stem/ short petals ($A$–$B$–) | Green stem/ short petals ($aaB$–) | Purple stem/ long petals ($A$–$bb$) | Green stem/ long petals ($aabb$) |
|---|---|---|---|---|
| Expected ratio if the genes are unlinked | 1 | 1 | 1 | 1 |
| Expected number of offspring (of 900) | | | | |
| Observed number of offspring (of 900) | 220 | 210 | 231 | 239 |

**Interpret the Data**

1. The results in the data table are from a simulated $F_1$ dihybrid testcross. The hypothesis that the two genes are unlinked predicts the offspring phenotypic ratio will be 1:1:1:1. Using this ratio, calculate the expected number of each phenotype out of the 900 total offspring, and enter the values in the data table.

2. The goodness of fit is measured by $\chi^2$. This statistic measures the amounts by which the observed values differ from their respective predictions to indicate how closely the two sets of values match. The formula for calculating this value is

$$\chi^2 = \Sigma \frac{(o - e)^2}{e}$$

where $o$ = observed and $e$ = expected. Calculate the $\chi^2$ value for the data using the table below. Enter the data into the table, and carry out the operations indicated in the top row. Then add up the entries in the last column to find the $\chi^2$ value.

| Testcross offspring | Expected ($e$) | Observed ($o$) | Deviation ($o - e$) | $(o - e)^2$ | $(o - e)^2/e$ |
|---|---|---|---|---|---|
| Purple stem/ short petals ($A$–$B$–) | | 220 | | | |
| Green stem/ short petals ($aaB$–) | | 210 | | | |
| Purple stem/ long petals ($A$–$bb$) | | 231 | | | |
| Green stem/ long petals ($aabb$) | | 239 | | | |
| | | | | $\chi^2$ = Sum | |

3. The $\chi^2$ value means nothing on its own—it is used to find the probability that, assuming the hypothesis is true, the observed data set could have resulted from random fluctuations. A low probability suggests the observed data is not consistent with the hypothesis, and thus the hypothesis should be rejected. A standard cut-off point biologists use is a probability of 0.05 (5%). If the probability corresponding to the $\chi^2$ value is 0.05 or less, the differences between observed and expected values are considered statistically significant and the hypothesis (that the genes are unlinked) should be rejected. If the probability is above 0.05, the results are not statistically significant; the observed data is consistent with the hypothesis. To find the probability, locate your $\chi^2$ value in the $\chi^2$ Distribution Table in Appendix F. The "degrees of freedom" (df) of your data set is the number of categories (here, 4 phenotypes) minus 1, so df = 3. (a) Determine which values on the df = 3 line of the table your calculated $\chi^2$ value lies between. (b) The column headings for these values show the probability range for your $\chi^2$ number. Based on whether there are nonsignificant ($p > 0.05$) or significant ($p \le 0.05$) differences between the observed and expected values, are the data consistent with the hypothesis that the two genes are unlinked and assorting independently, or is there enough evidence to reject this hypothesis?

(MB) A version of this Scientific Skills Exercise can be assigned in MasteringBiology.

Based on these assumptions, Sturtevant predicted that *the farther apart two genes are, the higher the probability that a crossover will occur between them and therefore the higher the recombination frequency*. His reasoning was simple: The greater the distance between two genes, the more points there are between them where crossing over can occur. Using recombination data from various fruit fly crosses, Sturtevant proceeded to assign relative positions to genes on the same chromosomes—that is, to *map* genes to their locations on the chromosomes.

## Constructing a Linkage Map

**Application**  A linkage map shows the relative locations of genes along a chromosome.

**Technique**  A linkage map is based on the assumption that the probability of a crossover between two genetic loci is proportional to the distance separating the loci. The recombination frequencies used to construct a linkage map for a particular chromosome are obtained from experimental crosses, such as the cross depicted in Figures 12.9 and 12.10. The distances between genes are expressed as map units, with one map unit equivalent to a 1% recombination frequency. Genes are arranged on the chromosome in the order that best fits the data.

**Results**  In this example, the observed recombination frequencies between three *Drosophila* gene pairs (*b–cn* 9%, *cn–vg* 9.5%, and *b–vg* 17%) best fit a linear order in which *cn* is positioned about halfway between the other two genes:

The *b–vg* recombination frequency (17%) is slightly less than the sum of the *b–cn* and *cn–vg* frequencies (9 + 9.5 = 18.5%) because of the few times that one crossover occurs between *b* and *cn* and another crossover occurs between *cn* and *vg*. The second crossover would "cancel out" the first, reducing the observed *b–vg* recombination frequency while contributing to the frequency between each of the closer pairs of genes. The value of 18.5% (18.5 map units) is closer to the actual distance between the genes, so a geneticist would add the smaller distances in constructing a map.

A genetic map based on recombination frequencies is called a **linkage map**. **Figure 12.11** shows Sturtevant's linkage map of three genes: the body-color (*b*) and wing-size (*vg*) genes depicted in Figure 12.10 and a third gene, called cinnabar (*cn*). Cinnabar is one of many *Drosophila* genes affecting eye color. Cinnabar eyes, a mutant phenotype, are a brighter red than the wild-type color. The recombination frequency between *cn* and *b* is 9%; that between *cn* and *vg*, 9.5%; and that between *b* and *vg*, 17%. In other words, crossovers between *cn* and *b* and between *cn* and *vg* are about half as frequent as crossovers between *b* and *vg*. Only a map that locates *cn* about midway between *b* and *vg* is consistent with these data, as you can prove to yourself by drawing alternative maps. Sturtevant expressed the distances between genes in **map units**, defining one map unit as equivalent to a 1% recombination frequency.

In practice, the interpretation of recombination data is more complicated than this example suggests. Some genes on a chromosome are so far from each other that a crossover between them is virtually certain. The observed frequency of recombination in crosses involving two such genes can have a maximum value of 50%, a result indistinguishable from that for genes on different chromosomes. In this case, the physical connection between genes on the same chromosome is not reflected in the results of genetic crosses. Despite being on the same chromosome and thus being *physically connected*, the genes are *genetically unlinked*; alleles of such genes assort independently, as if they were on different chromosomes. In fact, at least two of the genes for pea characters that Mendel studied are now known to be on the same chromosome, but the distance between them is so great that linkage is not observed in genetic crosses. Consequently, the two genes behaved as if they were on different chromosomes in Mendel's experiments. Genes located far apart on a chromosome are mapped by adding the recombination frequencies from crosses involving closer pairs of genes lying between the two distant genes.

Using recombination data, Sturtevant and his colleagues were able to map numerous *Drosophila* genes in linear arrays. They found that the genes clustered into four groups of linked genes (*linkage groups*). Light microscopy had revealed four pairs of chromosomes in *Drosophila*, so the linkage map provided additional evidence that genes are located on chromosomes. Each chromosome has a linear array of specific genes, each gene with its own locus (**Figure 12.12**).

▲ **Figure 12.12  A partial genetic (linkage) map of a *Drosophila* chromosome.** This simplified map shows just a few of the many genes that have been mapped on *Drosophila* chromosome II. The number at each gene locus indicates the number of map units between that locus and the locus for arista length (left). Notice that more than one gene can affect a given phenotypic characteristic, such as eye color. Also, note that in contrast to the homologous autosomes (II–IV), the X and Y sex chromosomes (I) have distinct shapes.

Because a linkage map is based strictly on recombination frequencies, it gives only an approximate picture of a chromosome. The frequency of crossing over is not actually uniform over the length of a chromosome, as Sturtevant assumed, and therefore map units do not correspond to actual physical distances (in nanometers, for instance). A linkage map does portray the order of genes along a chromosome, but it does not accurately portray the precise locations of those genes. Other methods enable geneticists to construct **cytogenetic maps** of chromosomes, which locate genes with respect to chromosomal features, such as stained bands, that can be seen in the microscope. The ultimate maps display the physical distances between gene loci in DNA nucleotides. Comparing a linkage map with such a physical map or with a cytogenetic map of the same chromosome, we find that the linear order of genes is identical in all the maps, but the spacing between genes is not.

**CONCEPT CHECK 12.3**

1. When two genes are located on the same chromosome, what is the physical basis for the production of recombinant offspring in a testcross between a dihybrid parent and a double-mutant (recessive) parent?

2. For each type of offspring of the testcross in Figure 12.9, explain the relationship between its phenotype and the alleles contributed by the female parent. (It will be useful to draw out the chromosomes of each fly and follow the alleles throughout the cross.)

3. **WHAT IF?** Genes $A$, $B$, and $C$ are located on the same chromosome. Testcrosses show that the recombination frequency between $A$ and $B$ is 28% and between $A$ and $C$ is 12%. Can you determine the linear order of these genes? Explain.

For suggested answers, see Appendix A.

**CONCEPT** 12.4

# Alterations of chromosome number or structure cause some genetic disorders

As you have learned so far in this chapter, the phenotype of an organism can be affected by small-scale changes involving individual genes. Random mutations are the source of all new alleles, which can lead to new phenotypic traits.

Large-scale chromosomal changes can also affect an organism's phenotype. Physical and chemical disturbances, as well as errors during meiosis, can damage chromosomes in major ways or alter their number in a cell. Large-scale chromosomal alterations in humans and other mammals often lead to spontaneous abortion (miscarriage) of a fetus, and individuals born with these types of genetic defects commonly exhibit various developmental disorders. Plants may tolerate such genetic defects better than animals do.

## Abnormal Chromosome Number

Ideally, the meiotic spindle distributes chromosomes to daughter cells without error. But there is an occasional mishap, called a **nondisjunction**, in which the members of a pair of homologous chromosomes do not move apart properly during meiosis I or sister chromatids fail to separate during meiosis II (**Figure 12.13**). In these cases, one gamete receives two of the same type of chromosome and another gamete receives no copy. The other chromosomes are usually distributed normally.

If either of the aberrant gametes unites with a normal one at fertilization, the zygote will also have an abnormal number of a particular chromosome, a condition known as **aneuploidy**. (Aneuploidy may involve more than one chromosome.) Fertilization involving a gamete that has no copy of a particular chromosome will lead to a missing chromosome in the zygote (so that the cell has $2n - 1$ chromosomes); the aneuploid zygote is said to be **monosomic** for that chromosome. If a chromosome is present in triplicate in the zygote (so that the cell has $2n + 1$ chromosomes), the aneuploid cell is **trisomic** for that chromosome. Mitosis will subsequently transmit the anomaly to all embryonic cells. If the organism survives, it usually has a set of traits caused by the abnormal dose of the genes associated with the extra or missing chromosome. Down syndrome is an example of trisomy in humans that will be discussed shortly. Nondisjunction can also

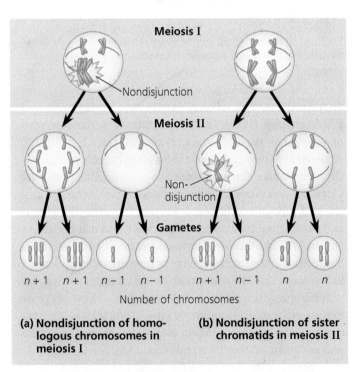

▲ **Figure 12.13 Meiotic nondisjunction.** Gametes with an abnormal chromosome number can arise by nondisjunction in either meiosis I or meiosis II. For simplicity, the figure does not show the spores formed by meiosis in plants. Ultimately, spores form gametes that have the defects shown.

occur during mitosis. If such an error takes place early in embryonic development, then the aneuploid condition is passed along by mitosis to a large number of cells and is likely to have a substantial effect on the organism.

Some organisms have more than two complete chromosome sets in all somatic cells. The general term for this chromosomal alteration is **polyploidy**; the specific terms *triploidy* (3*n*) and *tetraploidy* (4*n*) indicate three or four chromosomal sets, respectively. One way a triploid cell may arise is by the fertilization of an abnormal diploid egg produced by nondisjunction of all its chromosomes. Tetraploidy could result from the failure of a 2*n* zygote to divide after replicating its chromosomes. Subsequent normal mitotic divisions would then produce a 4*n* embryo.

Polyploidy is fairly common in plants; the spontaneous origin of polyploid individuals plays an important role in the evolution of plants. Many of the plant species we eat are polyploid; for example, bananas are triploid, wheat is hexaploid (6*n*), and strawberries are octoploid (8*n*).

## Alterations of Chromosome Structure

Errors in meiosis or damaging agents such as radiation can cause breakage of a chromosome, which can lead to four types of changes in chromosome structure **(Figure 12.14)**. A **deletion** occurs when a chromosomal fragment is lost. The affected chromosome is then missing certain genes. The "deleted" fragment may become attached as an extra segment to a sister chromatid, producing a **duplication**. Alternatively, a detached fragment could attach to a nonsister chromatid of a homologous chromosome. In that case, though, the "duplicated" segments might not be identical because the homologs could carry different alleles of certain genes. A chromosomal fragment may also reattach to the original chromosome but in the reverse orientation, producing an **inversion**. A fourth possible result of chromosomal breakage is for the fragment to join a nonhomologous chromosome, a rearrangement called a **translocation**.

Deletions and duplications are especially likely to occur during meiosis. In crossing over, nonsister chromatids sometimes exchange unequal-sized segments of DNA, so that one partner gives up more genes than it receives. The products of such an unequal crossover are one chromosome with a deletion and one chromosome with a duplication.

A diploid embryo that is homozygous for a large deletion (or has a single X chromosome with a large deletion, in a male) is usually missing a number of essential genes, a condition that is ordinarily lethal. Duplications and translocations also tend to be harmful. In reciprocal translocations, in which segments are exchanged between nonhomologous chromosomes, and in inversions, the balance of genes is not abnormal—all genes are present in their normal doses. Nevertheless, translocations and inversions can alter phenotype because a gene's expression can be influenced by its location among neighboring genes; such events sometimes have devastating effects.

▼ **Figure 12.14 Alterations of chromosome structure.** Red arrows indicate breakage points. Dark purple highlights the chromosomal parts affected by the rearrangements.

**(a) Deletion**

A **deletion** removes a chromosomal segment.

**(b) Duplication**

A **duplication** repeats a segment.

**(c) Inversion**

An **inversion** reverses a segment within a chromosome.

**(d) Translocation**

A **translocation** moves a segment from one chromosome to a nonhomologous chromosome. In a reciprocal translocation, the most common type, nonhomologous chromosomes exchange fragments.

Less often, a nonreciprocal translocation occurs: A chromosome transfers a fragment but receives none in return (not shown).

## Human Disorders Due to Chromosomal Alterations

Alterations of chromosome number and structure are associated with a number of serious human disorders. As described earlier, nondisjunction in meiosis results in aneuploidy in gametes and subsequently in any resulting zygotes. Although the frequency of aneuploid zygotes may be quite high in humans, most of these chromosomal alterations are so disastrous to development that the affected embryos are spontaneously aborted long before birth. However, some types of aneuploidy appear to upset the genetic balance less than others, with the result that individuals with certain aneuploid conditions can survive to birth and beyond. These individuals have a set of traits—a *syndrome*—characteristic of the type of aneuploidy. Genetic disorders caused by aneuploidy can be diagnosed before birth by genetic testing of the fetus.

### Down Syndrome (Trisomy 21) ~Translocation~

One aneuploid condition, **Down syndrome**, affects approximately one out of every 700 children born in the United States (**Figure 12.15**). Down syndrome is usually the result of an extra chromosome 21, so that each body cell has a total of 47 chromosomes. Because the cells are trisomic for chromosome 21, Down syndrome is often called *trisomy 21*. Down syndrome includes characteristic facial features, short stature, correctable heart defects, and developmental delays. Individuals with Down syndrome have an increased chance of developing leukemia and Alzheimer's disease but have a lower rate of high blood pressure, atherosclerosis (hardening of the arteries), stroke, and many types of solid tumors. Although people with Down syndrome, on average, have a life span shorter than normal, most, with proper medical treatment, live to middle age and beyond. Many live independently or at home with their families, are employed, and are valuable contributors to their communities. Almost all males and about half of females with Down syndrome are sexually underdeveloped and sterile.

The frequency of Down syndrome increases with the age of the mother. While the disorder occurs in just 0.04% of children born to women under age 30, the risk climbs to 0.92% for mothers at age 40 and is even higher for older mothers. The correlation of Down syndrome with maternal age has not yet been explained. Most cases result from nondisjunction during meiosis I, and some research points to an age-dependent abnormality in meiosis. Due to its low risk and its potential for providing useful information, prenatal screening for trisomies in the embryo is now offered to all pregnant women. Passed in 2008, the Prenatally and Postnatally Diagnosed Conditions

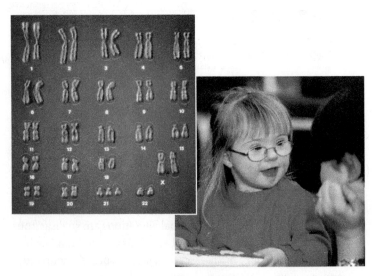

▲ **Figure 12.15 Down syndrome.** The karyotype shows trisomy 21, the most common cause of Down syndrome. The child exhibits the facial features characteristic of this disorder.

Awareness Act stipulates that medical practitioners give accurate, up-to-date information about any prenatal or postnatal diagnosis received by parents and that they connect parents with appropriate support services.

### Aneuploidy of Sex Chromosomes

Aneuploid conditions involving sex chromosomes appear to upset the genetic balance less than those involving autosomes. This may be because the Y chromosome carries relatively few genes. Also, extra copies of the X chromosome simply become inactivated as Barr bodies in somatic cells.

An extra X chromosome in a male, producing XXY, occurs approximately once in every 500 to 1,000 live male births. People with this disorder, called *Klinefelter syndrome*, have male sex organs, but the testes are abnormally small and the man is sterile. Even though the extra X is inactivated, some breast enlargement and other female body characteristics are common. Affected individuals may have subnormal intelligence. About one of every 1,000 males is born with an extra Y chromosome (XYY). These males undergo normal sexual development and do not exhibit any well-defined syndrome.

Females with trisomy X (XXX), which occurs once in approximately 1,000 live female births, are healthy and have no unusual physical features other than being slightly taller than average. Triple-X females are at risk for learning disabilities but are fertile. Monosomy X, called *Turner syndrome*, occurs about once in every 2,500 female births and is the only known viable monosomy in humans. Although these X0 individuals are phenotypically female, they are sterile because their sex organs do not mature. When provided with estrogen replacement therapy, girls with Turner syndrome do develop secondary sex characteristics. Most have normal intelligence.

### Disorders Caused by Structurally Altered Chromosomes

Many deletions in human chromosomes, even in a heterozygous state, cause severe problems. One such syndrome, known as *cri du chat* ("cry of the cat"), results from a specific deletion in chromosome 5. A child born with this deletion is severely intellectually disabled, has a small head with unusual facial features, and has a cry that sounds like the mewing of a distressed cat. Such individuals usually die in infancy or early childhood.

Chromosomal translocations have been implicated in certain cancers, including *chronic myelogenous leukemia* (CML). This disease occurs when a reciprocal translocation happens during mitosis of cells that will become white blood cells. In these cells, the exchange of a large portion of chromosome 22 with a small fragment from a tip of chromosome 9 produces a much shortened, easily recognized chromosome 22, called the *Philadelphia chromosome* (**Figure 12.16**). Such an exchange causes cancer by activating a gene that leads to uncontrolled cell cycle progression.

Normal chromosome 9

Normal chromosome 22

Reciprocal translocation

Translocated chromosome 9

Translocated chromosome 22
(Philadelphia chromosome)

▲ **Figure 12.16 Translocation associated with chronic myelogenous leukemia (CML).** The cancerous cells in nearly all CML patients contain an abnormally short chromosome 22, the so-called Philadelphia chromosome, and an abnormally long chromosome 9. These altered chromosomes result from the reciprocal translocation shown here, which presumably occurred in a single white blood cell precursor undergoing mitosis and was then passed along to all descendant cells.

**CONCEPT CHECK 12.4**

1. About 5% of individuals with Down syndrome have a chromosomal translocation in which a third copy of chromosome 21 is attached to chromosome 14. If this translocation occurred in a parent's gonad, how could it lead to Down syndrome in a child?
2. **WHAT IF?** The ABO blood type locus has been mapped on chromosome 9. A father who has type AB blood and a mother who has type O blood have a child with trisomy 9 and type A blood. Using this information, can you tell in which parent the nondisjunction occurred? Explain your answer.
3. **MAKE CONNECTIONS** The gene that is activated on the Philadelphia chromosome codes for an intracellular kinase. Review the discussion of cell cycle control and cancer in Concept 9.3, and explain how the activation of this gene could contribute to the development of cancer.
4. Women born with an extra X chromosome (XXX) are generally healthy and indistinguishable in appearance from normal XX women. What is a likely explanation for this finding? How could you test this explanation?

*For suggested answers, see Appendix A.*

# 12 Chapter Review

## SUMMARY OF KEY CONCEPTS

### CONCEPT 12.1

**Mendelian inheritance has its physical basis in the behavior of chromosomes (pp. 234–237)**

- The **chromosome theory of inheritance** states that genes are located on chromosomes and that the behavior of chromosomes during meiosis accounts for Mendel's laws of segregation and independent assortment.
- Morgan's discovery that transmission of the X chromosome in *Drosophila* correlates with inheritance of an eye-color trait was the first solid evidence indicating that a specific gene is associated with a specific chromosome.

? *What characteristic of the sex chromosomes allowed Morgan to correlate their behavior with that of the alleles of the eye-color gene?*

### CONCEPT 12.2

**Sex-linked genes exhibit unique patterns of inheritance (pp. 237–240)**

- Sex is often chromosomally based. Humans and other mammals have an X-Y system in which sex is determined by whether a Y chromosome is present.
- The sex chromosomes carry **sex-linked genes**, virtually all of which are on the X chromosome (X-linked). Any male who inherits a recessive X-linked allele (from his mother) will express the trait, such as color blindness.
- In mammalian females, one of the two X chromosomes in each cell is randomly inactivated during early embryonic development, becoming highly condensed into a **Barr body**.

? *Why are males affected much more often than females by X-linked disorders?*

### CONCEPT 12.3

**Linked genes tend to be inherited together because they are located near each other on the same chromosome (pp. 240–246)**

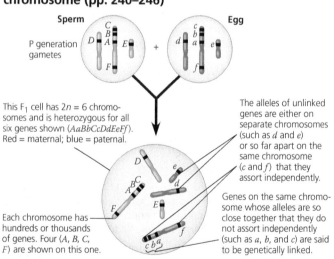

Sperm          Egg

P generation gametes

This F$_1$ cell has 2n = 6 chromosomes and is heterozygous for all six genes shown (*AaBbCcDdEeFf*). Red = maternal; blue = paternal.

Each chromosome has hundreds or thousands of genes. Four (*A, B, C, F*) are shown on this one.

The alleles of unlinked genes are either on separate chromosomes (such as *d* and *e*) or so far apart on the same chromosome (*c* and *f*) that they assort independently.

Genes on the same chromosome whose alleles are so close together that they do not assort independently (such as *a, b,* and *c*) are said to be genetically linked.

- An F$_1$ testcross yields **parental types** with the same combination of traits as those in the P generation parents and **recombinant types** with new combinations of traits. Unlinked genes exhibit a 50% frequency of recombination in the gametes. For genetically **linked genes**, **crossing over** accounts for the observed recombinants, always less than 50%.
- Recombination frequencies observed in genetic crosses allow construction of a **linkage map** (a type of **genetic map**).

? *Why are specific alleles of two genes that are farther apart more likely to show recombination than those of two closer genes?*

**CONCEPT** 12.4

## Alterations of chromosome number or structure cause some genetic disorders (pp. 246–249)

- **Aneuploidy**, an abnormal chromosome number, results from **nondisjunction** during meiosis. When a normal gamete unites with one containing two copies or no copies of a particular chromosome, the resulting zygote and its descendant cells either have one extra copy of that chromosome (**trisomy**, $2n + 1$) or are missing a copy (**monosomy**, $2n - 1$). **Polyploidy** (extra sets of chromosomes) can result from complete nondisjunction.
- Chromosome breakage can result in alterations of chromosome structure: **deletions**, **duplications**, **inversions**, and **translocations**.

**?** *Why are inversions and reciprocal translocations less likely to be lethal than are aneuploidy, duplications, and deletions?*

## TEST YOUR UNDERSTANDING

### Level 1: Knowledge/Comprehension

1. A man with hemophilia (a recessive, sex-linked condition) has a normal daughter, who marries a normal man. What is the probability that a daughter will be a hemophiliac? A son? If the couple has four sons, that all will be affected?

2. Pseudohypertrophic muscular dystrophy is an inherited disorder that causes gradual deterioration of the muscles. It is seen almost exclusively in boys born to apparently normal parents and usually results in death in the early teens. Is this disorder caused by a dominant or a recessive allele? Is its inheritance sex-linked or autosomal? How do you know? Explain why this disorder is almost never seen in girls.

3. A space probe discovers a planet inhabited by creatures that reproduce with the same hereditary patterns seen in humans. Three phenotypic characters are height ($T$ = tall, $t$ = dwarf), head appendages ($A$ = antennae, $a$ = no antennae), and nose morphology ($S$ = upturned snout, $s$ = downturned snout). Since the creatures are not "intelligent," Earth scientists are able to do some controlled breeding experiments using various heterozygotes in testcrosses. For tall heterozygotes with antennae, the offspring are tall-antennae, 46; dwarf-antennae, 7; dwarf–no antennae, 42; tall–no antennae, 5. For heterozygotes with antennae and an upturned snout, the offspring are antennae–upturned snout, 47; antennae–downturned snout, 2; no antennae–downturned snout, 48; no antennae–upturned snout, 3. Calculate the recombination frequencies for both experiments.

### Level 2: Application/Analysis

4. Using the information from problem 3, scientists do a further testcross using a heterozygote for height and nose morphology. The offspring are tall–upturned snout, 40; dwarf–upturned snout, 9; dwarf–downturned snout, 42; tall–downturned snout, 9. Calculate the recombination frequency from these data; then use your answer from problem 3 to determine the correct sequence of the three linked genes.

5. A man with red-green color blindness (a recessive, sex-linked condition) marries a woman with normal vision whose father was color-blind. What is the probability that they will have a color-blind daughter? That their first son will be color-blind? (Note the different wording in the two questions.)

6. You design *Drosophila* crosses to provide recombination data for gene *a*, which is located on the chromosome shown in Figure 12.12. Gene *a* has recombination frequencies of 14% with the vestigial-wing locus and 26% with the brown-eye locus. Approximately where is gene *a* located along the chromosome?

7. A wild-type fruit fly (heterozygous for gray body color and red eyes) is mated with a black fruit fly with purple eyes. The offspring are wild-type, 721; black-purple, 751; gray-purple, 49; black-red, 45. What is the recombination frequency between these genes for body color and eye color? Using information from Figure 12.9, what fruit flies (genotypes and phenotypes) would you mate to determine the sequence of the body-color, wing-size, and eye-color genes on the chromosome?

8. Assume that genes *A* and *B* are 50 map units apart on the same chromosome. An animal heterozygous at both loci is crossed with one that is homozygous recessive at both loci. What percentage of the offspring will show recombinant phenotypes? Without knowing that these genes are on the same chromosome, how would you interpret the results of this cross?

9. Two genes of a flower, one controlling blue (*B*) versus white (*b*) petals and the other controlling round (*R*) versus oval (*r*) stamens, are linked and are 10 map units apart. You cross a homozygous blue-oval plant with a homozygous white-round plant. The resulting $F_1$ progeny are crossed with homozygous white-oval plants, and 1,000 $F_2$ progeny are obtained. How many $F_2$ plants of each of the four phenotypes do you expect?

### Level 3: Synthesis/Evaluation

10. **SCIENTIFIC INQUIRY**
Butterflies have an X-Y sex determination system that is different from that of flies or humans. Female butterflies may be either XY or XO, while butterflies with two or more X chromosomes are males. This photograph shows a tiger swallowtail *gynandromorph*, an individual that is half male (left side) and half female (right side). Given that the first division of the zygote divides the embryo into the future right and left halves of the butterfly, propose a hypothesis that explains how nondisjunction during the first mitosis might have produced this unusual-looking butterfly.

11. **FOCUS ON EVOLUTION**
Crossing over, or recombination, is thought to be evolutionarily advantageous because it continually shuffles genetic alleles into novel combinations. Until recently, it was thought that Y-linked genes might degenerate because they have no homologous genes on the X chromosome with which to recombine. However, when the Y chromosome was sequenced, eight large regions were found to be internally homologous to each other, and quite a few of the 78 genes represent duplicates. How might this be beneficial?

12. **FOCUS ON INFORMATION**
The continuity of life is based on heritable information in the form of DNA. In a short essay (100–150 words), relate the structure and behavior of chromosomes to inheritance in both asexually and sexually reproducing species.

*For selected answers, see Appendix A.*

## MasteringBiology®

**Students** Go to **MasteringBiology** for assignments, the eText, and the Study Area with practice tests, animations, and activities.

**Instructors** Go to **MasteringBiology** for automatically graded tutorials and questions that you can assign to your students, plus Instructor Resources.

# 13

# The Molecular Basis of Inheritance

▼ **Figure 13.1** How was the structure of DNA determined?

OVERVIEW

## Life's Operating Instructions

In April 1953, James Watson and Francis Crick shook the scientific world with an elegant double-helical model for the three-dimensional structure of deoxyribonucleic acid, or DNA. **Figure 13.1** shows Watson (left) and Crick admiring their DNA model, which they built from tin and wire. Over the past 60 years or so, their model has evolved from a novel proposition to an icon of modern biology. Mendel's heritable factors and Morgan's genes on chromosomes are, in fact, composed of DNA. Chemically speaking, your genetic endowment is the DNA you inherited from your parents. DNA, the substance of inheritance, is the most celebrated molecule of our time.

Of all nature's molecules, nucleic acids are unique in their ability to direct their own replication from monomers. Indeed, the resemblance of offspring to their parents has its basis in the precise replication of DNA and its transmission from one generation to the next. Hereditary information is encoded in the chemical language of DNA and reproduced in all the cells of your body. It is this DNA program that directs the development of your biochemical, anatomical, physiological, and, to some extent, behavioral traits. In this chapter, you'll discover how biologists deduced that DNA is the genetic material and how Watson and Crick worked out its structure. You'll also learn how a molecule of DNA is copied during **DNA replication** and how cells repair their DNA. Next, you'll see how DNA is packaged with proteins in a chromosome. Finally, you'll explore how an understanding of DNA-related processes has allowed scientists to directly manipulate genes for practical purposes.

CONCEPT 13.1

## DNA is the genetic material

Today, even schoolchildren have heard of DNA, and scientists routinely manipulate DNA in the laboratory, often to change the heritable traits of cells in their experiments. Early in the 20th century, however, identifying the molecules of inheritance loomed as a major challenge to biologists.

## The Search for the Genetic Material:
### *Scientific Inquiry*

Once T. H. Morgan's group showed that genes exist as parts of chromosomes (described in Chapter 12), the two chemical components of chromosomes—DNA and protein—emerged as the leading candidates for the genetic material. Until the 1940s, the case for proteins seemed stronger, especially since biochemists had identified them as a class of macromolecules with great heterogeneity and specificity of function, essential requirements for the hereditary material. Moreover, little was known about nucleic acids, whose physical and chemical properties seemed far too uniform to account for the multitude of specific inherited traits exhibited by every organism. This view gradually changed as experiments with microorganisms yielded unexpected results. As with the work of Mendel and Morgan, a key factor in determining the identity of the genetic material was the choice of appropriate experimental organisms. The role of DNA in heredity was first worked out while studying bacteria and the viruses that infect them, which are far simpler than pea plants, fruit flies, or humans. In this section, we'll trace the search for the genetic material in some detail as a case study in scientific inquiry.

### *Evidence That DNA Can Transform Bacteria*

In 1928, a British medical officer named Frederick Griffith was trying to develop a vaccine against pneumonia. He was studying *Streptococcus pneumoniae*, a bacterium that causes pneumonia in mammals. Griffith had two strains (varieties) of the bacterium, one pathogenic (disease-causing) and one nonpathogenic (harmless). He was surprised to find that when he killed the pathogenic bacteria with heat and then mixed the cell remains with living bacteria of the nonpathogenic strain, some of the living cells became pathogenic **(Figure 13.2)**. Furthermore, this newly acquired trait of pathogenicity was inherited by all the descendants of the transformed bacteria. Clearly, some chemical component of the dead pathogenic cells caused this heritable change, although the identity of the substance was not known. Griffith called the phenomenon **transformation**, now defined as a change in genotype and phenotype due to the assimilation of external DNA by a cell. Later work by Oswald Avery and others identified the transforming substance as DNA.

Scientists remained skeptical, however, many viewing proteins as better candidates for the genetic material. Moreover, many biologists were not convinced that the genes of bacteria would be similar in composition and function to those of more complex organisms. But the major reason for the continued doubt was that so little was known about DNA.

### *Evidence That Viral DNA Can Program Cells*

Additional evidence for DNA as the genetic material came from studies of viruses that infect bacteria. These viruses are called **bacteriophages** (meaning "bacteria-eaters"), or **phages**

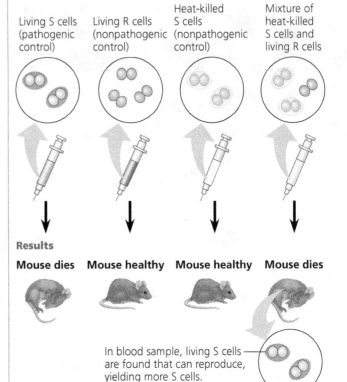

▼ **Figure 13.2** **Inquiry**

### Can a genetic trait be transferred between different bacterial strains?

**Experiment** Frederick Griffith studied two strains of the bacterium *Streptococcus pneumoniae*. Bacteria of the S (smooth) strain can cause pneumonia in mice; they are pathogenic because they have an outer capsule that protects them from an animal's immune system. Bacteria of the R (rough) strain lack a capsule and are nonpathogenic. To test for the trait of pathogenicity, Griffith injected mice with the two strains:

Living S cells (pathogenic control) — Living R cells (nonpathogenic control) — Heat-killed S cells (nonpathogenic control) — Mixture of heat-killed S cells and living R cells

**Results**

Mouse dies — Mouse healthy — Mouse healthy — Mouse dies

In blood sample, living S cells are found that can reproduce, yielding more S cells.

**Conclusion** Griffith concluded that the living R bacteria had been transformed into pathogenic S bacteria by an unknown, heritable substance from the dead S cells that allowed the R cells to make capsules.

**Source** F. Griffith, The significance of pneumococcal types, *Journal of Hygiene* 27:113–159 (1928).

**WHAT IF?** How did this experiment rule out the possibility that the R cells could have simply used the capsules of the dead S cells to become pathogenic?

for short. Viruses are much simpler than cells. A **virus** is little more than DNA (or sometimes RNA) enclosed by a protective coat, which is often simply protein **(Figure 13.3)**. To produce more viruses, a virus must infect a cell and take over the cell's metabolic machinery.

Phages have been widely used as tools by researchers in molecular genetics. In 1952, Alfred Hershey and Martha Chase performed experiments showing that DNA is the genetic material of a phage known as T2. This is one of many phages that

**▶ Figure 13.3 Viruses infecting a bacterial cell.** Phages called T2 attach to the host cell and inject their genetic material through the plasma membrane while the head and tail parts remain on the outer bacterial surface (colorized TEM).

Labels: Phage head, Tail sheath, Tail fiber, DNA, Bacterial cell, 100 nm

infect *Escherichia coli* (*E. coli*), a bacterium that normally lives in the intestines of mammals and is a model organism for molecular biologists. At that time, biologists already knew that T2, like many other phages, was composed almost entirely of DNA and protein. They also knew that the T2 phage could quickly turn an *E. coli* cell into a T2-producing factory that released many copies when the cell ruptured. Somehow, T2 could reprogram its host cell to produce viruses. But which viral component—protein or DNA—was responsible?

Hershey and Chase answered this question by devising an experiment showing that only one of the two components of T2 actually enters the *E. coli* cell during infection (**Figure 13.4**).

---

**▼ Figure 13.4** Inquiry

## Is protein or DNA the genetic material of phage T2?

**Experiment** Alfred Hershey and Martha Chase used radioactive sulfur and phosphorus to trace the fates of protein and DNA, respectively, of T2 phages that infected bacterial cells. They wanted to see which of these molecules entered the cells and could reprogram them to make more phages.

**1** Mixed radioactively labeled phages with bacteria. The phages infected the bacterial cells.

**2** Agitated the mixture in a blender to free phage parts outside the bacteria from the cells.

**3** Centrifuged the mixture so that bacteria formed a pellet at the bottom of the test tube; free phages and phage parts, which are lighter, remained suspended in the liquid.

**4** Measured the radioactivity in the pellet and the liquid.

**Batch 1:** Phages were grown with radioactive sulfur (³⁵S), which was incorporated into phage protein (pink).

**Batch 2:** Phages were grown with radioactive phosphorus (³²P), which was incorporated into phage DNA (blue).

Labels: Phage, Bacterial cell, Radioactive protein, DNA, Empty protein shell, Phage DNA, Centrifuge, Pellet (bacterial cells and contents), Radioactivity (phage protein) found in liquid, Radioactive DNA, Pellet, Radioactivity (phage DNA) found in pellet

**Results** When proteins were labeled (batch 1), radioactivity remained outside the cells; but when DNA was labeled (batch 2), radioactivity was found inside the cells. Bacterial cells with radioactive phage DNA released new phages with some radioactive phosphorus.

**Conclusion** Phage DNA entered bacterial cells, but phage proteins did not. Hershey and Chase concluded that DNA, not protein, functions as the genetic material of phage T2.

**Source** A. D. Hershey and M. Chase, Independent functions of viral protein and nucleic acid in growth of bacteriophage, *Journal of General Physiology* 36:39–56 (1952).

**WHAT IF?** *How would the results have differed if proteins carried the genetic information?*

In their experiment, they used a radioactive isotope of sulfur to tag protein in one batch of T2 and a radioactive isotope of phosphorus to tag DNA in a second batch. Because protein, but not DNA, contains sulfur, radioactive sulfur atoms were incorporated only into the protein of the phage. In a similar way, the atoms of radioactive phosphorus labeled only the DNA, not the protein, because nearly all the phage's phosphorus is in its DNA. In the experiment, separate samples of nonradioactive *E. coli* cells were allowed to be infected by the protein-labeled and DNA-labeled batches of T2. The researchers then tested the two samples shortly after the onset of infection to see which type of molecule—protein or DNA—had entered the bacterial cells and would therefore have been capable of reprogramming them.

Hershey and Chase found that the phage DNA entered the host cells but the phage protein did not. Moreover, when these bacteria were returned to a culture medium, the infection ran its course, and the *E. coli* released phages that contained some radioactive phosphorus, further showing that the DNA inside the cell played an ongoing role during the infection process.

Hershey and Chase concluded that the DNA injected by the phage must be the molecule carrying the genetic information that makes the cells produce new viral DNA and proteins. The Hershey-Chase experiment was a landmark study because it provided powerful evidence that nucleic acids, rather than proteins, are the hereditary material, at least for viruses.

### Additional Evidence That DNA Is the Genetic Material

Further evidence that DNA is the genetic material came from the laboratory of biochemist Erwin Chargaff. It was already known that DNA is a polymer of nucleotides, each consisting of three components: a nitrogenous (nitrogen-containing) base, a pentose sugar called deoxyribose, and a phosphate group (Figure 13.5). The base can be adenine (A), thymine (T), guanine (G), or cytosine (C). Chargaff analyzed the base composition of DNA from a number of different organisms. In 1950, he reported that the base composition of DNA varies from one species to another. For example, 32.8% of sea urchin DNA nucleotides have the base A, whereas only 24.7% of the DNA nucleotides from the bacterium *E. coli* have an A. This evidence of molecular diversity among species, which had been presumed absent from DNA, made DNA a more credible candidate for the genetic material.

Chargaff also noticed a peculiar regularity in the ratios of nucleotide bases. In the DNA of each species he studied, the number of adenines approximately equaled the number of thymines, and the number of guanines approximately equaled the number of cytosines. In sea urchin DNA, for example, the four bases are present in these percentages: A = 32.8% and T = 32.1%; G = 17.7% and C = 17.3%.

These two findings became known as *Chargaff's rules*: (1) the base composition varies between species, and

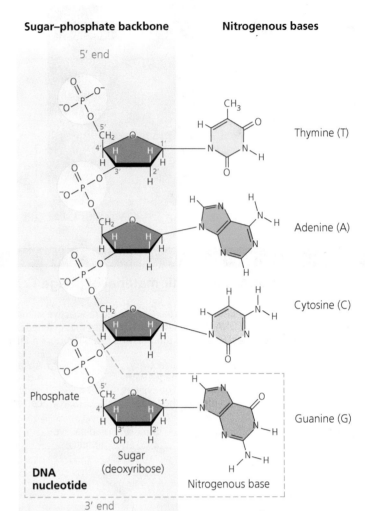

**Sugar–phosphate backbone**     **Nitrogenous bases**

5′ end

Thymine (T)

Adenine (A)

Cytosine (C)

Guanine (G)

Phosphate

**DNA nucleotide**

Sugar (deoxyribose)

Nitrogenous base

3′ end

▲ **Figure 13.5 The structure of a DNA strand.** Each DNA nucleotide monomer consists of a nitrogenous base (T, A, C, or G), the sugar deoxyribose (blue), and a phosphate group (yellow). The phosphate group of one nucleotide is attached to the sugar of the next, forming a "backbone" of alternating phosphates and sugars from which the bases project. The polynucleotide strand has directionality, from the 5′ end (with the phosphate group) to the 3′ end (with the —OH group of the sugar). 5′ and 3′ refer to the numbers assigned to the carbons in the sugar ring.

(2) within a species, the number of A and T bases are roughly equal and the number of G and C bases are roughly equal. In the **Scientific Skills Exercise**, you can use Chargaff's rules to predict unknown percentages of nucleotide bases. The rationale for these rules remained unexplained until the discovery of the double helical structure of DNA.

### Building a Structural Model of DNA: *Scientific Inquiry*

Once most biologists were convinced that DNA was the genetic material, the challenge was to determine how the structure of DNA could account for its role in inheritance. By the early 1950s, the arrangement of covalent bonds in a single nucleic acid polymer was well established (see Figure 13.5), and researchers focused on discovering the three-dimensional

# Working with Data in a Table

**Given the Percentage Composition of One Nucleotide in a Genome, Can We Predict the Percentages of the Other Three Nucleotides?** Even before the structure of DNA was elucidated, Erwin Chargaff and his coworkers noticed a pattern in the base composition of nucleotides from different organisms: the number of adenine (A) bases roughly equaled the number of thymine (T) bases, and the number of cytosine (C) bases roughly equaled the number of guanine (G) bases. Further, each species they studied had a different distribution of A/T and C/G bases. We now know that these consistent ratios are due to complementary base pairing between A and T and between C and G in the DNA double helix, and interspecies differences are due to the unique sequences of bases along a DNA strand. In this exercise, you will apply Chargaff's rules to predict the composition of nucleotide bases in a genome.

**How the Experiments Were Done** In Chargaff's experiments, DNA was extracted from the given organism, denatured, and hydrolyzed to break apart the individual nucleotides before analyzing them chemically. These experiments provided approximate values for each type of nucleotide. Today, the availability of whole-genome sequencing has allowed base composition analysis to be done more precisely directly from the sequence data.

**Data from the Experiments** Tables are useful for organizing sets of data representing a common set of values (here percentages of A, G, C, and T) for a number of different samples (in this case, species). You can apply the patterns that you see in the known data to predict unknown values. In the table in the upper right, complete base distribution data are given for sea urchin DNA and salmon DNA; you will use Chargaff's rules to fill in the rest of the table with predicted values.

| Source of DNA | Adenine | Guanine | Cytosine | Thymine |
|---|---|---|---|---|
| Sea urchin | 32.8% | 17.7% | 17.3% | 32.1% |
| Salmon | 29.7 | 20.8 | 20.4 | 29.1 |
| Wheat | 28.1 | 21.8 | 22.7 | |
| *E. coli* | 24.7 | 26.0 | | |
| Human | 30.4 | | | 30.1 |
| Ox | 29.0 | | | |

**Interpret the Data**

1. Explain how the sea urchin and salmon data demonstrate both of Chargaff's rules.
2. Based on Chargaff's rules, fill in the table with your predictions of the missing percentages of bases, starting with the wheat genome and proceeding through *E. coli*, human, and ox. Show how you arrived at your answers.
3. If Chargaff's rule is valid, that the amount of A equals the amount of T and the amount of C equals the amount of G, then hypothetically we could extrapolate this to the combined DNA of all species on Earth (like one huge Earth genome). To see whether the data in the table support this hypothesis, calculate the average percentage for each base in your completed table by averaging the values in each column. Does Chargaff's equivalence rule still hold true?

**Data from** several papers by Chargaff: for example, E. Chargaff et al., Composition of the desoxypentose nucleic acids of four genera of sea-urchin, *Journal of Biological Chemistry* 195:155–160 (1952).

(MB) A version of this Scientific Skills Exercise can be assigned in MasteringBiology.

---

structure of DNA. Among the scientists working on the problem were Linus Pauling, at the California Institute of Technology, and Maurice Wilkins and Rosalind Franklin, at King's College in London. First to come up with the correct answer, however, were two scientists who were relatively unknown at the time—the American James Watson and the Englishman Francis Crick.

The brief but celebrated partnership that solved the puzzle of DNA structure began soon after Watson journeyed to Cambridge University, where Crick was studying protein structure with a technique called X-ray crystallography (see Figure 2.24). While visiting the laboratory of Maurice Wilkins, Watson saw an X-ray diffraction image of DNA produced by Wilkins's accomplished colleague Rosalind Franklin **(Figure 13.6a)**. Images produced by X-ray crystallography are not actually pictures of molecules. The spots and smudges in **Figure 13.6b** were produced by X-rays that were diffracted (deflected) as they passed through aligned fibers of purified DNA. Watson was familiar with the type of X-ray diffraction pattern that helical molecules produce, and an examination of the photo that Wilkins showed him confirmed that DNA was helical in shape. It also augmented earlier data obtained by Franklin and others suggesting the

width of the helix and the spacing of the nitrogenous bases along it. The pattern in this photo implied that the helix was made up of two strands, contrary to a three-stranded model that Linus Pauling had proposed a short time earlier. The

**(a) Rosalind Franklin**  **(b) Franklin's X-ray diffraction photograph of DNA**

▲ **Figure 13.6 Rosalind Franklin and her X-ray diffraction photo of DNA.** Franklin, a very accomplished X-ray crystallographer, conducted critical experiments resulting in the photograph that allowed Watson and Crick to deduce the double-helical structure of DNA.

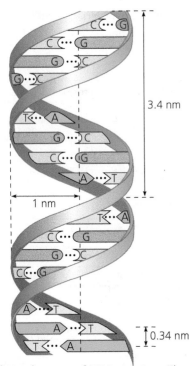

3.4 nm

1 nm

0.34 nm

**(a) Key features of DNA structure.** The "ribbons" in this diagram represent the sugar-phosphate backbones of the two DNA strands. The helix is "right-handed," curving up to the right. The two strands are held together by hydrogen bonds (dotted lines) between the nitrogenous bases, which are paired in the interior of the double helix.

5' end

Hydrogen bond

3' end

OH

3' end

OH

5' end

**(b) Partial chemical structure.** For clarity, the two DNA strands are shown untwisted in this partial chemical structure. Strong covalent bonds link the units of each strand, while weaker hydrogen bonds between the bases hold one strand to the other. Notice that the strands are antiparallel, meaning that they are oriented in opposite directions.

**(c) Space-filling model.** The tight stacking of the base pairs is clear in this computer model. Van der Waals interactions between the stacked pairs play a major role in holding the molecule together.

▲ **Figure 13.7  The double helix.**

presence of two strands accounts for the now-familiar term **double helix (Figure 13.7)**.

Watson and Crick began building models of a double helix that would conform to the X-ray measurements and what was then known about the chemistry of DNA, including Chargaff's rules. They knew that Franklin had concluded that the sugar-phosphate backbones were on the outside of the DNA molecule. This arrangement was appealing because it put the negatively charged phosphate groups facing the aqueous surroundings, while the relatively hydrophobic nitrogenous bases were hidden in the interior. Watson constructed such a model (see Figure 13.1). In this model, the two sugar-phosphate backbones are **antiparallel**—that is, their subunits run in opposite directions (see Figure 13.7b). You can imagine the overall arrangement as a rope ladder with rigid rungs. The side ropes represent the sugar-phosphate backbones, and the rungs represent pairs of nitrogenous bases. Now imagine twisting the ladder to form a helix. Franklin's X-ray data indicated that the helix makes one full turn every 3.4 nm along its length. With the bases stacked just 0.34 nm apart, there are ten "rungs" of base pairs in each full turn of the helix.

The nitrogenous bases of the double helix are paired in specific combinations: adenine (A) with thymine (T), and

guanine (G) with cytosine (C). It was mainly by trial and error that Watson and Crick arrived at this key feature of DNA. At first, Watson imagined that the bases paired like with like—for example, A with A and C with C. But this model did not fit the X-ray data, which suggested that the double helix had a uniform diameter. Why is this requirement inconsistent with like-with-like pairing of bases? Adenine and guanine are purines, nitrogenous bases with two organic rings, while cytosine and thymine are nitrogenous bases called pyrimidines, which have a single ring. Thus, purines (A and G) are about twice as wide as pyrimidines (C and T). A purine-purine pair is too wide and a pyrimidine-pyrimidine pair too narrow to account for the 2-nm diameter of the double helix. Always pairing a purine with a pyrimidine, however, results in a uniform diameter:

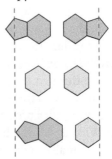

Purine + purine: too wide

Pyrimidine + pyrimidine: too narrow

Purine + pyrimidine: width consistent with X-ray data

**Adenine (A)**          **Thymine (T)**

**Guanine (G)**          **Cytosine (C)**

▲ **Figure 13.8 Base pairing in DNA.** The pairs of nitrogenous bases in a DNA double helix are held together by hydrogen bonds, shown here as black dotted lines.

Watson and Crick reasoned that there must be additional specificity of pairing dictated by the structure of the bases. Each base has chemical side groups that can form hydrogen bonds with its appropriate partner: Adenine forms two hydrogen bonds with thymine and only thymine; guanine forms three hydrogen bonds with cytosine and only cytosine. In shorthand, A pairs with T, and G pairs with C (**Figure 13.8**).

The Watson-Crick model took into account Chargaff's ratios and ultimately explained them. Wherever one strand of a DNA molecule has an A, the partner strand has a T. Similarly, a G in one strand is always paired with a C in the complementary strand. Therefore, in the DNA of any organism, the amount of adenine equals the amount of thymine, and the amount of guanine equals the amount of cytosine. Although the base-pairing rules dictate the combinations of nitrogenous bases that form the "rungs" of the double helix, they do not restrict the sequence of nucleotides *along* each DNA strand. The

linear sequence of the four bases can be varied in countless ways, and each gene has a unique order, or base sequence.

In April 1953, Watson and Crick surprised the scientific world with a succinct, one-page paper that reported their molecular model for DNA: the double helix, which has since become the symbol of molecular biology. Watson and Crick, along with Maurice Wilkins, were awarded the Nobel Prize in 1962 for this work. (Sadly, Rosalind Franklin had died at the age of 38 in 1958 and was thus ineligible for the prize.) The beauty of the double helix model was that the structure of DNA suggested the basic mechanism of its replication.

**CONCEPT CHECK 13.1**

1. Given a polynucleotide sequence such as GAATTC, can you tell which is the 5′ end? If not, what further information do you need to identify the ends? (See Figure 13.5.)

2. **WHAT IF?** Griffith did not expect transformation to occur in his experiment. What results was he expecting? Explain.

For suggested answers, see Appendix A.

**CONCEPT 13.2**

# Many proteins work together in DNA replication and repair

The relationship between structure and function is manifest in the double helix. The idea that there is specific pairing of nitrogenous bases in DNA was the flash of inspiration that led Watson and Crick to the double helix. At the same time, they saw the functional significance of the base-pairing rules. They ended their classic paper with this wry statement: "It has not escaped our notice that the specific pairing we have postulated immediately suggests a possible copying mechanism for the genetic material." In this section, you'll learn about the basic principle of DNA replication (**Figure 13.9**), as well as some important details of the process.

*[handwritten note: uracil replaces a H with CH3 at the 5' o/ in the nitrogenous base.]*

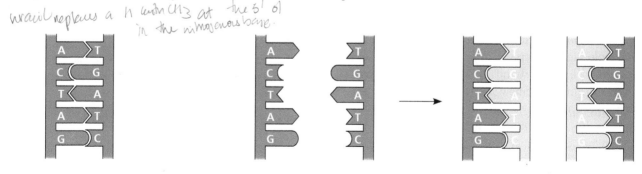

**(a)** The parental molecule (dark blue) has two complementary strands of DNA. Each base is paired by hydrogen bonding with its specific partner, A with T and G with C.

**(b)** First, the two DNA strands are separated. Each parental strand can now serve as a template for a new, complementary strand.

**(c)** Nucleotides complementary to the parental strands are connected to form the sugar-phosphate backbones of the new (light blue) strands.

▲ **Figure 13.9 A model for DNA replication: the basic concept.** In this simplified illustration, a short segment of DNA has been untwisted. Simple shapes symbolize the four kinds of bases, here represented as ladder rungs. Dark blue represents DNA strands present in the parental molecule; light blue represents newly synthesized DNA.

## The Basic Principle: Base Pairing to a Template Strand

In a second paper, Watson and Crick stated their hypothesis for how DNA replicates:

> Now our model for deoxyribonucleic acid is, in effect, a pair of templates, each of which is complementary to the other. We imagine that prior to duplication the hydrogen bonds are broken, and the two chains unwind and separate. Each chain then acts as a template for the formation onto itself of a new companion chain, so that eventually we shall have two pairs of chains, where we only had one before. Moreover, the sequence of the pairs of bases will have been duplicated exactly.*

Figure 13.9 illustrates Watson and Crick's basic idea. To make it easier to follow, only a short section of double helix is shown, in untwisted form. Notice that if you cover one of the two DNA strands of Figure 13.9a, you can still determine its linear sequence of nucleotides by referring to the uncovered strand and applying the base-pairing rules. The two strands are complementary; each stores the information necessary to reconstruct the other. When a cell copies a DNA molecule, each strand serves as a template for ordering nucleotides into a new, complementary strand. Nucleotides line up along the template strand according to the base-pairing rules and are linked to form the new strands. Where there was one double-stranded DNA molecule at the beginning of the process, there are soon two, each an exact replica of the "parental" molecule. The copying mechanism is analogous to using a photographic negative to make a positive image, which can in turn be used to make another negative, and so on.

This model of DNA replication remained untested for several years following publication of the DNA structure. The requisite experiments were simple in concept but difficult to perform. Watson and Crick's model predicts that when a double helix replicates, each of the two daughter molecules will have one old strand, from the parental molecule, and one newly made strand. This **semiconservative model** can be distinguished from a conservative model of replication, in which the two parental strands somehow come back together after the process (that is, the parental molecule is conserved). In yet a third model, called the dispersive model, all four strands of DNA following replication have a mixture of old and new DNA. These three models are shown in **Figure 13.10**. Although mechanisms for conservative or dispersive DNA replication are not easy to come up with, these models remained possibilities until they could be ruled out. After two years of preliminary work in the late 1950s, Matthew Meselson and Franklin Stahl devised a clever experiment that distinguished between the three models, described in detail in **Figure 13.11**. Their experiment supported the semiconservative model of DNA replication, as predicted by Watson and Crick,

---

*F. H. C. Crick and J. D. Watson, The complementary structure of deoxyribonucleic acid, *Proceedings of the Royal Society of London A* 223:80 (1954).

| | Parent cell | First replication | Second replication |

**(a) Conservative model.** The two parental strands reassociate after acting as templates for new strands, thus restoring the parental double helix.

**(b) Semiconservative model.** The two strands of the parental molecule separate, and each functions as a template for synthesis of a new, complementary strand.

**(c) Dispersive model.** Each strand of *both* daughter molecules contains a mixture of old and newly synthesized DNA.

▲ **Figure 13.10  Three alternative models of DNA replication.** Each short segment of double helix symbolizes the DNA within a cell. Beginning with a parent cell, we follow the DNA for two more generations of cells—two rounds of DNA replication. Newly made DNA is light blue.

and is widely acknowledged among biologists to be a classic example of elegant experimental design.

The basic principle of DNA replication is conceptually simple. However, the actual process involves some complicated biochemical gymnastics, as we will now see.

## DNA Replication: *A Closer Look*

The bacterium *E. coli* has a single chromosome of about 4.6 million nucleotide pairs. In a favorable environment, an *E. coli* cell can copy all this DNA and divide to form two genetically identical daughter cells in less than an hour. Each of *your* cells has 46 DNA molecules in its nucleus, one long double-helical molecule per chromosome. In all, that represents about 6 billion nucleotide pairs, or over a thousand times more DNA than is found in a bacterial cell. If we were to print the one-letter symbols for these bases (A, G, C, and T) the size of the

## ▼ Figure 13.11 Inquiry

### Does DNA replication follow the conservative, semiconservative, or dispersive model?

**Experiment** At the California Institute of Technology, Matthew Meselson and Franklin Stahl cultured *E. coli* for several generations in a medium containing nucleotide precursors labeled with a heavy isotope of nitrogen, $^{15}N$. They then transferred the bacteria to a medium with only $^{14}N$, a lighter isotope. A sample was taken after DNA replicated once; another sample was taken after DNA replicated again. They extracted DNA from the bacteria in the samples and then centrifuged each DNA sample to separate DNA of different densities.

① Bacteria cultured in medium with $^{15}N$ (heavy isotope)

② Bacteria transferred to medium with $^{14}N$ (lighter isotope)

**Results**

③ DNA sample centrifuged after first replication

④ DNA sample centrifuged after second replication

Less dense

More dense

**Conclusion** Meselson and Stahl compared their results with those predicted by each of the three models in Figure 13.10, as shown below. The first replication in the $^{14}N$ medium produced a band of hybrid ($^{15}N$–$^{14}N$) DNA. This result eliminated the conservative model. The second replication produced both light and hybrid DNA, a result that refuted the dispersive model and supported the semiconservative model. They therefore concluded that DNA replication is semiconservative.

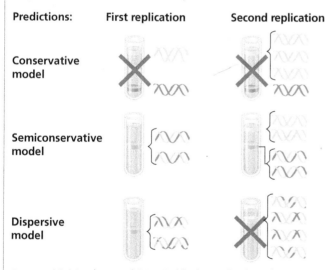

| Predictions: | First replication | Second replication |
|---|---|---|
| Conservative model | | |
| Semiconservative model | | |
| Dispersive model | | |

**Source** M. Meselson and F. W. Stahl, The replication of DNA in *Escherichia coli*, *Proceedings of the National Academy of Sciences USA* 44:671–682 (1958).

**Inquiry in Action** Read and analyze the original paper in *Inquiry in Action: Interpreting Scientific Papers*.

(MB) A related Experimental Inquiry Tutorial can be assigned in MasteringBiology.

**WHAT IF?** If Meselson and Stahl had first grown the cells in $^{14}N$-containing medium and then moved them into $^{15}N$-containing medium before taking samples, what would have been the result?

---

type you are now reading, the 6 billion nucleotide pairs of information in a diploid human cell would fill about 1,200 books as thick as this text. Yet it takes one of your cells just a few hours to copy all of this DNA. This replication of an enormous amount of genetic information is achieved with very few errors—only about one per 10 billion nucleotides. The copying of DNA is remarkable in its speed and accuracy.

More than a dozen enzymes and other proteins participate in DNA replication. Much more is known about how this "replication machine" works in bacteria (such as *E. coli*) than in eukaryotes, and we will describe the basic steps of the process for *E. coli*, except where otherwise noted. What scientists have learned about eukaryotic DNA replication suggests, however, that most of the process is fundamentally similar for prokaryotes and eukaryotes.

### Getting Started

The replication of a DNA molecule begins at particular sites called **origins of replication**, short stretches of DNA having a specific sequence of nucleotides. Proteins that initiate DNA replication recognize this sequence and attach to the DNA, separating the two strands and opening up a replication "bubble." At each end of a bubble is a **replication fork**, a Y-shaped region where the parental strands of DNA are being unwound. Several kinds of proteins participate in the unwinding (**Figure 13.12**). **Helicases** are enzymes that untwist the double helix at the replication forks, separating the two parental strands and making them available as template strands. After the parental strands separate, **single-strand binding proteins** bind to the unpaired DNA strands, keeping them from re-pairing. The untwisting of the double helix causes tighter twisting and strain ahead of the replication fork. **Topoisomerase** helps relieve this strain by breaking, swiveling, and rejoining DNA strands.

*[handwritten annotations]* covalently attached to phosphates, breaking the phosphodiester bond. The energy from the breakage in phosphotyrosine linkage making the nick...

Topoisomerase breaks, swivels, and rejoins the parental DNA ahead of the replication fork, relieving the strain caused by unwinding. *[handwritten: The strands can be nicked]*

Primase synthesizes RNA primers, using the parental DNA as a template.

*[handwritten: relative to each other, regenerate DNA helix and DNA polymerase]*

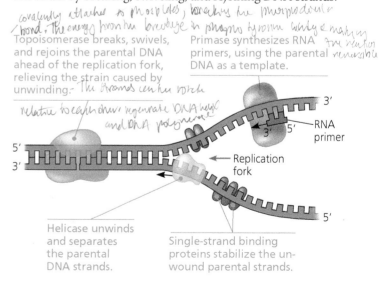

3′

RNA primer

Replication fork

5′

3′

5′

Helicase unwinds and separates the parental DNA strands.

Single-strand binding proteins stabilize the unwound parental strands.

▲ **Figure 13.12 Some of the proteins involved in the initiation of DNA replication.** The same proteins function at both replication forks in a replication bubble. For simplicity, only the left-hand fork is shown, and the DNA bases are drawn much larger in relation to the proteins than they are in reality.

The *E. coli* chromosome, like many other bacterial chromosomes, is circular and has a single origin of replication, forming one replication bubble (Figure 13.13a). Replication of DNA then proceeds in both directions until the entire molecule is copied. In contrast to a bacterial chromosome, a eukaryotic chromosome may have hundreds or even a few thousand replication origins. Multiple replication bubbles form and eventually fuse, thus speeding up the copying of the very long DNA molecules (Figure 13.13b). As in bacteria, eukaryotic DNA replication proceeds in both directions from each origin.

## Synthesizing a New DNA Strand

Within a bubble, the unwound sections of parental DNA strands are available to serve as templates for the synthesis of new complementary DNA strands. However, the enzymes that synthesize DNA cannot *initiate* the synthesis of a polynucleotide; they can only add nucleotides to the end of an already existing chain that is base-paired with the template strand. The initial nucleotide chain that is produced during DNA synthesis

is actually a short stretch of RNA, not DNA. This RNA chain is called a **primer** and is synthesized by the enzyme **primase** (see Figure 13.12). Primase starts a complementary RNA chain from a single RNA nucleotide, adding RNA nucleotides one at a time, using the parental DNA strand as a template. The completed primer, generally 5–10 nucleotides long, is thus base-paired to the template strand. The new DNA strand will start from the 3′ end of the RNA primer.

Enzymes called **DNA polymerases** catalyze the synthesis of new DNA by adding nucleotides to a preexisting chain. In *E. coli*, there are several different DNA polymerases, but two appear to play the major roles in DNA replication: DNA polymerase III and DNA polymerase I. The situation in eukaryotes is more complicated, with at least 11 different DNA polymerases discovered so far; however, the general principles are the same.

Most DNA polymerases require a primer and a DNA template strand along which complementary DNA nucleotides line up. In *E. coli*, DNA polymerase III (abbreviated DNA pol

▼ **Figure 13.13 Origins of replication in *E. coli* and eukaryotes.** The red arrows indicate the movement of the replication forks and thus the overall directions of DNA replication within each bubble.

**(a) Origin of replication in an *E. coli* cell**

In the circular chromosome of *E. coli* and many other bacteria, only one origin of replication is present. The parental strands separate at the origin, forming a replication bubble with two forks. Replication proceeds in both directions until the forks meet on the other side, resulting in two daughter DNA molecules. The TEM shows a bacterial chromosome with a replication bubble.

**(b) Origins of replication in a eukaryotic cell**

In each linear chromosome of eukaryotes, DNA replication begins when replication bubbles form at many sites along the giant DNA molecule. The bubbles expand as replication proceeds in both directions. Eventually, the bubbles fuse and synthesis of the daughter strands is complete. The TEM shows three replication bubbles along the DNA of a cultured Chinese hamster cell.

**DRAW IT** *In the TEM above, add arrows for the third bubble.*

III) adds a DNA nucleotide to the RNA primer and then continues adding DNA nucleotides, complementary to the parental DNA template strand, to the growing end of the new DNA strand. The rate of elongation is about 500 nucleotides per second in bacteria and 50 per second in human cells.

Each nucleotide to be added to a growing DNA strand consists of a sugar attached to a base and three phosphate groups. You have already encountered such a molecule—ATP (adenosine triphosphate; see Figure 5.8). The only difference between the ATP of energy metabolism and dATP, the adenine nucleotide used to make DNA, is the sugar component, which is deoxyribose in the building block of DNA but ribose in ATP. Like ATP, the nucleotides used for DNA synthesis are chemically reactive, partly because their triphosphate tails have an unstable cluster of negative charge. As each monomer joins the growing end of a DNA strand, two phosphate groups are lost as a molecule of pyrophosphate (℗—℗ᵢ). Subsequent hydrolysis of the pyrophosphate to two molecules of inorganic phosphate ℗ᵢ is a coupled exergonic reaction that helps drive the polymerization reaction (Figure 13.14).

### Antiparallel Elongation

As we have noted previously, the two ends of a DNA strand are different, giving each strand directionality, like a one-way street (see Figure 13.5). In addition, the two strands of DNA in a double helix are antiparallel, meaning that they are oriented in opposite directions to each other, like a divided highway (see Figure 13.14). Therefore, the two new strands formed during DNA replication must also end up antiparallel to their template strands.

How does the antiparallel arrangement of the double helix affect replication? Because of their structure, DNA polymerases can add nucleotides only to the free 3′ end of a primer or growing DNA strand, never to the 5′ end (see Figure 13.14). Thus, a new DNA strand can elongate only in the 5′ → 3′ direction. With this in mind, let's examine one of the two replication forks in a bubble (Figure 13.15). Along one template strand, DNA polymerase III can synthesize a complementary strand continuously by elongating the new DNA in the mandatory 5′ → 3′ direction. DNA pol III remains in the replication fork on that template strand and continuously adds nucleotides to the new complementary strand as the fork progresses. The DNA strand made by this mechanism is called the **leading strand**. Only one primer is required for DNA pol III to synthesize the leading strand.

To elongate the other new strand of DNA in the mandatory 5′ → 3′ direction, DNA pol III must work along the other

**Overview**

▲ **Figure 13.15 Synthesis of the leading strand during DNA replication.** This diagram focuses on the left replication fork shown in the overview box. DNA polymerase III (DNA pol III), shaped like a cupped hand, is shown closely associated with a protein called the "sliding clamp" that encircles the newly synthesized double helix like a doughnut. The sliding clamp moves DNA pol III along the DNA template strand.

▲ **Figure 13.14 Addition of a nucleotide to a DNA strand.** DNA polymerase catalyzes the addition of a nucleotide to the 3′ end of a growing DNA strand, with the release of two phosphates.

**?** Use this diagram to explain what we mean when we say that each DNA strand has directionality.

template strand in the direction *away from* the replication fork. The DNA strand elongating in this direction is called the **lagging strand**.* In contrast to the leading strand, which elongates continuously, the lagging strand is synthesized discontinuously, as a series of segments. These segments of the lagging strand are called **Okazaki fragments**, after the Japanese scientist who discovered them. The fragments are about 1,000–2,000 nucleotides long in *E. coli* and 100–200 nucleotides long in eukaryotes.

**Figure 13.16** illustrates the steps in the synthesis of the lagging strand at one fork. Whereas only one primer is required on the leading strand, each Okazaki fragment on the lagging strand must be primed separately (❶ and ❹). After DNA pol III forms an Okazaki fragment (❷–❹), another DNA polymerase, DNA polymerase I (DNA pol I), replaces the RNA nucleotides of the adjacent primer with DNA nucleotides (❺). But DNA pol I cannot join the final nucleotide of this replacement DNA segment to the first DNA nucleotide of the adjacent Okazaki fragment. Another enzyme, **DNA ligase**, accomplishes this task, joining the sugar-phosphate backbones of all the Okazaki fragments into a continuous DNA strand (❻).

**Figure 13.17** summarizes DNA replication. Study it carefully before proceeding.

## The DNA Replication Complex

It is traditional—and convenient—to represent DNA polymerase molecules as locomotives moving along a DNA "railroad track," but such a model is inaccurate in two important ways. First, the various proteins that participate in DNA replication actually form a single large complex, a "DNA replication machine." Many protein-protein interactions facilitate the efficiency of this complex. For example, by interacting with other proteins at the fork, primase apparently acts as a molecular brake, slowing progress of the replication fork and coordinating the placement of primers and the rates of replication on the leading and lagging strands. Second, the DNA replication complex may not move along the DNA; rather, the DNA may move through the complex during the replication process. In eukaryotic cells, multiple copies of the complex, perhaps grouped into "factories," may be anchored to the nuclear matrix, a framework of fibers extending through the interior of the nucleus. Recent studies support a model in which two DNA polymerase molecules, one on each template strand, "reel in" the parental DNA and extrude newly made daughter DNA molecules. Additional evidence suggests that the lagging strand is looped back through the complex (**Figure 13.18**).

---

*Synthesis of the leading strand and synthesis of the lagging strand occur concurrently and at the same rate. The lagging strand is so named because its synthesis is delayed slightly relative to synthesis of the leading strand; each new fragment of the lagging strand cannot be started until enough template has been exposed at the replication fork.

**Overview**

Origin of replication

Leading strand / Lagging strand

Lagging strand

Leading strand

Overall directions of replication

❶ Primase joins RNA nucleotides into a primer.

Template strand

❷ DNA pol III adds DNA nucleotides to the primer, forming Okazaki fragment 1.

RNA primer for fragment 1

❸ After reaching the next RNA primer to the right, DNA pol III detaches.

Okazaki fragment 1

RNA primer for fragment 2

Okazaki fragment 2

❹ Fragment 2 is primed. Then DNA pol III adds DNA nucleotides, detaching when it reaches the fragment 1 primer.

❺ DNA pol I replaces the RNA with DNA, adding to the 3' end of fragment 2.

❻ DNA ligase forms a bond between the newest DNA and the DNA of fragment 1.

❼ The lagging strand in this region is now complete.

Overall direction of replication

▲ **Figure 13.16 Synthesis of the lagging strand.**

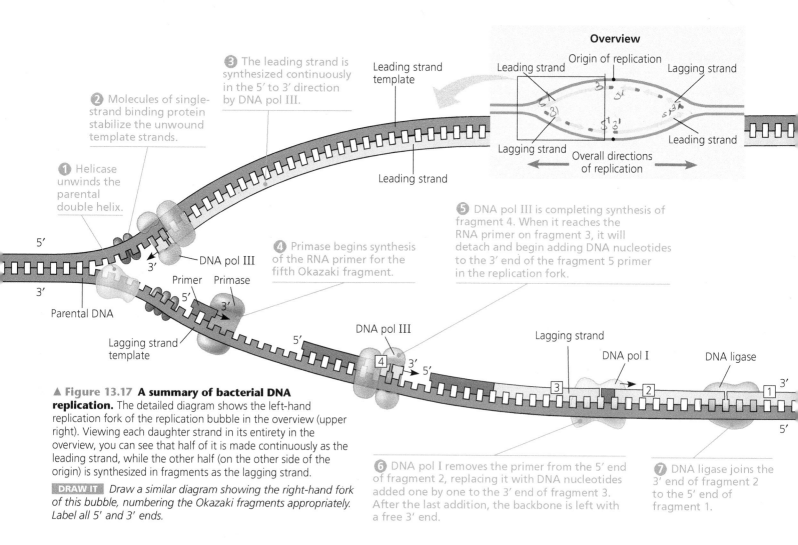

③ The leading strand is synthesized continuously in the 5′ to 3′ direction by DNA pol III.

② Molecules of single-strand binding protein stabilize the unwound template strands.

Leading strand template

**Overview**

Origin of replication

Leading strand

Lagging strand

Lagging strand

Leading strand

Overall directions of replication

① Helicase unwinds the parental double helix.

Leading strand

5′

3′

DNA pol III

3′

Parental DNA

Primer   Primase

5′

④ Primase begins synthesis of the RNA primer for the fifth Okazaki fragment.

⑤ DNA pol III is completing synthesis of fragment 4. When it reaches the RNA primer on fragment 3, it will detach and begin adding DNA nucleotides to the 3′ end of the fragment 5 primer in the replication fork.

Lagging strand template

5′

DNA pol III

3′

4

3′ 5′

Lagging strand

DNA pol I

DNA ligase

3

2

3′

1

5′

▲ **Figure 13.17 A summary of bacterial DNA replication.** The detailed diagram shows the left-hand replication fork of the replication bubble in the overview (upper right). Viewing each daughter strand in its entirety in the overview, you can see that half of it is made continuously as the leading strand, while the other half (on the other side of the origin) is synthesized in fragments as the lagging strand.

**DRAW IT** *Draw a similar diagram showing the right-hand fork of this bubble, numbering the Okazaki fragments appropriately. Label all 5′ and 3′ ends.*

⑥ DNA pol I removes the primer from the 5′ end of fragment 2, replacing it with DNA nucleotides added one by one to the 3′ end of fragment 3. After the last addition, the backbone is left with a free 3′ end.

⑦ DNA ligase joins the 3′ end of fragment 2 to the 5′ end of fragment 1.

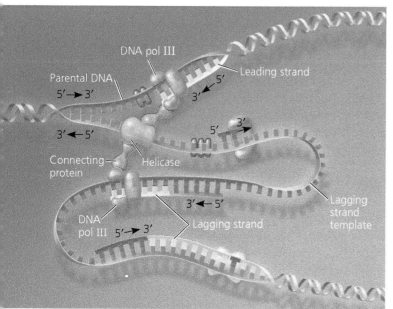

▲ **Figure 13.18 A current model of the DNA replication complex.** Two DNA polymerase III molecules work together in a complex, one on each template strand. The lagging strand template DNA loops through the complex.

 **ANIMATION**   ***BioFlix*** Visit the Study Area in **MasteringBiology** for the BioFlix ® 3-D Animation on DNA Replication.

## Proofreading and Repairing DNA

We cannot attribute the accuracy of DNA replication solely to the specificity of base pairing. Initial pairing errors between incoming nucleotides and those in the template strand occur at a rate of one in $10^5$ nucleotides. However, errors in the completed DNA molecule amount to only one in $10^{10}$ (10 billion) nucleotides, an error rate that is 100,000 times lower. This is because during DNA replication, DNA polymerases proofread each nucleotide against its template as soon as it is added to the growing strand. Upon finding an incorrectly paired nucleotide, the polymerase removes the nucleotide and then resumes synthesis. (This action is similar to fixing a typing error by deleting the wrong letter and then entering the correct letter.)

Mismatched nucleotides sometimes do evade proofreading by a DNA polymerase. In **mismatch repair**, other enzymes remove and replace incorrectly paired nucleotides resulting from replication errors. Researchers spotlighted the importance of such repair enzymes when they found that a hereditary defect in one of them is associated with a form of colon cancer. Apparently, this defect allows cancer-causing errors to accumulate in the DNA faster than normal.

Incorrectly paired or altered nucleotides can also arise after replication. In fact, maintenance of the genetic information encoded in DNA requires frequent repair of various kinds of damage to existing DNA. DNA molecules are constantly subjected to potentially harmful chemical and physical agents, such as cigarette smoke and X-rays (as we'll discuss in Chapter 14). In addition, DNA bases often undergo spontaneous chemical changes under normal cellular conditions. However, these changes in DNA are usually corrected before they become permanent changes—*mutations*—perpetuated through successive replications. Each cell continuously monitors and repairs its genetic material. Because repair of damaged DNA is so important to the survival of an organism, it is no surprise that many different DNA repair enzymes have evolved. Almost 100 are known in *E. coli*, and about 130 have been identified so far in humans.

Most cellular systems for repairing incorrectly paired nucleotides, whether they are due to DNA damage or to replication errors, use a mechanism that takes advantage of the base-paired structure of DNA. In many cases, a segment of the strand containing the damage is cut out (excised) by a DNA-cutting enzyme—a **nuclease**—and the resulting gap is then filled in with nucleotides, using the undamaged strand as a template. The enzymes involved in filling the gap are a DNA polymerase and DNA ligase. One such DNA repair system, shown in **Figure 13.19**, is called **nucleotide excision repair**.

1 Teams of enzymes detect and repair damaged DNA, such as this thymine dimer (often caused by ultraviolet radiation), which distorts the DNA molecule.

Nuclease

2 A nuclease enzyme cuts the damaged DNA strand at two points, and the damaged section is removed.

DNA polymerase

3 Repair synthesis by a DNA polymerase fills in the missing nucleotides.

DNA ligase

4 DNA ligase seals the free end of the new DNA to the old DNA, making the strand complete.

▲ **Figure 13.19 Nucleotide excision repair of DNA damage.**

An important function of the DNA repair enzymes in our skin cells is to repair genetic damage caused by the ultraviolet rays of sunlight. One example of this damage is when adjacent thymine bases on a DNA strand become covalently linked. Such *thymine dimers* cause the DNA to buckle (see Figure 13.19) and interfere with DNA replication. The importance of repairing this kind of damage is underscored by the disorder xeroderma pigmentosum, which in most cases is caused by an inherited defect in a nucleotide excision repair enzyme. Individuals with this disorder are hypersensitive to sunlight; mutations in their skin cells caused by ultraviolet light are left uncorrected, resulting in skin cancer.

## Evolutionary Significance of Altered DNA Nucleotides

**EVOLUTION** Faithful replication of the genome and repair of DNA damage are important for the functioning of the organism and for passing on a complete, accurate genome to the next generation. The error rate after proofreading and repair is extremely low, but rare mistakes do slip through. Once a mismatched nucleotide pair is replicated, the sequence change is permanent in the daughter molecule that has the incorrect nucleotide as well as in any subsequent copies. As you know, a permanent change in the DNA sequence is called a mutation.

Mutations can change the phenotype of an organism (as you'll learn in Chapter 14). And if they occur in germ cells (which give rise to gametes), mutations can be passed on from generation to generation. The vast majority of such changes are harmful, but a very small percentage can be beneficial. In either case, mutations are the source of the variation on which natural selection operates during evolution and are ultimately responsible for the appearance of new species. (You'll learn more about this process in Unit Three.) The balance between complete fidelity of DNA replication or repair and a low mutation rate has, over long periods of time, allowed the evolution of the rich diversity of species we see on Earth today.

## Replicating the Ends of DNA Molecules

For linear DNA, such as the DNA of eukaryotic chromosomes, the usual replication machinery cannot complete the 5′ ends of daughter DNA strands. (This is a consequence of the fact that a DNA polymerase can add nucleotides only to the 3′ ends.) As a result, repeated rounds of replication produce shorter and shorter DNA molecules with uneven ends.

What protects the genes near the ends of eukaryotic chromosomes from being eroded away during successive replications? Eukaryotic chromosomal DNA molecules have special nucleotide sequences called telomeres at their ends **(Figure 13.20)**. Telomeres do not contain genes; instead, the DNA typically consists of multiple repetitions of one short nucleotide sequence. In each human telomere, for example, the sequence

▲ **Figure 13.20 Telomeres.** Eukaryotes have repetitive, noncoding sequences called telomeres at the ends of their DNA. Telomeres are stained orange in these mouse chromosomes (LM).

TTAGGG is repeated 100 to 1,000 times. Telomeric DNA acts as a buffer zone that protects the organism's genes.

Telomeres do not prevent the erosion of genes near ends of chromosomes; they merely postpone it. As you would expect, telomeres tend to be shorter in cultured cells that have divided many times and in dividing somatic cells of older individuals. Shortening of telomeres is proposed to play a role in the aging process of some tissues and even of the organism as a whole.

If the chromosomes of germ cells became shorter in every cell cycle, essential genes would eventually be missing from the gametes they produce. However, this does not occur: An enzyme called **telomerase** catalyzes the lengthening of telomeres in eukaryotic germ cells, thus restoring their original length and compensating for the shortening that occurs during DNA replication. Telomerase is not active in most human somatic cells, but shows inappropriate activity in some cancer cells that may remove limits to a cell's normal life span. Thus, telomerase is under study as a target for cancer therapies.

**CONCEPT CHECK 13.2**

1. What role does base pairing play in the replication of DNA?
2. Make a table listing the functions of seven proteins involved in DNA replication in *E. coli*.
3. **MAKE CONNECTIONS** What is the relationship between DNA replication and the S phase of the cell cycle?

For suggested answers, see Appendix A.

CONCEPT 13.3

# A chromosome consists of a DNA molecule packed together with proteins

Now that you have learned about the structure and replication of DNA, let's take a step back and examine how DNA is packaged into chromosomes, the structures that carry genetic information. The main component of the genome in most bacteria is one double-stranded, circular DNA

molecule that is associated with a small amount of protein. Although we refer to this structure as a bacterial chromosome, it is very different from a eukaryotic chromosome, which consists of one linear DNA molecule associated with a large amount of protein. In *E. coli*, the chromosomal DNA consists of about 4.6 million nucleotide pairs, representing about 4,400 genes. This is 100 times more DNA than is found in a typical virus, but only about one-thousandth as much DNA as in a human somatic cell. Still, that is a lot of DNA to be packaged in such a small container.

Stretched out, the DNA of an *E. coli* cell would measure about a millimeter in length, 500 times longer than the cell. Within a bacterium, however, certain proteins cause the chromosome to coil and "supercoil," densely packing it so that it fills only part of the cell. Unlike the nucleus of a eukaryotic cell, this dense region of DNA in a bacterium, called the **nucleoid**, is not surrounded by membrane (see Figure 3.5).

Each eukaryotic chromosome contains a single linear DNA double helix that, in humans, averages about $1.5 \times 10^8$ nucleotide pairs. This is an enormous amount of DNA relative to a chromosome's condensed length. If completely stretched out, such a DNA molecule would be about 4 cm long, thousands of times the diameter of a cell nucleus—and that's not even considering the DNA of the other 45 human chromosomes!

In the cell, eukaryotic DNA is precisely combined with a large amount of protein. Together, this complex of DNA and protein, called **chromatin**, fits into the nucleus through an elaborate, multilevel system of packing.

Chromatin undergoes striking changes in its degree of packing during the course of the cell cycle. In interphase cells stained for light microscopy, the chromatin usually appears as a diffuse mass within the nucleus, suggesting that the chromatin is highly extended. As a cell prepares for mitosis, its chromatin coils and folds up (condenses), eventually forming a characteristic number of short, thick metaphase chromosomes that are distinguishable from each other with the light microscope. Our current view of the successive levels of DNA packing in a chromosome is outlined in **Figure 13.21**. Study this figure carefully before reading further.

Though interphase chromatin is generally much less condensed than the chromatin of mitotic chromosomes, it shows several of the same levels of higher-order packing. Some of the chromatin comprising a chromosome seems to be present as a 10-nm fiber, but much is compacted into a 30-nm fiber, which in some regions is further folded into looped domains. Even during interphase, the centromeres of chromosomes, as well as other chromosomal regions in some cells, exist in a highly condensed state similar to that seen in a metaphase chromosome. This type of interphase chromatin, visible as irregular clumps with a light microscope, is called **heterochromatin**, to distinguish it from the less compacted, more dispersed **euchromatin** ("true chromatin"). Because of its compaction, heterochromatic DNA is largely inaccessible to the machinery

This series of diagrams and transmission electron micrographs depicts a current model for the progressive levels of DNA coiling and folding. The illustration zooms out from a single molecule of DNA to a metaphase chromosome, which is large enough to be seen with a light microscope.

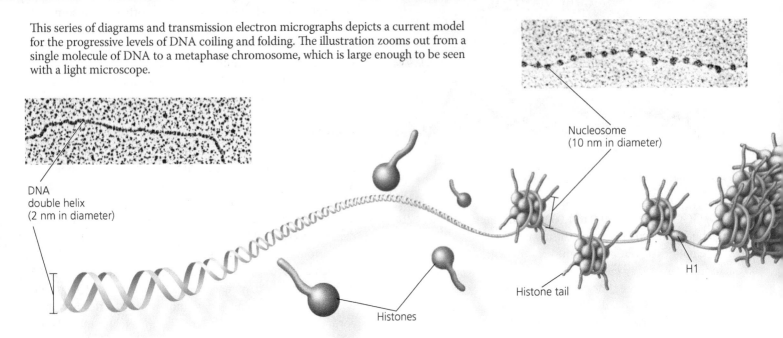

Nucleosome
(10 nm in diameter)

DNA
double helix
(2 nm in diameter)

H1

Histone tail

Histones

## DNA, the double helix

Shown here is a ribbon model of DNA, with each ribbon representing one of the sugar-phosphate backbones. As you will recall from Figure 13.7, the phosphate groups along the backbone contribute a negative charge along the outside of each strand. The TEM shows a molecule of naked DNA; the double helix alone is 2 nm across.

## Histones

Proteins called **histones** are responsible for the first level of DNA packing in chromatin. Although each histone is small—containing only about 100 amino acids—the total mass of histone in chromatin approximately equals the mass of DNA. More than a fifth of a histone's amino acids are positively charged (lysine or arginine) and therefore bind tightly to the negatively charged DNA.

Four types of histones are most common in chromatin: H2A, H2B, H3, and H4. The histones are very similar among eukaryotes; for example, all but two of the amino acids in cow H4 are identical to those in pea H4. The apparent conservation of histone genes during evolution probably reflects the important role of histones in organizing DNA within cells.

The four main types of histones are critical to the next level of DNA packing. (A fifth type of histone, called H1, is involved in a further stage of packing.)

## Nucleosomes, or "beads on a string" (10-nm fiber)

In electron micrographs, unfolded chromatin is 10 nm in diameter (the *10-nm fiber*). Such chromatin resembles beads on a string (see the TEM). Each "bead" is a **nucleosome**, the basic unit of DNA packing; the "string" between beads is called *linker DNA*.

A nucleosome consists of DNA wound twice around a protein core composed of two molecules each of the four main histone types. The amino end (N-terminus) of each histone (the *histone tail*) extends outward from the nucleosome.

In the cell cycle, the histones leave the DNA only briefly during DNA replication. Generally, they do the same during transcription, another process that requires access to the DNA by the cell's molecular machinery.

in the cell responsible for transcribing the genetic information coded in the DNA, a crucial early step in gene expression. In contrast, the looser packing of euchromatin makes its DNA accessible to this machinery, so the genes present in euchromatin can be transcribed.

The chromosome is a dynamic structure that is condensed, loosened, modified, and remodeled as necessary for various cell processes, including mitosis, meiosis, and gene activity. Certain chemical modifications of histones affect the state of

chromatin condensation and also have multiple effects on gene activity.

**CONCEPT CHECK 13.3**

1. Describe the structure of a nucleosome, the basic unit of DNA packing in eukaryotic cells.
2. What two properties, one structural and one functional, distinguish heterochromatin from euchromatin?

For suggested answers, see Appendix A.

30-nm fiber

Chromatid (700 nm)

Loops

Scaffold

300-nm fiber

Replicated chromosome (1,400 nm)

## 30-nm fiber

The next level of packing results from interactions between the histone tails of one nucleosome and the linker DNA and nucleosomes on either side. A fifth histone, H1, is involved at this level. These interactions cause the extended 10-nm fiber to coil or fold, forming a chromatin fiber roughly 30 nm in thickness, the *30-nm fiber*. Although the 30-nm fiber is quite prevalent in the interphase nucleus, the packing arrangement of nucleosomes in this form of chromatin is still a matter of some debate.

## Looped domains (300-nm fiber)

The 30-nm fiber, in turn, forms loops called *looped domains* attached to a chromosome scaffold composed of proteins, thus making up a *300-nm fiber*. The scaffold is rich in one type of topoisomerase, and H1 molecules also appear to be present.

## Metaphase chromosome

In a mitotic chromosome, the looped domains themselves coil and fold in a manner not yet fully understood, further compacting all the chromatin to produce the characteristic metaphase chromosome shown in the micrograph above. The width of one chromatid is 700 nm. Particular genes always end up located at the same places in metaphase chromosomes, indicating that the packing steps are highly specific and precise.

# Understanding DNA structure and replication makes genetic engineering possible

The discovery of the structure of DNA marked a milestone in biology and changed the course of biological research. Most notable was the realization that the two strands of a DNA molecule are complementary to each other. This fundamental structural property of DNA is the basis for **nucleic acid hybridization**, the base pairing of one strand of a nucleic acid to a complementary sequence on another strand. Nucleic acid hybridization forms the foundation of virtually every technique used in **genetic engineering**, the direct manipulation of genes for practical purposes. Genetic engineering has launched a revolution in fields ranging from agriculture to criminal law to medical and basic biological research. In this section, we'll describe several of the most important techniques and their uses.

## DNA Cloning: Making Multiple Copies of a Gene or Other DNA Segment

The molecular biologist studying a particular gene faces a challenge. Naturally occurring DNA molecules are very long, and a single molecule usually carries many genes. Moreover, in many eukaryotic genomes, genes occupy only a small proportion of the chromosomal DNA, the rest being noncoding nucleotide sequences. A single human gene, for example, might constitute only 1/100,000 of a chromosomal DNA molecule. As a further complication, the distinctions between a gene and the surrounding DNA are subtle, consisting only of differences in nucleotide sequence. To work directly with specific genes, scientists have developed methods for preparing well-defined segments of DNA in multiple identical copies, a process called *DNA cloning*.

Most methods for cloning pieces of DNA in the laboratory share certain general features. One common approach uses bacteria, most often *E. coli*. Recall from Figure 13.13 that the *E. coli* chromosome is a large circular molecule of DNA. In addition, *E. coli* and many other bacteria have **plasmids**, small circular DNA molecules that replicate separately from the bacterial chromosome. A plasmid has only a small number of genes; these genes may be useful when the bacterium is in a particular environment but may not be required for survival or reproduction under most conditions.

To clone pieces of DNA in the laboratory, researchers first obtain a plasmid (originally isolated from a bacterial cell and genetically engineered for efficient cloning) and insert DNA from another source ("foreign" DNA) into it **(Figure 13.22)**. The resulting plasmid is now **recombinant DNA**, a DNA molecule formed when segments of DNA from two different sources—often different species—are combined *in vitro* (in a test tube). The plasmid is then returned to a bacterial cell, producing a *recombinant bacterium*. This single cell reproduces through repeated cell divisions to form a clone of cells, a population of genetically identical cells. Because the dividing bacteria replicate the recombinant plasmid and pass it on to their descendants, the foreign DNA and any genes it carries are cloned at the same time. The production of multiple copies of a single gene is called **gene cloning**.

Gene cloning is useful for two basic purposes: to make many copies of, or *amplify*, a particular gene and to produce a protein product. Researchers can isolate copies of a cloned gene from bacteria for use in basic research or to endow an organism with a new metabolic trait, such as pest resistance. For example, a resistance gene present in one crop species might be cloned and transferred into plants of another species. Alternatively, a protein with medical uses, such as human growth hormone, can be harvested in large quantities from cultures of bacteria carrying the cloned gene for the protein. Since a single gene is usually a very small part of the total DNA in a cell, the ability to amplify such rare DNA fragments is therefore crucial for any application involving a single gene.

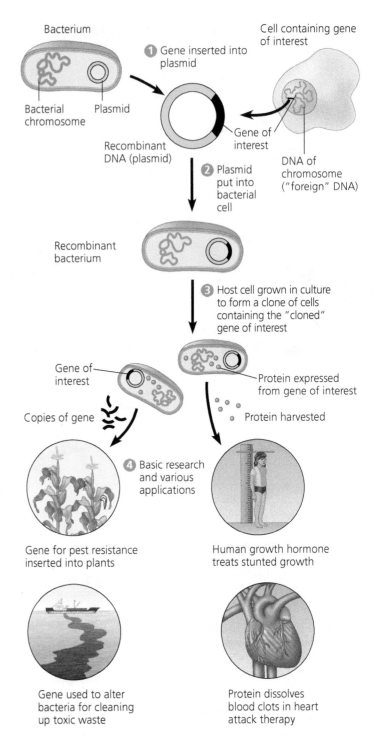

▲ **Figure 13.22 An overview of gene cloning and some uses of cloned genes.** In this simplified diagram of gene cloning, we start with a plasmid (originally isolated from a bacterial cell) and a gene of interest from another organism. Only one plasmid and one copy of the gene of interest are shown at the top of the figure, but the starting materials would include many of each.

## Using Restriction Enzymes to Make Recombinant DNA

Gene cloning and genetic engineering rely on the use of enzymes that cut DNA molecules at a limited number of specific locations. These enzymes, called restriction endonucleases, or **restriction enzymes**, were discovered in the late 1960s by biologists doing basic research on bacteria. Restriction enzymes protect the bacterial cell by cutting up foreign DNA from other organisms or phages.

Hundreds of different restriction enzymes have been identified and isolated. Each restriction enzyme is very specific, recognizing a particular short DNA sequence, or **restriction site**, and cutting both DNA strands at precise points within this restriction site. The DNA of a bacterial cell is protected from the cell's own restriction enzymes by the addition of methyl groups ($-CH_3$) to adenines or cytosines within the sequences recognized by the enzymes.

The top of **Figure 13.23** illustrates a restriction site recognized by a particular restriction enzyme from *E. coli*. As shown in this example, most restriction sites are symmetric. That is, the sequence of nucleotides is the same on both strands when read in the $5' \rightarrow 3'$ direction. The most commonly used restriction enzymes recognize sequences containing 4–8 nucleotides. Because any sequence this short usually occurs (by chance) many times in a long DNA molecule, a restriction enzyme will make many cuts in a DNA molecule, yielding a set of **restriction fragments**. All copies of a particular DNA molecule always yield the same set of restriction fragments when exposed to the same restriction enzyme. To see the fragments, researchers carry out a technique called **gel electrophoresis**, which can separate a mixture of nucleic acid fragments by length (**Figure 13.24**).

**(a)** Each sample, a mixture of DNA molecules, is placed in a separate well near one end of a thin slab of agarose gel. The gel is set into a small plastic support and immersed in an aqueous, buffered solution in a tray with electrodes at each end. The current is then turned on, causing the negatively charged DNA molecules to move toward the positive electrode.

**(b)** Shorter molecules are impeded less than longer ones, so they move faster through the gel. After the current is turned off, a DNA-binding dye is added that fluoresces pink in ultraviolet light. Each pink band corresponds to many thousands of DNA molecules of the same length. The horizontal ladder of bands at the bottom of the gel is a set of restriction fragments used as size standards.

▲ **Figure 13.24 Gel electrophoresis.** A gel made of a polymer acts as a molecular sieve to separate nucleic acids or proteins differing in size, electrical charge, or other physical properties as they move in an electric field. In the example shown here, DNA molecules are separated by length in a gel made of the polysaccharide agarose.

① Restriction enzyme cuts the sugar-phosphate backbones at each arrow.

Sticky end

② DNA fragment from another source is added. Base pairing of sticky ends produces various combinations.

Fragment from different DNA molecule cut by the same restriction enzyme

One possible combination

③ DNA ligase seals the strands.

Recombinant DNA molecule

▲ **Figure 13.23 Using a restriction enzyme and DNA ligase to make recombinant DNA.** The restriction enzyme in this example (called *Eco*RI) recognizes a specific six-base-pair sequence, the restriction site, and makes staggered cuts in the sugar-phosphate backbones within this sequence, producing fragments with sticky ends. Any fragments with complementary sticky ends can base-pair, including the two original fragments. If the fragments come from different DNA molecules, the ligated product is recombinant DNA.

**DRAW IT** *The restriction enzyme HindIII recognizes the sequence 5'-AAGCTT-3', cutting between the two A's. Draw the double-stranded sequence before and after the enzyme cuts.*

The most useful restriction enzymes cleave the sugar-phosphate backbones in the two DNA strands in a staggered manner, as indicated in Figure 13.23. The resulting double-stranded restriction fragments have at least one single-stranded end, called a **sticky end**. These short extensions can form hydrogen-bonded base pairs (hybridize) with complementary sticky ends on any other DNA molecules cut with the same enzyme. The associations formed in this way are only temporary but can be made permanent by DNA ligase. As you saw in Figure 13.16, this enzyme catalyzes the formation of covalent bonds that close up the sugar-phosphate backbones of DNA strands; for example, it joins Okazaki fragments during replication.

You can see at the bottom of Figure 13.23 that the ligase-catalyzed joining of DNA from two different sources produces a stable recombinant DNA molecule. In gene cloning, the two DNA molecules to be joined are a **cloning vector**—a DNA molecule that can carry foreign DNA into a host cell and replicate there—and the gene to be cloned (see Figure 13.22). The cloning vector is often a bacterial plasmid that has one copy of a restriction site recognized by a particular restriction enzyme, selected by the researcher and purchased from a commercial source. The most common way to obtain many copies of the gene to be cloned is described next.

## Amplifying DNA *in Vitro*: The Polymerase Chain Reaction (PCR) and Its Use in Cloning

Today, most researchers have some information about the sequence of the gene or DNA fragment they want to clone. Using this information, they can start with the entire collection of genomic DNA from the particular species of interest and obtain enough copies of the desired gene by using a technique called the **polymerase chain reaction**, or **PCR**. **Figure 13.25** illustrates the steps in PCR. Within a few hours, this technique can make billions of copies of a specific target DNA segment in a sample, even if that segment makes up less than 0.001% of the total DNA in the sample.

In the PCR procedure, a three-step cycle brings about a chain reaction that produces

▼ **Figure 13.25**  **Research Method**

### The Polymerase Chain Reaction (PCR)

**Application** With PCR, any specific segment—the target sequence—within a DNA sample can be copied many times (amplified), completely *in vitro*.

**Technique** PCR requires double-stranded DNA containing the target sequence, a heat-resistant DNA polymerase, all four nucleotides, and two 15- to 20-nucleotide DNA strands that serve as primers. One primer is complementary to one end of the target sequence on one strand; the second primer is complementary to the other end of the sequence on the other strand.

**Results** After 3 cycles, two molecules match the target sequence exactly. After 30 more cycles, over 1 billion ($10^9$) molecules match the target sequence.

an exponentially growing population of identical DNA molecules. During each cycle, the reaction mixture is heated to denature (separate) the DNA strands and then cooled to allow annealing (hybridization) of short, single-stranded DNA primers complementary to sequences on opposite strands at each end of the target segment; finally, a DNA polymerase extends the primers in the $5' \rightarrow 3'$ direction. If a standard DNA polymerase were used, the protein would be denatured along with the DNA during the first heating step and would have to be replaced after each cycle. The key to automating PCR was the discovery of an unusually heat-stable DNA polymerase called Taq polymerase, named after the bacterial species from which it was first isolated. This bacterial species, *Thermus aquaticus*, lives in hot springs, and the stability of its DNA polymerase at high temperatures is an evolutionary adaptation that enables the bacterium to survive at temperatures up to 95°C.

PCR is speedy and very specific. Only minuscule amounts of DNA need be present in the starting material, and this DNA can be partially degraded, as long as a few molecules contain the complete target segment. The key to this high specificity is the primers, the sequences of which are chosen so they hybridize *only* with complementary sequences at opposite ends of the target segment. (For high specificity, the primers must be at least 15 or so nucleotides long.) By the end of the third cycle, one-fourth of the molecules are identical to the target segment, with both strands the appropriate length. With each successive cycle, the number of target segment molecules of the correct length doubles, so the number of molecules equals $2^n$, where *n* is the number of cycles. After 30 more cycles, about a billion copies of the target sequence are present!

Despite its speed and specificity, PCR amplification alone cannot substitute for gene cloning in cells to make large amounts of a gene. This is because occasional errors during PCR replication limit the number of good copies and the length of DNA fragments that can be copied. Instead, PCR is used to provide the specific DNA fragment for cloning. PCR primers are synthesized to include a restriction site at each end of the DNA fragment that matches the site in the cloning vector, and the fragment and vector are cut and ligated together **(Figure 13.26)**. The resulting clones are sequenced so that clones with error-free inserts can be selected.

Devised in 1985, PCR has had a major impact on biological research and genetic engineering. PCR has been used to amplify DNA from a wide variety of sources: a 40,000-year-old frozen woolly mammoth; fingerprints or tiny amounts of blood, tissue, or semen found at crime scenes; single embryonic cells for rapid prenatal diagnosis of genetic disorders; and cells infected with viruses that are difficult to detect, such as HIV (in the latter case, viral genes are amplified).

## DNA Sequencing

Once a gene is cloned, researchers can exploit the principle of complementary base pairing to determine the gene's

▲ Figure 13.26 **Use of restriction enzymes and PCR in gene cloning.** In a closer look at the process shown at the top of Figure 13.22, PCR is used to produce the DNA fragment or gene of interest that will be ligated into a cloning vector, in this case a bacterial plasmid. Both the plasmid and the DNA fragments are cut with the same restriction enzyme, combined so the sticky ends can hybridize, ligated together, and introduced into bacterial cells.

complete nucleotide sequence, a process called **DNA sequencing**. In the last ten years, "next-generation" sequencing techniques have been developed that are rapid and inexpensive. A single template strand is immobilized, and DNA polymerase and other reagents are added that allow so-called *sequencing by synthesis* of the complementary strand, one nucleotide at a time. A chemical trick enables electronic monitors to identify which of the four nucleotides is being added, allowing determination of the sequence. Technical advances continue to produce "third-generation" sequencing techniques, with each new technique being faster and less expensive than the previous.

In this chapter, you've learned how DNA molecules are arranged in chromosomes and how DNA replication provides the copies of genes that parents pass to offspring. However, it is not enough that genes be copied and transmitted; the information they carry must be used by the cell. In other words, genes must also be "expressed." In the next few chapters, we'll examine how the cell expresses the genetic information encoded in DNA. We'll also return to the subject of genetic engineering by exploring a few techniques for analyzing gene expression.

### CONCEPT CHECK 13.4

1. The restriction site for an enzyme called *Pvu*I is the following sequence:

    5'-C G A T C G-3'
    3'-G C T A G C-5'

    Staggered cuts are made between the T and C on each strand. What type of bonds are being cleaved?

2. **DRAW IT** One strand of a DNA molecule has the following sequence: 5'-CCTTGACGATCGTTACCG-3'. Draw the other strand. Will *Pvu*I cut this molecule? If so, draw the products.

3. Describe the role of complementary base pairing during cloning, DNA sequencing, and PCR.

    **For suggested answers, see Appendix A.**

## SUMMARY OF KEY CONCEPTS

### CONCEPT 13.1

#### DNA is the genetic material (pp. 251–257)

- Experiments with bacteria and **phages** provided the first strong evidence that the genetic material is DNA.
- Watson and Crick deduced that DNA is a **double helix** and built a structural model. Two **antiparallel** sugar-phosphate chains wind around the outside of the molecule; the nitrogenous bases project into the interior, where they hydrogen-bond in specific pairs: A with T, G with C.

*What does it mean when we say that the two DNA strands in the double helix are antiparallel? What would an end of the double helix look like if the strands were parallel?*

### CONCEPT 13.2

#### Many proteins work together in DNA replication and repair (pp. 257–265)

- The Meselson-Stahl experiment showed that **DNA replication** is **semiconservative**: The parental molecule unwinds, and each strand then serves as a template for the synthesis of a new strand according to base-pairing rules.
- DNA replication at one **replication fork** is summarized here:

- DNA polymerases proofread new DNA, replacing incorrect nucleotides. In **mismatch repair**, enzymes correct errors that persist. **Nucleotide excision repair** is a general process by which **nucleases** cut out and replace damaged stretches of DNA.

*Compare DNA replication on the leading and lagging strands, including both similarities and differences.*

### CONCEPT 13.3

#### A chromosome consists of a DNA molecule packed together with proteins (pp. 265–267)

- The chromosome of most bacterial species is a circular DNA molecule with some associated proteins, making up the **nucleoid**

of the cell. The **chromatin** making up a eukaryotic chromosome is composed of DNA, **histones**, and other proteins. The histones bind to each other and to the DNA to form **nucleosomes**, the most basic units of DNA packing. Additional coiling and folding lead ultimately to the highly condensed chromatin of the metaphase chromosome. In interphase cells, most chromatin is less compacted (**euchromatin**), but some remains highly condensed (**heterochromatin**). Euchromatin, but not heterochromatin, is generally accessible for transcription of genes.

*Describe the levels of chromatin packing you would expect to see in an interphase nucleus.*

### CONCEPT 13.4

#### Understanding DNA structure and replication makes genetic engineering possible (pp. 267–271)

- **Gene cloning** (or DNA cloning) produces multiple copies of a gene (or DNA fragment) that can be used to manipulate and analyze DNA and to produce useful new products or organisms with beneficial traits.
- In **genetic engineering**, bacterial **restriction enzymes** are used to cut DNA molecules within short, specific nucleotide sequences (**restriction sites**), yielding a set of double-stranded **restriction fragments** with single-stranded **sticky ends**.

- DNA fragments of different lengths can be separated and their lengths assessed by **gel electrophoresis**.
- The sticky ends on restriction fragments from one DNA source—such as a bacterial **plasmid** or other **cloning vector**—can base-pair with complementary sticky ends on fragments from other DNA molecules; sealing the base-paired fragments with DNA ligase produces **recombinant DNA** molecules.
- The **polymerase chain reaction (PCR)** can produce many copies of (amplify) a specific target segment of DNA *in vitro* for use as a DNA fragment for cloning. PCR uses primers that bracket the desired segment and requires a heat-resistant DNA polymerase.
- The rapid development of fast, inexpensive techniques for **DNA sequencing** is based on *sequencing by synthesis*: DNA polymerase is used to replicate a stretch of DNA from a single-stranded template, and the order in which nucleotides are added reveals the sequence.

*Describe how the process of gene cloning results in a cell clone containing a recombinant plasmid.*

## TEST YOUR UNDERSTANDING

### Level 1: Knowledge/Comprehension

1. In his work with pneumonia-causing bacteria and mice, Griffith found that
   a. the protein coat from pathogenic cells was able to transform nonpathogenic cells.
   b. heat-killed pathogenic cells caused pneumonia.
   c. some substance from pathogenic cells was transferred to nonpathogenic cells, making them pathogenic.
   d. the polysaccharide coat of bacteria caused pneumonia.
   e. bacteriophages injected DNA into bacteria.

**2.** What is the basis for the difference in how the leading and lagging strands of DNA molecules are synthesized?

   **a.** The origins of replication occur only at the 5′ end.

   **b.** Helicases and single-strand binding proteins work at the 5′ end.

   **c.** DNA polymerase can join new nucleotides only to the 3′ end of a growing strand.

   **d.** DNA ligase works only in the 3′ → 5′ direction.

   **e.** Polymerase can work on only one strand at a time.

**3.** In analyzing the number of different bases in a DNA sample, which result would be consistent with the base-pairing rules?

   **a.** A = G

   **b.** A + G = C + T

   **c.** A + T = G + T

   **d.** A = C

   **e.** G = T

**4.** The elongation of the leading strand during DNA synthesis

   **a.** progresses away from the replication fork.

   **b.** occurs in the 3′ → 5′ direction.

   **c.** produces Okazaki fragments.

   **d.** depends on the action of DNA polymerase.

   **e.** does not require a template strand.

**5.** In a nucleosome, the DNA is wrapped around

   **a.** polymerase molecules.

   **b.** ribosomes.

   **c.** histones.

   **d.** a thymine dimer.

   **e.** satellite DNA.

**6.** Which of the following sequences in double-stranded DNA is most likely to be recognized as a cutting site for a restriction enzyme?

   **a.** AAGG   **b.** AGTC   **c.** GGCC   **d.** ACCA   **e.** AAAA
       TTCC        TCAG      CCGG     TGGT     TTTT

## Level 2: Application/Analysis

**7.** *E. coli* cells grown on $^{15}N$ medium are transferred to $^{14}N$ medium and allowed to grow for two more generations (two rounds of DNA replication). DNA extracted from these cells is centrifuged. What density distribution of DNA would you expect in this experiment?

   **a.** one high-density and one low-density band

   **b.** one intermediate-density band

   **c.** one high-density and one intermediate-density band

   **d.** one low-density and one intermediate-density band

   **e.** one low-density band

**8.** A biochemist isolates, purifies, and combines in a test tube a variety of molecules needed for DNA replication. When she adds some DNA to the mixture, replication occurs, but each DNA molecule consists of a normal strand paired with numerous segments of DNA a few hundred nucleotides long. What has she probably left out of the mixture?

   **a.** DNA polymerase

   **b.** DNA ligase

   **c.** nucleotides

   **d.** Okazaki fragments

   **e.** primase

**9.** The spontaneous loss of amino groups from adenine in DNA results in hypoxanthine, an uncommon base, opposite thymine. What combination of proteins could repair such damage?

   **a.** nuclease, DNA polymerase, DNA ligase

   **b.** topoisomerase, primase, DNA polymerase

   **c.** topoisomerase, helicase, single-strand binding protein

   **d.** DNA ligase, replication fork proteins, adenylyl cyclase

   **e.** nuclease, topoisomerase, primase

**10.** **MAKE CONNECTIONS** Although the proteins that cause the *E. coli* chromosome to coil are not histones, what property would you expect them to share with histones, given their ability to bind to DNA (see Figure 2.17)?

## Level 3: Synthesis/Evaluation

**11. SCIENTIFIC INQUIRY**

**DRAW IT** Model building can be an important part of the scientific process. The illustration shown above is a computer-generated model of a DNA replication complex. The parental and newly synthesized DNA strands are color-coded differently, as are each of the following three proteins: DNA pol III, the sliding clamp, and single-strand binding protein. Use what you've learned in this chapter to clarify this model by labeling each DNA strand and each protein and indicating the overall direction of DNA replication.

**12. FOCUS ON EVOLUTION**

Some bacteria may be able to respond to environmental stress by increasing the rate at which mutations occur during cell division. How might this be accomplished? Might there be an evolutionary advantage of this ability? Explain.

**13. FOCUS ON ORGANIZATION**

The continuity of life is based on heritable information in the form of DNA, and structure and function are correlated at all levels of biological organization. In a short essay (100–150 words), describe how the structure of DNA is correlated with its role as the molecular basis of inheritance.

*For selected answers, see Appendix A.*

## MasteringBiology®

**Students** Go to **MasteringBiology** for assignments, the eText, and the Study Area with practice tests, animations, and activities.

**Instructors** Go to **MasteringBiology** for automatically graded tutorials and questions that you can assign to your students, plus Instructor Resources.

# Gene Expression: From Gene to Protein

OVERVIEW

## The Flow of Genetic Information

In 2006, a young albino deer seen frolicking with several brown deer in the mountains of eastern Germany elicited a public outcry **(Figure 14.1)**. A local hunting organization announced that the albino deer suffered from a "genetic disorder" and should be shot. Some argued that the deer should merely be prevented from mating with other deer to safeguard the population's gene pool. Others favored relocating the albino deer to a nature reserve because they worried that it might be more noticeable to predators if left in the wild. A German rock star even held a benefit concert to raise funds for the relocation. What led to the striking phenotype of this deer, the cause of this lively debate?

Inherited traits are determined by genes, and the trait of albinism is caused by a recessive allele of a pigmentation gene (see Chapter 11). The information content of genes is in the form of specific sequences of nucleotides along strands of DNA, the genetic material. But how does this information determine an organism's traits? Put another way, what does a gene actually say? And how is its message translated by cells into a specific trait, such as brown hair, type A blood, or, in the case of an albino deer, a total lack of pigment? The albino deer has a faulty version of a key protein, an enzyme required for pigment synthesis, and this protein is faulty because the gene that codes for it contains incorrect information.

This example illustrates the main point of this chapter: The DNA inherited by an organism leads to specific traits by dictating the synthesis of proteins and of RNA molecules involved in protein synthesis. In other words, proteins are the link between genotype and phenotype. **Gene expression** is the process by which DNA directs the synthesis of proteins (or, in some cases, just RNAs). The expression of genes that code for proteins includes two stages: transcription and translation. This chapter describes the flow of information from gene to protein in detail and explains how genetic mutations affect organisms through their proteins. Understanding the processes of gene expression, which are similar in all three domains of life, will allow us to revisit the concept of the gene in more detail at the end of the chapter.

▼ **Figure 14.1** How does a single faulty gene result in the dramatic appearance of an albino deer?

## CONCEPT 14.1

# Genes specify proteins via transcription and translation

Before going into the details of how genes direct protein synthesis, let's step back and examine how the fundamental relationship between genes and proteins was discovered.

## Evidence from the Study of Metabolic Defects

In 1902, British physician Archibald Garrod was the first to suggest that genes dictate phenotypes through enzymes that catalyze specific chemical reactions in the cell. Garrod postulated that the symptoms of an inherited disease reflect a person's inability to make a particular enzyme. He later referred to such diseases as "inborn errors of metabolism." Garrod gave as one example the hereditary condition called alkaptonuria. In this disorder, the urine is black because it contains the chemical alkapton, which darkens upon exposure to air. Garrod reasoned that most people have an enzyme that metabolizes alkapton, whereas people with alkaptonuria have inherited an inability to make that enzyme.

Garrod may have been the first to recognize that Mendel's principles of heredity apply to humans as well as peas. Garrod's realization was ahead of its time, but research several decades later supported his hypothesis that a gene dictates the production of a specific enzyme. Biochemists accumulated much evidence that cells synthesize and degrade most organic molecules via metabolic pathways, in which each chemical reaction in a sequence is catalyzed by a specific enzyme (see Concept 5.1). Such metabolic pathways lead, for instance, to the synthesis of the pigments that give the brown deer in Figure 14.1 their fur

color or fruit flies (*Drosophila*) their eye color (see Figure 12.3). In the 1930s, the American geneticist George Beadle and his French colleague Boris Ephrussi speculated that in *Drosophila*, each of the mutations affecting eye color blocks pigment synthesis at a specific step by preventing production of the enzyme that catalyzes that step. But neither the chemical reactions nor the enzymes that catalyze them were known at the time.

### *Nutritional Mutants in Neurospora:* Scientific Inquiry

A breakthrough in demonstrating the relationship between genes and enzymes came a few years later at Stanford University, where Beadle and Edward Tatum began working with the bread mold *Neurospora crassa* to investigate the role of genes in this organism's metabolic pathways. Their experimental approach still plays a central role in genetic research today: They disabled genes one by one and looked for changes in each mutant's phenotype, thereby revealing the normal function of the gene.

Like Mendel and T. H. Morgan before them, Beadle and Tatum chose their experimental organism carefully. They elected to work with *Neurospora*, a haploid species. They realized that it would be easier to detect a disabled gene in a haploid species than in a diploid species like *Drosophila*. In a diploid species, two copies of each gene are present, and both would need to be disabled for an effect to be seen on the organism's phenotype. In *Neurospora*, though, disabling a single gene would allow them to see the consequences and thus to deduce what the function of the wild-type gene might be. (In other words, haploidy makes it easier to detect recessive mutations.)

What was known about metabolism in *Neurospora* also made it a good choice. Wild-type *Neurospora* has modest food requirements. It can grow in the laboratory on a simple solution of inorganic salts, glucose, and the vitamin biotin (Figure 14.2). From this *minimal medium*, the mold cells use their metabolic

▲ Figure 14.2 **The experimental approach of Beadle and Tatum.** To obtain nutritional mutants, Beadle and Tatum exposed *Neurospora* cells to X-rays to induce mutations. They then screened mutants with new nutritional requirements, such as arginine, as shown here.

**WHAT IF?** *What do you predict would happen if the same mutant were tested in a tube of minimal medium plus the amino acid glycine?*

pathways to produce all the other molecules they need. Wild-type cells grow and divide repeatedly on this medium.

*Neurospora* cells can be plated individually on a petri dish containing minimal medium embedded in a gel-like substance called agar. Although single cells are microscopic, after many divisions the resulting daughter cells can be seen by eye on the surface of the agar. Thus their ability to grow and divide on a particular medium can easily be monitored. Any change in their ability to grow on minimal medium would be easy to recognize in the lab simply as a new food requirement for growth (cell division).

Because any mutant that could not synthesize an essential nutrient would be unable to grow on minimal medium, Beadle and Tatum placed single *Neurospora* cells on a *complete growth medium*, which consisted of minimal medium supplemented with all 20 amino acids and a few other nutrients. As diagrammed in Figure 14.2 they bombarded the cells with X-rays, shown in the 1920s to cause mutations. Each of the surviving cells formed a visible colony of genetically identical cells. Next, the researchers screened the surviving colonies for "nutritional mutants" that grew well on complete medium but not at all on minimal medium. Apparently, each nutritional mutant was unable to synthesize a certain essential molecule from the minimal ingredients. In the final step of this experimental approach, Beadle and Tatum took cells from each mutant colony growing on complete medium and distributed them to a number of different vials. Each vial contained minimal medium plus a single additional nutrient. The particular supplement that allowed growth indicated the nutrient that the mutant could not synthesize.

Thus, the researchers amassed a valuable collection of mutant strains of *Neurospora*, catalogued by their defects. The collection would prove useful for focusing in on particular metabolic pathways in which the individual steps were either known or strongly suspected. For example, a series of experiments on mutants requiring the amino acid arginine revealed that they could be grouped into classes, each corresponding to a particular step in the biochemical pathway for arginine synthesis. These results, along with the results of similar experiments with other nutritional mutants, suggested that each class was blocked at a different step in the pathway because mutants in that class lacked the enzyme that catalyzes the blocked step due to a faulty gene **(Figure 14.3)**.

Because each mutant was defective in a single gene, Beadle and Tatum saw that, taken together, the collected results provided strong support for a working hypothesis they had proposed earlier. The *one gene–one enzyme hypothesis*, as they dubbed it, states that the function of a gene is to dictate the production of a specific enzyme. Further support for this hypothesis came from experiments that identified the specific enzymes lacking in the mutants. Beadle and Tatum shared a Nobel Prize in 1958 for "their discovery that genes act by regulating definite chemical events," in the words of the Nobel committee.

▲ **Figure 14.3** **The one gene–one protein hypothesis.** Based on results from work in their lab on nutritional mutants, Beadle and Tatum proposed that the function of a specific gene is to dictate production of a specific enzyme that catalyzes a particular reaction. The model shown here for the arginine-synthesizing pathway illustrates their hypothesis.

### The Products of Gene Expression: A Developing Story

As researchers learned more about proteins, they made revisions to the one gene–one enzyme hypothesis. First of all, not all proteins are enzymes. Keratin, the structural protein of animal hair, and the hormone insulin are two examples of nonenzyme proteins. Because proteins that are not enzymes are nevertheless gene products, molecular biologists began to think in terms of one gene–one protein. However, many proteins are constructed from two or more different polypeptide chains, and each polypeptide is specified by its own gene. For example, hemoglobin, the oxygen-transporting protein of vertebrate red blood cells, contains two kinds of polypeptides, and thus two genes code for this protein (see Figure 2.21). Beadle and Tatum's idea was therefore restated as the *one gene–one polypeptide hypothesis*. Even this description is not entirely accurate, though. First, many eukaryotic genes can each code for a set of closely related polypeptides via a process called alternative splicing, which you will learn about later in this chapter. Second, quite a few genes code for RNA molecules that have important functions in cells even though they are never translated into protein. For now, we will focus on genes that do code for polypeptides. (Note that it is common to refer to these gene products as proteins—a practice you'll encounter in this text—rather than more precisely as polypeptides.)

## Basic Principles of Transcription and Translation

Genes provide the instructions for making specific proteins. But a gene does not build a protein directly. The bridge between DNA and protein synthesis is the nucleic acid RNA. RNA is chemically similar to DNA except that it contains ribose instead of deoxyribose as its sugar and has the nitrogenous base uracil rather than thymine (see Chapter 2). Thus, each nucleotide along a DNA strand has A, G, C, or T as its base, and each nucleotide along an RNA strand has A, G, C, or U as its base. An RNA molecule usually consists of a single strand.

It is customary to describe the flow of information from gene to protein in linguistic terms because both nucleic acids and proteins are polymers with specific sequences of monomers that convey information, much as specific sequences of letters communicate information in a language like English. In

DNA or RNA, the monomers are the four types of nucleotides, which differ in their nitrogenous bases. Genes are typically hundreds or thousands of nucleotides long, each gene having a specific sequence of nucleotides. Each polypeptide of a protein also has monomers arranged in a particular linear order (the protein's primary structure), but its monomers are amino acids. Thus, nucleic acids and proteins contain information written in two different chemical languages. Getting from DNA to protein requires two major stages: transcription and translation.

**Transcription** is the synthesis of RNA using information in the DNA. The two nucleic acids are written in different forms of the same language, and the information is simply transcribed, or "rewritten," from DNA to RNA. Just as a DNA strand provides a template for making a new complementary strand during DNA replication, it also can serve as a template for assembling a complementary sequence of RNA nucleotides. For a protein-coding gene, the resulting RNA molecule is a faithful transcript of the gene's protein-building instructions. This type of RNA molecule is called **messenger RNA (mRNA)** because it carries a genetic message from the DNA to the protein-synthesizing machinery of the cell. (Transcription is the general term for the synthesis of *any* kind of RNA on a DNA template. Later, you'll learn about some other types of RNA produced by transcription.)

**Translation** is the synthesis of a polypeptide using the information in the mRNA. During this stage, there is a change in language: The cell must translate the nucleotide sequence of an mRNA molecule into the amino acid sequence of a polypeptide. The sites of translation are **ribosomes**, complex particles that facilitate the orderly linking of amino acids into polypeptide chains.

Transcription and translation occur in all organisms—those that lack a membrane-enclosed nucleus (bacteria and archaea) and those that have one (eukaryotes). Because most studies of transcription and translation have used bacteria and eukaryotic cells, they are our main focus in this chapter. While our understanding of transcription and translation in archaea lags behind, we do know that archaeal cells share some features of gene expression with bacteria, and others with eukaryotes.

The basic mechanics of transcription and translation are similar for bacteria and eukaryotes, but there is an important difference in the flow of genetic information within the cells. Because bacteria do not have nuclei, their DNA is not separated by nuclear membranes from ribosomes and the other protein-synthesizing equipment (**Figure 14.4a**). As you will see later, this lack of compartmentalization allows translation of an mRNA to begin while its transcription is still in progress. In a eukaryotic cell, by contrast, the nuclear envelope separates transcription from translation in space and time (**Figure 14.4b**). Transcription occurs in the nucleus, and mRNA is then transported to the cytoplasm, where translation occurs. But before eukaryotic RNA transcripts from protein-coding genes can leave the nucleus, they are modified in various ways to produce the final, functional mRNA.

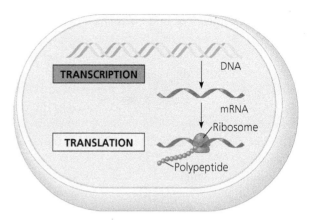

**(a) Bacterial cell.** In a bacterial cell, which lacks a nucleus, mRNA produced by transcription is immediately translated without additional processing.

**(b) Eukaryotic cell.** The nucleus provides a separate compartment for transcription. The original RNA transcript, called pre-mRNA, is processed in various ways before leaving the nucleus as mRNA.

▲ **Figure 14.4 Overview: the roles of transcription and translation in the flow of genetic information.** In a cell, inherited information flows from DNA to RNA to protein. The two main stages of information flow are transcription and translation. A miniature version of part (a) or (b) accompanies several figures later in the chapter as an orientation diagram to help you see where a particular figure fits into the overall scheme.

The transcription of a protein-coding eukaryotic gene results in *pre-mRNA*, and further processing yields the finished mRNA. The initial RNA transcript from any gene, including those specifying RNA that is not translated into protein, is more generally called a **primary transcript**.

To summarize: Genes program protein synthesis via genetic messages in the form of messenger RNA. Put another way, cells are governed by a molecular chain of command with a directional flow of genetic information, shown here by arrows:

This concept was dubbed the *central dogma* by Francis Crick in 1956. How has the concept held up over time? In the 1970s, scientists were surprised to discover that some RNA molecules can act as templates for DNA synthesis (a process you'll read about in Chapter 15). However, these exceptions do not invalidate the idea that, in general, genetic information flows from DNA to RNA to protein. Now let's discuss how the instructions for assembling amino acids into a specific order are encoded in nucleic acids.

## The Genetic Code

When biologists began to suspect that the instructions for protein synthesis were encoded in DNA, they recognized a problem: There are only four nucleotide bases to specify 20 amino acids. Thus, the genetic code cannot be a language like Chinese, where each written symbol corresponds to a word. How many nucleotides, then, correspond to an amino acid?

### Codons: Triplets of Nucleotides

If each kind of nucleotide base were translated into an amino acid, only four amino acids could be specified, one per nucleotide base. Would a language of two-letter code words suffice? The two-nucleotide sequence AG, for example, could specify one amino acid, and GT could specify another. Since there are four possible nucleotide bases in each position, this would give us 16 (that is, $4^2$) possible arrangements—still not enough to code for all 20 amino acids.

Triplets of nucleotide bases are the smallest units of uniform length that can code for all the amino acids. If each arrangement of three consecutive nucleotide bases specifies an amino acid, there can be 64 (that is, $4^3$) possible code words—more than enough to specify all the amino acids. Experiments have verified that the flow of information from gene to protein is based on a **triplet code**: The genetic instructions for a polypeptide chain are written in the DNA as a series of nonoverlapping, three-nucleotide words. The series of words in a gene is transcribed into a complementary series of nonoverlapping, three-nucleotide words in mRNA, which is then translated into a chain of amino acids **(Figure 14.5)**.

During transcription, the gene determines the sequence of nucleotide bases along the length of the RNA molecule that is being synthesized. For each gene, only one of the two DNA strands is transcribed. This strand is called the **template strand** because it provides the pattern, or template, for the sequence of nucleotides in an RNA transcript. For any given gene, the same strand is used as the template every time the gene is transcribed. For other genes on the same DNA molecule, however, the opposite strand may be the one that always functions as the template.

▶ **Figure 14.5** **The triplet code.** For each gene, one DNA strand functions as a template for transcription of RNAs, such as mRNA. The base-pairing rules for DNA synthesis also guide transcription, except that uracil (U) takes the place of thymine (T) in RNA. During translation, the mRNA is read as a sequence of nucleotide triplets, called codons. Each codon specifies an amino acid to be added to the growing polypeptide chain. The mRNA is read in the 5′ → 3′ direction.

**?** *Compare the sequence of the mRNA to that of the nontemplate DNA strand, in both cases reading from 5′ → 3′.*

An mRNA molecule is complementary rather than identical to its DNA template because RNA nucleotides are assembled on the template according to base-pairing rules (see Figure 14.5). The pairs are similar to those that form during DNA replication, except that U, the RNA substitute for T, pairs with A and the mRNA nucleotides contain ribose instead of deoxyribose. Like a new strand of DNA, the RNA molecule is synthesized in an antiparallel direction to the template strand of DNA. (To review what is meant by "antiparallel" and the 5′ and 3′ ends of a nucleic acid chain, see Figure 13.7.) In the example in Figure 14.5, the nucleotide triplet ACC along the DNA (written as 3′-ACC-5′) provides a template for 5′-UGG-3′ in the mRNA molecule. The mRNA nucleotide triplets are called **codons**, and they are customarily written in the 5′ → 3′ direction. In our example, UGG is the codon for the amino acid tryptophan (abbreviated Trp). The term *codon* is also used for the DNA nucleotide triplets along the *nontemplate* strand. These codons are complementary to the template strand and thus identical in sequence to the mRNA, except that they have T instead of U. (For this reason, the nontemplate DNA strand is sometimes called the "coding strand.")

During translation, the sequence of codons along an mRNA molecule is decoded, or translated, into a sequence of amino acids making up a polypeptide chain. The codons are read by the translation machinery in the 5′ → 3′ direction along the mRNA. Each codon specifies which one of the 20 amino acids will be incorporated at the corresponding position along a polypeptide. Because codons are nucleotide triplets, the number of nucleotides making up a genetic message must be three times the number of amino acids in the protein product. For example, it takes 300 nucleotides along an mRNA strand to code for the amino acids in a polypeptide that is 100 amino acids long.

### Cracking the Code

Molecular biologists cracked the genetic code of life in the early 1960s when a series of elegant experiments disclosed the amino acid translations of each of the RNA codons. The first codon was deciphered in 1961 by Marshall Nirenberg, of the National Institutes of Health, and his colleagues. Nirenberg synthesized an artificial mRNA by linking identical RNA nucleotides containing uracil as their base. No matter where this message started or stopped, it could contain only one codon in repetition: UUU. Nirenberg added this "poly-U" to a test-tube mixture containing amino acids, ribosomes, and the other components required for protein synthesis. His artificial system translated the poly-U into a polypeptide containing many units of the amino acid phenylalanine (Phe), strung together as a long polyphenylalanine chain. Thus, Nirenberg determined that the mRNA codon UUU specifies the amino acid phenylalanine. Soon, the amino acids specified by the codons AAA, GGG, and CCC were determined in the same way.

Although more elaborate techniques were required to decode mixed triplets such as AUA and CGA, all 64 codons were deciphered by the mid-1960s. As **Figure 14.6** shows, 61 of the 64 triplets code for amino acids. The three codons that do not designate amino acids are "stop" signals, or termination codons, marking the end of translation. Notice that the codon AUG has a dual function: It codes for the amino acid methionine (Met) and also functions as a "start" signal, or initiation codon. Genetic messages usually begin with the mRNA codon AUG, which signals the protein-synthesizing machinery to begin translating the mRNA at that location. (Because AUG also stands for methionine, polypeptide chains begin with methionine when they are synthesized. However, an enzyme may subsequently remove this starter amino acid from the chain.)

Notice in Figure 14.6 that there is redundancy in the genetic code, but no ambiguity. For example, although codons GAA and GAG both specify glutamic acid (redundancy), neither of them ever specifies any other amino acid (no ambiguity). The redundancy in the code is not altogether random. In many cases, codons that are synonyms for a particular amino acid differ only in the third nucleotide base of the triplet. We'll consider a possible benefit of this redundancy later in the chapter.

Our ability to extract the intended message from a written language depends on reading the symbols in the correct

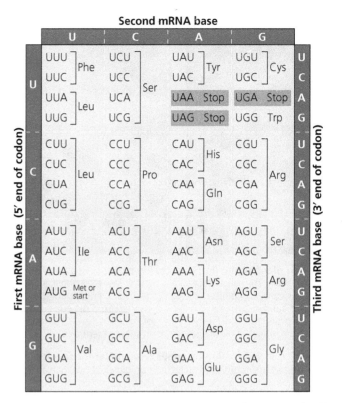

▲ **Figure 14.6 The codon table for mRNA.** The three nucleotide bases of an mRNA codon are designated here as the first, second, and third bases, reading in the 5′ → 3′ direction along the mRNA. (Practice using this table by finding the codons in Figure 14.5.) The codon AUG not only stands for the amino acid methionine (Met) but also functions as a "start" signal for ribosomes to begin translating the mRNA at that point. Three of the 64 codons function as "stop" signals, marking where ribosomes end translation. See Figure 2.17 for a list of the full names of all the amino acids.

groupings—that is, in the correct **reading frame**. Consider this statement: "The red dog ate the bug." Group the letters incorrectly by starting at the wrong point, and the result will probably be gibberish: for example, "her edd oga tet heb ug." The reading frame is also important in the molecular language of cells. The short stretch of polypeptide shown in Figure 14.5, for instance, will be made correctly only if the mRNA nucleotides are read from left to right (5′ → 3′) in the groups of three shown in the figure: UGG UUU GGC UCA. Although a genetic message is written with no spaces between the codons, the cell's protein-synthesizing machinery reads the message as a series of nonoverlapping three-letter words. The message is *not* read as a series of overlapping words—UGGUUU, and so on—which would convey a very different message.

### Evolution of the Genetic Code

**EVOLUTION** The genetic code is nearly universal, shared by organisms from the simplest bacteria to the most complex plants and animals. The RNA codon CCG, for instance, is translated as the amino acid proline in all organisms whose genetic code has been examined. In laboratory experiments, genes can be transcribed and translated after being transplanted from one species to another, sometimes with quite

**(a) Tobacco plant expressing a firefly gene.** The yellow glow is produced by a chemical reaction catalyzed by the protein product of the firefly gene.

**(b) Pig expressing a jellyfish gene.** Researchers injected the gene for a fluorescent protein into fertilized pig eggs. One of the eggs developed into this fluorescent pig.

▲ **Figure 14.7 Expression of genes from different species.** Because diverse forms of life share a common genetic code, one species can be programmed to produce proteins characteristic of a second species by introducing DNA from the second species into the first.

striking results, as shown in **Figure 14.7**. Bacteria can be programmed by the insertion of human genes to synthesize certain human proteins for medical use, such as insulin. Such applications have produced many exciting developments in the area of genetic engineering (see Chapter 13).

Despite a small number of exceptions in which a few codons differ from the standard ones, the evolutionary significance of the code's *near* universality is clear. A language shared by all living things must have been operating very early in the history of life—early enough to be present in the common ancestor of all present-day organisms. A shared genetic vocabulary is a reminder of the kinship that bonds all life on Earth.

### CONCEPT CHECK 14.1

1. **MAKE CONNECTIONS** In a research article about alkaptonuria published in 1902, Garrod suggested that humans inherit two "characters" (alleles) for a particular enzyme and that both parents must contribute a faulty version for the offspring to have the disorder. Today, would this disorder be called dominant or recessive? (See Concept 11.4.)

2. What polypeptide product would you expect from a poly-G mRNA that is 30 nucleotides long?

3. **DRAW IT** The template strand of a gene contains the sequence 3'-TTCAGTCGT-5'. Imagine that the nontemplate sequence was transcribed instead of the template sequence. Draw the mRNA sequence and translate it using Figure 14.6. (Be sure to pay attention to the 5' and 3' ends.) Predict how well the protein synthesized from the nontemplate strand would function, if at all.

*For suggested answers, see Appendix A.*

# Transcription is the DNA-directed synthesis of RNA: *a closer look*

Now that we have considered the linguistic logic and evolutionary significance of the genetic code, we are ready to reexamine transcription, the first stage of gene expression, in more detail.

## Molecular Components of Transcription

Messenger RNA, the carrier of information from DNA to the cell's protein-synthesizing machinery, is transcribed from the template strand of a gene. An enzyme called an **RNA polymerase** pries the two strands of DNA apart and joins together RNA nucleotides complementary to the DNA template strand, thus elongating the RNA polynucleotide **(Figure 14.8)**. Like the DNA polymerases that function in DNA replication, RNA polymerases can assemble a polynucleotide only in its $5' \rightarrow 3'$ direction. Unlike DNA polymerases, however, RNA polymerases are able to start a chain from scratch; they don't need a primer.

Specific sequences of nucleotides along the DNA mark where transcription of a gene begins and ends. The DNA sequence where RNA polymerase attaches and initiates transcription is known as the **promoter**; in bacteria, the sequence that signals the end of transcription is called the **terminator**. (The termination mechanism is different in eukaryotes; we'll describe it later.) Molecular biologists refer to the direction of transcription as "downstream" and the other direction as "upstream." These terms are also used to describe the positions of nucleotide sequences within the DNA or RNA. Thus, the promoter sequence in DNA is said to be upstream from the terminator. The stretch of DNA that is transcribed into an RNA molecule is called a **transcription unit**.

Bacteria have a single type of RNA polymerase that synthesizes not only mRNA but also other types of RNA that function in protein synthesis, such as ribosomal RNA. In contrast, eukaryotes have at least three types of RNA polymerase in their nuclei; the one used for mRNA synthesis is called RNA polymerase II. In the discussion of transcription that follows, we start with the features of mRNA synthesis common to both bacteria and eukaryotes and then describe some key differences.

## Synthesis of an RNA Transcript

The three stages of transcription, as shown in Figure 14.8 and described next, are initiation, elongation, and termination of the RNA chain. Study Figure 14.8 to familiarize yourself with the stages and the terms used to describe them.

### RNA Polymerase Binding and Initiation of Transcription

The promoter of a gene includes within it the transcription **start point** (the nucleotide where RNA synthesis actually begins) and typically extends several dozen or more nucleotide pairs upstream from the start point. RNA polymerase binds in a precise location and orientation on the promoter, thereby determining where transcription starts and which of the two strands of the DNA helix is used as the template.

Certain sections of a promoter are especially important for binding RNA polymerase. In bacteria, the RNA polymerase itself specifically recognizes and binds to the promoter. In eukaryotes, a collection of proteins called **transcription factors** mediate the binding of RNA polymerase and the initiation of transcription. Only after transcription factors are attached to the promoter does RNA polymerase II bind to it. The whole complex of transcription factors and RNA polymerase II bound to the promoter is called a **transcription initiation complex**. **Figure 14.9** shows the role of transcription factors and a crucial

**▲ Figure 14.8 The stages of transcription: initiation, elongation, and termination.** This general depiction of transcription applies to both bacteria and eukaryotes, but the details of termination differ, as described in the text. Also, in a bacterium, the RNA transcript is immediately usable as mRNA; in a eukaryote, the RNA transcript must first undergo processing.

**MAKE CONNECTIONS** *Compare the use of a template strand during transcription and replication. See Figure 13.17.*

**Promoter** — Transcription unit

5′
3′
DNA

Start point
RNA polymerase

**❶ Initiation.** After RNA polymerase binds to the promoter, the DNA strands unwind, and the polymerase initiates RNA synthesis at the start point on the template strand.

Nontemplate strand of DNA

5′
3′

Template strand of DNA

Unwound DNA

RNA transcript

**❷ Elongation.** The polymerase moves downstream, unwinding the DNA and elongating the RNA transcript 5′ → 3′. In the wake of transcription, the DNA strands re-form a double helix.

Rewound DNA

5′
3′

5′

RNA transcript

**❸ Termination.** Eventually, the RNA transcript is released, and the polymerase detaches from the DNA.

5′
3′

5′          Completed RNA transcript          3′

Direction of transcription ("downstream")

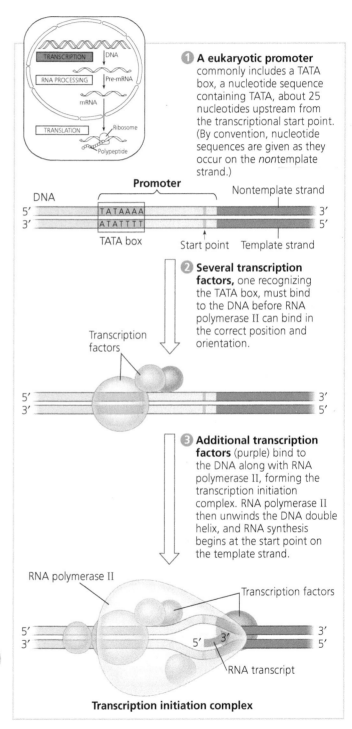

**❶ A eukaryotic promoter** commonly includes a TATA box, a nucleotide sequence containing TATA, about 25 nucleotides upstream from the transcriptional start point. (By convention, nucleotide sequences are given as they occur on the *non*template strand.)

DNA          **Promoter**          Nontemplate strand

5′  TATAAAA  3′
3′  ATATTTT  5′

TATA box          Start point   Template strand

**❷ Several transcription factors,** one recognizing the TATA box, must bind to the DNA before RNA polymerase II can bind in the correct position and orientation.

Transcription factors

5′
3′

**❸ Additional transcription factors** (purple) bind to the DNA along with RNA polymerase II, forming the transcription initiation complex. RNA polymerase II then unwinds the DNA double helix, and RNA synthesis begins at the start point on the template strand.

RNA polymerase II                    Transcription factors

5′                                              3′
3′              5′  3′                          5′

RNA transcript

**Transcription initiation complex**

**▲ Figure 14.9 The initiation of transcription at a eukaryotic promoter.** In eukaryotic cells, proteins called transcription factors mediate the initiation of transcription by RNA polymerase II.

**?** *Explain how the interaction of RNA polymerase with the promoter would differ if the figure showed transcription initiation for bacteria.*

DNA sequence in the promoter—the so-called **TATA box**—in forming the initiation complex at a eukaryotic promoter.

The interaction between eukaryotic RNA polymerase II and transcription factors is an example of the importance of protein-protein interactions in controlling eukaryotic transcription. Once the appropriate transcription factors are firmly attached to the promoter DNA and the polymerase is bound in the correct orientation, the enzyme unwinds the two DNA strands and starts transcribing the template strand.

### Elongation of the RNA Strand

As RNA polymerase moves along the DNA, it continues to untwist the double helix, exposing about 10–20 DNA nucleotides at a time for pairing with RNA nucleotides **(Figure 14.10)**. The enzyme adds nucleotides to the 3′ end of the growing RNA molecule as it continues along the double helix. In the wake of this advancing wave of RNA synthesis, the new RNA molecule peels away from its DNA template, and the DNA double helix re-forms. Transcription progresses at a rate of about 40 nucleotides per second in eukaryotes.

A single gene can be transcribed simultaneously by several molecules of RNA polymerase following each other like trucks in a convoy. A growing strand of RNA trails off from each polymerase, with the length of each new strand reflecting how far along the template the enzyme has traveled from the start point (see the mRNA molecules in Figure 14.23). The congregation of many polymerase molecules simultaneously transcribing a single gene increases the amount of mRNA transcribed from it, which helps the cell make the encoded protein in large amounts.

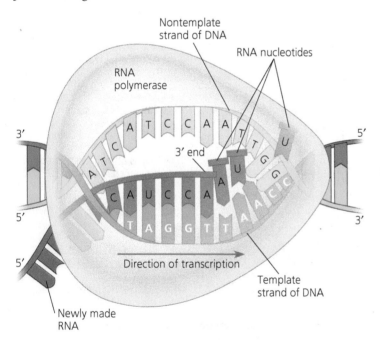

▲ **Figure 14.10 Transcription elongation.** RNA polymerase moves along the DNA template strand, joining complementary RNA nucleotides to the 3′ end of the growing RNA transcript. Behind the polymerase, the new RNA peels away from the template strand, which re-forms a double helix with the nontemplate strand.

### Termination of Transcription

The mechanism of termination differs between bacteria and eukaryotes. In bacteria, transcription proceeds through a terminator sequence in the DNA. The transcribed terminator (an RNA sequence) functions as the termination signal, causing the polymerase to detach from the DNA and release the transcript, which requires no further modification before translation. In eukaryotes, RNA polymerase II transcribes a sequence on the DNA called the polyadenylation signal sequence, which codes for a polyadenylation signal (AAUAAA) in the pre-mRNA. Then, at a point about 10–35 nucleotides downstream from the AAUAAA signal, proteins associated with the growing RNA transcript cut it free from the polymerase, releasing the pre-mRNA. The pre-mRNA then undergoes processing, the topic of the next section.

**CONCEPT CHECK 14.2**

1. What is a promoter, and is it located at the upstream or downstream end of a transcription unit?
2. What enables RNA polymerase to start transcribing a gene at the right place on the DNA in a bacterial cell? In a eukaryotic cell?
3. **WHAT IF?** Suppose X-rays caused a sequence change in the TATA box of a particular gene's promoter. How would that affect transcription of the gene? (See Figure 14.9.)

For suggested answers, see Appendix A.

**CONCEPT 14.3**

# Eukaryotic cells modify RNA after transcription

Enzymes in the eukaryotic nucleus modify pre-mRNA in specific ways before the genetic messages are dispatched to the cytoplasm. During this **RNA processing**, both ends of the primary transcript are altered. Also, in most cases, certain interior sections of the RNA molecule are cut out and the remaining parts spliced together. These modifications produce an mRNA molecule ready for translation.

## Alteration of mRNA Ends

Each end of a pre-mRNA molecule is modified in a particular way **(Figure 14.11)**. The 5′ end is synthesized first; it receives a **5′ cap**, a modified form of a guanine (G) nucleotide added onto the 5′ end after transcription of the first 20–40 nucleotides. The 3′ end of the pre-mRNA molecule is also modified before the mRNA exits the nucleus. Recall that the pre-mRNA is released soon after the polyadenylation signal, AAUAAA, is transcribed. At the 3′ end, an enzyme adds 50–250 more adenine (A) nucleotides, forming a **poly-A tail**. The 5′ cap and poly-A tail share several important functions. First, they seem to facilitate the export of the mature mRNA from the nucleus. Second, they help protect the mRNA from degradation by hydrolytic enzymes. And third, they help ribosomes attach to the

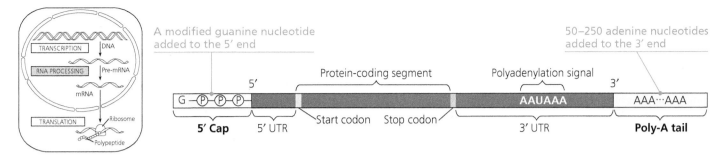

**▲ Figure 14.11** **RNA processing: Addition of the 5' cap and poly-A tail.** Enzymes modify the two ends of a eukaryotic pre-mRNA molecule. The modified ends may promote the export of mRNA from the nucleus, and they help protect the mRNA from degradation. When the mRNA reaches the cytoplasm, the modified ends, in conjunction with certain cytoplasmic proteins, facilitate ribosome attachment. The 5' cap and poly-A tail are not translated into protein, nor are the regions called the 5' untranslated region (5' UTR) and 3' untranslated region (3' UTR).

5' end of the mRNA once the mRNA reaches the cytoplasm. Figure 14.11 shows a diagram of a eukaryotic mRNA molecule with cap and tail. The figure also shows the untranslated regions (UTRs) at the 5' and 3' ends of the mRNA (referred to as the 5' UTR and 3' UTR). The UTRs are parts of the mRNA that will not be translated into protein, but they have other functions, such as ribosome binding.

## Split Genes and RNA Splicing

A remarkable stage of RNA processing in the eukaryotic nucleus is the removal of large portions of the RNA molecule that is initially synthesized—a cut-and-paste job called **RNA splicing**, similar to editing a video **(Figure 14.12)**. The average length of a transcription unit along a human DNA molecule is about 27,000 nucleotide pairs, so the primary RNA transcript is also that long. However, the average-sized protein of 400 amino acids requires only 1,200 nucleotides in RNA to code for it. (Remember, each amino acid is encoded by a *triplet* of nucleotides.) This means that most eukaryotic genes and their RNA transcripts have long noncoding stretches of nucleotides, regions that are not translated. Even more surprising is that most of these noncoding sequences are interspersed between

coding segments of the gene and thus between coding segments of the pre-mRNA. In other words, the sequence of DNA nucleotides that codes for a eukaryotic polypeptide is usually not continuous; it is split into segments. The noncoding segments of nucleic acid that lie between coding regions are called *in*tervening sequences, or **introns**. The other regions are called **exons**, because they are eventually *ex*pressed, usually by being translated into amino acid sequences. (Exceptions include the UTRs of the exons at the ends of the RNA, which make up part of the mRNA but are not translated into protein. Because of these exceptions, you may find it helpful to think of exons as sequences of RNA that *exit* the nucleus.) The terms *intron* and *exon* are used for both RNA sequences and the DNA sequences that encode them.

In making a primary transcript from a gene, RNA polymerase II transcribes both introns and exons from the DNA, but the mRNA molecule that enters the cytoplasm is an abridged version. The introns are cut out from the molecule and the exons joined together, forming an mRNA molecule with a continuous coding sequence. This is the process of RNA splicing.

One important consequence of the presence of introns in genes is that a single gene can encode more than one kind of

© 1996 Pearson Education, Inc.

**▲ Figure 14.12** **RNA processing: RNA splicing.** The RNA molecule shown here codes for β-globin, one of the polypeptides of hemoglobin. The numbers under the RNA refer to codons; β-globin is 146 amino acids long. The β-globin gene and its pre-mRNA transcript have three exons, corresponding to sequences that will leave the nucleus as mRNA. (The 5' UTR and 3' UTR are parts of exons because they are included in the mRNA; however, they do not code for protein.) During RNA processing, the introns are cut out and the exons spliced together. In many genes, the introns are much larger than the exons.

polypeptide. Many genes are known to give rise to two or more different polypeptides, depending on which segments are treated as exons during RNA processing; this is called **alternative RNA splicing**. Because of alternative splicing, the number of different protein products an organism produces can be much greater than its number of genes.

How is pre-mRNA splicing carried out? The removal of introns is accomplished by a large complex made of proteins and small RNAs called a **spliceosome**. This complex binds to several short nucleotide sequences along the intron, including key sequences at each end **(Figure 14.13)**. The intron is then released (and rapidly degraded), and the spliceosome joins together the two exons that flanked the intron. It turns out that the small RNAs in the spliceosome catalyze these processes, as well as participating in spliceosome assembly and splice site recognition.

### Ribozymes

The idea of a catalytic role for the RNAs in the spliceosome arose from the discovery of **ribozymes**, RNA molecules that function as enzymes. In some organisms, RNA splicing can occur without proteins or even additional RNA molecules: The intron RNA functions as a ribozyme and catalyzes its own excision! For example, in the ciliate protist *Tetrahymena*, self-splicing occurs in the production of ribosomal RNA (rRNA), a component of the organism's ribosomes. The pre-rRNA actually removes its own introns. The discovery of ribozymes rendered obsolete the idea that all biological catalysts are proteins.

Three properties of RNA enable some RNA molecules to function as enzymes. First, because RNA is single-stranded, a region of an RNA molecule may base-pair with a complementary region elsewhere in the same molecule, which gives the molecule a particular three-dimensional structure. A specific

structure is essential to the catalytic function of ribozymes, just as it is for enzymatic proteins. Second, like certain amino acids in an enzymatic protein, some of the bases in RNA contain functional groups that may participate in catalysis. Third, the ability of RNA to hydrogen-bond with other nucleic acid molecules (either RNA or DNA) adds specificity to its catalytic activity. For example, complementary base pairing between the RNA of the spliceosome and the RNA of a primary RNA transcript precisely locates the region where the ribozyme catalyzes splicing. Later in this chapter, you'll see how these properties of RNA also allow it to perform important noncatalytic roles in the cell, such as recognition of the three-nucleotide codons on mRNA.

CONCEPT 14.4

# Translation is the RNA-directed synthesis of a polypeptide: *a closer look*

We will now examine in greater detail how genetic information flows from mRNA to protein—the process of translation. As we did for transcription, we'll concentrate on the basic steps of translation that occur in both bacteria and eukaryotes, while pointing out key differences.

## Molecular Components of Translation

In the process of translation, a cell "reads" a genetic message and builds a polypeptide accordingly. The message is a series of codons along an mRNA molecule, and the translator is called **transfer RNA (tRNA)**. The function of tRNA is to transfer amino acids from the cytoplasmic pool of amino acids to a growing polypeptide in a ribosome. A cell keeps its cytoplasm stocked with all 20 amino acids, either by synthesizing them from other compounds or by taking them up from the surrounding solution. The ribosome, a structure made of proteins and RNAs, adds each amino acid brought to it by tRNA to the growing end of a polypeptide chain **(Figure 14.14)**.

Translation is simple in principle but complex in its biochemistry and mechanics, especially in the eukaryotic cell. In dissecting translation, we'll concentrate on the slightly less complicated version of the process that occurs in bacteria. We'll begin by looking at the major players in this cellular process and then see how they act together in making a polypeptide.

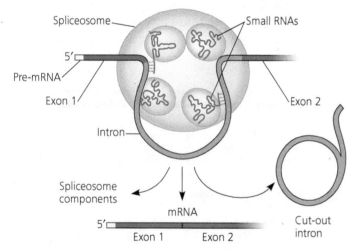

▲ **Figure 14.13 A spliceosome splicing a pre-mRNA.** The diagram shows a portion of a pre-mRNA transcript, with an intron (pink) flanked by two exons (red). Small RNAs within the spliceosome base-pair with nucleotides at specific sites along the intron. Next, the spliceosome catalyzes cutting of the pre-mRNA and the splicing together of the exons, releasing the intron for rapid degradation.

**(a) Two-dimensional structure.** The four base-paired regions and three loops are characteristic of all tRNAs, as is the base sequence of the amino acid attachment site at the 3′ end. The anticodon triplet is unique to each tRNA type, as are some sequences in the other two loops. (The asterisks mark bases that have been chemically modified, a characteristic of tRNA. The modified bases contribute to tRNA function in a way that is not yet understood.)

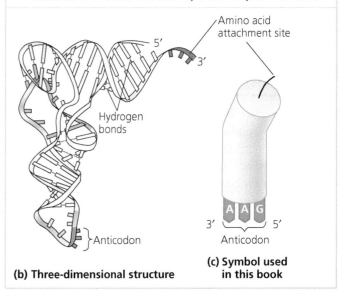

**(b) Three-dimensional structure**

**(c) Symbol used in this book**

▲ **Figure 14.15   The structure of transfer RNA (tRNA).** Anticodons are conventionally written 3′ → 5′ to align properly with codons written 5′ → 3′ (see Figure 14.14). For base pairing, RNA strands must be antiparallel, like DNA. For example, anticodon 3′-AAG-5′ pairs with mRNA codon 5′-UUC-3′.

▲ **Figure 14.14   Translation: the basic concept.** As a molecule of mRNA is moved through a ribosome, codons are translated into amino acids, one by one. The interpreters are tRNA molecules, each type with a specific nucleotide triplet called an anticodon at one end and a corresponding amino acid at the other end. A tRNA adds its amino acid cargo to a growing polypeptide chain after the anticodon hydrogen-bonds to a complementary codon on the mRNA. The figures that follow show some of the details of translation in a bacterial cell.

 **ANIMATION**   ***BioFlix***   Visit the Study Area in **MasteringBiology** for the BioFlix® 3-D Animation on Protein Synthesis.

### The Structure and Function of Transfer RNA

The key to translating a genetic message into a specific amino acid sequence is the fact that each tRNA can translate a particular mRNA codon into a given amino acid. This is possible because a tRNA bears a specific amino acid at one end, while at the other end is a nucleotide triplet that can base-pair with the complementary codon on mRNA.

A tRNA molecule consists of a single RNA strand that is only about 80 nucleotides long (compared to hundreds of nucleotides for most mRNA molecules). Because of the presence of complementary stretches of nucleotide bases that can hydrogen-bond to each other, this single strand can fold back on itself and form a molecule with a three-dimensional structure. Flattened into one plane to clarify this base pairing, a tRNA molecule looks like a cloverleaf **(Figure 14.15a)**. The tRNA actually twists and folds into a

compact three-dimensional structure that is roughly L-shaped **(Figure 14.15b)**. The loop extending from one end of the L includes the **anticodon**, the  particular nucleotide triplet that base-pairs to a specific mRNA codon. From the other end of the L-shaped tRNA molecule protrudes its 3′ end, which is the attachment site for an amino acid. Thus, the structure of a tRNA molecule fits its function.

As an example, consider the mRNA codon GGC, which is translated as the amino acid glycine. The tRNA that base-pairs with this codon by hydrogen bonding has CCG as its anticodon and carries glycine at its other end (see the incoming tRNA approaching the ribosome in Figure 14.14). As an mRNA molecule is moved through a ribosome, glycine will be added to the polypeptide chain whenever the codon GGC is presented for translation. Codon by codon, the genetic message is translated as tRNAs deposit amino acids in the order prescribed, and the ribosome joins the amino acids into a chain. The tRNA molecule is a translator in the sense that it can read a nucleic acid word (the mRNA codon) and interpret it as a protein word (the amino acid).

Like mRNA and other types of cellular RNA, transfer RNA molecules are transcribed from DNA templates. In a eukaryotic cell, tRNA, like mRNA, is made in the nucleus and then travels from the nucleus to the cytoplasm, where translation occurs. In both bacterial and eukaryotic cells, each tRNA molecule is used repeatedly, picking up its designated amino acid in the cytosol, depositing this cargo onto a polypeptide chain at the ribosome, and then leaving the ribosome, ready to pick up another of the same amino acid.

The accurate translation of a genetic message requires two instances of molecular recognition. First, a tRNA that binds to an mRNA codon specifying a particular amino acid must carry that amino acid, and no other, to the ribosome. The correct matching up of tRNA and amino acid is carried out by a family of related enzymes called **aminoacyl-tRNA synthetases (Figure 14.16)**. The active site of each type of aminoacyl-tRNA synthetase fits only a specific combination of amino acid and tRNA. (Regions of both the amino acid attachment end and the anticodon end of the tRNA are instrumental in ensuring the specific fit.) There are 20 different synthetases, one for each amino acid; each synthetase is able to bind to all the different tRNAs that match the codons for its particular amino acid. The synthetase catalyzes the covalent attachment of the amino acid to its tRNA in a process driven by the hydrolysis of ATP. The resulting aminoacyl tRNA, also called a charged tRNA, is released from the enzyme and is then available to deliver its amino acid to a growing polypeptide chain on a ribosome.

The second instance of molecular recognition is the pairing of the tRNA anticodon with the appropriate mRNA codon. If one tRNA variety existed for each mRNA codon specifying an amino acid, there would be 61 tRNAs (see Figure 14.6). In fact, there are only about 45, signifying that some tRNAs must be able to bind to more than one codon. Such versatility is possible because the rules for base pairing between the third nucleotide base of a codon and the corresponding base of a tRNA anticodon are relaxed compared to those at other codon positions. For example, the nucleotide base U at the 5′ end of a tRNA anticodon can pair with either A or G in the third position (at the 3′ end) of an mRNA codon. The flexible base pairing at

▲ **Figure 14.16 Aminoacyl-tRNA synthetases provide specificity in joining amino acids to their tRNAs.** Linkage of a tRNA to its amino acid is an endergonic process that occurs at the expense of ATP (which loses two phosphate groups, becoming AMP). Shown as an example is the joining of the amino acid tyrosine (Tyr) to the appropriate tRNA by the aminoacyl-tRNA synthetase specific for tyrosine.

this codon position is called **wobble**. Wobble explains why the synonymous codons for a given amino acid most often differ in their third nucleotide base, but not in the other bases. For example, a tRNA with the anticodon 3′-UCU-5′ can base-pair with either the mRNA codon 5′-AGA-3′ or 5′-AGG-3′, both of which code for arginine (see Figure 14.6).

### Ribosomes

Ribosomes facilitate the specific coupling of tRNA anticodons with mRNA codons during protein synthesis. A ribosome consists of a large subunit and a small subunit, each made up of proteins and one or more **ribosomal RNAs (rRNAs) (Figure 14.17)**. In eukaryotes, the subunits are made in the nucleolus. Ribosomal RNA genes are transcribed, and the RNA is processed and assembled with proteins imported from the cytoplasm. The resulting ribosomal subunits are then exported via nuclear pores to the cytoplasm. In both bacteria and eukaryotes, large and small subunits join to form a functional ribosome only when they attach to an mRNA molecule. About one-third of the mass of a ribosome is made up of proteins; the rest consists of rRNAs, either three molecules (in bacteria) or four

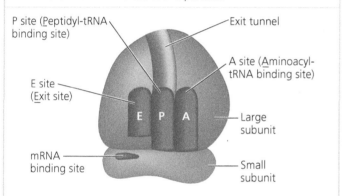

**(a) Computer model of functioning ribosome.** This is a model of a bacterial ribosome, showing its overall shape. The eukaryotic ribosome is roughly similar. A ribosomal subunit is a complex of ribosomal RNA molecules and proteins.

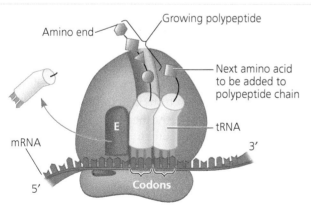

**(b) Schematic model showing binding sites.** A ribosome has an mRNA binding site and three tRNA binding sites, known as the A, P, and E sites. This schematic ribosome will appear in later diagrams.

**(c) Schematic model with mRNA and tRNA.** A tRNA fits into a binding site when its anticodon base-pairs with an mRNA codon. The P site holds the tRNA attached to the growing polypeptide. The A site holds the tRNA carrying the next amino acid to be added to the polypeptide chain. Discharged tRNAs leave from the E site. The polypeptide grows at its carboxyl end.

▲ **Figure 14.17** **The anatomy of a functioning ribosome.**

(in eukaryotes). Because most cells contain thousands of ribosomes, rRNA is the most abundant type of cellular RNA.

Although the ribosomes of bacteria and eukaryotes are very similar in structure and function, eukaryotic ribosomes are slightly larger, and they differ somewhat from bacterial ribosomes in their molecular composition. The differences are medically significant. Certain antibiotic drugs can inactivate bacterial ribosomes without inhibiting the ability of eukaryotic ribosomes to make proteins. These drugs, including tetracycline and streptomycin, are used to combat bacterial infections.

The structure of a ribosome reflects its function of bringing mRNA together with tRNAs carrying amino acids. In addition to a binding site for mRNA, each ribosome has three binding sites for tRNA, as described in Figure 14.17. The **P site** (peptidyl-tRNA binding site) holds the tRNA carrying the growing polypeptide chain, while the **A site** (aminoacyl-tRNA binding site) holds the tRNA carrying the next amino acid to be added to the chain. Discharged tRNAs leave the ribosome from the **E site** (exit site). The ribosome holds the tRNA and mRNA in close proximity and positions the new amino acid so it can be added to the carboxyl end of the growing polypeptide. It then catalyzes the formation of the peptide bond. As the polypeptide becomes longer, it passes through an *exit tunnel* in the ribosome's large subunit. When the polypeptide is complete, it is released through the exit tunnel.

There is strong evidence supporting the hypothesis that rRNA, not protein, is primarily responsible for both the structure and the function of the ribosome. The proteins, which are largely on the exterior, support the shape changes of the rRNA molecules as they carry out catalysis during translation. Ribosomal RNA is the main constituent of the A and P sites and of the interface between the two ribosomal subunits; it also acts as the catalyst of peptide bond formation. Thus, a ribosome can be regarded as one colossal ribozyme!

## Building a Polypeptide

We can divide translation, the synthesis of a polypeptide chain, into three stages (analogous to those of transcription): initiation, elongation, and termination. All three stages require protein "factors" that aid in the translation process. For certain aspects of chain initiation and elongation, energy is also required. It is provided by the hydrolysis of guanosine triphosphate (GTP), a molecule closely related to ATP.

### Ribosome Association and Initiation of Translation

The initiation stage of translation brings together mRNA, a tRNA bearing the first amino acid of the polypeptide, and the two subunits of a ribosome. First, a small ribosomal subunit binds to both mRNA and a specific initiator tRNA, which carries the amino acid methionine. In bacteria, the small subunit can bind these two in either order; it binds the mRNA at a specific RNA sequence, just upstream of the start codon, AUG. In eukaryotes, the small subunit, with the initiator tRNA already bound, binds to the 5′ cap of the mRNA and then moves, or *scans*, downstream along the mRNA until it reaches the start codon; the initiator tRNA then hydrogen-bonds to the AUG start codon (**Figure 14.18**). In either case, the start codon signals the start of translation; this is important because it establishes the codon reading frame for the mRNA. In the **Scientific Skills Exercise**, you can work with DNA sequences encoding the ribosomal binding sites on the mRNAs of a group of *E. coli* genes.

The union of mRNA, initiator tRNA, and a small ribosomal subunit is followed by the attachment of a large ribosomal subunit, completing the *translation initiation complex*. Proteins called *initiation factors* are required to bring all these components together. The cell also expends energy obtained by hydrolysis of a GTP molecule to form the initiation complex. At the completion of the initiation process, the initiator tRNA sits in the P site of the ribosome, and the vacant A site is ready for the next aminoacyl tRNA. Note that a polypeptide is always synthesized in one direction, from the initial methionine at the amino end, also called the N-terminus, toward the final amino acid at the carboxyl end, also called the C-terminus (see Figure 2.18).

① A small ribosomal subunit binds to a molecule of mRNA. In a bacterial cell, the mRNA binding site on this subunit recognizes a specific nucleotide sequence on the mRNA just upstream of the start codon. An initiator tRNA, with the anticodon UAC, base-pairs with the start codon, AUG. This tRNA carries the amino acid methionine (Met).

② The arrival of a large ribosomal subunit completes the initiation complex. Proteins called initiation factors (not shown) are required to bring all the translation components together. Hydrolysis of GTP provides the energy for the assembly. The initiator tRNA is in the P site; the A site is available to the tRNA bearing the next amino acid.

▲ **Figure 14.18 The initiation of translation.**

### Elongation of the Polypeptide Chain

In the elongation stage of translation, amino acids are added one by one to the previous amino acid at the C-terminus of the growing chain. Each addition involves the participation of several proteins called *elongation factors* and occurs in a three-step cycle described in **Figure 14.19**. Energy expenditure occurs in the first and third steps. Codon recognition requires hydrolysis of one molecule of GTP, which increases the accuracy and efficiency of this step. One more GTP is hydrolyzed to provide energy for the translocation step.

The mRNA is moved through the ribosome in one direction only, 5′ end first; this is equivalent to the ribosome moving 5′ → 3′ on the mRNA. The important point is that the ribosome and the mRNA move relative to each other, unidirectionally, codon by codon. The elongation cycle takes less than a tenth of a second in bacteria and is repeated as each amino acid is added to the chain until the polypeptide is completed.

### Termination of Translation

The final stage of translation is termination (**Figure 14.20**). Elongation continues until a stop codon in the mRNA reaches the A site of the ribosome. The nucleotide base triplets UAG, UAA, and UGA do not code for amino acids but instead act as signals to stop translation. A *release factor*, a protein shaped like an aminoacyl tRNA, binds directly to the stop codon in the A site. The release factor causes the addition of a water molecule instead of an amino acid to the polypeptide chain. (There are plenty of water molecules available in the aqueous cellular environment.) This reaction breaks (hydrolyzes) the bond between the completed polypeptide and the tRNA in the P site, releasing the polypeptide through the exit tunnel of the ribosome's large subunit. The remainder of the translation assembly then comes apart in a multistep process, aided by other protein factors. Breakdown of the translation assembly requires the hydrolysis of two more GTP molecules.

## Completing and Targeting the Functional Protein

The process of translation is often not sufficient to make a functional protein. In this section, you'll learn about modifications that polypeptide chains undergo after the translation process as well as some of the mechanisms used to target completed proteins to specific sites in the cell.

### Protein Folding and Post-Translational Modifications

During its synthesis, a polypeptide chain begins to coil and fold spontaneously as a consequence of its amino acid sequence (primary structure), forming a protein with a specific shape: a three-dimensional molecule with secondary and tertiary structure (see Figure 2.21). Thus, a gene determines primary structure, and primary structure in turn determines shape. In many cases, a chaperone protein helps the polypeptide fold correctly.

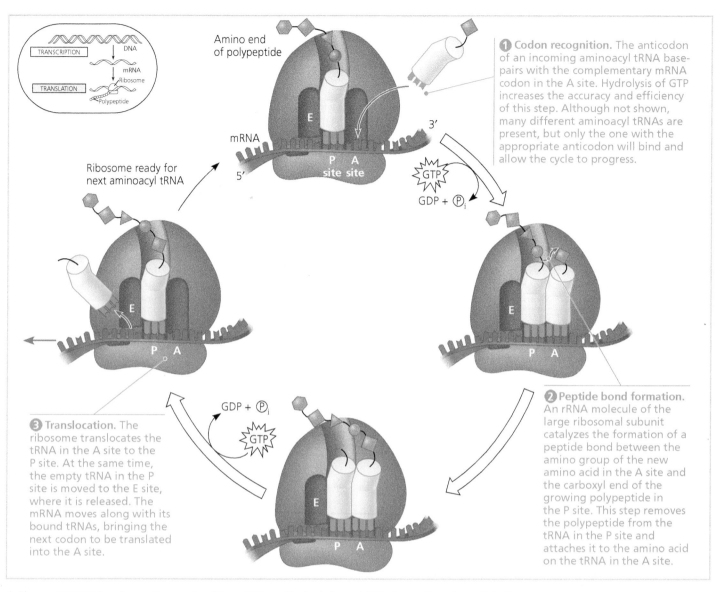

**▲ Figure 14.19 The elongation cycle of translation.** The hydrolysis of GTP plays an important role in the elongation process. Not shown are the proteins called elongation factors.

Text labels within Figure 14.19:

Amino end of polypeptide

mRNA

Ribosome ready for next aminoacyl tRNA

**1** **Codon recognition.** The anticodon of an incoming aminoacyl tRNA base-pairs with the complementary mRNA codon in the A site. Hydrolysis of GTP increases the accuracy and efficiency of this step. Although not shown, many different aminoacyl tRNAs are present, but only the one with the appropriate anticodon will bind and allow the cycle to progress.

**2** **Peptide bond formation.** An rRNA molecule of the large ribosomal subunit catalyzes the formation of a peptide bond between the amino group of the new amino acid in the A site and the carboxyl end of the growing polypeptide in the P site. This step removes the polypeptide from the tRNA in the P site and attaches it to the amino acid on the tRNA in the A site.

**3** **Translocation.** The ribosome translocates the tRNA in the A site to the P site. At the same time, the empty tRNA in the P site is moved to the E site, where it is released. The mRNA moves along with its bound tRNAs, bringing the next codon to be translated into the A site.

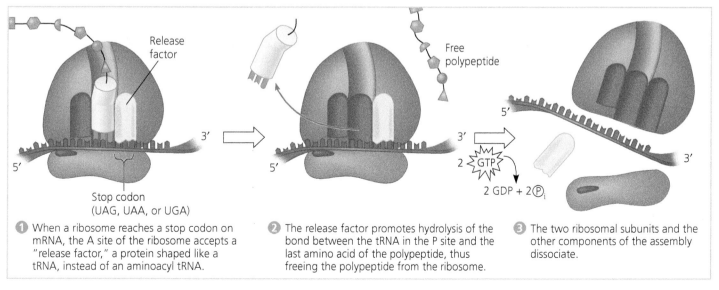

Text labels within Figure 14.20:

Release factor

Stop codon (UAG, UAA, or UGA)

Free polypeptide

**1** When a ribosome reaches a stop codon on mRNA, the A site of the ribosome accepts a "release factor," a protein shaped like a tRNA, instead of an aminoacyl tRNA.

**2** The release factor promotes hydrolysis of the bond between the tRNA in the P site and the last amino acid of the polypeptide, thus freeing the polypeptide from the ribosome.

**3** The two ribosomal subunits and the other components of the assembly dissociate.

**▲ Figure 14.20 The termination of translation.** Like elongation, termination requires GTP hydrolysis as well as additional protein factors, which are not shown here.

# Interpreting a Sequence Logo

**How Can a Sequence Logo Be Used to Identify Ribosome-Binding Sites?** When initiating translation, ribosomes bind to an mRNA at a ribosome-binding site upstream of the AUG start codon. Because mRNAs from different genes all bind to a ribosome, the genes encoding these mRNAs are likely to have a similar base sequence where the ribosomes bind. Therefore, candidate ribosome-binding sites on mRNA can be identified by comparing DNA sequences (and thus the mRNA sequences) of multiple genes in a species, searching the region upstream of the start codon for shared ("conserved") stretches of bases. In this exercise you will analyze DNA sequences from multiple such genes, represented by a visual graphic called a sequence logo.

**How the Experiment Was Done** The DNA sequences of 149 genes from the *E. coli* genome were aligned and analyzed using computer software. The aim was to identify similar base sequences—at the appropriate location in each gene—that might be potential ribosome-binding sites. Rather than presenting the data as a series of 149 sequences aligned in a column (a sequence alignment), the researchers used a sequence logo.

**Data from the Experiment** To show how sequence logos are made, the potential ribosome-binding regions from 10 of the *E. coli* genes are shown in a sequence alignment below, followed by the sequence logo derived from the aligned sequences. Note that the DNA shown is the nontemplate (coding) strand, which is how DNA sequences are typically given.

| | |
|---|---|
| *thrA* | G G T A A C G A G G T A A C A A C C A T G C G A G T G |
| *lacA* | C A T A A C G G A G T G A T C G C A T T G A A C A T G |
| *lacY* | C G C G T A A G G A A A T C C A T T A T G T A C T A T |
| *lacZ* | T T C A C A C A G G A A A C A G C T A T G A C C A T G |
| *lacI* | C A A T T C A G G G T G G T G A A T G T G A A A C C A |
| *recA* | G G C A T G A C A G G A G T A A A A A T G G C T A T C |
| *galR* | A C C C A C T A A G G T A T T T T C A T G G C G A C C |
| *metJ* | A A G A G G A T T A A G T A T C T C A T G G C T G A A |
| *lexA* | A T A C A C C C A G G G G G C G G A A T G A A A G C G |
| *trpR* | T A A C A A T G G C G A C A T A T T A T G G C C C A A |

**Interpret the Data**

1. In the sequence logo (bottom, left), the horizontal axis shows the primary sequence of the DNA by nucleotide position. Letters for each base are stacked on top of each other according to their relative frequency at that position among the aligned sequences, with the most common base as the largest letter at the top of the stack. The height of each letter represents the relative frequency of that base *at that position*. (a) In the sequence alignment, count the number of each base at position −9 and order them from most to least frequent. Compare this to the size and placement of each base at −9 in the logo. (b) Do the same for positions 0 and 1.

2. The height of a stack of letters in a logo indicates the predictive power of that stack (determined statistically). If the stack is tall, we can be more confident in predicting what base will be in that position if a new sequence is added to the logo. For example, at position 2, all 10 sequences have a G; the probability of finding a G there in a new sequence is very high, as is the stack. For short stacks, the bases all have about the same frequency, and so it's hard to predict a base at those positions. (a) Which two positions have the most predictable bases? What bases do you predict would be at those positions in a newly sequenced gene? (b) Which 12 positions have the least predictable bases? How do you know? How does this reflect the relative frequencies of the bases shown in the 10 sequences? Answer only for the two left-most of the 12 positions.

3. In the actual experiment, the researchers used 149 sequences to build their sequence logo (shown below). There is a stack at each position, even if short, because the sequence logo includes more data. (a) Which three positions in the sequence logo have the most predictable bases? Name the most frequent base at each. (b) Which positions have the least predictable bases? How can you tell?

4. A consensus sequence identifies the base occurring most often at each position in the set of sequences. (a) Write out the consensus sequence of this (the nontemplate) strand. In any position where the base can't be determined, put a dash. (b) Which provides more information—the consensus sequence or the sequence logo? What is lost in the less informative method?

5. (a) Based on the logo, what five adjacent base positions in the 5′ UTR region are most likely to be involved in ribosome binding? Explain. (b) What is represented by the bases in positions 0–2?

**Further Reading** T.D. Schneider and R.M. Stephens, Sequence logos: A new way to display consensus sequences, *Nucleic Acids Research* 18:6097–6100 (1990).

(MB) A version of this Scientific Skills Exercise can be assigned in MasteringBiology.

Additional steps—*post-translational modifications*—may be required before the protein can begin doing its particular job in the cell. Certain amino acids may be chemically modified by the attachment of sugars, lipids, phosphate groups, or other additions. Enzymes may remove one or more amino acids from the leading (amino) end of the polypeptide chain. In some cases, a polypeptide chain may be enzymatically cleaved into two or more pieces. For example, the protein insulin is first synthesized as a single polypeptide chain but becomes active only after an enzyme cuts out a central part of the chain, leaving a protein made up of two shorter polypeptide chains connected by disulfide bridges. In other cases, two or more polypeptides that are synthesized separately may come together, becoming the subunits of a protein that has quaternary structure. A familiar example is hemoglobin (see Figure 2.21).

## Targeting Polypeptides to Specific Locations

In electron micrographs of eukaryotic cells active in protein synthesis, two populations of ribosomes (and polyribosomes) are evident: free and bound (see Figure 4.9). Free ribosomes are suspended in the cytosol and mostly synthesize proteins that stay in the cytosol and function there. In contrast, bound ribosomes are attached to the cytosolic side of the endoplasmic reticulum (ER) or to the nuclear envelope. Bound ribosomes make proteins of the endomembrane system (the nuclear envelope, ER, Golgi apparatus, lysosomes, vacuoles, and plasma membrane) as well as proteins secreted from the cell, such as insulin. It is important to note that the ribosomes themselves are identical and can alternate between being free and bound.

What determines whether a ribosome is free in the cytosol or bound to rough ER? Polypeptide synthesis always begins in the cytosol as a free ribosome starts to translate an mRNA molecule. There the process continues to completion—*unless* the growing polypeptide itself cues the ribosome to attach to the ER. The polypeptides of proteins destined for the endomembrane system or for secretion are marked by a **signal peptide**, which targets the protein to the ER **(Figure 14.21)**. The signal peptide, a sequence of about 20 amino acids at or near the leading end (N-terminus) of the polypeptide, is recognized as it emerges from the ribosome by a protein-RNA complex called a **signal-recognition particle (SRP)**. This particle functions as an escort that brings the ribosome to a receptor protein built into the ER membrane. The receptor is part of a multiprotein translocation complex. Polypeptide synthesis continues there, and the growing polypeptide snakes across the membrane into the ER lumen via a protein pore. The signal peptide is usually removed by an enzyme. The rest of the completed polypeptide, if it is to be secreted from the cell, is released into solution within the ER lumen (as in Figure 14.21). Alternatively, if the polypeptide is to be a membrane protein,

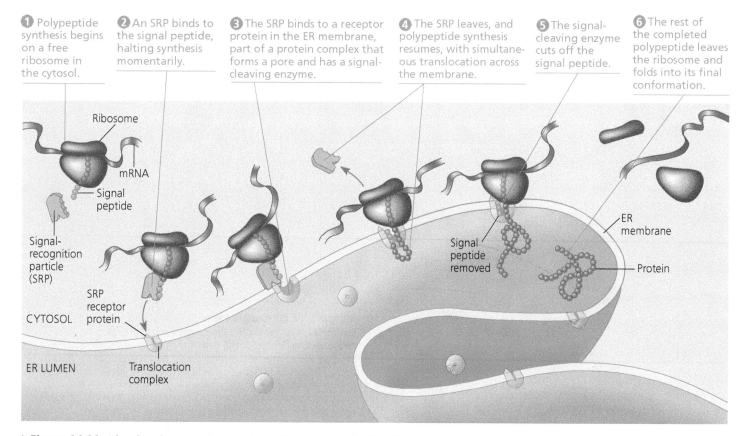

**1** Polypeptide synthesis begins on a free ribosome in the cytosol.

**2** An SRP binds to the signal peptide, halting synthesis momentarily.

**3** The SRP binds to a receptor protein in the ER membrane, part of a protein complex that forms a pore and has a signal-cleaving enzyme.

**4** The SRP leaves, and polypeptide synthesis resumes, with simultaneous translocation across the membrane.

**5** The signal-cleaving enzyme cuts off the signal peptide.

**6** The rest of the completed polypeptide leaves the ribosome and folds into its final conformation.

▲ **Figure 14.21** **The signal mechanism for targeting proteins to the ER.**

it remains partially embedded in the ER membrane. In either case, it travels in a transport vesicle to the plasma membrane.

Other kinds of signal peptides are used to target polypeptides to mitochondria, chloroplasts, the interior of the nucleus, and other organelles that are not part of the endomembrane system. The critical difference in these cases is that translation is completed in the cytosol before the polypeptide is imported into the organelle. Translocation mechanisms also vary, but in all cases studied to date, the "postal zip codes" that address proteins for secretion or to cellular locations are signal peptides of some sort. Bacteria also employ signal peptides to target proteins to the plasma membrane for secretion.

## Making Multiple Polypeptides in Bacteria and Eukaryotes

In previous sections, you have learned how a single polypeptide is synthesized using the information encoded in an mRNA molecule. When a polypeptide is required in a cell, though, the need is for many copies, not just one.

In both bacteria and eukaryotes, multiple ribosomes translate an mRNA at the same time **(Figure 14.22)**; that is, a single mRNA is used to make many copies of a polypeptide

simultaneously. Once a ribosome is far enough past the start codon, a second ribosome can attach to the mRNA, eventually resulting in a number of ribosomes trailing along the mRNA. Such strings of ribosomes, called polyribosomes (or polysomes), can be seen with an electron microscope (see Figure 14.22). They enable a cell to make many copies of a polypeptide very quickly.

Another way both bacteria and eukaryotes augment the number of copies of a polypeptide is by transcribing multiple mRNAs from the same gene, as we mentioned earlier. However, the coordination of the two processes—transcription and translation—differ in the two groups. The most important differences between bacteria and eukaryotes arise from the bacterial cell's lack of compartmental organization. Like a one-room workshop, a bacterial cell ensures a streamlined operation by coupling the two processes. In the absence of a nuclear envelope, it can simultaneously transcribe and translate the same gene **(Figure 14.23)**, and the newly made protein can then diffuse to its site of function.

In contrast, the eukaryotic cell's nuclear envelope segregates transcription from translation and provides a compartment for extensive RNA processing. This processing stage includes additional steps whose regulation can help coordinate the eukaryotic cell's elaborate activities. **Figure 14.24** summarizes the path from gene to polypeptide in a eukaryotic cell.

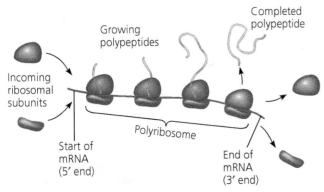

**(a)** An mRNA molecule is generally translated simultaneously by several ribosomes in clusters called polyribosomes.

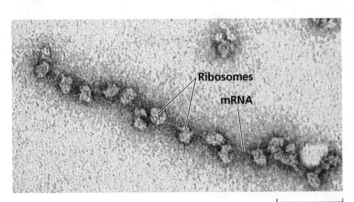

**(b)** This micrograph shows a large polyribosome in a bacterial cell. Growing polypeptides are not visible here (TEM).

0.1 µm

▲ **Figure 14.22 Polyribosomes.**

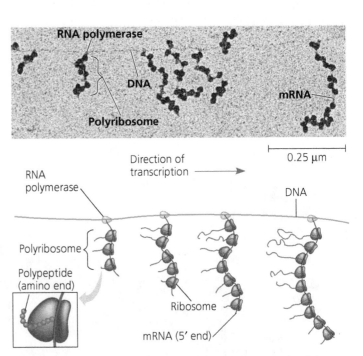

0.25 µm

▲ **Figure 14.23 Coupled transcription and translation in bacteria.** In bacterial cells, the translation of mRNA can begin as soon as the leading (5') end of the mRNA molecule peels away from the DNA template. The micrograph (TEM) shows a stretch of *E. coli* DNA being transcribed by RNA polymerase molecules. Attached to each RNA polymerase molecule is a growing strand of mRNA, which is already being translated by ribosomes. The newly synthesized polypeptides are not visible in the micrograph but are shown in the diagram.

? *Which one of the mRNA molecules started being transcribed first? On that mRNA, which ribosome started translating first?*

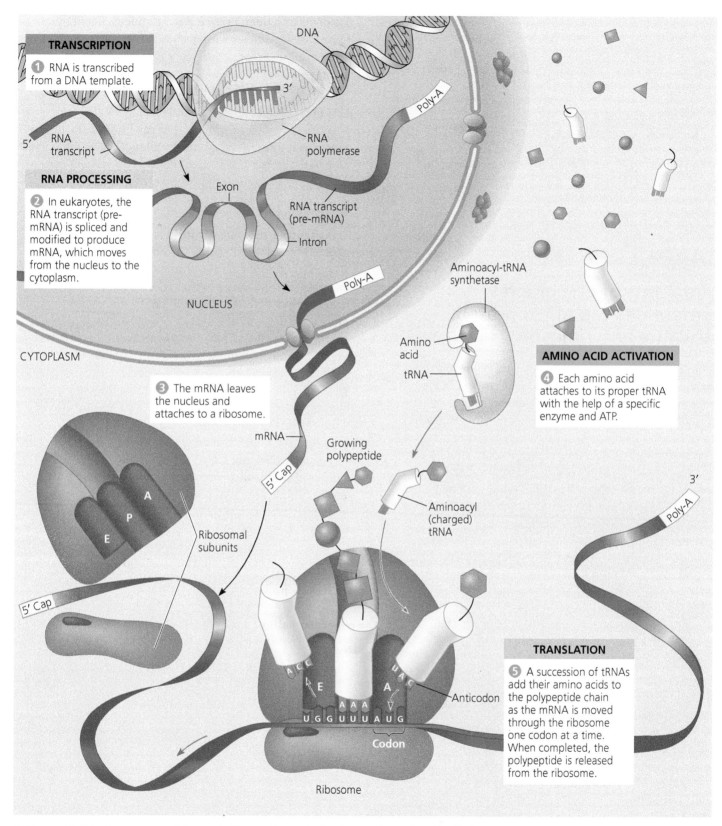

**TRANSCRIPTION**

① RNA is transcribed from a DNA template.

DNA

RNA polymerase

RNA transcript

Poly-A

5′

**RNA PROCESSING**

② In eukaryotes, the RNA transcript (pre-mRNA) is spliced and modified to produce mRNA, which moves from the nucleus to the cytoplasm.

Exon

RNA transcript (pre-mRNA)

Intron

Poly-A

NUCLEUS

CYTOPLASM

③ The mRNA leaves the nucleus and attaches to a ribosome.

Aminoacyl-tRNA synthetase

Amino acid

tRNA

**AMINO ACID ACTIVATION**

④ Each amino acid attaches to its proper tRNA with the help of a specific enzyme and ATP.

mRNA

Growing polypeptide

5′ Cap

Ribosomal subunits

5′ Cap

Aminoacyl (charged) tRNA

3′

Poly-A

**TRANSLATION**

⑤ A succession of tRNAs add their amino acids to the polypeptide chain as the mRNA is moved through the ribosome one codon at a time. When completed, the polypeptide is released from the ribosome.

Anticodon

A C C

E

A

U A C

A A A

U G G U U U A U G

Codon

Ribosome

▲ **Figure 14.24  A summary of transcription and translation in a eukaryotic cell.** This diagram shows the path from one gene to one polypeptide. Keep in mind that each gene in the DNA can be transcribed repeatedly into many identical RNA molecules and that each mRNA can be translated repeatedly to yield many identical polypeptide molecules. (Also, remember that the final products of some genes are not polypeptides but RNA molecules, including tRNA and rRNA.) In general, the steps of transcription and translation are similar in bacterial, archaeal, and eukaryotic cells. The major difference is the occurrence of RNA processing in the eukaryotic nucleus. Other significant differences are found in the initiation stages of both transcription and translation and in the termination of transcription.

1. What two processes ensure that the correct amino acid is added to a growing polypeptide chain?
2. Discuss the ways in which rRNA structure likely contributes to ribosomal function.
3. Describe how a polypeptide to be secreted is transported to the endomembrane system.
4. **DRAW IT** Draw a tRNA with the anticodon 3'-CGU-5'. What two different codons could it bind to? Draw each codon on an mRNA, labeling all 5' and 3' ends, the tRNA, and the amino acid it carries.

For suggested answers, see Appendix A.

**CONCEPT** 14.5

# Mutations of one or a few nucleotides can affect protein structure and function

Now that you have explored the process of gene expression, you are ready to understand the effects of changes to the genetic information of a cell (or virus). These changes, called **mutations**, are responsible for the huge diversity of genes found among organisms because mutations are the ultimate source of new genes. Chromosomal rearrangements that affect long segments of DNA are considered large-scale mutations (see Figure 12.14). Here we'll examine small-scale mutations of one or a few nucleotide pairs, including **point mutations**, changes in a single nucleotide pair of a gene.

If a point mutation occurs in a gamete or in a cell that gives rise to gametes, it may be transmitted to offspring and to a succession of future generations. If the mutation has an adverse effect on the phenotype of an organism, the mutant condition is referred to as a genetic disorder or hereditary disease. For example, we can trace the genetic basis of sickle-cell disease to the mutation of a single nucleotide pair in the gene that encodes the β-globin polypeptide of hemoglobin. The change of a single nucleotide in the DNA's template strand leads to the production of an abnormal protein (**Figure 14.25**; also see Figure 2.22). In individuals who are homozygous for the mutant allele, the sickling of red blood cells caused by the altered hemoglobin produces the multiple symptoms associated with sickle-cell disease (see Chapter 11). Another disorder caused by a point mutation is a heart condition, familial cardiomyopathy, that is responsible for some incidents of sudden death in young athletes. Point mutations in several genes have been identified, any of which can lead to this disorder.

## Types of Small-Scale Mutations

Let's now consider how small-scale mutations affect proteins. Small-scale mutations within a gene can be divided into two general categories: (1) single nucleotide-pair substitutions and (2) nucleotide-pair insertions or deletions. Insertions and deletions can involve one or more nucleotide pairs.

### Substitutions

A **nucleotide-pair substitution** is the replacement of one nucleotide and its partner with another pair of nucleotides (**Figure 14.26a**). Some substitutions have no effect on the encoded protein, owing to the redundancy of the genetic code. For example, if 3'-CCG-5' on the template strand mutated to 3'-CCA-5', the mRNA codon that used to be GGC would become GGU, but a glycine would still be inserted at the proper location in the protein (see Figure 14.6). In other words, a change in a nucleotide pair may transform one codon into another that is translated into the same amino acid. Such a change is an example of a **silent mutation**, which has no observable effect on the phenotype. (Silent mutations can occur outside genes as well.) Substitutions that change one amino acid to another one are called **missense mutations**. Such a mutation may have little effect on the protein: The new amino acid may have properties similar to those of the amino acid it replaces, or it may be in a region of the protein where the exact sequence of amino acids is not essential to the protein's function.

However, the nucleotide-pair substitutions of greatest interest are those that cause a major change in a protein. The

---

▼ **Figure 14.25 The molecular basis of sickle-cell disease: a point mutation.** The allele that causes sickle-cell disease differs from the wild-type (normal) allele by a single DNA nucleotide pair.

**Wild-type hemoglobin**

Wild-type hemoglobin DNA

3' — C T C — 5'
5' — G A G — 3'

mRNA

5' — G A G — 3'

Normal hemoglobin
Glu

**Sickle-cell hemoglobin**

Mutant hemoglobin DNA

3' — C A C — 5'
5' — G T G — 3'

mRNA

5' — G U G — 3'

Sickle-cell hemoglobin
Val

In the DNA, the mutant (sickle-cell) template strand (top) has an A where the wild-type template has a T.

The mutant mRNA has a U instead of an A in one codon.

The mutant hemoglobin has a valine (Val) instead of a glutamic acid (Glu).

alteration of a single amino acid in a crucial area of a protein—such as in the part of hemoglobin shown in Figure 14.25 or in the active site of an enzyme—will significantly alter protein activity. Occasionally, such a mutation leads to an improved protein or one with novel capabilities, but much more often such mutations are detrimental, leading to a useless or less active protein that impairs cellular function.

Substitution mutations are usually missense mutations; that is, the altered codon still codes for an amino acid and thus makes sense, although not necessarily the *right* sense. But a point mutation can also change a codon for an amino acid into a stop codon. This is called a **nonsense mutation**, and it causes translation to be terminated prematurely; the resulting polypeptide will be shorter than the polypeptide encoded by the normal gene. Nearly all nonsense mutations lead to nonfunctional proteins.

### Insertions and Deletions

**Insertions** and **deletions** are additions or losses of nucleotide pairs in a gene (**Figure 14.26b**). These mutations have

▼ **Figure 14.26 Types of small-scale mutations that affect mRNA sequence.** All but one of the types shown here also affect the amino acid sequence of the encoded polypeptide.

a disastrous effect on the resulting protein more often than substitutions do. Insertion or deletion of nucleotides may alter the reading frame of the genetic message, the triplet grouping of nucleotides on the mRNA that is read during translation. Such a mutation, called a **frameshift mutation**, will occur whenever the number of nucleotides inserted or deleted is not a multiple of three. All the nucleotides that are downstream of the deletion or insertion will be improperly grouped into codons, and the result will be extensive missense, usually ending sooner or later in nonsense and premature termination. Unless the frameshift is very near the end of the gene, the protein is almost certain to be nonfunctional.

## Mutagens

Mutations can arise in a number of ways. Errors during DNA replication or recombination can lead to nucleotide-pair substitutions, insertions, or deletions, as well as to mutations affecting longer stretches of DNA. If an incorrect nucleotide is added to a growing chain during replication, for example, the base on that nucleotide will then be mismatched with the nucleotide base on the other strand. In many cases, the error will be corrected by proofreading and repair systems (see Chapter 13). Otherwise, the incorrect base will be used as a template in the next round of replication, resulting in a mutation. Such mutations are called *spontaneous mutations*. It is difficult to calculate the rate at which such mutations occur. Rough estimates have been made of the rate of mutation during DNA replication for both *E. coli* and eukaryotes, and the numbers are similar: About one nucleotide in every $10^{10}$ is altered, and the change is passed on to the next generation of cells.

A number of physical and chemical agents, called **mutagens**, interact with DNA in ways that cause mutations. In the 1920s, Hermann Muller discovered that X-rays caused genetic changes in fruit flies, and he used X-rays to make *Drosophila* mutants for his genetic studies. But he also recognized an alarming implication of his discovery: X-rays and other forms of high-energy radiation pose hazards to the genetic material of people as well as laboratory organisms. Mutagenic radiation, a physical mutagen, includes ultraviolet (UV) light, which can cause disruptive thymine dimers in DNA (see Figure 13.19).

Chemical mutagens fall into several categories. Nucleotide analogs are chemicals that are similar to normal DNA nucleotides but that pair incorrectly during DNA replication. Some other chemical mutagens interfere with correct DNA replication by inserting themselves into the DNA and distorting the double helix. Still other mutagens cause chemical changes in bases that change their pairing properties.

Researchers have developed a variety of methods to test the mutagenic activity of chemicals. A major application of these tests is the preliminary screening of chemicals to identify those that may cause cancer. This approach makes sense because most carcinogens (cancer-causing chemicals) are mutagenic, and conversely, most mutagens are carcinogenic.

**CONCEPT CHECK 14.5**

1. What happens when one nucleotide pair is lost from the middle of the coding sequence of a gene?
2. **MAKE CONNECTIONS** Individuals heterozygous for the sickle-cell allele show effects of the allele under some circumstances (see Concept 11.4). Explain in terms of gene expression.
3. **DRAW IT** The template strand of a gene includes this sequence: 3'-TACTTGTCCGATATC-5'. It is mutated to 3'-TACTTGTCCAATATC-5'. For both versions, draw the DNA, the mRNA, and the encoded amino acid sequence. What is the effect on the amino acid sequence?

For suggested answers, see Appendix A.

## What Is a Gene? *Revisiting the Question*

Our definition of a gene has evolved over the past few chapters, as it has through the history of genetics. We began with the Mendelian concept of a gene as a discrete unit of inheritance that affects a phenotypic character (Chapter 11). We saw that Morgan and his colleagues assigned such genes to specific loci on chromosomes (Chapter 12). We went on to view a gene as a region of specific nucleotide sequence along the length of the DNA molecule of a chromosome (Chapter 13). Finally, in this chapter, we have considered a functional definition of a gene as a DNA sequence that codes for a specific polypeptide chain. All these definitions are useful, depending on the context in which genes are being studied.

Clearly, the statement that a gene codes for a polypeptide is too simple. Most eukaryotic genes contain noncoding segments (such as introns), so large portions of these genes have no corresponding segments in polypeptides. Molecular biologists also often include promoters and certain other regulatory regions of DNA within the boundaries of a gene. These DNA sequences are not transcribed, but they can be considered part of the functional gene because they must be present for transcription to occur. Our definition of a gene must also be broad enough to include the DNA that is transcribed into rRNA, tRNA, and other RNAs that are not translated. These genes have no polypeptide products but play crucial roles in the cell. Thus, we arrive at the following definition: *A gene is a region of DNA that can be expressed to produce a final functional product that is either a polypeptide or an RNA molecule.*

When considering phenotypes, however, it is useful to focus on genes that code for polypeptides. In this chapter, you have learned how a typical gene is expressed—by transcription into RNA and then translation into a polypeptide that forms a protein of specific structure and function. Proteins, in turn, bring about an organism's observable phenotype.

A given type of cell expresses only a subset of its genes. This is an essential feature in multicellular organisms: Gene expression is precisely regulated. We'll explore gene regulation in the next chapter, beginning with the simpler case of bacteria and continuing with eukaryotes.

# 14 Chapter Review

## SUMMARY OF KEY CONCEPTS

### CONCEPT 14.1
**Genes specify proteins via transcription and translation (pp. 275–280)**

- DNA controls metabolism by directing cells to make specific enzymes and other proteins, via the process of **gene expression**. Beadle and Tatum's studies of mutant strains of *Neurospora* led to the one gene–one polypeptide hypothesis. Genes code for polypeptide chains or specify RNA molecules.
- **Transcription** is the synthesis of RNA complementary to a **template strand** of DNA, providing a nucleotide-to-nucleotide transfer of information. **Translation** is the synthesis of a polypeptide whose amino acid sequence is specified by the nucleotide sequence in **mRNA**; this informational transfer involves a change of language, from that of nucleotides to that of amino acids.
- Genetic information is encoded as a sequence of nonoverlapping nucleotide triplets, or **codons**. A codon in messenger RNA (mRNA) either is translated into an amino acid (61 of the 64 codons) or serves as a stop signal (3 codons). Codons must be read in the correct **reading frame**.

**?** *Describe the process of gene expression, by which a gene affects the phenotype of an organism.*

### CONCEPT 14.2
**Transcription is the DNA-directed synthesis of RNA: *a closer look* (pp. 280–282)**

- RNA synthesis is catalyzed by **RNA polymerase**, which links together RNA nucleotides complementary to a DNA template strand. This process follows the same base-pairing rules as DNA replication, except that in RNA, uracil substitutes for thymine.

- The three stages of transcription are initiation, elongation, and termination. A **promoter**, often including a **TATA box** in eukaryotes, establishes where RNA synthesis is initiated. **Transcription factors** help eukaryotic RNA polymerase recognize promoter sequences,

forming a **transcription initiation complex**. The mechanisms of termination are different in bacteria and eukaryotes.

**?** *What are the similarities and differences in the initiation of gene transcription in bacteria and eukaryotes?*

### CONCEPT 14.3
**Eukaryotic cells modify RNA after transcription (pp. 282–284)**

- Eukaryotic pre-mRNAs undergo **RNA processing**, which includes RNA splicing, the addition of a modified nucleotide **5′ cap** to the 5′ end, and the addition of a **poly-A tail** to the 3′ end.
- Most eukaryotic genes are split into segments: They have **introns** interspersed among the **exons** (regions included in the mRNA). In **RNA splicing**, introns are removed and exons joined. RNA splicing is typically carried out by **spliceosomes**, but in some cases, RNA alone catalyzes its own splicing. The catalytic ability of some RNA molecules, called **ribozymes**, derives from the properties of RNA. The presence of introns allows for **alternative RNA splicing**.

**?** *What function do the 5′ cap and the poly-A tail serve on a eukaryotic mRNA?*

### CONCEPT 14.4
**Translation is the RNA-directed synthesis of a polypeptide: *a closer look* (pp. 284–294)**

- A cell translates an mRNA message into protein using **transfer RNAs (tRNAs)**. After being bound to a specific amino acid by an **aminoacyl-tRNA synthetase**, a tRNA lines up via its **anticodon** at the complementary codon on mRNA. A **ribosome**, made up of **ribosomal RNAs (rRNAs)** and proteins, facilitates this coupling with binding sites for mRNA and tRNA.
- Ribosomes coordinate the three stages of translation: initiation, elongation, and termination. The formation of peptide bonds between amino acids is catalyzed by rRNA as tRNAs move through the **A** and **P sites** and exit through the **E site**.

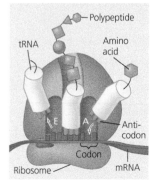

- After translation, modifications to proteins can affect their shape. Free ribosomes in the cytosol initiate synthesis of all proteins, but proteins with a **signal peptide** are synthesized on the ER.
- A gene can be transcribed by multiple RNA polymerases simultaneously. A single mRNA molecule can be translated simultaneously by a number of ribosomes, forming a **polyribosome**. In bacteria, these processes are coupled, but in eukaryotes they are separated in time and space by the nuclear membrane.

 *What function do tRNAs serve in the process of translation?*

CONCEPT 14.5

## Mutations of one or a few nucleotides can affect protein structure and function (pp. 294–297)

- Small-scale **mutations** include **point mutations**, changes in one DNA nucleotide pair, which may lead to production of nonfunctional proteins. **Nucleotide-pair substitutions** can cause **missense** or **nonsense mutations**. Nucleotide-pair **insertions** or **deletions** may produce **frameshift mutations**.
- Spontaneous mutations can occur during DNA replication, recombination, or repair. Chemical and physical **mutagens** cause DNA damage that can alter genes.

 *What will be the results of chemically modifying one nucleotide base of a gene? What role is played by DNA repair systems in the cell?*

# TEST YOUR UNDERSTANDING

### Level 1: Knowledge/Comprehension

1. In eukaryotic cells, transcription cannot begin until
   a. the two DNA strands have completely separated and exposed the promoter.
   b. several transcription factors have bound to the promoter.
   c. the 5′ caps are removed from the mRNA.
   d. the DNA introns are removed from the template.
   e. DNA nucleases have isolated the transcription unit.

2. Which of the following is *not* true of a codon?
   a. It consists of three nucleotides.
   b. It may code for the same amino acid as another codon.
   c. It never codes for more than one amino acid.
   d. It extends from one end of a tRNA molecule.
   e. It is the basic unit of the genetic code.

3. The anticodon of a particular tRNA molecule is
   a. complementary to the corresponding mRNA codon.
   b. complementary to the corresponding triplet in rRNA.
   c. the part of tRNA that bonds to a specific amino acid.
   d. changeable, depending on the amino acid that attaches to the tRNA.
   e. catalytic, making the tRNA a ribozyme.

4. Which of the following is *not* true of RNA processing?
   a. Exons are cut out before mRNA leaves the nucleus.
   b. Nucleotides may be added at both ends of the RNA.
   c. Ribozymes may function in RNA splicing.
   d. RNA splicing can be catalyzed by spliceosomes.
   e. A primary transcript is often much longer than the final RNA molecule that leaves the nucleus.

5. Which component is *not* directly involved in translation?
   a. mRNA
   b. DNA
   c. tRNA
   d. ribosomes
   e. GTP

### Level 2: Application/Analysis

6. Using Figure 14.6, identify a 5′ → 3′ sequence of nucleotides in the DNA template strand for an mRNA coding for the polypeptide sequence Phe-Pro-Lys.
   a. 5′-UUUGGGAAA-3′
   b. 5′-GAACCCCTT-3′
   c. 5′-AAAACCTTT-3′
   d. 5′-CTTCGGGAA-3′
   e. 5′-AAACCCUUU-3′

7. Which of the following mutations would be *most* likely to have a harmful effect on an organism?
   a. a nucleotide-pair substitution
   b. a deletion of three nucleotides near the middle of a gene
   c. a single nucleotide deletion in the middle of an intron
   d. a single nucleotide deletion near the end of the coding sequence
   e. a single nucleotide insertion downstream of, and close to, the start of the coding sequence

8. Fill in the following table:

| Type of RNA | Functions |
|---|---|
| Messenger RNA (mRNA) | |
| Transfer RNA (tRNA) | |
| | Plays catalytic (ribozyme) roles and structural roles in ribosomes |
| Primary transcript | |
| Small RNAs in spliceosome | |

### Level 3: Synthesis/Evaluation

9. **SCIENTIFIC INQUIRY**
   Knowing that the genetic code is almost universal, a scientist uses molecular biological methods to insert the human β-globin gene (shown in Figure 14.12) into bacterial cells, hoping the cells will express it and synthesize functional β-globin protein. Instead, the protein produced is nonfunctional and is found to contain many fewer amino acids than does β-globin made by a eukaryotic cell. Explain why.

10. **FOCUS ON EVOLUTION**
    Most amino acids are coded for by a set of similar codons (see Figure 14.6). What evolutionary explanations can you give for this pattern? (*Hint*: There is one explanation relating to ancestry, and some less obvious ones of a "form-fits-function" type.)

11. **FOCUS ON INFORMATION**
    Evolution accounts for the unity and diversity of life, and the continuity of life is based on heritable information in the form of DNA. In a short essay (100–150 words), discuss how the fidelity with which DNA is inherited is related to the processes of evolution. (Review the discussion of proofreading and DNA repair in Concept 13.2.)

*For selected answers, see Appendix A.*

## MasteringBiology®

**Students** Go to **MasteringBiology** for assignments, the eText, and the Study Area with practice tests, animations, and activities.

**Instructors** Go to **MasteringBiology** for automatically graded tutorials and questions that you can assign to your students, plus Instructor Resources.

# Viruses

15

**KEY CONCEPTS**

15.1 A virus consists of a nucleic acid surrounded by a protein coat

15.2 Viruses replicate only in host cells

15.3 Viruses are formidable pathogens in animals and plants

**OVERVIEW**

## A Borrowed Life

The photo in **Figure 15.1** shows a remarkable event: a cell under siege, releasing thousands more of its attackers, each capable of infecting another cell. The attackers (red) are human immunodeficiency viruses (HIV) emerging from a human immune cell. By injecting its genetic information into the infected cell, a single virus hijacks the cell, recruiting cellular machinery to manufacture many new viruses and promote further infection. Left untreated, HIV causes acquired immunodeficiency syndrome (AIDS) by destroying the immune system.

Compared to eukaryotic and even prokaryotic cells, viruses are much smaller and simpler in structure. Lacking the metabolic machinery found in a cell, a **virus** is an infectious particle consisting of little more than genes packaged in a protein coat.

Are viruses living or nonliving? Because viruses are capable of causing many diseases, researchers in the late 1800s saw a parallel with bacteria and proposed that viruses were the simplest of living forms. However, viruses cannot reproduce or carry out metabolism outside of a host cell. Most biologists studying viruses today would likely agree that they are not alive but exist in a shady area between life-forms and chemicals. The simple phrase used recently by two researchers describes them aptly enough: Viruses lead "a kind of borrowed life."

In this chapter, we'll explore the biology of viruses, beginning with their structure and then describing how they replicate. We'll end the chapter with a look at the role of viruses as disease-causing agents, or pathogens, of plants and animals.

▼ **Figure 15.1** Are the tiny viruses (red) budding from this cell alive?

0.25 μm

**CONCEPT** 15.1

## A virus consists of a nucleic acid surrounded by a protein coat

The tiniest viruses are only 20 nm in diameter—smaller than a ribosome. Millions could easily fit on a pinhead. Even the largest known virus, which has a diameter of several hundred nanometers, is barely visible under the light microscope. An early discovery that some viruses could be crystallized was exciting and puzzling news. Not even the simplest of cells can aggregate into regular crystals. But if viruses are not cells, then what are they? Examining the structure of a virus more closely reveals that it is an infectious particle consisting of nucleic acid enclosed in a protein coat and, for some viruses, surrounded by a membranous envelope.

## Viral Genomes

We usually think of genes as being made of double-stranded DNA—the conventional double helix—but many viruses defy this convention. Their genomes may consist of double-stranded DNA, single-stranded DNA, double-stranded RNA, or single-stranded RNA, depending on the type of virus. A virus is called a DNA virus or an RNA virus, based on the kind of nucleic acid that makes up its genome. In either case, the genome is usually organized as a single linear or circular molecule of nucleic acid, although the genomes of some viruses consist of multiple molecules of nucleic acid. The smallest viruses known have only four genes in their genome, while the largest have several hundred to a thousand. For comparison, bacterial genomes contain about 200 to a few thousand genes.

## Capsids and Envelopes

The protein shell enclosing the viral genome is called a **capsid**. Depending on the type of virus, the capsid may be rod-shaped, polyhedral, or more complex in shape. Capsids are built from a large number of protein subunits called *capsomeres*, but the number of different *kinds* of proteins in a capsid is usually small. Tobacco mosaic virus (TMV), for example, has a rigid, rod-shaped capsid made from over a thousand molecules of a single type of protein arranged in a helix; rod-shaped viruses are commonly called *helical viruses* for this reason **(Figure 15.2a)**. Adenoviruses, which infect the respiratory tracts of animals, have 252 identical protein molecules arranged in a polyhedral capsid with 20 triangular facets—an icosahedron; thus, these and other similarly shaped viruses are referred to as *icosahedral viruses* **(Figure 15.2b)**.

Some viruses have accessory structures that help them infect their hosts. For instance, a membranous envelope surrounds

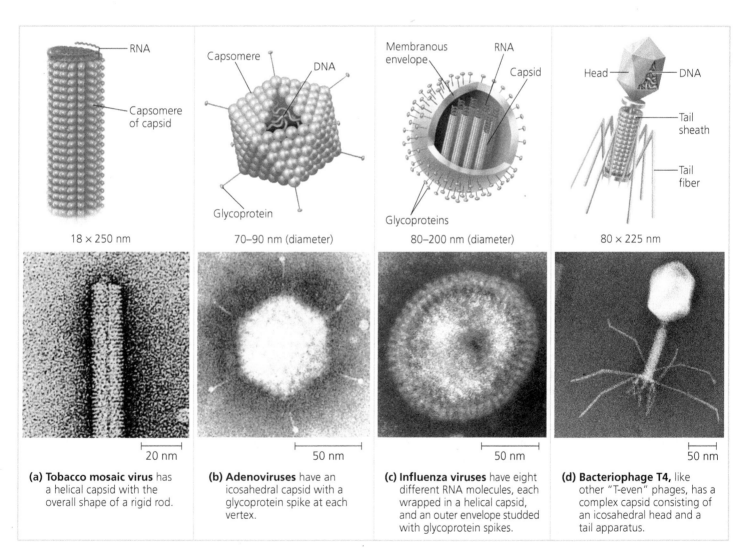

**(a) Tobacco mosaic virus** has a helical capsid with the overall shape of a rigid rod.

RNA
Capsomere of capsid
18 × 250 nm
20 nm

**(b) Adenoviruses** have an icosahedral capsid with a glycoprotein spike at each vertex.

Capsomere
DNA
Glycoprotein
70–90 nm (diameter)
50 nm

**(c) Influenza viruses** have eight different RNA molecules, each wrapped in a helical capsid, and an outer envelope studded with glycoprotein spikes.

Membranous envelope
RNA
Capsid
Glycoproteins
80–200 nm (diameter)
50 nm

**(d) Bacteriophage T4,** like other "T-even" phages, has a complex capsid consisting of an icosahedral head and a tail apparatus.

Head
DNA
Tail sheath
Tail fiber
80 × 225 nm
50 nm

▲ **Figure 15.2 Viral structure.** Viruses are made up of nucleic acid (DNA or RNA) enclosed in a protein coat (the capsid) and sometimes further wrapped in a membranous envelope. The individual protein subunits making up the capsid are called capsomeres. Although diverse in size and shape, viruses have many common structural features. (All micrographs are colorized TEMs.)

the capsids of influenza viruses and many other viruses found in animals **(Figure 15.2c)**. These **viral envelopes**, which are derived from the membranes of the host cell, contain host cell phospholipids and membrane proteins. They also contain proteins and glycoproteins of viral origin. (Glycoproteins are proteins with carbohydrates covalently attached.) Some viruses carry a few viral enzyme molecules within their capsids.

Many of the most complex capsids are found among the viruses that infect bacteria, called **bacteriophages**, or simply **phages**. The first phages studied included seven that infect *E. coli*. These seven phages were named type 1 (T1), type 2 (T2), and so forth, in the order of their discovery. The three T-even phages (T2, T4, and T6) turned out to be very similar in structure. Their capsids have elongated icosahedral heads enclosing their DNA. Attached to the head is a protein tail piece with fibers by which the phages attach to a bacterium **(Figure 15.2d)**. In the next section, we'll examine how these few viral parts function together with cellular components to produce large numbers of viral progeny.

### CONCEPT CHECK 15.1

1. Compare the structures of tobacco mosaic virus and influenza virus (see Figure 15.2).

2. **MAKE CONNECTIONS** Bacteriophages were used to provide evidence that DNA carries genetic information (see Figure 13.4). Briefly describe the experiment carried out by Hershey and Chase, including in your description why the researchers chose to use phages.

*For suggested answers, see Appendix A.*

**CONCEPT** 15.2

# Viruses replicate only in host cells

Viruses lack metabolic enzymes and equipment for making proteins, such as ribosomes. They are obligate intracellular parasites; in other words, they can replicate only within a host cell. It is fair to say that viruses in isolation are merely packaged sets of genes in transit from one host cell to another.

Each particular virus can infect cells of only a limited number of host species, called the **host range** of the virus. This host specificity results from the evolution of recognition systems by the virus. Viruses usually identify host cells by a "lock-and-key" fit between viral surface proteins and specific receptor molecules on the outside of cells. Some viruses have broad host ranges. For example, West Nile virus and equine encephalitis virus are distinctly different viruses that can each infect mosquitoes, birds, horses, and humans. Other viruses have host ranges so narrow that they infect only a single species. Measles virus, for instance, can infect only humans. Furthermore, viral infection of multicellular eukaryotes is usually limited to particular tissues. Human cold viruses infect only the cells lining the upper respiratory tract, and the HIV virus binds to receptors present only on certain types of white blood cells (see Figure 15.1).

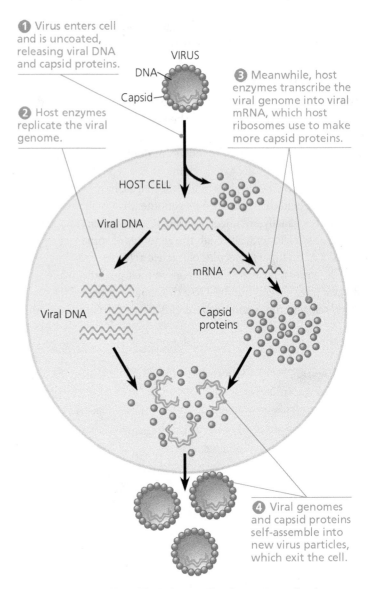

1 Virus enters cell and is uncoated, releasing viral DNA and capsid proteins.

2 Host enzymes replicate the viral genome.

3 Meanwhile, host enzymes transcribe the viral genome into viral mRNA, which host ribosomes use to make more capsid proteins.

4 Viral genomes and capsid proteins self-assemble into new virus particles, which exit the cell.

VIRUS

DNA

Capsid

HOST CELL

Viral DNA

Viral DNA

mRNA

Capsid proteins

▲ **Figure 15.3 A simplified viral replicative cycle.** A virus is an obligate intracellular parasite that uses the equipment and small molecules of its host cell to replicate. In this simplest of viral cycles, the parasite is a DNA virus with a capsid consisting of a single type of protein.

**MAKE CONNECTIONS** *Label each of the straight black arrows with one word representing the name of the process that is occurring. (Review Figure 14.24.)*

## General Features of Viral Replicative Cycles

A viral infection begins when a virus binds to a host cell and the viral genome makes its way inside **(Figure 15.3)**. The mechanism of genome entry depends on the type of virus and the type of host cell. For example, T-even phages use their elaborate tail apparatus to inject DNA into a bacterium (see Figure 15.2d). Other viruses are taken up by endocytosis or, in the case of enveloped viruses, by fusion of the viral envelope with the host's plasma membrane. Once the viral genome is inside, the proteins it encodes can commandeer the host, reprogramming the cell to copy the viral nucleic acid and manufacture viral proteins. The host provides the nucleotides for making viral nucleic acids, as well as enzymes, ribosomes, tRNAs, amino acids, ATP, and other components needed for making the viral proteins. Many DNA viruses use the DNA polymerases of the host cell to synthesize new genomes along the templates provided by the viral DNA. In contrast, to replicate their genomes, RNA viruses use virally encoded RNA polymerases that can use RNA as a template. (Uninfected cells generally make no enzymes for carrying out this process.)

After the viral nucleic acid molecules and capsomeres are produced, they spontaneously self-assemble into new viruses. In fact, researchers can separate the RNA and capsomeres of TMV and then reassemble complete viruses simply by mixing the components together under the right conditions. The simplest type of viral replicative cycle ends with the exit of hundreds or thousands of viruses from the infected host cell, a process that often damages or destroys the cell. Such cellular damage and death, as well as the body's responses to this destruction, cause many of the symptoms associated with viral infections. The viral progeny that exit a cell have the potential to infect additional cells, spreading the viral infection.

There are many variations on the simplified viral replicative cycle we have just described. We'll now take a look at some of these variations in bacterial viruses (phages) and animal viruses; later in the chapter, we'll consider plant viruses.

## Replicative Cycles of Phages

Phages are the best understood of all viruses, although some of them are also among the most complex. Research on phages led to the discovery that some double-stranded DNA viruses can replicate by two alternative mechanisms: the lytic cycle and the lysogenic cycle.

### The Lytic Cycle

A phage replicative cycle that culminates in death of the host cell is known as a **lytic cycle**. The term refers to the last stage of infection, during which the bacterium lyses (breaks open) and releases the phages that were produced within the cell. Each of these phages can then infect a healthy cell, and a few successive lytic cycles can destroy an entire bacterial population in just a few hours. A phage that replicates only by a lytic cycle is called a **virulent phage**. Figure 15.4 illustrates the major steps in the lytic cycle of T4, a typical virulent phage. Study this figure before proceeding.

After reading about the lytic cycle, you may wonder why phages haven't exterminated all bacteria. The reason is that bacteria have their own defenses. First, natural selection favors bacterial mutants with receptors that are no longer recognized by a particular type of phage. Second, when phage DNA does

▶ **Figure 15.4 The lytic cycle of phage T4, a virulent phage.** Phage T4 has almost 300 genes, which are transcribed and translated using the host cell's machinery. One of the first phage genes translated after the viral DNA enters the host cell codes for an enzyme that degrades the host cell's DNA (step 2); the phage DNA is protected from breakdown because it contains a modified form of cytosine that is not recognized by the enzyme. The entire lytic cycle, from the phage's first contact with the cell surface to cell lysis, takes only 20–30 minutes at 37°C.

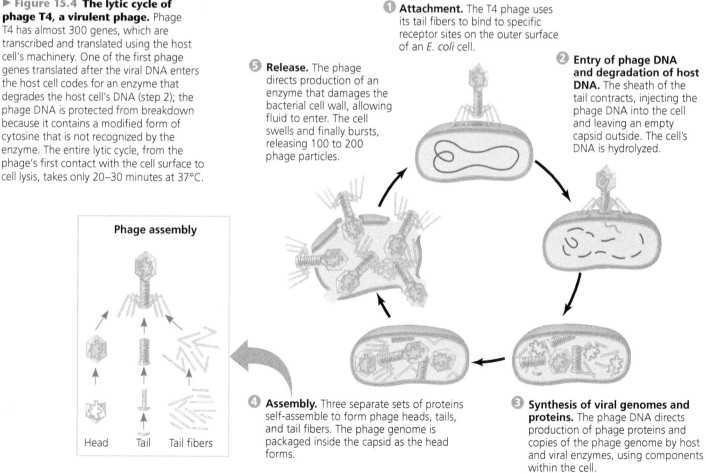

① **Attachment.** The T4 phage uses its tail fibers to bind to specific receptor sites on the outer surface of an *E. coli* cell.

② **Entry of phage DNA and degradation of host DNA.** The sheath of the tail contracts, injecting the phage DNA into the cell and leaving an empty capsid outside. The cell's DNA is hydrolyzed.

③ **Synthesis of viral genomes and proteins.** The phage DNA directs production of phage proteins and copies of the phage genome by host and viral enzymes, using components within the cell.

④ **Assembly.** Three separate sets of proteins self-assemble to form phage heads, tails, and tail fibers. The phage genome is packaged inside the capsid as the head forms.

⑤ **Release.** The phage directs production of an enzyme that damages the bacterial cell wall, allowing fluid to enter. The cell swells and finally bursts, releasing 100 to 200 phage particles.

**Phage assembly**

Head        Tail        Tail fibers

enter a bacterium, the DNA often is identified as foreign and cut up by cellular enzymes called **restriction enzymes**, which are so named because their activity *restricts* the ability of the phage to infect the bacterium. (These enzymes are used in molecular biology and DNA cloning techniques; see Concept 13.4.) The bacterial cell's own DNA is methylated in a way that prevents attack by its own restriction enzymes. But just as natural selection favors bacteria with mutant receptors or effective restriction enzymes, it also favors phage mutants that can bind the altered receptors or are resistant to particular restriction enzymes. Thus, the parasite-host relationship is in constant evolutionary flux.

There is yet a third important reason bacteria have been spared from extinction as a result of phage activity. Instead of lysing their host cells, many phages coexist with them in a state called lysogeny, which we'll now discuss.

### The Lysogenic Cycle

In contrast to the lytic cycle, which kills the host cell, the **lysogenic cycle** allows replication of the phage genome without destroying the host. Phages capable of using both modes of replicating within a bacterium are called **temperate phages**. A temperate phage called lambda, written with the Greek letter λ, is widely used in biological research. Phage λ resembles T4, but its tail has only one short tail fiber.

Infection of an *E. coli* cell by phage λ begins when the phage binds to the surface of the cell and injects its linear DNA genome **(Figure 15.5)**. Within the host, the λ DNA molecule forms a circle. What happens next depends on the replicative mode: lytic cycle or lysogenic cycle. During a lytic cycle, the viral genes immediately turn the host cell into a λ-producing factory, and the cell soon lyses and releases its viral products. During a lysogenic cycle, however, the λ DNA molecule is incorporated into a specific site on the *E. coli* chromosome by viral proteins that break both circular DNA molecules and join them to each other. When integrated into the bacterial chromosome in this way, the viral DNA is known as a **prophage**. One prophage gene codes for a protein that prevents transcription of most of the other prophage genes. Thus, the phage genome is mostly silent within the bacterium. Every time the *E. coli* cell prepares to divide, it replicates the phage DNA along with its own and passes the copies on to daughter cells. A single infected cell can quickly give rise to a large population of bacteria carrying the virus in prophage form. This mechanism enables viruses to propagate without killing the host cells on which they depend.

The term *lysogenic* implies that prophages are capable of generating active phages that lyse their host cells. This occurs when the λ genome is induced to exit the bacterial chromosome and initiate a lytic cycle. An environmental signal, such

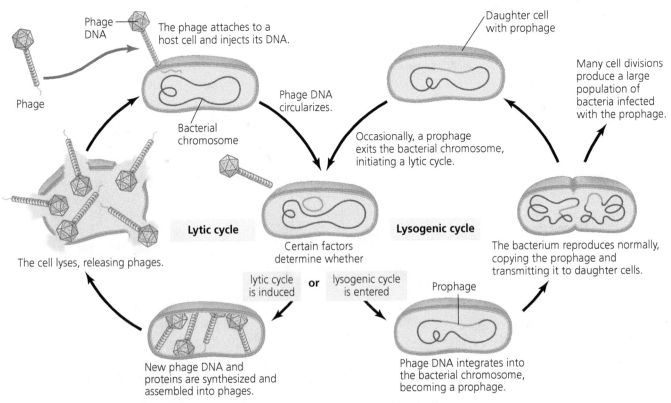

▲ **Figure 15.5 The lytic and lysogenic cycles of phage λ, a temperate phage.** After entering the bacterial cell and circularizing, the λ DNA can immediately initiate the production of a large number of progeny phages (lytic cycle) or integrate into the bacterial chromosome (lysogenic cycle). In most cases, phage λ follows the lytic pathway, which is similar to that detailed in Figure 15.4. However, once a lysogenic cycle begins, the prophage may be carried in the host cell's chromosome for many generations. Phage λ has one main tail fiber, which is short.

as a certain chemical or high-energy radiation, usually triggers the switchover from the lysogenic to the lytic mode.

In addition to the gene for the transcription-preventing protein, a few other prophage genes may be expressed during lysogeny. Expression of these genes may alter the host's phenotype, a phenomenon that can have important medical significance. For example, the three species of bacteria that cause the human diseases diphtheria, botulism, and scarlet fever would not be so harmful to humans without certain prophage genes that cause the host bacteria to make toxins. And the difference between the *E. coli* strain that resides in our intestines and the O157:H7 strain that has caused several deaths by food poisoning appears to be the presence of prophages in the O157:H7 strain.

## Replicative Cycles of Animal Viruses

Everyone has suffered from viral infections, whether cold sores, influenza, or the common cold. Like all viruses, those that cause illness in humans and other animals can replicate only inside host cells. Many variations on the basic scheme of viral infection and replication are represented among the animal viruses. Key variables are the nature of the viral genome

(double- or single-stranded DNA or RNA) and the presence or absence of an envelope.

Whereas few bacteriophages have an RNA genome or envelope, many animal viruses have both. In fact, nearly all animal viruses with RNA genomes have an envelope, as do some with DNA genomes. Rather than consider all the mechanisms of viral infection and replication, we'll focus on the roles of viral envelopes and on the functioning of RNA as the genetic material of many animal viruses.

### Viral Envelopes

An animal virus equipped with an envelope—that is, an outer membrane—uses it to enter the host cell. Protruding from the outer surface of this envelope are viral glycoproteins that bind to specific receptor molecules on the surface of a host cell. **Figure 15.6** outlines the events in the replicative cycle of an enveloped virus with an RNA genome. Ribosomes bound to the endoplasmic reticulum (ER) of the host cell make the protein parts of the envelope glycoproteins; cellular enzymes in the ER and Golgi apparatus then add the sugars. The resulting viral glycoproteins, embedded in membrane derived from the

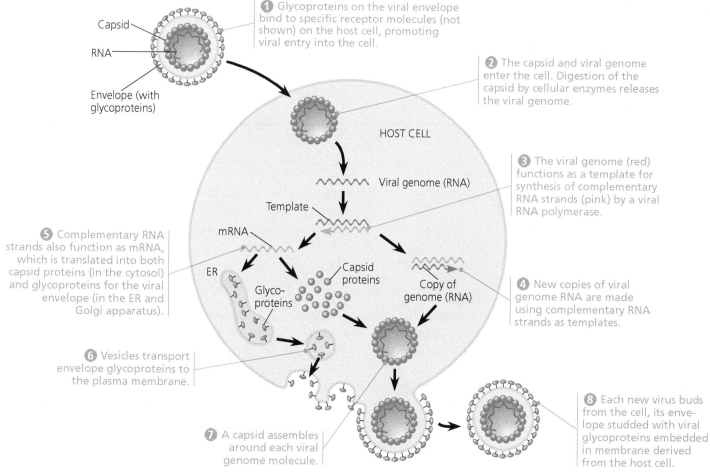

Capsid

RNA

Envelope (with glycoproteins)

**1** Glycoproteins on the viral envelope bind to specific receptor molecules (not shown) on the host cell, promoting viral entry into the cell.

**2** The capsid and viral genome enter the cell. Digestion of the capsid by cellular enzymes releases the viral genome.

HOST CELL

Viral genome (RNA)

Template

mRNA

ER

Glyco-proteins

Capsid proteins

Copy of genome (RNA)

**3** The viral genome (red) functions as a template for synthesis of complementary RNA strands (pink) by a viral RNA polymerase.

**5** Complementary RNA strands also function as mRNA, which is translated into both capsid proteins (in the cytosol) and glycoproteins for the viral envelope (in the ER and Golgi apparatus).

**4** New copies of viral genome RNA are made using complementary RNA strands as templates.

**6** Vesicles transport envelope glycoproteins to the plasma membrane.

**7** A capsid assembles around each viral genome molecule.

**8** Each new virus buds from the cell, its envelope studded with viral glycoproteins embedded in membrane derived from the host cell.

▲ **Figure 15.6 The replicative cycle of an enveloped RNA virus.** Shown here is a virus with a single-stranded RNA genome that functions as a template for synthesis of mRNA. Some enveloped viruses enter the host cell by fusion of the envelope with the cell's plasma membrane; others enter by endocytosis. For all enveloped RNA viruses, the formation of new envelopes for progeny viruses occurs by the mechanism depicted in this figure.

host cell, are transported to the cell surface. In a process much like exocytosis, new viral capsids are wrapped in membrane as they bud from the cell. In other words, the viral envelope is derived from the host cell's plasma membrane, although some of the molecules of this membrane are specified by viral genes. The enveloped viruses are now free to infect other cells. This replicative cycle does not necessarily kill the host cell, in contrast to the lytic cycles of phages.

Some viruses have envelopes that are not derived from plasma membrane. Herpesviruses, for example, are temporarily cloaked in membrane derived from the nuclear envelope of the host; they then shed this membrane in the cytoplasm and acquire a new envelope made from membrane of the Golgi apparatus. These viruses have a double-stranded DNA genome and replicate within the host cell nucleus, using a combination of viral and cellular enzymes to replicate and transcribe their DNA. In the case of herpesviruses, copies of the viral DNA can remain behind as mini-chromosomes in the nuclei of certain nerve cells. There they remain latent until some sort of physical or emotional stress triggers a new round of active virus production. The infection of other cells by these new viruses causes the blisters characteristic of herpes, such as cold sores or genital sores. Once someone acquires a herpesvirus infection, flare-ups may recur throughout the person's life.

### RNA as Viral Genetic Material

Although some phages and most plant viruses are RNA viruses, the broadest variety of RNA genomes is found among the viruses that infect animals. There are three types of single-stranded RNA genomes found in animal viruses. In the first type, the viral genome can directly serve as mRNA and thus can be translated into viral protein immediately after infection. In a second type, the RNA genome serves as a *template* for mRNA synthesis. The RNA genome is transcribed into complementary RNA strands, which function both as mRNA and as templates for the synthesis of additional copies of genomic RNA. All viruses that require RNA → RNA synthesis to make mRNA use a viral enzyme capable of carrying out this process; there are no such enzymes in most cells. The viral enzyme is packaged with the genome inside the viral capsid.

The RNA animal viruses with the most complicated replicative cycles are the third type, the **retroviruses**. These viruses are equipped with an enzyme called **reverse transcriptase**, which transcribes an RNA template into DNA, providing an RNA → DNA information flow, the opposite of the usual direction. (Reverse transcriptase is the enzyme used in the technique called RT-PCR, described in Concept 15.4.) This unusual phenomenon is the source of the name retroviruses (*retro* means "backward"). Of particular medical importance is **HIV (human immunodeficiency virus)**, the retrovirus that causes **AIDS (acquired immunodeficiency syndrome)**. HIV and other retroviruses are enveloped viruses that contain two identical molecules of single-stranded RNA and two molecules of reverse transcriptase.

The HIV replicative cycle (traced in **Figure 15.7**) is typical of a retrovirus. After HIV enters a host cell, its reverse transcriptase molecules are released into the cytoplasm, where they catalyze synthesis of viral DNA. The newly made viral DNA then enters the cell's nucleus and integrates into the DNA of a chromosome. The integrated viral DNA, called a **provirus**, never leaves the host's genome, remaining a permanent resident of the cell. (Recall that a prophage, in contrast, leaves the host's genome at the start of a lytic cycle.) The host's RNA polymerase transcribes the proviral DNA into RNA molecules, which can function both as mRNA for the synthesis of viral proteins and as genomes for the new viruses that will be assembled and released from the cell. We'll describe how HIV causes the deterioration of the immune system that occurs in AIDS.

### Evolution of Viruses

**EVOLUTION** We began this chapter by asking whether or not viruses are alive. Viruses do not really fit our definition of living organisms. An isolated virus is biologically inert, unable to replicate its genes or regenerate its own supply of ATP. Yet it has a genetic program written in the universal language of life. Do we think of viruses as nature's most complex associations of molecules or as the simplest forms of life? Either way, we must bend our usual definitions. Although viruses cannot replicate or carry out metabolic activities independently, their use of the genetic code makes it hard to deny their evolutionary connection to the living world.

How did viruses originate? Viruses have been found that infect every form of life—not just bacteria, animals, and plants, but also archaea, fungi, and algae and other protists. Because they depend on cells for their own propagation, it seems likely that viruses are not the descendants of precellular forms of life but evolved—possibly multiple times—*after* the first cells appeared. Most molecular biologists favor the hypothesis that viruses originated from naked bits of cellular nucleic acids that moved from one cell to another, perhaps via injured cell surfaces. The evolution of genes coding for capsid proteins may have facilitated the infection of uninjured cells.

Candidates for the original sources of viral genomes include plasmids and transposons. *Plasmids* are small, circular DNA molecules found in bacteria and in the unicellular eukaryotes called yeasts. Plasmids exist apart from the cell's genome, can replicate independently of the genome, and are occasionally transferred between cells. (Use of plasmids in gene cloning was discussed in Concept 13.4.) *Transposons* are DNA segments that can move from one location to another within a cell's genome. Thus, plasmids, transposons, and viruses all share an important feature: They are *mobile genetic elements*.

Consistent with this vision of pieces of DNA shuttling from cell to cell is the observation that a viral genome can have more

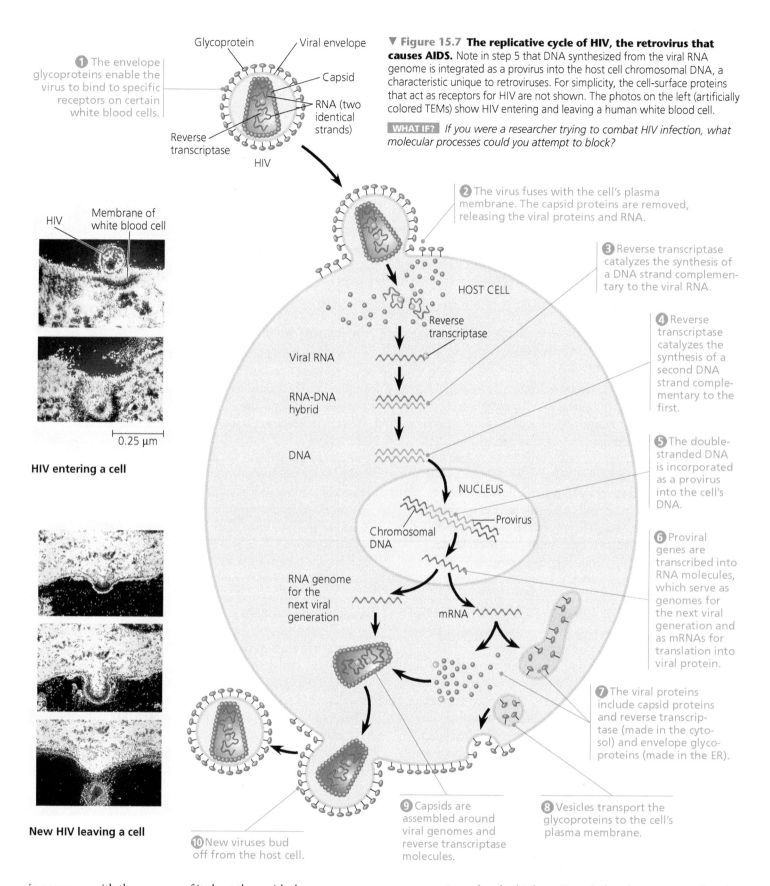

**1** The envelope glycoproteins enable the virus to bind to specific receptors on certain white blood cells.

Glycoprotein — Viral envelope
— Capsid
— RNA (two identical strands)
Reverse transcriptase
HIV

**▼ Figure 15.7 The replicative cycle of HIV, the retrovirus that causes AIDS.** Note in step 5 that DNA synthesized from the viral RNA genome is integrated as a provirus into the host cell chromosomal DNA, a characteristic unique to retroviruses. For simplicity, the cell-surface proteins that act as receptors for HIV are not shown. The photos on the left (artificially colored TEMs) show HIV entering and leaving a human white blood cell.

**WHAT IF?** *If you were a researcher trying to combat HIV infection, what molecular processes could you attempt to block?*

**2** The virus fuses with the cell's plasma membrane. The capsid proteins are removed, releasing the viral proteins and RNA.

HIV — Membrane of white blood cell

0.25 μm

**HIV entering a cell**

HOST CELL

Reverse transcriptase

Viral RNA

RNA-DNA hybrid

DNA

**3** Reverse transcriptase catalyzes the synthesis of a DNA strand complementary to the viral RNA.

**4** Reverse transcriptase catalyzes the synthesis of a second DNA strand complementary to the first.

**5** The double-stranded DNA is incorporated as a provirus into the cell's DNA.

NUCLEUS

Chromosomal DNA
Provirus

**6** Proviral genes are transcribed into RNA molecules, which serve as genomes for the next viral generation and as mRNAs for translation into viral protein.

RNA genome for the next viral generation

mRNA

**7** The viral proteins include capsid proteins and reverse transcriptase (made in the cytosol) and envelope glycoproteins (made in the ER).

**New HIV leaving a cell**

**10** New viruses bud off from the host cell.

**9** Capsids are assembled around viral genomes and reverse transcriptase molecules.

**8** Vesicles transport the glycoproteins to the cell's plasma membrane.

in common with the genome of its host than with the genomes of viruses that infect other hosts. The ongoing evolutionary relationship between viruses and the genomes of their host cells is an association that makes viruses very useful experimental systems in molecular biology. Knowledge about viruses also allows many practical applications, since viruses have a tremendous impact on all organisms through their ability to cause disease.

## CONCEPT 15.3

# Viruses are formidable pathogens in animals and plants

Diseases caused by viral infections afflict humans, crops, and livestock worldwide. We'll first discuss animal viruses.

## Viral Diseases in Animals

A viral infection can produce symptoms by a number of different routes. Viruses may damage or kill cells by causing the release of hydrolytic enzymes from lysosomes. Some viruses cause infected cells to produce toxins that lead to disease symptoms, and some have molecular components that are toxic, such as envelope proteins. How much damage a virus causes depends partly on the ability of the infected tissue to regenerate by cell division. People usually recover completely from colds because the epithelium of the respiratory tract, which the viruses infect, can efficiently repair itself. In contrast, damage inflicted by poliovirus to mature nerve cells is permanent because these cells do not divide and usually cannot be replaced. Many of the temporary symptoms associated with viral infections, such as fever and aches, actually result from the body's own efforts at defending itself against infection rather than from cell death caused by the virus.

The immune system is a complex and critical part of the body's natural defenses. It is also the basis for the major medical tool for preventing viral infections—vaccines. A **vaccine** is a harmless variant or derivative of a pathogen that stimulates the immune system to mount defenses against the harmful pathogen. Smallpox, a viral disease that was at one time a devastating scourge in many parts of the world, was eradicated by a vaccination program carried out by the World Health Organization (WHO). The very narrow host range of the smallpox virus—it infects only humans—was a critical factor in the success of this program. Similar worldwide vaccination campaigns are currently under way to eradicate polio and measles. Effective vaccines are also available to protect against rubella, mumps, hepatitis A and B, and a number of other viral diseases.

Although vaccines can prevent certain viral illnesses, medical technology can do little, at present, to cure most viral infections once they occur. The antibiotics that help us recover from bacterial infections are powerless against viruses. Antibiotics kill bacteria by inhibiting enzymes specific to bacteria but have no effect on eukaryotic or virally encoded enzymes. However, the few enzymes that are encoded by viruses have provided targets for other drugs. Most antiviral drugs resemble nucleosides and as a result interfere with viral nucleic acid synthesis. One such drug is acyclovir, which impedes herpesvirus replication by inhibiting the viral polymerase that synthesizes viral DNA. Similarly, azidothymidine (AZT) curbs HIV replication by interfering with the synthesis of DNA by reverse transcriptase. In the past two decades, much effort has gone into developing drugs against HIV. Currently, multidrug treatments, sometimes called "cocktails," have been found to be most effective. Such treatments commonly include a combination of two nucleoside mimics and a protease inhibitor, which interferes with an enzyme required for assembly of the viruses.

## Emerging Viruses

Viruses that suddenly become apparent are often referred to as *emerging viruses*. HIV, the AIDS virus, is a classic example: This virus appeared in San Francisco in the early 1980s, seemingly out of nowhere, although later studies uncovered a case in the Belgian Congo in 1959. The deadly Ebola virus, recognized initially in 1976 in central Africa, is one of several emerging viruses that cause *hemorrhagic fever*, an often fatal syndrome (set of symptoms) characterized by fever, vomiting, massive bleeding, and circulatory system collapse. A number of other dangerous emerging viruses cause encephalitis, inflammation of the brain. One example is the West Nile virus, which appeared in North America for the first time in 1999 and has spread to all 48 contiguous states in the United States.

In 2009, a general outbreak, or **epidemic**, of a flu-like illness appeared in Mexico and the United States. The infectious agent was quickly identified as an influenza virus related to viruses that cause the seasonal flu **(Figure 15.8a)**. This particular virus was named H1N1 for reasons that will be explained shortly. The viral disease spread rapidly, prompting WHO to declare a global epidemic, or **pandemic**, shortly thereafter. Half a year later, the disease had reached 207 countries, infecting over 600,000 people and killing almost 8,000. Public health agencies responded rapidly with guidelines for shutting down schools and other public places, and vaccine development and screening efforts were accelerated **(Figure 15.8b)**.

How do such viruses burst on the human scene, giving rise to harmful diseases that were previously rare or even unknown? Three processes contribute to the emergence of viral diseases. The first, and perhaps most important, is the mutation of existing viruses. RNA viruses tend to have an unusually high rate of mutation because errors in replicating their RNA genomes are not corrected by proofreading. Some mutations change existing viruses into new genetic varieties (strains) that can cause disease, even in individuals who are immune to the ancestral virus. For instance, seasonal flu epidemics are caused by new strains of influenza virus

(a) **2009 pandemic H1N1 influenza A virus.** Viruses (blue) are seen on an infected cell (green) in this colorized SEM.

(b) **2009 pandemic screening.** At a South Korean airport, thermal scans were used to detect passengers with a fever who might have the H1N1 flu.

▲ **Figure 15.8 Influenza in humans.**

genetically different enough from earlier strains that people have little immunity to them. You'll see an example of this process in the **Scientific Skills Exercise**, where you'll analyze genetic changes in variants of the 2009 flu virus and correlate them with spread of the disease.

A second process that can lead to the emergence of viral diseases is the dissemination of a viral disease from a small, isolated human population. For instance, AIDS went unnamed and virtually unnoticed for decades before it began to spread around the world. In this case, technological and social factors, including affordable international travel, blood transfusions, sexual promiscuity, and the abuse of intravenous drugs, allowed a previously rare human disease to become a global scourge.

A third source of new viral diseases in humans is the spread of existing viruses from other animals. Scientists estimate that about three-quarters of new human diseases originate in this way. Animals that harbor and can transmit a particular virus but are generally unaffected by it are said to act as a natural reservoir for that virus. For example, the 2009 flu pandemic mentioned earlier was likely passed to humans from pigs; for this reason, it was originally called "swine flu."

In general, flu epidemics provide an instructive example of the effects of viruses moving between species. There are three types of influenza virus: types B and C, which infect only humans and have never caused an epidemic, and type A, which infects a wide range of animals, including birds, pigs, horses, and humans. Influenza A strains have caused four major flu epidemics among humans in the last 100 years. The worst was the first one, the "Spanish flu" pandemic of 1918–1919, which killed between 10 and 20% of those infected—about 40 million people, including many World War I soldiers.

Different strains of influenza A are given standardized names; for example, both the strain that caused the 1918 flu and the one that caused the 2009 pandemic flu are called H1N1. The name identifies which forms of two viral surface proteins are present: hemagglutinin (H) and neuraminidase (N). There are 16 different types of hemagglutinin, a protein that helps the flu virus attach to host cells, and 9 types of neuraminidase, an enzyme that helps release new virus particles from infected cells. Waterbirds have been found that carry viruses with all possible combinations of H and N.

A likely scenario for the 1918 pandemic is that the virus mutated as it passed from one host species to another. When an animal like a pig or a bird is infected with more than one strain of flu virus, the different strains can undergo genetic recombination if the RNA molecules of their genomes mix and match during viral assembly. Pigs were probably the breeding ground for the 2009 flu virus, which contains sequences from bird, pig, and human flu viruses. Coupled with mutation, these reassortments can lead to the emergence of a viral strain capable of infecting human cells. People who have never been exposed to that particular strain before will lack immunity, and the recombinant virus has the potential to be highly pathogenic. If such a flu virus recombines with viruses that circulate widely among humans, it may acquire the ability to spread easily from person to person, dramatically increasing the potential for a major human outbreak.

One potential long-term threat is the avian flu caused by an H5N1 virus carried by wild and domestic birds. The first documented transmission from birds to humans occurred in Hong Kong in 1997. Since then, the overall mortality rate of the H5N1 virus has been greater than 50% of those infected, an alarming number. Also, the host range of H5N1 is expanding, which provides increasing chances for reassortment between different strains. If the H5N1 avian flu virus evolves so that it can spread easily from person to person, it could represent a major global health threat akin to that of the 1918 pandemic.

How easily could this happen? Recently, scientists working with ferrets, small mammals that are animal models for human flu, found that only a few mutations of the avian flu virus would allow infection of cells in the human nasal cavity and windpipe. Furthermore, when the scientists transferred nasal swabs serially from ferret to ferret, the virus became transmissible through the air. Reports of this startling discovery at a scientific conference in 2011 ignited a firestorm of debate about whether to publish the results. Ultimately, the scientific community decided the benefits of potentially understanding how to prevent pandemics would outweigh the risks of the information being used for harmful purposes, and the work was published in 2012.

As we have seen, emerging viruses are generally not new; rather, they are existing viruses that mutate, disseminate more widely in the current host species, or spread to new host species. Changes in host behavior or environmental changes can increase the viral traffic responsible for emerging diseases. For instance, new roads built through remote areas can allow viruses to spread between previously isolated human populations. Also, the destruction of forests to expand cropland can bring humans into contact with other animals that may host viruses capable of infecting humans.

# Analyzing a DNA Sequence-Based Phylogenetic Tree to Understand Viral Evolution

**How Can DNA Sequence Data Be Used to Track Flu Virus Evolution During Pandemic Waves?** In 2009, an influenza A H1N1 virus caused a pandemic, and the virus has continued to resurface in outbreaks across the world. Researchers in Taiwan were curious about why the virus kept appearing despite widespread flu vaccine initiatives. They hypothesized that newly evolved variants of the H1N1 virus were able to evade human immune system defenses. To test this hypothesis, they needed to determine if each wave of the flu outbreak was caused by a different H1N1 variant.

**How the Experiment Was Done** Scientists obtained the genome sequences for 4,703 virus isolates collected from patients with H1N1 flu in Taiwan. They compared the sequences in different strains for the viral hemagglutinin (HA) gene, and based on mutations that had occurred, arranged the isolates into a phylogenetic tree.

**Data from the Experiment** The figure below, left, shows a phylogenetic tree; each branch tip is one variant of the H1N1 virus with a unique HA gene sequence. The tree is a way to visualize a working hypothesis about the evolutionary relationships between H1N1 variants.

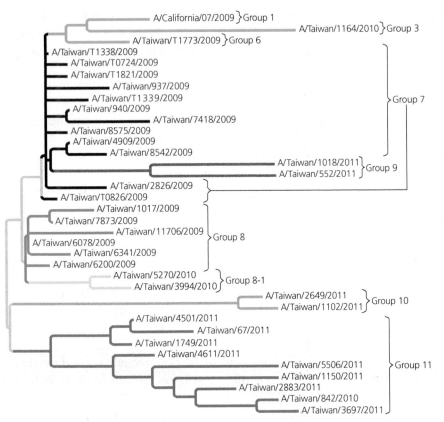

### Interpret the Data

1. The phylogenetic tree shows the hypothesized evolutionary relationship between the variant strains of H1N1 virus. The more closely connected two variants are, the more alike they are in terms of HA gene sequence. Each fork in a branch, called a node, shows where two lineages separate due to different accumulated mutations. The length of the branches is a measure of how many DNA sequence differences there are between the variants, thus how distantly related they are. Referring to the phylogenetic tree, which variants are more closely related to each other: A/Taiwan1018/2011 and A/Taiwan/552/2011 or A/Taiwan1018/2011 and A/Taiwan/8542/2009? Explain your answer.

2. The scientists arranged the branches into groups made up of one ancestral variant and all of its descendant, mutated variants. They are color-coded in the figure. Using Group 11 as an example, trace the lineage of its variants. (a) Do all of the nodes have the same number of branches or branch tips? (b) Are all of the branches in the group the same length? (c) What do these results indicate?

3. The graph shows the number of isolates collected from ill patients on the *y*-axis and the month and year that the isolates were collected on the *x*-axis. Each group of variants is plotted separately with a line color that matches the tree diagram. (a) Which group of variants was the earliest to cause H1N1 flu in over 100 patients in Taiwan? (b) Once a group of variants had a peak number of infections, did members of that same group cause another wave of infection? (c) One variant in Group 1 was used to make a vaccine very early in the pandemic. Based on the graphed data, does it look like the vaccine was effective?

4. Groups 9, 10, and 11 all had H1N1 variants that caused a large number of infections at the same time in Taiwan. Does this mean that the scientists' hypothesis, that new variants cause new waves of infection, was incorrect? Explain your answer.

**Data from** J-R. Yang et al., New variants and age shift to high fatality groups contribute to severe successive waves in the 2009 influenza pandemic in Taiwan, *PLoS ONE* 6(11): e28288 (2011). doi:10.1371/journal.pone.0028288.

(MB) A version of this Scientific Skills Exercise can be assigned in MasteringBiology.

Scientists also graphed the isolates by the month and year of isolate collection, which reflects the time period in which each viral variant was actively causing illness in people.

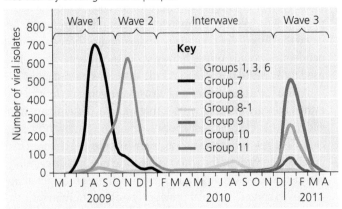

## Viral Diseases in Plants

More than 2,000 types of viral diseases of plants are known, and together they account for an estimated annual loss of $15 billion worldwide due to their destruction of agricultural and horticultural crops. Common signs of viral infection include bleached or brown spots on leaves and fruits (as on the squash to the right), stunted growth, and damaged flowers or roots, all tending to diminish the yield and quality of crops.

Plant viruses have the same basic structure and mode of replication as animal viruses. Most plant viruses discovered thus far, including tobacco mosaic virus (TMV), have an RNA genome. Many have a helical capsid, like TMV, while others have an icosahedral capsid (see Figure 15.2).

Viral diseases of plants spread by two major routes. In the first route, called *horizontal transmission*, a plant is infected from an external source of the virus. Because the invading virus must get past the plant's outer protective layer of cells (the epidermis), a plant becomes more susceptible to viral infections if it has been damaged by wind, injury, or herbivores. Herbivores, especially insects, pose a double threat because they can also act as carriers of viruses, transmitting disease from plant to plant. Moreover, farmers and gardeners may transmit plant viruses inadvertently on pruning shears and other tools. The other route of viral infection is *vertical transmission*, in which a plant inherits a viral infection from a parent. Vertical transmission can occur in asexual propagation (for example, through cuttings) or in sexual reproduction via infected seeds.

Once a virus enters a plant cell and begins replicating, viral genomes and associated proteins can spread throughout the plant by means of plasmodesmata, the cytoplasmic connections that penetrate the walls between adjacent plant cells (see Figure 3.25). The passage of viral macromolecules from cell to cell is facilitated by virally encoded proteins that cause enlargement of plasmodesmata. Scientists have not yet devised cures for most viral plant diseases. Consequently, research efforts are focused largely on reducing the transmission of such diseases and on breeding resistant varieties of crop plants.

Earlier in this chapter, we mentioned the ongoing evolutionary relationship between viruses and the genomes of their host cells. In fact, the original source of viral genetic material may have been transposons, mobile genetic elements that are present in multiple copies in many genomes..

### CONCEPT CHECK 15.3

1. Describe two ways a preexisting virus can become an emerging virus.
2. Contrast horizontal and vertical transmission of viruses in plants.
3. **WHAT IF?** TMV has been isolated from virtually all commercial tobacco products. Why, then, is TMV infection not an additional hazard for smokers?

For suggested answers, see Appendix A.

---

# 15 Chapter Review

## SUMMARY OF KEY CONCEPTS

**CONCEPT** 15.1

### A virus consists of a nucleic acid surrounded by a protein coat (pp. 300–302)

- A **virus** is a small nucleic acid genome enclosed in a protein **capsid** and sometimes a membranous **viral envelope** containing viral proteins that help the virus enter a cell. The genome may be single- or double-stranded DNA or RNA.

**?** *Are viruses generally considered living or nonliving? Explain.*

**CONCEPT** 15.2

### Viruses replicate only in host cells (pp. 302–308)

- Viruses use enzymes, ribosomes, and small molecules of host cells to synthesize progeny viruses during replication. Each type of virus has a characteristic **host range**.
- **Phages** (viruses that infect bacteria) can replicate by two alternative mechanisms: the **lytic cycle** and the **lysogenic cycle**.

**Lytic cycle**
- **Virulent** or **temperate phage**
- Destruction of host DNA
- Production of new phages
- Lysis of host cell causes release of progeny phages

**Lysogenic cycle**
- **Temperate phage** only
- Genome integrates into bacterial chromosome as **prophage**, which
  (1) is replicated and passed on to daughter cells and
  (2) can be induced to leave the chromosome and initiate a lytic cycle

- Many animal viruses have an envelope. **Retroviruses** (such as **HIV**) use the enzyme **reverse transcriptase** to copy their RNA genome into DNA, which can be integrated into the host genome as a **provirus**.

- Since viruses can replicate only within cells, they probably evolved after the first cells appeared, perhaps as packaged fragments of cellular nucleic acid. The origin of viruses is still being debated.

> **?** *Describe enzymes that are not found in most cells but are necessary for the replication of certain viruses.*

CONCEPT 15.3

## Viruses are formidable pathogens in animals and plants (pp. 308–311)

- Symptoms of viral diseases in animals may be caused by direct viral harm to cells or by the body's immune response. **Vaccines** stimulate the immune system to defend the host against specific viruses.
- Outbreaks of "new" viral diseases in humans are usually caused by existing viruses that expand their host territory. The H1N1 2009 flu virus was a new combination of pig, human, and avian viral genes that caused a pandemic.
- Viruses enter plant cells through damaged cell walls (horizontal transmission) or are inherited from a parent (vertical transmission).

> **?** *What aspect of an RNA virus makes it more likely than a DNA virus to become an emerging virus?*

## TEST YOUR UNDERSTANDING

### Level 1: Knowledge/Comprehension

1. Which of the following characteristics, structures, or processes is common to both bacteria and viruses?
   a. metabolism
   b. ribosomes
   c. genetic material composed of nucleic acid
   d. cell division
   e. independent existence

2. Emerging viruses arise by
   a. mutation of existing viruses.
   b. the spread of existing viruses to new host species.
   c. the spread of existing viruses more widely within their host species.
   d. all of the above
   e. none of the above

3. A human pandemic is
   a. a viral disease that infects all humans.
   b. a flu that kills more than 1 million people.
   c. an epidemic that extends around the world.
   d. a viral disease that can infect multiple species.
   e. a virus that increases in mortality rate as it spreads.

### Level 2: Application/Analysis

4. A bacterium is infected with an experimentally constructed bacteriophage composed of the T2 phage protein coat and T4 phage DNA. The new phages produced will have
   a. T2 protein and T4 DNA.
   b. T2 protein and T2 DNA.
   c. a mixture of the DNA and proteins of both phages.
   d. T4 protein and T4 DNA.
   e. T4 protein and T2 DNA.

5. RNA viruses require their own supply of certain enzymes because
   a. host cells rapidly destroy the viruses.
   b. host cells lack enzymes that can replicate the viral genome.
   c. these enzymes translate viral mRNA into proteins.
   d. these enzymes penetrate host cell membranes.
   e. these enzymes cannot be made in host cells.

6. **DRAW IT** Redraw Figure 15.6 to show the replicative cycle of a virus with a single-stranded genome that can function as mRNA.

### Level 3: Synthesis/Evaluation

7. **SCIENTIFIC INQUIRY**
   When bacteria infect an animal, the number of bacteria in the body increases in an exponential fashion (graph A). After infection by a virulent animal virus with a lytic replicative cycle, there is no evidence of infection for a while. Then the number of viruses rises suddenly and subsequently increases in a series of steps (graph B). Explain the difference in the curves.

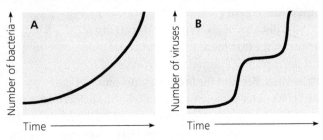

8. **FOCUS ON EVOLUTION**
   The success of some viruses lies in their ability to evolve rapidly within the host. Such a virus evades the host's defenses by mutating and producing many altered progeny viruses before the body can mount an attack. Thus, the viruses present late in infection differ from those that initially infected the body. Discuss this as an example of evolution in microcosm. Which viral lineages tend to predominate?

9. **FOCUS ON ORGANIZATION**
   While viruses are considered by most scientists to be nonliving, they do show some characteristics of life, including the correlation of structure and function. In a short essay (100–150 words), discuss how the structure of a virus correlates with its function.

*For selected answers, see Appendix A.*

## MasteringBiology®

**Students** Go to **MasteringBiology** for assignments, the eText, and the Study Area with practice tests, animations, and activities.

**Instructors** Go to **MasteringBiology** for automatically graded tutorials and questions that you can assign to your students, plus Instructor Resources.

## Chapter 1

### Figure Questions

**Figure 1.4** Possible answers include the match between the shape of the hummingbird's beak and the flower from which it obtains nectar; the streamlined shape of the bird's body and ability to fold up its legs for efficient flight; the color and appearance of the flower, which attract the hummingbird. **Figure 1.19** The resident mice might have a more reddish coat color. Both beach and mainland mice would probably suffer higher predation rates in the new habitat than in their native environments. However, the dark mainland mice might be expected to stand out less against the background, so might have a lower predation rate than the beach mice.

### Concept Check 1.1

**1.** Examples: A molecule consists of *atoms* bonded together. Each organelle has an orderly arrangement of *molecules*. Photosynthetic plant cells contain *organelles* called chloroplasts. A tissue consists of a group of similar *cells*. Organs such as the heart are constructed from several *tissues*. A complex multicellular organism, such as a plant, has several types of *organs*, such as leaves and roots. A population is a set of *organisms* of the same species. A community consists of *populations* of the various species inhabiting a specific area. An ecosystem consists of a biological *community* along with the nonliving factors important to life, such as air, soil, and water. The biosphere is made up of all of Earth's *ecosystems*. **2.** (a) Organization: Structure and function are correlated. (b) Organization: The cell is an organism's basic unit of structure and function, *and* Information: Life's processes involve the expression and transmission of genetic information. (c) Energy and Matter: Life requires transfer and transformation of energy, *and* Interactions: Organisms interact with other organisms and with the physical environment. **3.** Some possible answers: *Organization*: The ability of a human heart to pump blood requires an intact heart; it is not a capability of any of the heart's tissues or cells working alone. *Information*: Human eye color is determined by the combination of genes inherited from the two parents. *Energy and Matter*: A plant, such as a grass, absorbs energy from the sun and transforms it into molecules that act as stored fuel. Animals can eat parts of the plant and use the food for energy to carry out their activities. *Interactions*: A mouse eats food, such as nuts or grasses, and deposits some of the food material as feces and urine. Construction of a nest rearranges the physical environment and may hasten degradation of some of its components. The mouse may also act as food for a predator. *Evolution*: All plants have chloroplasts, indicating their descent from a common ancestor.

### Concept Check 1.2

**1.** An address pinpoints a location by tracking from broader to narrower categories—a state, city, zip, street, and building number. This is analogous to the groups-subordinate-to-groups structure of biological taxonomy. **2.** The naturally occurring heritable variation in a population is "edited" by natural selection because individuals with heritable traits better suited to the environment survive and reproduce more successfully than others. Over time, better-suited individuals persist and their percentage in the population increases, while less suited individuals become less prevalent—a type of population editing. **3.**

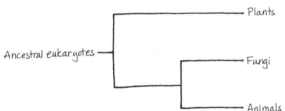

### Concept Check 1.3

**1.** Inductive reasoning derives generalizations from specific cases; deductive reasoning predicts specific outcomes from general premises. **2.** The coloration pattern of the mice **3.** A scientific theory is usually more general than a hypothesis and substantiated by a much greater amount of evidence. Natural selection is an explanatory idea that applies to all kinds of organisms and is supported by vast amounts of evidence of various kinds. **4.** Science aims to understand natural phenomena and how they work, while technology involves application of scientific discoveries for a particular purpose or to solve a specific problem.

### Summary of Key Concepts Questions

**1.1** Finger movements rely on the coordination of the many structural components of the hand (muscles, nerves, bones, etc.), each of which is composed of elements from lower levels of biological *organization* (cells, molecules). The development of the hand relies on the genetic *information* encoded in chromosomes found in cells throughout the body. To power the finger movements that result in a text message, muscle and nerve cells require chemical *energy* that they transform in powering muscle contraction or in propagating nerve impulses. Finally, all of the anatomical and physiological features that allow the activity of texting are the outcome of a process of natural selection that resulted in the *evolution* of hands and of the mental facilities for use of language. **1.2** Ancestors of the beach mouse may have exhibited variations in their coat color. Because of the prevalence of visual predators, the better camouflaged (lighter) mice may have survived longer and been able to produce more offspring. Over time,

a higher and higher proportion of individuals in the population would have had the adaptation of lighter fur that acted to camouflage the mouse. **1.3** Inductive reasoning is used in forming hypotheses, while deductive reasoning leads to predictions that are used to test hypotheses.

### Test Your Understanding

**1.** b **2.** c **3.** b **4.** c **5.** c **6.** d
**7.** Your figure should show the following: (1) For the biosphere, Earth with an arrow coming out of a tropical ocean; (2) for the ecosystem, a distant view of a coral reef; (3) for the community, a collection of reef animals and algae, with corals, fishes, some seaweed, and any other organisms you can think of; (4) for the population, a group of fish of the same species; (5) for the organism, one fish from your population; (6) for the organ, the fish's stomach, and for the organ system, the whole digestive tract (see Chapter 33 for help); (7) for a tissue, a group of similar cells from the stomach; (8) for a cell, one cell from the tissue, showing its nucleus and a few other organelles; (9) for an organelle, the nucleus, where most of the cell's DNA is located; and (10) for a molecule, a DNA double helix. Your sketches can be very rough!

## Chapter 2

### Figure Questions

**Figure 2.8**

Note that the oxygen on carbon 5 lost its proton and that the oxygen on carbon 2, which used to be the carbonyl oxygen, gained a proton. Four carbons are in the fructose ring, and two are not. (The latter two carbons are attached to carbons 2 and 5, which are in the ring.) The fructose ring differs from the glucose ring, which has five carbons in the ring and one that is not. (Note that the orientation of this fructose molecule is flipped relative to that of the one in Figure 2.9.)

**Figure 2.9**

**Figure 2.14**

**Figure 2.18**

**Figure 2.22** The R group of glutamic acid is acidic and hydrophilic, whereas that of valine is nonpolar and hydrophobic. Therefore, it is unlikely that valine can participate in the same intramolecular interactions that glutamic acid can. A change in these interactions would be expected to cause a disruption of molecular structure. **Figure 2.24** The spirals are α helices.

**Concept Check 2.1**

**1.** Both consist largely of hydrocarbon chains.   **2.** It has both an amino group (—NH$_2$), which makes it an amine, and a carboxyl group (—COOH), which makes it a carboxylic acid.   **3.** A chemical group that can act as a base (by picking up H$^+$) has been replaced with a group that can act as an acid, increasing the acidic properties of the molecule. The shape of the molecule would also change, likely changing the molecules with which it can interact.

**Concept Check 2.2**

**1.** Nine, with one water molecule required to hydrolyze each connected pair of monomers   **2.** The amino acids in the fish protein must be released in hydrolysis reactions and incorporated into other proteins in dehydration reactions.

**Concept Check 2.3**

**1.** C$_3$H$_6$O$_3$   **2.** C$_{12}$H$_{22}$O$_{11}$   **3.** The antibiotic treatment is likely to have killed the cellulose-digesting prokaryotes in the cow's stomach. The absence of these prokaryotes would hamper the cow's ability to obtain energy from food and could lead to weight loss and possibly death. Thus, prokaryotic species are reintroduced, in appropriate combinations, in the gut culture given to treated cows.

**Concept Check 2.4**

**1.** Both have a glycerol molecule attached to fatty acids. The glycerol of a fat has three fatty acids attached, whereas the glycerol of a phospholipid is attached to two fatty acids and one phosphate group.   **2.** Human sex hormones are steroids, a type of hydrophobic compound.   **3.** The oil droplet membrane could consist of a single layer of phospholipids rather than a bilayer, because an arrangement in which the hydrophobic tails of the membrane phospholipids were in contact with the hydrocarbon regions of the oil molecules would be more stable.

**Concept Check 2.5**

**1.** The function of a protein is a consequence of its specific shape, which is lost when a protein becomes denatured.   **2.** Secondary structure involves hydrogen bonds between atoms of the polypeptide backbone. Tertiary structure involves interactions between atoms of the side chains of the amino acid monomers.   **3.** These are all nonpolar amino acids, so you would expect this region to be located in the interior of the folded polypeptide, where it would not contact the aqueous environment inside the cell.

**Concept Check 2.6**

**1.**

**2.**

5'—T A G G C C T—3'
3'—A T C C G G A—5'

**3.** a.

Mismatch

5'—T A A G C C T—3'
3'—A T C C G G A—5'

b.

3'—A T T C G G A—5'

**Summary of Key Concepts Questions**

**2.1** The methyl group is nonpolar and not reactive. The other six groups are called functional groups and can participate in chemical reactions. Except for the sulfhydryl group, these functional groups are hydrophilic; they increase the solubility of organic compounds in water.   **2.2** The polymers of carbohydrates, proteins, and nucleic acids are built from three different types of monomers: monosaccharides, amino acids, and nucleotides, respectively.   **2.3** Both starch and cellulose are polymers of glucose, but the glucose monomers are in the α configuration in starch and the β configuration in cellulose. The glycosidic linkages thus have different geometries, giving the polymers different shapes and thus different properties. Starch is an energy-storage compound in plants; cellulose is a structural component of plant cell walls. Humans can hydrolyze starch to provide energy but cannot hydrolyze cellulose. Cellulose aids in the passage of food through the digestive tract.   **2.4** Lipids are not polymers because they do not exist as a chain of linked monomers. They are not considered macromolecules because they do not reach the giant size of many polysaccharides, proteins, and nucleic acids.   **2.5** A polypeptide, which may consist of hundreds of amino acids in a specific sequence (primary structure), has regions of coils and pleats (secondary structure), which are then folded into irregular contortions (tertiary structure) and may be noncovalently associated with other polypeptides (quaternary structure). The linear order of amino acids, with the varying properties of their side chains (R groups), determines what secondary and tertiary structures will form to produce a protein. The resulting unique three-dimensional shapes of proteins are key to their specific and diverse functions.   **2.6** The complementary base pairing of the two strands of DNA makes possible the precise replication of DNA every time a cell divides, ensuring that genetic information is faithfully transmitted. In some types of RNA, complementary base pairing enables RNA molecules to assume specific three-dimensional shapes that facilitate diverse functions.

**Test Your Understanding**

**1.** b   **2.** d   **3.** d   **4.** b   **5.** a   **6.** d   **7.** c

**8.**

| | Monomers or Components | Polymer or larger molecule | Type of linkage |
|---|---|---|---|
| Carbohydrates | Monosaccharides | Polysaccharides | Glycosidic linkages |
| Lipids | Fatty acids | Triacylglycerols | Ester linkages |
| Proteins | Amino acids | Polypeptides | Peptide bonds |
| Nucleic acids | Nucleotides | Polynucleotides | Phosphodiester linkages |

# Chapter 3

## Figure Questions

**Figure 3.5** A phospholipid is a lipid, consisting of a glycerol molecule joined to two fatty acids and one phosphate group. Together, the glycerol and phosphate end of the phospholipid form the "head," which is hydrophilic, while the hydrocarbon chains on the fatty acids form hydrophobic "tails." The presence in a single molecule of both a hydrophilic and a hydrophobic region makes the molecule ideal as the main building block of a membrane.   **Figure 3.8** The DNA in a chromosome dictates synthesis of a messenger RNA (mRNA) molecule, which then moves out to the cytoplasm. There, the information is used for the production, on ribosomes, of proteins that carry out cellular functions.   **Figure 3.9** Any of the bound ribosomes (attached to the endoplasmic reticulum) could be circled, because any could be making a protein that will be secreted.

**Figure 3.22**

*1 microtubule*

*Triplet of microtubules*

Each centriole has 9 sets of 3 microtubules, so the entire centrosome (two centrioles) has 54 microtubules. Each microtubule consists of a helical array of tubulin dimers (as shown in Table 3.1).

**Figure 3.23**

*Central pair of microtubules*

*They terminate here*

The two central microtubules terminate above the basal body, so they aren't present at the level of the cross section through the basal body, indicated by the lower red rectangle in (a).

## Concept Check 3.1

**1.** Stains used for light microscopy are colored molecules that bind to cell components, affecting the light passing through, while stains used for electron microscopy involve heavy metals that affect the beams of electrons.   **2.** (a) Light microscope, (b) scanning electron microscope

## Concept Check 3.2

**1.** See Figure 3.7.
**2.**

This cell would have the same volume as the large cell in column 2 and the collection of small cells in column 3 but proportionally more surface area than that in column 2 and less than that in column 3. Thus, the surface-to-volume ratio should be greater than 1.2 but less than 6. To obtain the surface area, add the area of the six sides (the top, bottom, sides, and ends): $125 + 125 + 125 + 125 + 1 + 1 = 502$. The surface-to-volume ratio equals 502 divided by a volume of 125, or 4.0.

## Concept Check 3.3

**1.** Ribosomes in the cytoplasm translate the genetic message, carried from the DNA in the nucleus by mRNA, into a polypeptide chain.   **2.** Nucleoli consist of DNA and the ribosomal RNA (rRNA) made according to its instructions, as well as proteins imported from the cytoplasm. Together, the rRNA and proteins are assembled into large and small ribosomal subunits. (These are exported through nuclear pores to the cytoplasm, where they will participate in polypeptide synthesis.)   **3.** Each chromosome consists of one long DNA molecule attached to numerous protein molecules, a combination called chromatin. The chromosomes are "condensing" as their thin strands of chromatin coil up to form shorter, thicker structures.

## Concept Check 3.4

**1.** The primary distinction between rough and smooth ER is the presence of bound ribosomes on the rough ER. Both types of ER make phospholipids, but membrane proteins and secretory proteins are all produced on the ribosomes of the rough ER. The smooth ER also functions in detoxification, carbohydrate metabolism, and storage

of calcium ions.   **2.** Transport vesicles move membranes and substances they enclose between other components of the endomembrane system.   **3.** The mRNA is synthesized in the nucleus and then passes out through a nuclear pore to be translated on a bound ribosome, attached to the rough ER. The protein is synthesized into the lumen of the ER and perhaps modified there. A transport vesicle carries the protein to the Golgi apparatus. After further modification in the Golgi, another transport vesicle carries it back to the ER, where it will perform its cellular function.

## Concept Check 3.5

**1.** Both organelles are involved in energy transformation, mitochondria in cellular respiration and chloroplasts in photosynthesis. They both have multiple membranes that separate their interiors into compartments. In both organelles, the innermost membranes—cristae, or infoldings of the inner membrane, in mitochondria, and the thylakoid membranes in chloroplasts—have large surface areas with embedded enzymes that carry out their main functions.   **2.** Yes. Plant cells are able to make their own sugar by photosynthesis, but mitochondria in these eukaryotic cells are the organelles that are able to generate energy from sugars, a function required in all cells.   **3.** Mitochondria and chloroplasts are not derived from the ER, nor are they connected physically or via transport vesicles to organelles of the endomembrane system. Mitochondria and chloroplasts are structurally quite different from vesicles derived from the ER, which are bounded by a single membrane.

## Concept Check 3.6

**1.** Dynein arms, powered by ATP, move neighboring doublets of microtubules relative to each other. Because they are anchored within the organelle and with respect to one another, the doublets bend instead of sliding past each other. Synchronized bending of the nine microtubule doublets brings about bending of both structures.   **2.** Such individuals have defects in the microtubule-based movement of cilia and flagella. Thus, the sperm can't move because of malfunctioning or nonexistent flagella, and the airways are compromised because cilia that line the trachea malfunction or don't exist, and so mucus can't be cleared from the lungs.

## Concept Check 3.7

**1.** One obvious difference is the presence of direct cytoplasmic connections between cells of plants (plasmodesmata) and animals (gap junctions). These connections result in the cytoplasm being continuous between adjacent cells.   **2.** The cell would not be able to function properly and would probably soon die, as the cell wall or ECM must be permeable to allow the exchange of matter between the cell and its external environment. Molecules involved in energy production and use must be allowed entry, as well as those that provide information about the cell's environment. Other molecules, such as products synthesized by the cell for export and the by-products of cellular respiration, must be allowed to exit.   **3.** The parts of the protein that face aqueous regions would be expected to have polar or charged (hydrophilic) amino acids, while the parts that go through the membrane would be expected to have nonpolar (hydrophobic) amino acids. You would predict polar or charged amino acids at each end (tail), in the region of the cytoplasmic loop, and in the regions of the two extracellular loops. You would predict nonpolar amino acids in the four regions inside the membrane between the tails and loops.

## Summary of Key Concepts Questions

**3.1** Both light and electron microscopy allow cells to be studied visually, thus helping us understand internal cellular structure and the arrangement of cell components. Cell fractionation techniques separate out different groups of cell components, which can then be analyzed biochemically to determine their function. Performing microscopy on cell fractions helps to correlate the biochemical function of the cell with the cell component responsible.   **3.2** The separation of different functions in different organelles has several advantages. Reactants and enzymes can be concentrated in one area instead of spread throughout the cell. Reactions that require specific conditions, such as a lower pH, can be compartmentalized. And enzymes for specific reactions may be embedded in the membranes that enclose or partition an organelle.   **3.3** The nucleus contains the genetic material of the cell in the form of DNA, which codes for messenger RNA, which in turn provides instructions for the synthesis of proteins (including the proteins that make up part of the ribosomes). DNA also codes for ribosomal RNA, which is combined with proteins in the nucleolus into the subunits of ribosomes. Within the cytoplasm, ribosomes join with mRNA to build polypeptides, using the genetic information in the mRNA.   **3.4** Transport vesicles move proteins and membrane synthesized by the rough ER to the Golgi for further processing and then to the plasma membrane, lysosomes, or other locations in the cell, including back to the ER.   **3.5** According to the endosymbiont theory, mitochondria originated from an oxygen-using prokaryotic cell that was engulfed by an ancestral eukaryotic cell. Over time, the host and endosymbiont evolved into a single unicellular organism. Chloroplasts originated when at least one of these mitochondria-containing eukaryotic cells engulfed and then retained a photosynthetic prokaryote.   **3.6** Inside the cell, motor proteins interact with components of the cytoskeleton to move cellular parts. Motor proteins may "walk" vesicles along microtubules. The movement of cytoplasm within a cell involves interactions of the motor protein myosin and microfilaments (actin filaments). Whole cells can be moved by the rapid bending of flagella or cilia, which is caused by the motor-protein-powered sliding of microtubules in these structures. Some cells move by amoeboid movement, which involves interactions of microfilaments with myosin. Interactions of motor proteins and microfilaments in muscle cells can propel multicellular organisms.   **3.7** A plant cell wall is primarily composed of microfibrils of cellulose embedded in other polysaccharides and proteins. The ECM of animal cells is primarily composed of the glycoproteins collagen and fibronectin, as well as other protein fibers. These fibers are embedded in a network of carbohydrate-rich proteoglycans. A plant cell wall provides structural support for the cell and, collectively, for the plant body. In addition to giving support, the ECM of an animal cell allows for communication of environmental changes into the cell.

## Test Your Understanding

**1.** b  **2.** d  **3.** b  **4.** e  **5.** a  **6.** d  **7.** c  **8.** See Figure 3.7.

# Chapter 4

Hydrophilic portion

Hydrophobic portion

The hydrophilic portion is in contact with an aqueous environment (cytosol or extracellular fluid), and the hydrophobic portion is in contact with the hydrophobic portions of other phospholipids in the interior of the bilayer. **Figure 4.4** You couldn't rule out movement of proteins within membranes of the same species. You might propose that the membrane lipids and proteins from one species weren't able to mingle with those from the other species because of some incompatibility.

**Figure 4.7** A transmembrane protein like the dimer in (f) might change its shape upon binding to a particular ECM molecule. The new shape might enable the interior portion of the protein to bind to a second, cytoplasmic protein that would relay the message to the inside of the cell, as shown in (c). **Figure 4.8** The shape of a protein on the HIV surface is likely to be complementary to the shape of the receptor (CD4) and also to that of the co-receptor (CCR5). A molecule that was a similar shape to the HIV surface protein could bind CCR5, blocking HIV binding. (Another answer would be a molecule that bound to CCR5 and changed the shape of CCR5 so it could no longer bind HIV.)

**Figure 4.9**

The protein would contact the extracellular fluid. The protein extends into the ER lumen. Once the vesicle fuses with the plasma membrane, the "inside" of the ER membrane, facing the lumen, will become the "outside" of the plasma membrane, facing the extracellular fluid. **Figure 4.11** The orange dye would be evenly distributed throughout the solution on both sides of the membrane. The solution levels would not be affected because the orange dye can diffuse through the membrane and equalize its concentration. Thus, no additional osmosis would take place in either direction. **Figure 4.16** The diamond solutes are moving into the cell (down), and the round solutes are moving out of the cell (up); both are moving against their concentration gradient.

## Concept Check 4.1

**1.** They are on the inner side of the transport vesicle membrane. **2.** The grasses living in the cooler region would be expected to have more unsaturated fatty acids in their membranes because those fatty acids remain fluid at lower temperatures. The grasses living immediately adjacent to the hot springs would be expected to have more saturated fatty acids, which would allow the fatty acids to "stack" more closely, making the membranes less fluid and therefore helping them to stay intact at higher temperatures. (Cholesterol could not be used to moderate the effects of temperature on membrane fluidity because it is not found within plant cell membranes.)

## Concept Check 4.2

**1.** $O_2$ and $CO_2$ are both nonpolar molecules that can easily pass through the hydrophobic interior of a membrane. **2.** Water is a polar molecule, so it cannot pass very rapidly through the hydrophobic region in the middle of a phospholipid bilayer. **3.** The hydronium ion is charged, while glycerol is not. Charge is probably more significant than size as a basis for exclusion by the aquaporin channel.

## Concept Check 4.3

**1.** $CO_2$ is a nonpolar molecule that can diffuse through the plasma membrane. As long as it diffuses away so that the concentration remains low outside the cell, it will continue to exit the cell in this way. (This is the opposite of the case for $O_2$, described in this section.) **2.** The activity of *Paramecium caudatum*'s contractile vacuole will decrease. The vacuole pumps out excess water that accumulates in the cell; this accumulation occurs only in a hypotonic environment.

## Concept Check 4.4

**1.** The pump uses ATP. To establish a voltage, ions have to be pumped against their gradients, which requires energy. **2.** Each ion is being transported against its electrochemical gradient. If either ion were transported down its electrochemical gradient, this *would* be considered cotransport. **3.** The internal environment of a lysosome is acidic, so it has a higher concentration of $H^+$ than does the cytoplasm. Therefore, you might expect the membrane of the lysosome to have a proton pump such as that shown in Figure 7.17 to pump $H^+$ into the lysosome.

## Concept Check 4.5

**1.** Exocytosis. When a transport vesicle fuses with the plasma membrane, the vesicle membrane becomes part of the plasma membrane.
**2.**

**3.** The glycoprotein would be synthesized in the ER lumen, move through the Golgi apparatus, and then travel in a vesicle to the plasma membrane, where it would undergo exocytosis and become part of the ECM.

## Summary of Key Concepts Questions

**4.1** Plasma membranes define the cell by separating the cellular components from the external environment. This allows conditions inside cells to be controlled by membrane proteins, which regulate entry and exit of molecules and even cell function (see Figure 4.7). The processes of life can be carried out inside the controlled environment of the cell, so membranes are crucial. In eukaryotes, membranes also function to subdivide the cytoplasm into different compartments where distinct processes can occur, even under differing conditions such as pH. **4.2** Aquaporins are channel proteins that greatly increase the permeability of a membrane to water molecules, which are polar and therefore do not readily diffuse through the hydrophobic interior of the membrane. **4.3** There will be a net diffusion of water out of a cell into a hypertonic solution. The free water concentration is higher inside the cell than in the solution (where water molecules are not free, but are clustered around the higher concentration of solute particles). **4.4** One of the solutes moved by the cotransporter is actively transported against its concentration gradient. The energy for this transport comes from the concentration gradient of the other solute, which was established by an electrogenic pump that used energy to transport the other solute across the membrane. **4.5** In receptor-mediated endocytosis, specific molecules act as ligands when they bind to receptors on the plasma membrane. The cell can acquire bulk quantities of those molecules when a coated pit forms a vesicle and carries the bound molecules into the cell.

## Test Your Understanding

**1.** b **2.** c **3.** a **4.** c **5.** b
**6.** (a)

(b) The solution outside is hypotonic. It has less sucrose, which is a nonpenetrating solute. (c) See answer for (a). (d) The artificial cell will become more turgid. (e) Eventually, the two solutions will have the same solute concentrations. Even though sucrose can't move through the membrane, water flow (osmosis) will lead to isotonic conditions.

## Chapter 5

**Figure 5.9** The R group of glutamine (Gln, or Q) is like that of glutamic acid (Glu, or E), except it has an amino group (–NH₂) in place of a hydroxyl group (–OH), so Gln is drawn as a Glu with an attached –NH₂.

**Figure 5.12**

**Figure 5.16**

### Concept Check 5.1
**1.** The second law is the trend toward randomization, or increasing entropy. When the concentrations of a substance on both sides of a membrane are equal, the distribution is more random than when they are unequal. Diffusion of a substance to a region where it is initially less concentrated increases entropy, making it an energetically favorable (spontaneous) process as described by the second law. **2.** The apple has potential energy in its position hanging on the tree, and the sugars and other nutrients it contains have chemical energy. The apple has kinetic energy as it falls from the tree to the ground. Finally, when the apple is digested and its molecules broken down, some of the chemical energy is used to do work, and the rest is lost as thermal energy.

### Concept Check 5.2
**1.** Cellular respiration is a spontaneous and exergonic process. The energy released from glucose is used to do work in the cell or is lost as heat. **2.** The reaction is exergonic because it releases energy—in this case, in the form of light. (This is a nonbiological version of the bioluminescence seen in Figure 5.1.)

### Concept Check 5.3
**1.** ATP usually transfers energy to endergonic processes by phosphorylating (adding phosphate groups to) other molecules. (Exergonic processes phosphorylate ADP to regenerate ATP.) **2.** A set of coupled reactions can transform the first combination into the second. Since this is an exergonic process overall, Δ*G* is negative and the first combination must have more free energy (see Figure 5.9). **3.** Active transport: The solute is being transported against its concentration gradient, which requires energy, provided by ATP hydrolysis.

### Concept Check 5.4
**1.** A spontaneous reaction is a reaction that is exergonic. However, if it has a high activation energy that is rarely attained, the rate of the reaction may be low. **2.** Only the specific substrate(s) will fit properly into the active site of an enzyme, the part of the enzyme that carries out catalysis. **3.** In the presence of malonate, increase the concentration of the normal substrate (succinate) and see whether the rate of reaction increases. If it does, malonate is a competitive inhibitor.

### Concept Check 5.5
**1.** The activator binds in such a way that it stabilizes the active form of an enzyme, whereas the inhibitor stabilizes the inactive form.

### Summary of Key Concepts Questions
**5.1** The process of "ordering" a cell's structure is accompanied by an increase in the entropy, or disorder, of the universe. For example, an animal cell takes in highly ordered organic molecules as the source of matter and energy used to build and maintain its structures. In the same process, however, the cell releases heat and the simple molecules of carbon dioxide and water to the surroundings. The increase in entropy of the latter process offsets the entropy decrease in the former. **5.2** Spontaneous reactions supply the energy to perform cellular work. **5.3** The free energy released from the hydrolysis of ATP may drive endergonic reactions through the transfer of a phosphate group to a reactant molecule, forming a more reactive phosphorylated intermediate. ATP hydrolysis also powers the mechanical and transport work of a cell, often by powering shape changes in the relevant motor proteins. Cellular respiration, the catabolic breakdown of glucose, provides the energy for the endergonic regeneration of ATP from ADP and Ⓟᵢ. **5.4** Activation energy barriers prevent the complex molecules of the cell, which are rich in free energy, from spontaneously breaking down to less ordered, more stable molecules. Enzymes permit a regulated metabolism by binding to specific substrates and forming enzyme-substrate complexes that selectively lower the E_A for the chemical reactions in a cell. **5.5** A cell tightly regulates its metabolic pathways in response to fluctuating needs for energy and materials. The binding of activators or inhibitors to regulatory sites on allosteric enzymes stabilizes either the active or

inactive form of the subunits. For example, the binding of ATP to a catabolic enzyme in a cell with excess ATP would inhibit that pathway. Such types of feedback inhibition preserve chemical resources within a cell. If ATP supplies are depleted, binding of ADP to the regulatory site of catabolic enzymes will activate that pathway.

### Test Your Understanding
**1.** b  **2.** c  **3.** b  **4.** a  **5.** c  **6.** e  **7.** c

**8.**

**A.** The substrate molecules are entering the cells, so no product is made yet.
**B.** There is sufficient substrate, so the reaction is proceeding at a maximum rate.
**C.** As the substrate is used up, the rate decreases (the slope is less steep).
**D.** The line is flat because no new substrate remains and thus no new product appears.

## Chapter 6

### Figure Questions
**Figure 6.7** Because there is no external source of energy for the reaction, it must be exergonic, and the reactants must be at a higher energy level than the products.
**Figure 6.14** At first, some ATP could be made, since electron transport could proceed as far as complex III, and a small H⁺ gradient could be built up. Soon, however, no more electrons could be passed to complex III because it could not be reoxidized by passing its electrons to complex IV. **Figure 6.15** First, there are 2 NADH from the oxidation of pyruvate plus 6 NADH from the citric acid cycle (CAC); 8 NADH × 2.5 ATP/NADH = 20 ATP. Second, there are 2 FADH₂ from the CAC; 2 FADH₂ × 1.5 ATP/FADH₂ = 3 ATP. Third, the 2 NADH from glycolysis enter the mitochondrion through one of two types of shuttle. They pass their electrons either to 2 FAD, which become FADH₂ and result in 3 ATP, or to 2 NAD⁺, which become NADH and result in 5 ATP. Thus, 20 + 3 + 3 = 26 ATP or 20 + 3 + 5 = 28 ATP from all NADH and FADH₂.

### Concept Check 6.1
**1.** Both processes include glycolysis, the citric acid cycle, and oxidative phosphorylation. In aerobic respiration, the final electron acceptor is molecular oxygen (O₂); in anaerobic respiration, the final electron acceptor is a different substance.
**2.** Substrate-level phosphorylation, which occurs during glycolysis and the citric acid cycle, involves the direct transfer of a phosphate group from an organic substrate to ADP by an enzyme. Oxidative phosphorylation occurs during the third stage of cellular respiration, which is called oxidative phosphorylation. In this process, the synthesis of ATP from ADP and inorganic phosphate (Ⓟᵢ) is powered by the redox reactions of the electron transport chain. **3.** C₄H₆O₅ would be oxidized, and NAD⁺ would be reduced.

### Concept Check 6.2
**1.** NAD⁺ acts as the oxidizing agent in step 6, accepting electrons from glyceraldehyde 3-phosphate, which thus acts as the reducing agent.

### Concept Check 6.3
**1.** NADH and FADH₂; they will donate electrons to the electron transport chain.
**2.** CO₂ is released from the pyruvate that is the end product of glycolysis, and CO₂ is also released during the citric acid cycle.

### Concept Check 6.4
**1.** Oxidative phosphorylation would eventually stop entirely, resulting in no ATP production by this process. Without oxygen to "pull" electrons down the electron transport chain, H⁺ would not be pumped into the mitochondrion's intermembrane space and chemiosmosis would not occur. **2.** Decreasing the pH means the addition of H⁺. This would establish a proton gradient even without the function of the electron transport chain, and we would expect ATP synthase to function and synthesize ATP. (In fact, it was experiments like this that provided support for chemiosmosis as an energy-coupling mechanism.) **3.** One of the components of the electron transport chain, ubiquinone (Q), must be able to diffuse within the membrane. It could not do so if the membrane were locked rigidly into place.

### Concept Check 6.5
**1.** A derivative of pyruvate, such as acetaldehyde during alcohol fermentation, or pyruvate itself during lactic acid fermentation; oxygen during aerobic respiration **2.** The cell would need to consume glucose at a rate about 16 times the consumption rate in the aerobic environment (2 ATP are generated by fermentation versus up to 32 ATP by cellular respiration).

### Concept Check 6.6
**1.** The fat is much more reduced; it has many —CH₂— units, and in all these bonds the electrons are equally shared. The electrons present in a carbohydrate molecule are already somewhat oxidized (shared unequally in bonds), as quite a few of them are bound to oxygen. **2.** When you consume more food than necessary for metabolic processes, your body synthesizes fat as a way of storing energy for later use. **3.** When oxygen is present, the fatty acid chains containing most of the energy of a fat are oxidized and fed into the citric acid cycle and the electron transport chain. During

intense exercise, however, oxygen is scarce in muscle cells, so ATP must be generated by glycolysis alone. A very small part of the fat molecule, the glycerol backbone, can be oxidized via glycolysis, but the amount of energy released by this portion is insignificant compared with that released by the fatty acid chains. (This is why moderate exercise, staying below 70% maximum heart rate, is better for burning fat—because enough oxygen remains available to the muscles.)

### Summary of Key Concepts Questions

**6.1** Most of the ATP produced in cellular respiration comes from oxidative phosphorylation, in which the energy released from redox reactions in an electron transport chain is used to produce ATP. In substrate-level phosphorylation, an enzyme directly transfers a phosphate group to ADP from an intermediate substrate. All ATP production in glycolysis occurs by substrate-level phosphorylation; this form of ATP production also occurs at one step in the citric acid cycle. **6.2** The oxidation of the three-carbon sugar glyceraldehyde 3-phosphate yields energy. In this oxidation, electrons and $H^+$ are transferred to $NAD^+$, forming NADH, and a phosphate group is attached to the oxidized substrate. ATP is then formed by substrate-level phosphorylation when this phosphate group is transferred to ADP. **6.3** The release of six molecules of $CO_2$ represents the complete oxidation of glucose. During the processing of two pyruvates to acetyl CoA, the fully oxidized carboxyl group ($-COO^-$) is given off as $CO_2$. The remaining four carbons are released as $CO_2$ in the citric acid cycle as citrate is oxidized back to oxaloacetate. **6.4** The flow of $H^+$ through the ATP synthase complex causes the rotor and attached rod to rotate, exposing catalytic sites in the knob portion that produce ATP from ADP and $Ⓟ_i$. ATP synthases are found in the inner mitochondrial membrane, the plasma membrane of prokaryotes, and membranes within chloroplasts. **6.5** Anaerobic respiration yields more ATP. The 2 ATP produced by substrate-level phosphorylation in glycolysis represent the total energy yield of fermentation. NADH passes its "high-energy" electrons to pyruvate or a derivative of pyruvate, recycling $NAD^+$ and allowing glycolysis to continue. Anaerobic respiration uses an electron transport chain to capture the energy of the electrons in NADH via a series of redox reactions; ultimately, the electrons are transferred to an electronegative molecule other than oxygen. Also, additional molecules of NADH are produced in anaerobic respiration as pyruvate is oxidized. **6.6** The ATP produced by catabolic pathways is used to drive anabolic pathways. Also, many of the intermediates of glycolysis and the citric acid cycle are used in the biosynthesis of a cell's molecules.

### Test Your Understanding
**1.** d **2.** c **3.** c **4.** a **5.** e **6.** a **7.** b
**8.**

## Chapter 7

### Figure Questions

**Figure 7.3** Situating containers of algae near sources of $CO_2$ emissions makes sense because algae need $CO_2$ to carry out photosynthesis. The higher their rate of photosynthesis, the more plant oil they will produce. At the same time, algae would be absorbing the $CO_2$ emitted from industrial plants or from car engines, reducing the amount of $CO_2$ entering the atmosphere. **Figure 7.12** In the leaf, most of the chlorophyll electrons excited by photon absorption are used to power the reactions of photosynthesis. **Figure 7.16** The person at the top of the photosystem I tower would not turn to his left and throw his electron into the bucket. Instead, he would throw it onto the top of the ramp at his right, next to the photosystem II tower. The electron would then roll down the ramp, get energized by a photon, and return to him. This cycle would continue as long as light was available. (This is why it's called cyclic electron flow.) **Figure 7.22** Yes, plants can break down the sugar (in the form of glucose) by cellular respiration, producing ATPs for various cellular processes such as endergonic chemical reactions, transport of substances across membranes, and movement of molecules in the cell. ATPs are also used for the movement of chloroplasts during cellular streaming in some plant cells. **Figure 7.23** The gene encoding hexokinase is part of the DNA of a chromosome in the nucleus. There, the gene is transcribed into mRNA, which is transported to the cytoplasm where it is translated on a free ribosome into a polypeptide. The polypeptide folds into a functional protein with secondary and tertiary structure. Once functional, it carries out the first reaction of glycolysis in the cytoplasm.

### Concept Check 7.1
**1.** $CO_2$ enters the leaves via stomata, and water enters via roots and is carried to the leaves through veins. **2.** Using $^{18}O$, a heavy isotope of oxygen, as a label, researchers

were able to confirm van Niel's hypothesis that the oxygen produced during photosynthesis comes from water, not from carbon dioxide. **3.** The light reactions could *not* keep producing NADPH and ATP without the $NADP^+$, ADP, and $\sim Pi$ that the Calvin cycle generates. The two cycles are interdependent.

### Concept Check 7.2
**1.** Green, because green light is mostly transmitted and reflected—not absorbed—by photosynthetic pigments **2.** Water ($H_2O$) is the initial electron donor; $NADP^+$ accepts electrons at the end of the electron transport chain, becoming reduced to NADPH. **3.** In this experiment, the rate of ATP synthesis would slow and eventually stop. Because the added compound would not allow a proton gradient to build up across the membrane, ATP synthase could not catalyze ATP production.

### Concept Check 7.3
**1.** 6, 18, 12 **2.** The more potential energy a molecule stores, the more energy and reducing power are required for the formation of that molecule. Glucose is a valuable energy source because it is highly reduced, storing lots of potential energy in its electrons. To reduce $CO_2$ to glucose, much energy and reducing power are required in the form of large numbers of ATP and NADPH molecules, respectively. **3.** The light reactions require ADP and $NADP^+$, which would not be formed in sufficient quantities from ATP and NADPH if the Calvin cycle stopped.
**4.**

$$3 \times 1 (=3)$$
$$3 \times 6 (=18)$$
$$3 \times 5 (=15)$$
$$6 \times 3 (=18)$$
$$6 \times 3 (=18)$$
$$5 \times 3 (=15)$$
$$6 \times 3 (=18)$$
$$1 \times 3 (=3)$$

Three carbon atoms enter the cycle, one by one, as individual $CO_2$ molecules, and leave the cycle in one three-carbon molecule (G3P) per three turns of the cycle.
**5.** In glycolysis, G3P acts as an intermediate. The 6-carbon sugar fructose 1,6-bisphosphate is cleaved into two 3-carbon sugars, one of which is G3P. The other is an isomer called dihydroxyacetone phosphate (DHAP), which can be converted to G3P by an isomerase. Because G3P is the substrate for the next enzyme, it is constantly removed, and the reaction equilibrium is pulled in the direction of conversion of DHAP to more G3P. In the Calvin cycle, G3P acts as both an intermediate and a product. For every three $CO_2$ molecules that enter the cycle, six G3P molecules are formed, five of which must remain in the cycle and become rearranged to regenerate three 5-carbon RuBP molecules. The one remaining G3P is a product, which can be thought of as the result of "reducing" the three $CO_2$ molecules that entered the cycle into a 3-carbon sugar that can later be used to generate energy.

### Concept Check 7.4
**1.** Photorespiration decreases photosynthetic output by adding oxygen, instead of carbon dioxide, to the Calvin cycle. As a result, no sugar is generated (no carbon is fixed), and $O_2$ is used rather than generated. **2.** Without PS II, no $O_2$ is generated in bundle-sheath cells. This avoids the problem of $O_2$ competing with $CO_2$ for binding to rubisco in these cells. **3.** Both problems are caused by a drastic change in Earth's atmosphere due to burning of fossil fuels. The increase in $CO_2$ concentration affects ocean chemistry by decreasing pH, thus affecting calcification by marine organisms. On land, $CO_2$ concentration and air temperature are conditions that plants have become adapted to, and changes in these characteristics have a strong effect on photosynthesis by plants. Thus, alteration of these two fundamental factors could have critical effects on organisms all around the planet, in all different habitats. **4.** $C_4$ and CAM species would replace many of the $C_3$ species.

### Summary of Key Concepts Questions
**7.1** $CO_2$ and $H_2O$ are the products of respiration; they are the reactants in photosynthesis. In respiration, glucose is oxidized to $CO_2$ and electrons are passed through an electron transfer chain from glucose to $O_2$, producing $H_2O$. In photosynthesis, $H_2O$ is the source of electrons, which are energized by light, temporarily stored in NADPH, and used to reduce $CO_2$ to carbohydrate. **7.2** The action spectrum of photosynthesis shows that some wavelengths of light that are not absorbed by chlorophyll *a* are still effective at promoting photosynthesis. The light-harvesting complexes of photosystems contain accessory pigments such as chlorophyll *b* and carotenoids, which absorb different wavelengths and pass the energy to chlorophyll *a*, broadening the spectrum of light usable for photosynthesis.

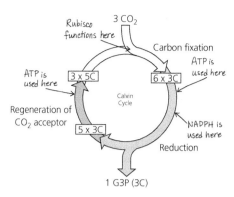

In the reduction phase of the Calvin cycle, ATP phosphorylates a three-carbon compound, and NADPH then reduces this compound to G3P. ATP is also used in the regeneration phase, when five molecules of G3P are converted to three molecules of the five-carbon compound RuBP. Rubisco catalyzes the first step of carbon fixation—the addition of $CO_2$ to RuBP. **7.4** Both $C_4$ photosynthesis and CAM photosynthesis involve initial fixation of $CO_2$ to produce a four-carbon compound (in mesophyll cells in $C_4$ plants and at night in CAM plants). These compounds are then broken down to release $CO_2$ (in the bundle-sheath cells in $C_4$ plants and during the day in CAM plants). ATP is required for recycling the molecule that is used initially to combine with $CO_2$. These pathways avoid the photorespiration that consumes ATP and reduces the photosynthetic output of $C_3$ plants when they close stomata on hot, dry, bright days. Thus, hot, arid climates would favor $C_4$ and CAM plants.

### Test Your Understanding
**1.** d **2.** b **3.** c **4.** a **5.** c **6.** b **7.** c
**10.**

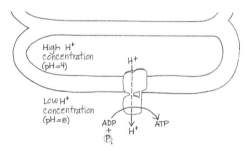

The ATP would end up outside the thylakoid. The thylakoids were able to make ATP in the dark because the researchers set up an artificial proton concentration gradient across the thylakoid membrane; thus, the light reactions were not necessary to establish the H$^+$ gradient required for ATP synthesis by ATP synthase.

## Chapter 8

### Figure Questions
**Figure 8.6** Epinephrine is a signaling molecule; presumably, it binds to a cell-surface receptor protein. **Figure 8.8** This is an example of passive transport. The ion is moving down its concentration gradient, and no energy is required. **Figure 8.9** The aldosterone molecule is hydrophobic and can therefore pass directly through the lipid bilayer of the plasma membrane into the cell. (Hydrophilic molecules cannot do this.) **Figure 8.10** The entire phosphorylation cascade wouldn't operate. Regardless of whether or not the signaling molecule was bound, protein kinase 3 would always be inactive and would not be able to activate the purple-colored protein leading to the cellular response. **Figure 8.11** The signaling molecule (cAMP) would remain in its active form and would continue to signal. **Figure 8.16** 100,000,000 (one hundred million or 108) glucose molecules are released. The first step results in 100* amplification (one epinephrine activates 100 G proteins); the next step does not amplify the response; the next step is a 100* amplification (102 active adenylyl cyclase molecules to 104 cyclic AMPs); the next step does not amplify; the next two steps are each 10* amplifications, and the final step is a 100* amplification. **Figure 8.17** The signaling pathway shown in Figure 8.14 leads to the splitting of PIP$_2$ into the second messengers DAG and IP$_3$, which produce different responses. (The response elicited by DAG is mentioned but not shown.) The pathway shown for cell B is similar in that it branches and leads to two responses.

### Concept Check 8.1
**1.** The two cells of opposite mating type (**a** and **α**) each secrete a certain signaling molecule, which can only be bound by receptors carried on cells of the opposite mating type. Thus, the **a** mating factor cannot bind to another **a** cell and cause it to grow toward the first **a** cell. Only an **α** cell can "receive" the signaling molecule and respond by directed growth (see the Scientific Skills Exercise). **2.** Glycogen phosphorylase acts in the third stage, the response to epinephrine signaling. **3.** Glucose 1-phosphate is not generated, because the activation of the enzyme requires an intact cell, with an intact

receptor in the membrane and an intact signal transduction pathway. The enzyme cannot be activated directly by interaction with the signaling molecule in the test tube.

### Concept Check 8.2
**1.** NGF is water-soluble (hydrophilic), so it cannot pass through the lipid membrane to reach intracellular receptors, as steroid hormones can. Therefore, you'd expect the NGF receptor to be in the plasma membrane—which is, in fact, the case. **2.** The cell with the faulty receptor would not be able to respond appropriately to the signaling molecule when it was present. This would most likely have dire consequences for the cell, since regulation of the cell's activities by this receptor would not occur appropriately. **3.** Binding of a ligand to a receptor changes the shape of the receptor, altering the ability of the receptor to transmit a signal. Binding of an allosteric regulator to an enzyme changes the shape of the enzyme, either promoting or inhibiting enzyme activity. **4.** When the receptor is actively transmitting a signal to the inside of the cell, it is bound to a G protein. To determine a structure corresponding to that state, it might be useful to crystallize the receptor in the presence of many copies of the G protein. (In fact, a research group used this approach successfully with a G protein-coupled receptor related to the one shown in Figure 8.8.)

### Concept Check 8.3
**1.** A protein kinase is an enzyme that transfers a phosphate group from ATP to a protein, usually activating that protein (often a second type of protein kinase). Many signal transduction pathways include a series of such interactions, in which each phosphorylated protein kinase in turn phosphorylates the next protein kinase in the series. Such phosphorylation cascades carry a signal from outside the cell to the cellular protein(s) that will carry out the response. **2.** Protein phosphatases reverse the effects of the kinases, and unless the signaling molecule is at a high enough concentration that it is continuously rebinding the receptor, the kinase molecules will all be returned to their inactive states by phosphatases. **3.** The signal that is being transduced is the *information* that a signaling molecule is bound to the cell-surface receptor. Information is transduced by way of sequential protein-protein interactions that change protein shapes, causing them to function in a way that passes the signal (the information) along. **4.** The IP$_3$-gated channel opens, allowing calcium ions to flow out of the ER and into the cytoplasm, which raises the cytosolic Ca$^{2+}$ concentration.

### Concept Check 8.4
**1.** At each step in a cascade of sequential activations, one molecule or ion may activate numerous molecules functioning in the next step. This causes the response to be amplified at each such step and overall results in a large amplification of the original signal. **2.** Scaffolding proteins hold molecular components of signaling pathways in a complex with each other. Different scaffolding proteins would assemble different collections of proteins, leading to different cellular responses in the two cells. **3.** A malfunctioning protein phosphatase would not be able to dephosphorylate a particular receptor or relay protein. As a result, the signaling pathway, once activated, would not be able to be terminated. (In fact, one study found altered protein phosphatases in cells from 25% of colorectal tumors.)

### Concept Check 8.5
**1.** In formation of the hand or paw in mammals, cells in the regions between the digits are programmed to undergo apoptosis. This serves to shape the digits of the hand or paw so that they are not webbed. (A lack of apoptosis in these regions in water birds results in webbed feet.) **2.** If a receptor protein for a death-signaling molecule were defective such that it was activated even in the absence of the death signal, this would lead to apoptosis when it wouldn't normally occur. Similar defects in any of the proteins in the signaling pathway would have the same effect if the defective proteins activated relay or response proteins in the absence of interaction with the previous protein or second messenger in the pathway. Conversely, if any protein in the pathway were defective in its ability to respond to an interaction with an early protein or other molecule or ion, apoptosis would not occur when it normally should. For example, a receptor protein for a death-signaling ligand might not be able to be activated, even when ligand was bound. This would stop the signal from being transduced into the cell.

### Summary of Key Concepts Questions
**8.1** A cell is able to respond to a hormone only if it has a receptor protein on the cell surface or inside the cell that can bind to the hormone. The response to a hormone depends on the specific signal transduction pathway within the cell, which will lead to the specific cellular response. The response can vary for different types of cells. **8.2** Both GPCRs and RTKs have an extracellular binding site for a signaling molecule (ligand) and one or more α helical regions of the polypeptide that span the membrane. A GPCR functions singly, while RTKs tend to dimerize or form larger groups of RTKs. GPCRs usually trigger a single transduction pathway, whereas the multiple activated tyrosines on an RTK dimer may trigger several different transduction pathways at the same time. **8.3** A protein kinase is an enzyme that adds a phosphate group to another protein. Protein kinases are often part of a phosphorylation cascade that transduces a signal. A second messenger is a small, nonprotein molecule or ion that rapidly diffuses and relays a signal throughout a cell. Both protein kinases and second messengers can operate in the same pathway. For example, the second messenger cAMP often activates protein kinase A, which then phosphorylates other proteins. **8.4** In G protein-coupled pathways, the GTPase portion of a G protein converts GTP to GDP and inactivates the G protein. Protein phosphatases remove phosphate groups from activated proteins, thus stopping a phosphorylation cascade of protein kinases. Phosphodiesterase converts cAMP to AMP, thus reducing the effect of cAMP in a signal transduction pathway. **8.5** The basic mechanism of controlled cell suicide evolved early in eukaryotic evolution, and the genetic basis for these pathways has been conserved during animal evolution. Such a mechanism is essential to the development and maintenance of all animals.

## Test Your Understanding

**1.** d **2.** a **3.** b **4.** a **5.** c **6.** c **7.** c

**8.** This is one possible drawing of the pathway. (Similar drawings would also be correct.)

Circling the other chromatid instead would also be correct. **Figure 9.5** The chromosome has four arms. **Figure 9.7** 12; 2; 2; 1

# Chapter 9

## Figure Questions

**Figure 9.4**

One sister chromatid

Circling the other chromatid instead would also be correct. **Figure 9.5** The chromosome has four arms. **Figure 9.7** 12; 2; 2; 1

**Figure 9.8**

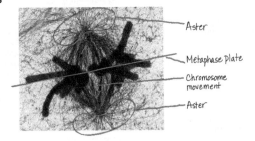

Aster

Metaphase plate

Chromosome movement

Aster

**Figure 9.9** The mark would have moved toward the nearer pole. The lengths of fluorescent microtubules between that pole and the mark would have decreased, while the lengths between the chromosomes and the mark would have remained the same. **Figure 9.14** In both cases, the $G_1$ nucleus would have remained in $G_1$ until the time it normally would have entered the S phase. Chromosome condensation and spindle formation would not have occurred until the S and $G_2$ phases had been completed. **Figure 9.16** Passing the $G_2$ checkpoint in the diagram corresponds to the beginning of the "Time" axis of the graph, and entry into the mitotic phase (yellow background on the diagram) corresponds to the peaks of MPF activity and cyclin concentration on the graph (see the yellow M banner over the peaks). During $G_1$ and S phase in the diagram, Cdk is present without cyclin, so on the graph both cyclin concentration and MPF activity are low. The curved purple arrow in the diagram shows increasing cyclin concentration, seen on the graph during the end of S phase and throughout $G_2$ phase. Then the cell cycle begins again. **Figure 9.17** The cell would divide under conditions where it was inappropriate to do so. If the daughter cells and their descendants also ignored either of the checkpoints and divided, there would soon be an abnormal mass of cells. (This type of inappropriate cell division can contribute to the development of cancer.) **Figure 9.18** The cells in the vessel with PDGF would not be able to respond to the growth factor signal and thus would not divide. The culture would resemble that without the added PDGF.

## Concept Check 9.1

**1.** 1; 1; 2 **2.** 39; 39; 78

## Concept Check 9.2

**1.** 6 chromosomes, duplicated; 12 chromatids **2.** Following mitosis, cytokinesis results in two genetically identical daughter cells in both plant cells and animal cells. However, the mechanism of dividing the cytoplasm is different in animals and plants. In an animal cell, cytokinesis occurs by cleavage, which divides the parent cell in two with a contractile ring of actin filaments. In a plant cell, a cell plate forms in the middle of the cell and grows until its membrane fuses with the plasma membrane of the parent cell. A new cell wall grows inside the cell plate. **3.** From the end of S phase in interphase through the end of metaphase in mitosis **4.** During eukaryotic cell division, tubulin is involved in spindle formation and chromosome movement, while actin functions during cytokinesis. In bacterial binary fission, it's the opposite: Tubulin-like molecules are thought to act in daughter cell separation, and actin-like molecules are thought to move the daughter bacterial chromosomes to opposite ends of the cell. **5.** A kinetochore connects the spindle (a motor; note that it has motor proteins) to a chromosome (the cargo it will move). **6.** Microtubules made up of tubulin in the cell provide "rails" along which vesicles and other organelles can travel, based on interactions of motor proteins with tubulin in the microtubules. In muscle cells, actin in microfilaments interacts with myosin filaments to cause muscle contraction.

## Concept Check 9.3

**1.** The nucleus on the right was originally in the $G_1$ phase; therefore, it had not yet duplicated its chromosomes. The nucleus on the left was in the M phase, so it had already duplicated its chromosomes. **2.** A sufficient amount of MPF has to exist for a cell to pass the $G_2$ checkpoint; this occurs through the accumulation of cyclin proteins, which combine with Cdk to form (active) MPF. **3.** The intracellular estrogen receptor, once activated, would be able to act as a transcription factor in the nucleus, turning on genes that may cause the cell to pass a checkpoint and divide. The HER2 receptor, when activated by a ligand, would form a dimer, and each subunit of the dimer would phosphorylate the other. This would lead to a series of signal transduction steps, ultimately turning on genes in the nucleus. As in the case of the estrogen receptor, the genes would code for proteins necessary to commit the cell to divide.

## Summary of Key Concepts Questions

**9.1** The DNA of a eukaryotic cell is packaged into structures called *chromosomes*. Each chromosome is a long molecule of DNA, which carries hundreds to thousands of genes, with associated proteins that maintain chromosome structure and help control gene activity. This DNA-protein complex is called *chromatin*. The chromatin of each chromosome is long and thin when the cell is not dividing. Prior to cell division, each chromosome is duplicated, and the resulting sister *chromatids* are attached to each other by proteins at the centromeres and, for many species, all along their lengths (a phenomenon called sister chromatid cohesion). **9.2** Chromosomes exist as single DNA molecules in $G_1$ of interphase and in anaphase and telophase of mitosis. During S phase, DNA replication produces sister chromatids, which persist during $G_2$ of interphase and through prophase, prometaphase, and metaphase of mitosis. **9.3** Checkpoints allow cellular surveillance mechanisms to determine whether the cell is prepared to go to the next stage. Internal and external signals move a cell past these checkpoints. The $G_1$ checkpoint, called the "restriction point" in mammalian cells, determines whether a cell will complete the cell cycle and divide or switch into the $G_0$ phase. The signals to pass this checkpoint often are external—such as growth factors. Passing the $G_2$ checkpoint requires sufficient numbers of active MPF complexes, which in turn orchestrate several mitotic events. MPF also initiates degradation of its cyclin component, terminating the M phase. The M phase will not begin again until sufficient cyclin is produced during the next S and $G_2$ phases. The signal to pass the M phase checkpoint is not activated until all chromosomes are attached to kinetochore fibers and are aligned at the metaphase plate. Only then will sister chromatid separation occur.

## Test Your Understanding

**1.** b **2.** a **3.** c **4.** c **5.** a **6.** b **7.** a **8.** d

**9.** See Figure 9.7 for a description of major events.

Prometaphase   Prophase   Telophase

Anaphase   Metaphase

Only one cell is indicated for each stage, but other correct answers are also present in this micrograph.

**10.**

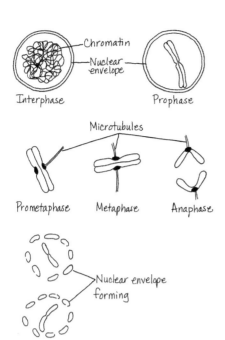

Interphase     Prophase

Microtubules

Prometaphase     Metaphase     Anaphase

Nuclear envelope forming

Telophase and cytokinesis

## Chapter 10

### Figure Questions
**Figure 10.4** Two sets of chromosomes are present. Three pairs of homologous chromosomes are present. **Figure 10.7**

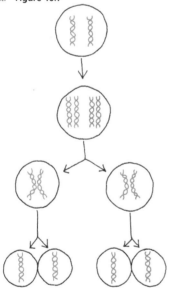

(A short strand of DNA is shown here for simplicity, but each chromosome or chromatid contains a very long coiled and folded DNA molecule.)
**Figure 10.8** If a cell with six chromosomes undergoes two rounds of mitosis, each of the four resulting cells will have six chromosomes, while the four cells resulting from meiosis in Figure 10.8 each have three chromosomes. In mitosis, DNA replication (and thus chromosome duplication) precedes each prophase, ensuring that daughter cells have the same number of chromosomes as the parent cell. In meiosis, in contrast, DNA replication occurs only before prophase I (not prophase II). Thus, in two rounds of mitosis, the chromosomes duplicate twice and divide twice, while in meiosis, the chromosomes duplicate once and divide twice. **Figure 10.10** Yes. Each of the six chromosomes (three per cell) shown in telophase I has one nonrecombinant chromatid and one recombinant chromatid. Therefore, eight possible sets of chromosomes can be generated for the cell on the left and eight for the cell on the right.

### Concept Check 10.1
**1.** Parents pass genes to their offspring; by dictating the production of messenger RNAs (mRNAs), the genes program cells to make specific enzymes and other proteins, whose cumulative action produces an individual's inherited traits. **2.** Such organisms reproduce by mitosis, which generates offspring whose genomes are exact copies of the

parent's genome (in the absence of mutation). **3.** She should clone it. Cross-breeding it with another plant would generate offspring that have additional variation, which she no longer desires now that she has obtained her ideal orchid.

### Concept Check 10.2
**1.** Each of the six chromosomes is duplicated, so each contains two DNA double helices. Therefore, there are 12 DNA molecules in the cell. The haploid number, $n$, is 3. One set is always haploid. **2.** 23; 2. **3.** This organism has the life cycle shown in Figure 10.6c. Therefore, it must be a fungus or a protist, perhaps an alga.

### Concept Check 10.3
**1.** The chromosomes are similar in that each is composed of two sister chromatids, and the individual chromosomes are positioned similarly at the metaphase plate. The chromosomes differ in that in a mitotically dividing cell, sister chromatids of each chromosome are genetically identical, but in a meiotically dividing cell, sister chromatids are genetically distinct because of crossing over in meiosis I. Moreover, the chromosomes in metaphase of mitosis can be a diploid set or a haploid set, but the chromosomes in metaphase of meiosis II always consist of a haploid set. **2.** If crossing over did not occur, the two homologs would not be associated in any way. This might result in incorrect arrangement of homologs during metaphase I and ultimately in formation of gametes with an abnormal number of chromosomes.

### Concept Check 10.4
**1.** Mutations in a gene lead to the different versions (alleles) of that gene.
**2.** Without crossing over, independent assortment of chromosomes during meiosis I theoretically can generate $2^n$ possible haploid gametes, and random fertilization can produce $2^n \times 2^n$ possible diploid zygotes. Because the haploid number ($n$) of grasshoppers is 23 and that of fruit flies is 4, two grasshoppers would be expected to produce a greater variety of zygotes than would two fruit flies. **3.** If the segments of the maternal and paternal chromatids that undergo crossing over are genetically identical and thus have the same two alleles for every gene, then the recombinant chromosomes will be genetically equivalent to the parental chromosomes. Crossing over contributes to genetic variation only when it involves the rearrangement of different alleles.

### Summary of Key Concepts Questions
**10.1** Genes program specific traits, and offspring inherit their genes from each parent, accounting for similarities in their appearance to one or the other parent. Humans reproduce sexually, which ensures new combinations of genes (and thus traits) in the offspring. Consequently, the offspring are not clones of their parents (which would be the case if humans reproduced asexually). **10.2** Animals and plants both reproduce sexually, alternating meiosis with fertilization. Both have haploid gametes that unite to form a diploid zygote, which then goes on to divide mitotically, forming a diploid multicellular organism. In animals, haploid cells become gametes and don't undergo mitosis, while in plants, the haploid cells resulting from meiosis undergo mitosis to form a haploid multicellular organism, the gametophyte. This organism then goes on to generate haploid gametes. (In plants such as trees, the gametophyte is quite reduced in size and not obvious to the casual observer.) **10.3** At the end of meiosis I, the two members of a homologous pair end up in different cells, so they cannot pair up and undergo crossing over. **10.4** First, during independent assortment in metaphase I, each pair of homologous chromosomes lines up independent of each other pair at the metaphase plate, so a daughter cell of meiosis I randomly inherits either a maternal or paternal chromosome. Second, due to crossing over, each chromosome is not exclusively maternal or paternal, but includes regions at the ends of the chromatid from a nonsister chromatid (a chromatid of the other homolog). (The nonsister segment can also be in an internal region of the chromatid if a second crossover occurs beyond the first one before the end of the chromatid.) This provides much additional diversity in the form of new combinations of alleles. Third, random fertilization ensures even more variation, since any sperm of a large number containing many possible genetic combinations can fertilize any egg of a similarly large number of possible combinations.

### Test Your Understanding
**1.** a   **2.** b   **3.** a   **4.** d   **5.** c
**6.** (a)

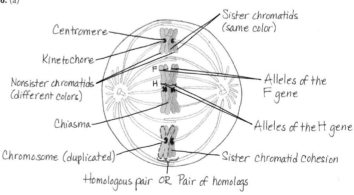

(b) A haploid set is made up of one long, one medium, and one short chromosome. For example, the chromosomes of one color make up a haploid set. (In cases where crossovers have occurred, a haploid set of one color may include segments of chromatids of the other color.) All red and blue chromosomes together make up a diploid set. (c) Metaphase I   **7.** This cell must be undergoing meiosis because homologous chromosomes are associated with each other at the metaphase plate; this does not occur in mitosis.

# Chapter 11

**Figure 11.3** All offspring would have purple flowers. (The ratio would be one purple to zero white.) The P generation plants are true-breeding, so mating two purple-flowered plants produces the same result as self-pollination: All the offspring have the same trait. **Figure 11.8**

Yes, this cross would also have allowed Mendel to make different predictions for the two hypotheses, thereby allowing him to distinguish the correct one. **Figure 11.10** Your classmate would probably point out that the F₁ generation hybrids show an intermediate phenotype between those of the homozygous parents, which supports the blending hypothesis. You could respond that crossing the F₁ hybrids results in the reappearance of the white phenotype, rather than identical pink offspring, which fails to support the idea of traits blending during inheritance. **Figure 11.11** Both the $I^A$ and $I^B$ alleles are dominant to the $i$ allele, which is recessive and results in no attached carbohydrate. The $I^A$ and $I^B$ alleles are codominant; both are expressed in the phenotype of $I^A I^B$ heterozygotes, who have type AB blood. **Figure 11.15** In the Punnett square, two of the three individuals with normal coloration are carriers, so the probability is $2/3$. (Note that you must take into account everything you know when you calculate probability: You know she is not $aa$, so there are only three possible genotypes to consider.)

## Concept Check 11.1

**1.** There are 423 round peas and 133 wrinkled peas, a ratio of 3.18:1, or roughly 3:1.
**2.** According to the law of independent assortment, 25 plants ($1/16$ of the offspring) are predicted to be $aatt$, or recessive for both characters. The actual result is likely to differ slightly from this value.

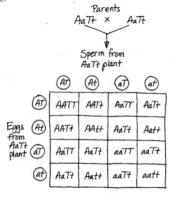

**3.** The plant could make eight different gametes (*YRI, YRi, YrI, Yri, yRI, yRi, yrI,* and *yri*). To fit all the possible gametes in a self-pollination, a Punnett square would need 8 rows and 8 columns. It would have spaces for the 64 possible unions of gametes in the offspring. **4.** Self-pollination is sexual reproduction because meiosis is involved in forming gametes, which unite during fertilization. As a result, the offspring in self-pollination are genetically different from the parent.

## Concept Check 11.2

**1.** $1/2$ homozygous dominant (*AA*), 0 homozygous recessive (*aa*), and $1/2$ heterozygous (*Aa*) **2.** $1/4$ *BBDD*; $1/4$ *BbDD*; $1/4$ *BBDd*; $1/4$ *BbDd* **3.** The genotypes that fulfill this condition are *ppyyIi, ppYyii, Ppyyii, ppYYii,* and *ppyyii*. Use the multiplication rule to find the probability of getting each genotype, and then use the addition rule to find the overall probability of meeting the conditions of this problem:

## Concept Check 11.3

**1.** Incomplete dominance describes the relationship between two alleles of a single gene, whereas epistasis relates to the genetic relationship between two genes (and the respective alleles of each). **2.** Half of the children would be expected to have type A blood and half type B blood. **3.** The black and white alleles are incompletely dominant, with heterozygotes being gray in color. A cross between a gray rooster and a black hen should yield approximately equal numbers of gray and black offspring.

## Concept Check 11.4

**1.** $1/9$ (Since cystic fibrosis is caused by a recessive allele, Beth and Tom's siblings who have CF must be homozygous recessive. Therefore, each parent must be a carrier of the recessive allele. Since neither Beth nor Tom has CF, this means they each have a $2/3$ chance of being a carrier. If they are both carriers, there is a $1/4$ chance that they will have a child with CF. $2/3 \times 2/3 \times 1/4 = 1/9$); 0 (Both Beth and Tom would have to be carriers to produce a child with the disease.) **2.** In the monohybrid cross involving flower color, the ratio is 3.15 purple : 1 white, while in the human family in the pedigree, the ratio in the third generation is 1 free : 1 attached earlobe. The difference is due to the small sample size (two offspring) in the human family. If the second-generation couple in this pedigree were able to have 929 offspring as in the pea plant cross, the ratio would likely be closer to 3:1. (Note that none of the pea plant crosses in Table 11.1 yielded *exactly* a 3:1 ratio.)

## Summary of Key Concepts Questions

**11.1** Alternative versions of genes, called alleles, are passed from parent to offspring during sexual reproduction. In a cross between purple- and white-flowered homozygous parents, the F₁ offspring are all heterozygous, each inheriting a purple allele from one parent and a white allele from the other. Because the purple allele is dominant, it determines the phenotype of all F₁ offspring to be purple, while the expression of the recessive white allele is masked. Only in the F₂ generation is it possible for a white allele to exist in a homozygous state, which causes the white trait to be expressed.
**11.2**

3/4 yellow × 3/4 round = 9/16 yellow-round
3/4 yellow × 1/4 wrinkled = 3/16 yellow-wrinkled
1/4 green × 3/4 round = 3/16 green-round
1/4 green × 1/4 wrinkled = 1/16 green-wrinkled

= 9 yellow-round : 3 yellow-wrinkled : 3 green-round : 1 green-wrinkled

**11.3** The ABO blood group is an example of multiple alleles because this single gene has more than two alleles ($I^A$, $I^B$, and $i$). Two of the alleles, $I^A$ and $I^B$, exhibit codominance, since both carbohydrates (A and B) are present when these two alleles exist together in a genotype. $I^A$ and $I^B$ each exhibit complete dominance over the $i$ allele. This situation is not an example of incomplete dominance because each allele affects the phenotype in a distinguishable way, so the result is not intermediate between the two phenotypes. Because this situation involves a single gene, it is not an example of epistasis or polygenic inheritance. **11.4** The chance of the fourth child having cystic fibrosis is $1/4$, as it was for each of the other children, because each birth is an independent event. We already know that both parents are carriers, so whether their first three children are carriers or not has no bearing on the probability that their next child will have the disease. The parents' genotypes provide the only relevant information.

## Test Your Understanding

**1.** Gene, l; Allele, e; Character, g; Trait, b; Dominant allele, j; Recessive allele, a; Genotype, k; Phenotype, h; Homozygous, c; Heterozygous, f; Testcross, i; Monohybrid cross, d
**2.**

Parents
GgIi × GgIi

Sperm

| | GI | Gi | gI | gi |
|---|---|---|---|---|
| **GI** | GGII | GGIi | GgII | GgIi |
| **Gi** | GGIi | GGii | GgIi | Ggii |
| **gI** | GgII | GgIi | ggII | ggIi |
| **gi** | GgIi | Ggii | ggIi | ggii |

Eggs

9 green-inflated : 3 green-constricted :
3 yellow-inflated : 1 yellow-constricted

**3.** Man $I^A i$; woman $I^B i$; child $ii$. Genotypes for future children are predicted to be $1/4$ $I^A I^B$, $1/4$ $I^A i$, $1/4$ $I^B i$, $1/4$ $ii$.   **4.** $1/2$   **5.** A cross of $Ii \times ii$ would yield offspring with a genotypic ratio of 1 $Ii$ : 1 $ii$ (2:2 is an equivalent answer) and a phenotypic ratio of 1 inflated : 1 constricted (2:2 is equivalent).

Parents

Ii × ii

Sperm from
ii plant

Eggs from Ii plant

| | i | i |
|---|---|---|
| **I** | Ii | Ii |
| **i** | ii | ii |

Genotypic ratio 1 Ii : 1 ii
(2:2 is equivalent)

Phenotypic ratio 1 inflated : 1 constricted
(2:2 is equivalent)

**6.** (a) $1/64$; (b) $1/64$; (c) $1/8$; (d) $1/32$   **7.** Albino ($b$) is a recessive trait; black ($B$) is dominant. First cross: parents $BB \times bb$; gametes $B$ and $b$; offspring all $Bb$ (black coat). The black guinea pig in the second cross is a heterozygote. Second cross: parents $Bb \times bb$; gametes $1/2$ $B$ and $1/2$ $b$ (heterozygous parent) and $b$; offspring $1/2$ $Bb$ (black) and $1/2$ $bb$ (white).   **8.** Parental cross is $AAC^R C^R \times aaC^W C^W$. $F_1$ genotype is $AaC^R C^W$, phenotype is all axial-pink. $F_2$ genotypes are 1 $AAC^R C^R$ : 2 $AAC^R C^W$ : 1 $AAC^W C^W$ : 2 $AaC^R C^R$ : 4 $AaC^R C^W$ : 2 $AaC^W C^W$ : 1 $aaC^R C^R$ : 2 $aaC^R C^W$ : 1 $aaC^W C^W$. $F_2$ phenotypes are 3 axial-red : 6 axial-pink : 3 axial-white : 1 terminal-red : 2 terminal-pink : 1 terminal-white.
**9.** (a) $PPLl \times PPLl$, $PPLl \times PpLl$, or $PPLl \times ppLl$; (b) $ppLl \times ppLl$; (c) $PPLL \times$ any of the 9 possible genotypes or $PPll \times ppLL$; (d) $PpLl \times Ppll$; (e) $PpLl \times PpLl$   **10.** (a) $3/4$ $\times 3/4 \times 3/4 = 27/64$; (b) $1 - 27/64 = 37/64$; (c) $3/4 \times 1/4 \times 1/4 = 1/64$; (d) $1/64 = 63/64$.
**11.** (a) $1/256$; (b) $1/16$; (c) $1/256$; (d) $1/64$; (e) $1/128$   **12.** (a) 1; (b) $1/32$; (c) $1/8$; (d) $1/2$   **13.** $1/9$
**14.** 25%, or $1/4$, will be cross-eyed; all (100%) of the cross-eyed offspring will also be white.   **15.** Matings of the original mutant cat with true-breeding noncurl cats will produce both curl and noncurl $F_1$ offspring if the curl allele is dominant, but only noncurl offspring if the curl allele is recessive. Whether the curl trait is dominant or recessive, you would obtain some true-breeding offspring homozygous for the curl allele from matings between the $F_1$ cats resulting from the original curl × noncurl crosses. If dominant, you wouldn't be able to tell truebreeding, homozygous offspring from heterozygotes without further crosses. You will know that cats are true-breeding when curl × curl matings produce only curl offspring for several generations. As it turns out, the allele that causes curled ears is dominant.   **16.** $1/16$   **17.** The dominant allele $I$ is epistatic to the $P/p$ locus, and thus the genotypic ratio for the $F_1$ generation will be 9 $I$–$P$– (colorless) : 3 $I$–$pp$ (colorless) : 3 $iiP$– (purple) : 1 $iipp$ (red). Overall, the phenotypic ratio is 12 colorless : 3 purple : 1 red.   **18.** Recessive. All affected individuals (Arlene, Tom, Wilma, and Carla) are homozygous recessive $aa$. George is $Aa$, since some of his children with Arlene are affected. Sam, Ann, Daniel, and Alan are each $Aa$, since they are all unaffected children with one affected parent. Michael also is $Aa$, since he has an affected child (Carla) with his heterozygous wife Ann. Sandra, Tina, and Christopher can each have either the $AA$ or $Aa$ genotype.   **19.** $1/6$   **20.** 9 $B$–$A$– (agouti) : 3 $B$–$aa$ (black) : 3 $bbA$– (white) : 1 $bbaa$ (white). Overall, 9 agouti : 3 black : 4 white.

## Chapter 12

### Figure Questions

**Figure 12.2** The ratio would be 1 yellow-round : 1 green-round : 1 yellow-wrinkled : 1 green-wrinkled.   **Figure 12.4** About $3/4$ of the $F_2$ offspring would have red eyes and about $1/4$ would have white eyes. About half of the white-eyed flies would be female and half would be male; similarly, about half of the red-eyed flies would be female and half would be male.   **Figure 12.7** All the males would be color-blind, and all the females would be carriers.   **Figure 12.9** The two largest classes would still be the parental-type offspring (offspring with the phenotypes of the true-breeding P generation flies), but now they would be gray-vestigial and black-normal because those were the specific allele combinations in the P generation.   **Figure 12.10** The two chromosomes below, left, are like the two chromosomes inherited by the $F_1$ female, one from each P generation fly. They are passed by the $F_1$ female intact to the offspring and thus could be called "parental" chromosomes. The other two chromosomes result from crossing over during meiosis in the $F_1$ female. Because they have combinations of alleles not seen in either of the $F_1$ female's chromosomes, they can be called "recombinant" chromosomes. (Note that in this example, the alleles on the recombinant chromosomes, $b^+ vg^+$ and $b vg$, are the allele combinations that were on the parental chromosomes in the cross shown in Figures 12.9 and 12.10. The basis for calling them parental chromosomes is the combination of alleles that was present on the P generation chromosomes.)

Parental chromosomes        Recombinant chromosomes

### Concept Check 12.1

**1.** The law of segregation relates to the inheritance of alleles for a single character. The law of independent assortment of alleles relates to the inheritance of alleles for two characters.   **2.** The physical basis for the law of segregation is the separation of homologs in anaphase I. The physical basis for the law of independent assortment is the alternative arrangements of all the homologous chromosome pairs in metaphase I.
**3.** To show the mutant phenotype, a male needs to possess only one mutant allele. If this gene had been on a pair of autosomes, *both* alleles would have had to be mutant for an individual to show the recessive mutant phenotype, a much less probable situation.

### Concept Check 12.2

**1.** Because the gene for this eye-color character is located on the X chromosome, all female offspring will be red-eyed and heterozygous ($X^{w+} X^w$); all male offspring will inherit a Y chromosome from the father and be white-eyed ($X^w Y$).   **2.** $1/4$ ($1/2$ chance that the child will inherit a Y chromosome from the father and be male × $1/2$ chance that he will inherit the X carrying the disease allele from his mother); if the child is a boy, there is a $1/2$ chance he will have the disease; a female will have zero chance (but $1/2$ chance of being a carrier).   **3.** With a disorder caused by a dominant allele, there is no such thing as a "carrier," since those with the allele have the disorder. Because the allele is dominant, the females lose any "advantage" in having two X chromosomes, since one disorder-associated allele is sufficient to result in the disorder. All fathers who have the dominant allele will pass it along to *all* their daughters, who will also have the disorder. A mother who has the allele (and thus the disorder) will pass it to half of her sons and half of her daughters.

### Concept Check 12.3

**1.** Crossing over during meiosis I in the heterozygous parent produces some gametes with recombinant genotypes for the two genes. Offspring with a recombinant phenotype arise from fertilization of the recombinant gametes by homozygous recessive gametes from the double-mutant parent.   **2.** In each case, the alleles contributed by the female parent (in the egg) determine the phenotype of the offspring because the male in this cross contributes only recessive alleles.   **3.** No. The order could be $A$-$C$-$B$ or $C$-$A$-$B$. To determine which possibility is correct, you need to know the recombination frequency between $B$ and $C$.

### Concept Check 12.4

**1.** In meiosis, a combined 14-21 chromosome behaves as one chromosome. If a gamete receives the combined 14-21 chromosome and a normal copy of chromosome 21, trisomy 21 will result when this gamete combines with a normal gamete during fertilization.   **2.** No. The child can be either $I^A I^A i$ or $I^A ii$. A sperm of genotype $I^A I^A$ could result from nondisjunction in the father during meiosis II, while an egg with the genotype $ii$ could result from nondisjunction in the mother during either meiosis I or meiosis II.   **3.** Activation of this gene could lead to the production of too much of this kinase. If the kinase is involved in a signaling pathway that triggers cell division, too much of it could trigger unrestricted cell division, which in turn could contribute to the development of a cancer (in this case, a cancer of one type of white blood cell).   **4.** The inactivation of two X chromosomes in XXX women would leave them with one genetically active X, as in women with the normal number of chromosomes. Microscopy should reveal two Barr bodies in XXX women.

**12.1** Because the sex chromosomes are different from each other and because they determine the sex of the offspring, Morgan could use the sex of the offspring as a phenotypic characteristic to follow the parental chromosomes. (He could also have followed them under a microscope, as the X and Y chromosomes look different.) At the same time, he could record eye color to follow the eye-color alleles. **12.2** Males have only one X chromosome, along with a Y chromosome, while females have two X chromosomes. The Y chromosome has very few genes on it, while the X has about 1,000. When a recessive X-linked allele that causes a disorder is inherited by a male on the X from his mother, there isn't a second allele present on the Y (males are hemizygous), so the male has the disorder. Because females have two X chromosomes, they must inherit two recessive alleles in order to have the disorder, a rarer occurrence. **12.3** Crossing over results in new combinations of alleles. Crossing over is a random occurrence, and the more distance there is between two genes, the more chances there are for crossing over to occur, leading to a new combination of alleles. **12.4** In inversions and reciprocal translocations, the same genetic material is present in the same relative amount but just organized differently. In aneuploidy, duplications, and deletions, the balance of genetic material is upset, as large segments are either missing or present in more than one copy. Apparently, this type of imbalance is very damaging to the organism. (Although it isn't lethal in the developing embryo, the reciprocal translocation that produces the Philadelphia chromosome can lead to a form of cancer by altering the expression of important genes.)

**Test Your Understanding**

**1.** $0$; $\frac{1}{2}$; $\frac{1}{16}$ **2.** Recessive; if the disorder were dominant, it would affect at least one parent of a child born with the disorder. The disorder's inheritance is sex-linked because it is seen only in boys. For a girl to have the disorder, she would have to inherit recessive alleles from *both* parents. This would be very rare, since males with the recessive allele on their X chromosome die in their early teens. **3.** Between $T$ and $A$, 12%; between $A$ and $S$, 5% **4.** Between $T$ and $S$, 18%; sequence of genes is $T$–$A$–$S$. **5.** $\frac{1}{4}$ for each daughter ($\frac{1}{2}$ chance that the child will be female × $\frac{1}{2}$ chance of a homozygous recessive genotype); $\frac{1}{2}$ for first son **6.** About one-third of the distance from the vestigial-wing locus to the brown-eye locus **7.** 6%; wild-type heterozygous for normal wings and red eyes × recessive homozygous for vestigial wings and purple eyes **8.** Fifty percent of the offspring will show phenotypes resulting from crossovers. These results would be the same as those from a cross where $A$ and $B$ were *not* on the same chromosome. Further crosses involving other genes on the same chromosome would reveal the genetic linkage and map distances. **9.** 450 each of blue-oval and white-round (parentals) and 50 each of blue-round and white-oval (recombinants)

## Chapter 13

### Figure Questions

**Figure 13.2** The living S cells found in the blood sample were able to reproduce to yield more S cells, indicating that the S trait is a permanent, heritable change, rather than just a one-time use of the dead S cells' capsules. **Figure 13.4** The radioactivity would have been found in the pellet when proteins were labeled (batch 1) because proteins would have had to enter the bacterial cells to program them with genetic instructions. It's hard for us to imagine now, but the DNA might have played a structural role that allowed some of the proteins to be injected while it remained outside the bacterial cell (resulting in no radioactivity in the pellet in batch 2). **Figure 13.11** The tube from the first replication would look the same, with a middle band of hybrid $^{15}$N-$^{14}$N DNA, but the second tube would not have the upper band of two light blue strands. Instead, it would have a bottom band of two dark blue strands, like the bottom band in the result predicted after one replication in the conservative model. **Figure 13.13** In the bubble at the top of the micrograph in (b), arrows should be drawn pointing left and right to indicate the two replication forks. **Figure 13.14** Looking at any of the DNA strands, we see that one end is called the 5′ end and the other the 3′ end. If we proceed from the 5′ end to the 3′ end on the left-most strand, for example, we list the components in this order: phosphate group → 5′ C of the sugar → 3′ C → phosphate → 5′ C → 3′ C. Going in the opposite direction on the same strand, the components proceed in the reverse order: 3′ C → 5′ C → phosphate. Thus, the two directions are distinguishable, which is what we mean when we say that the strands have directionality. (Review Figure 13.5 if necessary.)

**Figure 13.17**

**Figure 13.23**

**Concept Check 13.1**

**1.** You can't tell which end is the 5′ end. You need to know which end has a phosphate group on the 5′ carbon (the 5′ end) or which end has an —OH group on the 3′ carbon (the 3′ end). **2.** He was expecting that the mouse injected with the mixture of heat-killed S cells and living R cells would survive, since neither type of cell alone would kill the mouse.

**Concept Check 13.2**

**1.** Complementary base pairing ensures that the two daughter molecules are exact copies of the parental molecule. When the two strands of the parental molecule separate, each serves as a template on which nucleotides are arranged, by the base-pairing rules, into new complementary strands.

**2.**

| Protein | Function |
|---|---|
| Helicase | Unwinds parental double helix at replication forks |
| Single-strand binding protein | Binds to and stabilizes single-stranded DNA until it can be used as a template |
| Topoisomerase | Relieves "overwinding" strain ahead of replication forks by breaking, swiveling, and rejoining DNA strands |
| Primase | Synthesizes an RNA primer at 5′ end of leading strand and at 5′ end of each Okazaki fragment of lagging strand |
| DNA pol III | Using parental DNA as a template, synthesizes new DNA strand by covalently adding nucleotides to 3′ end of a preexisting DNA strand or RNA primer |
| DNA pol I | Removes RNA nucleotides of primer from 5′ end and replaces them with DNA nucleotides |
| DNA ligase | Joins 3′ end of DNA that replaces primer to rest of leading strand and joins Okazaki fragments of lagging strand |

**3.** In the cell cycle, DNA synthesis occurs during the S phase, between the $G_1$ and $G_2$ phases of interphase. DNA replication is therefore complete before the mitotic phase begins.

**Concept Check 13.3**

**1.** A nucleosome is made up of eight histone proteins, two each of four different types, around which DNA is wound. Linker DNA runs from one nucleosome to the next. **2.** Euchromatin is chromatin that becomes less compacted during interphase and is accessible to the cellular machinery responsible for gene activity. Heterochromatin, on the other hand, remains quite condensed during interphase and contains genes that are largely inaccessible to this machinery.

**Concept Check 13.4**

**1.** The covalent sugar-phosphate bonds of the DNA strands **2.** Yes, *Pvu*I will cut the molecule (at the position indicated by the dashed red line).

**3.** Cloning requires joining two pieces of DNA—a cloning vector, such as a bacterial plasmid, and a gene or DNA fragment from another source. Both pieces must be cut with the same restriction enzyme, creating sticky ends that will base-pair with complementary ends on other fragments. (The sugar-phosphate backbones will then be ligated together.) In DNA sequencing, primers base-pair to the template, allowing DNA synthesis to start, and then nucleotides are added to the growing strand based on complementarity of base pairing. In PCR, the primers must base-pair with their target sequences in the DNA mixture, locating one specific region among many, and complementary base pairing is the basis for the building of the new strand during the extension step.

## Summary of Key Concepts Questions

**13.1** Each strand in the double helix has polarity, the end with a phosphate group on the 5′ carbon of the sugar being called the 5′ end, and the end with an —OH group on the 3′ carbon of the sugar being called the 3′ end. The two strands run in opposite directions, so each end of the molecule has both a 5′ and a 3′ end. This arrangement is called "antiparallel." If the strands were parallel, they would both run 5′ → 3′ in the same direction, so an end of the molecule would have either two 5′ ends or two 3′ ends. **13.2** On both the leading and lagging strands, DNA polymerase adds onto the 3′ end of an RNA primer synthesized by primase, synthesizing DNA in the 5′ → 3′ direction. Because the parental strands are antiparallel, however, only on the leading strand does synthesis proceed continuously into the replication fork. The lagging strand is synthesized bit by bit in the direction away from the fork as a series of shorter Okazaki fragments, which are later joined together by DNA ligase. Each fragment is initiated by synthesis of an RNA primer by primase as soon as a given stretch of single-stranded template strand is opened up. Although both strands are synthesized at the same rate, synthesis of the lagging strand is delayed because initiation of each fragment begins only when sufficient template strand is available. **13.3** Most of the chromatin in an interphase nucleus is uncondensed. Much is present as the 30-nm fiber, with some in the form of the 10-nm fiber and some as looped domains of the 30-nm fiber. (These different levels of chromatin packing may reflect differences in gene expression occurring in these regions.) Also, a small percentage of the chromatin, such as that at the centromeres and telomeres, is highly condensed heterochromatin. **13.4** A plasmid vector and a source of foreign DNA to be cloned are both cut with the same restriction enzyme, generating restriction fragments with sticky ends. These fragments are mixed together, ligated, and reintroduced into bacterial cells, which can then make many copies of the foreign DNA or its product.

### Test Your Understanding

**1.** c  **2.** c  **3.** b  **4.** d  **5.** c  **6.** c  **7.** d  **8.** b  **9.** a

**10.** Like histones, the *E. coli* proteins would be expected to contain many basic (positively charged) amino acids, such as lysine and arginine, which can form weak bonds with the negatively charged phosphate groups on the sugar-phosphate backbone of the DNA molecule.

**11.**

New DNA strand (olive) / Parental DNA strand (purple) / Sliding clamp / DNA pol III / Single-strand binding protein / Direction of replication

## Chapter 14

### Figure Questions

**Figure 14.2** The mutant would not grow in the absence of arginine. **Figure 14.5** The mRNA sequence (5′-UGGUUUGGCUCA-3′) is the same as the nontemplate DNA strand sequence (5′-TGGTTTGGCTCA-3′), except there is U in the mRNA and T in the DNA. **Figure 14.8** The processes are similar in that polymerases form polynucleotides complementary to an antiparallel DNA template strand. In replication, however, both strands act as templates, whereas in transcription, only one DNA strand acts as a template. **Figure 14.9** The RNA polymerase would bind directly to the promoter, rather than depending on the previous binding of other factors. **Figure 14.23** The mRNA on the right (the longest one) started being transcribed first. The ribosome at the top, closest to the DNA, started translating first and thus has the longest polypeptide.

### Concept Check 14.1

**1.** Recessive  **2.** A polypeptide made up of 10 Gly (glycine) amino acids

**3.**

"Template sequence" (from nontemplate sequence in problem, written 3′ → 5′):    3′–ACGACTGAA–5′

mRNA sequence:    5′–UGCUGACUU–3′

Translated:    Cys-STOP-Leu

(Remember that the mRNA is antiparallel to the DNA strand.) A protein translated from the nontemplate sequence would have a completely different amino acid sequence and would most likely be nonfunctional. (It would also be shorter because of the stop signal shown in the mRNA sequence above—and possibly others earlier in the mRNA sequence.)

### Concept Check 14.2

**1.** The promoter is the region of DNA to which RNA polymerase binds to begin transcription, and it is at the upstream end of the gene (transcription unit). **2.** In a bacterial cell, RNA polymerase recognizes the gene's promoter and binds to it. In a eukaryotic cell, transcription factors mediate the binding of RNA polymerase to the promoter. In both cases, sequences in the promoter bind precisely to the RNA polymerase, so the enzyme is in the right location and orientation. **3.** The transcription

factor that recognizes the TATA sequence would be unable to bind, so RNA polymerase could not bind, and transcription of that gene probably would not occur.

### Concept Check 14.3

**1.** Due to alternative splicing of exons, each gene can result in multiple different mRNAs and can thus direct synthesis of multiple different proteins. **2.** In editing a video, segments are cut out and discarded (like introns), and the remaining segments are joined together (like exons) so that the regions of joining ("splicing") are not noticeable. **3.** Once the mRNA has exited the nucleus, the cap prevents it from being degraded by hydrolytic enzymes and facilitates its attachment to ribosomes. If the cap were removed from all mRNAs, the cell would no longer be able to synthesize any proteins and would probably die.

### Concept Check 14.4

**1.** First, each aminoacyl-tRNA synthetase specifically recognizes a single amino acid and attaches it only to an appropriate tRNA. Second, a tRNA charged with its specific amino acid binds only to an mRNA codon for that amino acid. **2.** The structure and function of the ribosome seem to depend more on the rRNAs than on the ribosomal proteins. Because it is single-stranded, an RNA molecule can hydrogen-bond with itself and with other RNA molecules. RNA molecules make up the interface between the two ribosomal subunits, so presumably RNA-RNA binding helps hold the ribosome together. The binding site for mRNA in the ribosome includes rRNA that can bind the mRNA. Also, complementary bonding within an RNA molecule allows it to assume a particular three-dimensional shape and, along with the RNA's functional groups, presumably enables rRNA to catalyze peptide bond formation during translation. **3.** A signal peptide on the leading end of the polypeptide being synthesized is recognized by a signal-recognition particle that brings the ribosome to the ER membrane. There the ribosome attaches and continues to synthesize the polypeptide, depositing it in the ER lumen. **4.** Because of wobble, the tRNA could bind to either 5′-GCA-3′ or 5′-GCG-3′, both of which code for alanine (Ala). Alanine would be attached to the tRNA.

tRNA    Ala

3′ CGU 5′

GCA    GCG
5′ ⌐⌐⌐ 3′    5′ ⌐⌐⌐ 3′

### Concept Check 14.5

**1.** In the mRNA, the reading frame downstream from the deletion is shifted, leading to a long string of incorrect amino acids in the polypeptide, and in most cases, a stop codon will arise, leading to premature termination. The polypeptide will most likely be nonfunctional. **2.** Heterozygous individuals, said to have sickle-cell trait, have a copy each of the wild-type allele and the sickle-cell allele. Both alleles will be expressed, so these individuals will have both normal and sickle-cell hemoglobin molecules. Apparently, having a mix of the two forms of β-globin has no effect under most conditions, but during prolonged periods of low blood oxygen (such as at higher altitudes), these individuals can show some signs of sickle-cell disease.

**3.**

Normal DNA sequence
(template strand is on top):    3′–TACTTGTCCGATATC–5′
                               5′–ATGAACAGGCTATAG–3′

mRNA sequence:    5′–AUGAACAGGCUAUAG–3′

Amino acid sequence:    Met-Asn-Arg-Leu-STOP

Mutated DNA sequence
(template strand is on top):    3′–TACTTGTCCAATATC–5′
                               5′–ATGAACAGGTTATAG–3′

mRNA sequence:    5′–AUGAACAGGUUAUAG–3′

Amino acid sequence:    Met-Asn-Arg-Leu-STOP

No effect: The amino acid sequence is Met-Asn-Arg-Leu both before and after the mutation because the mRNA codons 5′-CUA-3′ and 5′-UUA-3′ both code for Leu. (The fifth codon is a stop codon.)

### Summary of Key Concepts Questions

**14.1** A gene contains genetic information in the form of a nucleotide sequence. The gene is first transcribed into an RNA molecule, and a messenger RNA molecule is ultimately translated into a polypeptide. The polypeptide makes up part or all of a protein, which performs a function in the cell and contributes to the phenotype of the organism. **14.2** Both bacterial and eukaryotic genes have promoters, regions where RNA polymerase ultimately binds and begins transcription. In bacteria, RNA polymerase binds directly to the promoter; in eukaryotes, transcription factors bind first to the promoter, and then RNA polymerase binds to the transcription factors and promoter together. **14.3** Both the 5′ cap and the poly-A tail help the mRNA exit from the nucleus and then, in the cytoplasm, help ensure mRNA stability and allow it to bind to ribosomes. **14.4** tRNAs function as translators between the nucleotide-based language of mRNA and the amino-acid-based language of polypeptides. A tRNA carries a specific amino acid, and the anticodon on the tRNA is complementary to the codon on the mRNA that codes for that amino acid. In the ribosome, the tRNA binds to the A site, where the polypeptide being synthesized is joined to the new amino acid, which becomes the new (C-terminal) end of the polypeptide. Next, the tRNA moves to the P site. When the next amino acid is added via transfer of the polypeptide to the new tRNA, the now empty tRNA moves to the E site, where it exits the ribosome. **14.5** When a nucleotide base is altered chemically, its base-pairing characteristics may be changed. When that happens, an incorrect nucleotide is likely to be incorporated into the complementary strand during the next replication of the DNA, and successive rounds of replication will perpetuate the mutation. Once the gene is transcribed, the mutated codon may code for a different amino acid that inhibits or changes the function of a protein. If the chemical change in the base is detected and repaired by the DNA repair system before the next replication, no mutation will result.

**Test Your Understanding**
**1.** b **2.** d **3.** a **4.** a **5.** b **6.** d **7.** e
**8.**

| Type of RNA | Functions |
|---|---|
| Messenger RNA (mRNA) | Carries information specifying amino acid sequences of proteins from DNA to ribosomes |
| Transfer RNA (tRNA) | Serves as translator molecule in protein synthesis; translates mRNA codons into amino acids |
| Ribosomal RNA (rRNA) | Plays catalytic (ribozyme) roles and structural roles in ribosomes |
| Primary transcript | Is a precursor to mRNA, rRNA, or tRNA, before being processed; some intron RNA acts as a ribozyme, catalyzing its own splicing |
| Small RNAs in spliceosome | Play structural and catalytic roles in spliceosomes, the complexes of protein and RNA that splice pre-mRNA |

# Chapter 15

## Figure Questions
**Figure 15.3** Top vertical arrow: Infection. Left upper arrow: Replication. Right upper arrow: Transcription. Right middle arrow: Translation. Lower left and right arrows: Self-assembly. Bottom middle arrow: Exit. **Figure 15.7** There are many steps that could be interfered with: binding of the virus to the cell, reverse transcriptase function, integration into the host cell chromosome, genome synthesis (in this case, transcription of RNA from the integrated provirus), assembly of the virus inside the cell, and budding of the virus. (Many of these, if not all, are targets of actual medical strategies to block progress of the infection in HIV-infected people.)

## Concept Check 15.1
**1.** TMV consists of one molecule of RNA surrounded by a helical array of proteins. The influenza virus has eight molecules of RNA, each surrounded by a helical array of proteins, similar to the arrangement of the single RNA molecule in TMV. Another difference between the viruses is that the influenza virus has an outer envelope and TMV does not. **2.** The T2 phages were an excellent choice for use in the Hershey-Chase experiment because they consist of only DNA surrounded by a protein coat, and DNA and protein were the two candidates for macromolecules that carried genetic information. Hershey and Chase were able to radioactively label each type of molecule alone and follow it during separate infections of *E. coli* cells with T2. Only the DNA entered the bacterial cell during infection, and only labeled DNA showed up in some of the progeny phage. Hershey and Chase concluded that the DNA must carry the genetic information necessary for the phage to reprogram the cell and produce progeny phages.

## Concept Check 15.2
**1.** Lytic phages can only carry out lysis of the host cell, whereas lysogenic phages may either lyse the host cell or integrate into the host chromosome. In the latter case, the viral DNA (prophage) is simply replicated along with the host chromosome. Under certain conditions, a prophage may exit the host chromosome and initiate a lytic cycle. **2.** Both the viral RNA polymerase and the cellular RNA polymerase in Figure 14.10 synthesize an RNA molecule complementary to a template strand. However, the cellular RNA polymerase in Figure 14.10 uses one of the strands of the DNA double helix as a template, whereas the viral RNA polymerase uses the RNA of the viral genome as a template. **3.** Because it synthesizes DNA from its RNA genome. This is the reverse ("retro") of the usual DNA → RNA information flow.

## Concept Check 15.3
**1.** Mutations can lead to a new strain of a virus that can no longer be effectively fought by the immune system, even if an animal had been exposed to the original strain; a virus can jump from one species to a new host; and a rare virus can spread if a host population becomes less isolated. **2.** In horizontal transmission, a plant is infected from an external source of the virus, which can enter through a break in the plant's epidermis due to damage by herbivores. In vertical transmission, a plant inherits viruses from its parent either via infected seeds (sexual reproduction) or via an infected cutting (asexual reproduction). **3.** Humans are not within the host range of TMV, so they can't be infected by the virus.

## Summary of Key Concepts Questions
**15.1** Viruses are generally considered nonliving because they are not capable of replicating outside of a host cell. To replicate, they depend completely on host enzymes and resources. **15.2** Single-stranded RNA viruses require an RNA polymerase that can make RNA using an RNA template. (Cellular RNA polymerases make RNA using a DNA template.) Retroviruses require reverse transcriptases to make DNA using an RNA template. (Once the first DNA strand has been made, the same enzyme can promote synthesis of the second DNA strand.) **15.3** The mutation rate of RNA viruses is higher than that of DNA viruses because RNA polymerase has no proofreading function, so errors in replication are not corrected. Their higher mutation rate means that RNA viruses change faster than DNA viruses, allowing them to have an altered host range and to evade immune defenses in possible hosts.

## Test Your Understanding
**1.** c **2.** d **3.** c **4.** d **5.** b
**6.** As shown in the sketch, the viral genome would be translated into capsid proteins and envelope glycoproteins directly, rather than after a complementary RNA copy was made. A complementary RNA strand would still be made, however, that could be used as a template for many new copies of the viral genome.

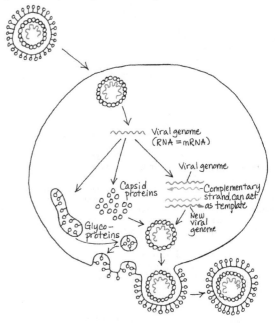

# Appendix B Periodic Table of the Elements

Atomic number (number of protons) → 6
Element symbol → C
Atomic mass (number of protons plus number of neutrons averaged over all isotopes) → 12.01

Metals   Metalloids   Nonmetals

— Representative elements —

**Groups:** Elements in a vertical column have the same number of electrons in their valence (outer) shell and thus have similar chemical properties.

**Periods:** Each horizontal row contains elements with the same total number of electron shells. Across each period, elements are ordered by increasing atomic number.

Alkali metals   Alkaline earth metals   Halogens   Noble gases

Transition elements

| Period number | Group 1A 1 | Group 2A 2 | 3 3B | 4 4B | 5 5B | 6 6B | 7 7B | 8 | 9 8B | 10 | 11 1B | 12 2B | 13 Group 3A | 14 Group 4A | 15 Group 5A | 16 Group 6A | 17 Group 7A | 18 Group 8A |
|---|---|---|---|---|---|---|---|---|---|---|---|---|---|---|---|---|---|---|
| 1 | 1 H 1.008 | | | | | | | | | | | | | | | | | 2 He 4.003 |
| 2 | 3 Li 6.941 | 4 Be 9.012 | | | | | | | | | | | 5 B 10.81 | 6 C 12.01 | 7 N 14.01 | 8 O 16.00 | 9 F 19.00 | 10 Ne 20.18 |
| 3 | 11 Na 22.99 | 12 Mg 24.31 | | | | | | | | | | | 13 Al 26.98 | 14 Si 28.09 | 15 P 30.97 | 16 S 32.07 | 17 Cl 35.45 | 18 Ar 39.95 |
| 4 | 19 K 39.10 | 20 Ca 40.08 | 21 Sc 44.96 | 22 Ti 47.87 | 23 V 50.94 | 24 Cr 52.00 | 25 Mn 54.94 | 26 Fe 55.85 | 27 Co 58.93 | 28 Ni 58.69 | 29 Cu 63.55 | 30 Zn 65.41 | 31 Ga 69.72 | 32 Ge 72.64 | 33 As 74.92 | 34 Se 78.96 | 35 Br 79.90 | 36 Kr 83.80 |
| 5 | 37 Rb 85.47 | 38 Sr 87.62 | 39 Y 88.91 | 40 Zr 91.22 | 41 Nb 92.91 | 42 Mo 95.94 | 43 Tc (98) | 44 Ru 101.1 | 45 Rh 102.9 | 46 Pd 106.4 | 47 Ag 107.9 | 48 Cd 112.4 | 49 In 114.8 | 50 Sn 118.7 | 51 Sb 121.8 | 52 Te 127.6 | 53 I 126.9 | 54 Xe 131.3 |
| 6 | 55 Cs 132.9 | 56 Ba 137.3 | 57* La 138.9 | 72 Hf 178.5 | 73 Ta 180.9 | 74 W 183.8 | 75 Re 186.2 | 76 Os 190.2 | 77 Ir 192.2 | 78 Pt 195.1 | 79 Au 197.0 | 80 Hg 200.6 | 81 Tl 204.4 | 82 Pb 207.2 | 83 Bi 209.0 | 84 Po (209) | 85 At (210) | 86 Rn (222) |
| 7 | 87 Fr (223) | 88 Ra (226) | 89† Ac (227) | 104 Rf (261) | 105 Db (262) | 106 Sg (266) | 107 Bh (264) | 108 Hs (269) | 109 Mt (268) | 110 Ds (271) | 111 Rg (272) | 112 Cn (285) | 113 — (284) | 114 — (289) | 115 — (288) | 116 — (293) | 117 — (294?) | 118 — (294) |

*Lanthanides

| 58 Ce 140.1 | 59 Pr 140.9 | 60 Nd 144.2 | 61 Pm (145) | 62 Sm 150.4 | 63 Eu 152.0 | 64 Gd 157.3 | 65 Tb 158.9 | 66 Dy 162.5 | 67 Ho 164.9 | 68 Er 167.3 | 69 Tm 168.9 | 70 Yb 173.0 | 71 Lu 175.0 |
|---|---|---|---|---|---|---|---|---|---|---|---|---|---|

†Actinides

| 90 Th 232.0 | 91 Pa 231.0 | 92 U 238.0 | 93 Np (237) | 94 Pu (244) | 95 Am (243) | 96 Cm (247) | 97 Bk (247) | 98 Cf (251) | 99 Es 252 | 100 Fm 257 | 101 Md 258 | 102 No 259 | 103 Lr 260 |
|---|---|---|---|---|---|---|---|---|---|---|---|---|---|

| Name (Symbol) | Atomic Number | Name (Symbol) | Atomic Number | Name (Symbol) | Atomic Number | Name (Symbol) | Atomic Number | Name (Symbol) | Atomic Number |
|---|---|---|---|---|---|---|---|---|---|
| Actinium (Ac) | 89 | Copernicium (Cn) | 112 | Iridium (Ir) | 77 | Palladium (Pd) | 46 | Sodium (Na) | 11 |
| Aluminum (Al) | 13 | Copper (Cu) | 29 | Iron (Fe) | 26 | Phosphorus (P) | 15 | Strontium (Sr) | 38 |
| Americium (Am) | 95 | Curium (Cm) | 96 | Krypton (Kr) | 36 | Platinum (Pt) | 78 | Sulfur (S) | 16 |
| Antimony (Sb) | 51 | Darmstadtium (Ds) | 110 | Lanthanum (La) | 57 | Plutonium (Pu) | 94 | Tantalum (Ta) | 73 |
| Argon (Ar) | 18 | Dubnium (Db) | 105 | Lawrencium (Lr) | 103 | Polonium (Po) | 84 | Technetium (Tc) | 43 |
| Arsenic (As) | 33 | Dysprosium (Dy) | 66 | Lead (Pb) | 82 | Potassium (K) | 19 | Tellurium (Te) | 52 |
| Astatine (At) | 85 | Einsteinium (Es) | 99 | Lithium (Li) | 3 | Praseodymium (Pr) | 59 | Terbium (Tb) | 65 |
| Barium (Ba) | 56 | Erbium (Er) | 68 | Lutetium (Lu) | 71 | Promethium (Pm) | 61 | Thallium (Tl) | 81 |
| Berkelium (Bk) | 97 | Europium (Eu) | 63 | Magnesium (Mg) | 12 | Protactinium (Pa) | 91 | Thorium (Th) | 90 |
| Beryllium (Be) | 4 | Fermium (Fm) | 100 | Manganese (Mn) | 25 | Radium (Ra) | 88 | Thulium (Tm) | 69 |
| Bismuth (Bi) | 83 | Fluorine (F) | 9 | Meitnerium (Mt) | 109 | Radon (Rn) | 86 | Tin (Sn) | 50 |
| Bohrium (Bh) | 107 | Francium (Fr) | 87 | Mendelevium (Md) | 101 | Rhenium (Re) | 75 | Titanium (Ti) | 22 |
| Boron (B) | 5 | Gadolinium (Gd) | 64 | Mercury (Hg) | 80 | Rhodium (Rh) | 45 | Tungsten (W) | 74 |
| Bromine (Br) | 35 | Gallium (Ga) | 31 | Molybdenum (Mo) | 42 | Roentgenium (Rg) | 111 | Uranium (U) | 92 |
| Cadmium (Cd) | 48 | Germanium (Ge) | 32 | Neodymium (Nd) | 60 | Rubidium (Rb) | 37 | Vanadium (V) | 23 |
| Calcium (Ca) | 20 | Gold (Au) | 79 | Neon (Ne) | 10 | Ruthenium (Ru) | 44 | Xenon (Xe) | 54 |
| Californium (Cf) | 98 | Hafnium (Hf) | 72 | Neptunium (Np) | 93 | Rutherfordium (Rf) | 104 | Ytterbium (Yb) | 70 |
| Carbon (C) | 6 | Hassium (Hs) | 108 | Nickel (Ni) | 28 | Samarium (Sm) | 62 | Yttrium (Y) | 39 |
| Cerium (Ce) | 58 | Helium (He) | 2 | Niobium (Nb) | 41 | Scandium (Sc) | 21 | Zinc (Zn) | 30 |
| Cesium (Cs) | 55 | Holmium (Ho) | 67 | Nitrogen (N) | 7 | Seaborgium (Sg) | 106 | Zirconium (Zr) | 40 |
| Chlorine (Cl) | 17 | Hydrogen (H) | 1 | Nobelium (No) | 102 | Selenium (Se) | 34 | | |
| Chromium (Cr) | 24 | Indium (In) | 49 | Osmium (Os) | 76 | Silicon (Si) | 14 | | |
| Cobalt (Co) | 27 | Iodine (I) | 53 | Oxygen (O) | 8 | Silver (Ag) | 47 | | |

# Appendix C The Metric System

Metric Prefixes:
| | | |
|---|---|---|
| $10^9$ = giga (G) | $10^{-2}$ = centi (c) | $10^{-9}$ = nano (n) |
| $10^6$ = mega (M) | $10^{-3}$ = milli (m) | $10^{-12}$ = pico (p) |
| $10^3$ = kilo (k) | $10^{-6}$ = micro (μ) | $10^{-15}$ = femto (f) |

| Measurement | Unit and Abbreviation | Metric Equivalent | Metric-to-English Conversion Factor | English-to-Metric Conversion Factor |
|---|---|---|---|---|
| Length | 1 kilometer (km) | = 1,000 ($10^3$) meters | 1 km = 0.62 mile | 1 mile = 1.61 km |
| | 1 meter (m) | = 100 ($10^2$) centimeters<br>= 1,000 millimeters | 1 m = 1.09 yards<br>1 m = 3.28 feet<br>1 m = 39.37 inches | 1 yard = 0.914 m<br>1 foot = 0.305 m |
| | 1 centimeter (cm) | = 0.01 ($10^{-2}$) meter | 1 cm = 0.394 inch | 1 foot = 30.5 cm<br>1 inch = 2.54 cm |
| | 1 millimeter (mm) | = 0.001 ($10^{-3}$) meter | 1 mm = 0.039 inch | |
| | 1 micrometer (μm)<br>(formerly micron, μ) | = $10^{-6}$ meter ($10^{-3}$ mm) | | |
| | 1 nanometer (nm)<br>(formerly millimicron, mμ) | = $10^{-9}$ meter ($10^{-3}$ μm) | | |
| | 1 angstrom (Å) | = $10^{-10}$ meter ($10^{-4}$ μm) | | |
| Area | 1 hectare (ha) | = 10,000 square meters | 1 ha = 2.47 acres | 1 acre = 0.405 ha |
| | 1 square meter ($m^2$) | = 10,000 square centimeters | 1 $m^2$ = 1.196 square yards<br>1 $m^2$ = 10.764 square feet | 1 square yard = 0.8361 $m^2$<br>1 square foot = 0.0929 $m^2$ |
| | 1 square centimeter ($cm^2$) | = 100 square millimeters | 1 $cm^2$ = 0.155 square inch | 1 square inch = 6.4516 $cm^2$ |
| Mass | 1 metric ton (t) | = 1,000 kilograms | 1 t = 1.103 tons | 1 ton = 0.907 t |
| | 1 kilogram (kg) | = 1,000 grams | 1 kg = 2.205 pounds | 1 pound = 0.4536 kg |
| | 1 gram (g) | = 1,000 milligrams | 1 g = 0.0353 ounce<br>1 g = 15.432 grains | 1 ounce = 28.35 g |
| | 1 milligram (mg) | = $10^{-3}$ gram | 1 mg = approx. 0.015 grain | |
| | 1 microgram (μg) | = $10^{-6}$ gram | | |
| Volume (solids) | 1 cubic meter ($m^3$) | = 1,000,000 cubic centimeters | 1 $m^3$ = 1.308 cubic yards<br>1 $m^3$ = 35.315 cubic feet | 1 cubic yard = 0.7646 $m^3$<br>1 cubic foot = 0.0283 $m^3$ |
| | 1 cubic centimeter ($cm^3$ or cc) | = $10^{-6}$ cubic meter | 1 $cm^3$ = 0.061 cubic inch | 1 cubic inch = 16.387 $cm^3$ |
| | 1 cubic millimeter ($mm^3$) | = $10^{-9}$ cubic meter<br>= $10^{-3}$ cubic centimeter | | |
| Volume (liquids and gases) | 1 kiloliter (kL or kl) | = 1,000 liters | 1 kL = 264.17 gallons | |
| | 1 liter (L or l) | = 1,000 milliliters | 1 L = 0.264 gallon<br>1 L = 1.057 quarts | 1 gallon = 3.785 L<br>1 quart = 0.946 L |
| | 1 milliliter (mL or ml) | = $10^{-3}$ liter<br>= 1 cubic centimeter | 1 mL = 0.034 fluid ounce<br>1 mL = approx. ¼ teaspoon<br>1 mL = approx. 15–16 drops (gtt.) | 1 quart = 946 mL<br>1 pint = 473 mL<br>1 fluid ounce = 29.57 mL<br>1 teaspoon = approx. 5 mL |
| | 1 microliter (μL or μl) | = $10^{-6}$ liter ($10^{-3}$ milliliter) | | |
| Pressure | 1 megapascal (MPa) | = 1,000 kilopascals | 1 MPa = 10 bars | 1 bar = 0.1 MPa |
| | 1 kilopascal (kPa) | = 1,000 pascals | 1 kPa = 0.01 bar | 1 bar = 100 kPa |
| | 1 pascal (Pa) | = 1 newton/$m^2$ ($N/m^2$) | 1 Pa = $1.0 \times 10^{-5}$ bar | 1 bar = $1.0 \times 10^5$ Pa |
| Time | 1 second (s or sec) | = ¹⁄₆₀ minute | | |
| | 1 millisecond (ms or msec) | = $10^{-3}$ second | | |
| Temperature | Degrees Celsius (°C) (0 K [Kelvin] = −273.15°C) | | °F = ⁹⁄₅°C + 32 | °C = ⁵⁄₉ (°F − 32) |

## Light Microscope

In light microscopy, light is focused on a specimen by a glass condenser lens; the image is then magnified by an objective lens and an ocular lens, for projection on the eye, digital camera, digital video camera, or photographic film.

## Electron Microscope

In electron microscopy, a beam of electrons (top of the microscope) is used instead of light, and electromagnets are used instead of glass lenses. The electron beam is focused on the specimen by a condenser lens; the image is magnified by an objective lens and a projector lens for projection on a digital detector, fluorescent screen, or photographic film.

# Appendix E Classification of Life

This appendix presents a taxonomic classification for the major extant groups of organisms discussed in this text; not all phyla are included. The classification presented here is based on the three-domain system, which assigns the two major groups of prokaryotes, bacteria and archaea, to separate domains (with eukaryotes making up the third domain).

Various alternative classification schemes are discussed in Unit Four of the text. The taxonomic turmoil includes debates about the number and boundaries of kingdoms and about the alignment of the Linnaean classification hierarchy with the findings of modern cladistic analysis. In this review, asterisks (*) indicate currently recognized phyla thought by some systematists to be paraphyletic.

## DOMAIN BACTERIA

- **Proteobacteria**
- **Chlamydia**
- **Spirochetes**
- **Cyanobacteria**
- **Gram-positive bacteria**

## DOMAIN ARCHAEA

- **Korarchaeota**
- **Euryarchaeota**
- **Crenarchaeota**
- **Nanoarchaeota**

## DOMAIN EUKARYA

In the phylogenetic hypothesis we present in Chapter 25, major clades of eukaryotes are grouped together in the four "supergroups" listed in blue type. Formerly, all the eukaryotes generally called protists were assigned to a single kingdom, Protista. However, advances in systematics have made it clear that some protists are more closely related to plants, fungi, or animals than they are to other protists. As a result, the kingdom Protista has been abandoned.

### Excavata
- Diplomonadida (diplomonads)
- Parabasala (parabasalids)
- Euglenozoa (euglenozoans)
  - Kinetoplastida (kinetoplastids)
  - Euglenophyta (euglenids)

### The "SAR" clade
- Stramenopila (stramenopiles)
  - Bacillariophyta (diatoms)
  - Phaeophyta (brown algae)
- Alveolata (alveolates)
  - Dinoflagellata (dinoflagellates)
  - Apicomplexa (apicomplexans)
  - Ciliophora (ciliates)

- Rhizaria
  - Foraminifera (forams)
  - Cercozoa (cercozoans)

### Archaeplastida
- Rhodophyta (red algae)
- Chlorophyta (green algae: chlorophytes)
- Charophyta (green algae: charophytes)
- Plantae
  - Phylum Hepatophyta (liverworts) ⎫
  - Phylum Bryophyta (mosses) ⎬ Nonvascular plants (bryophytes)
  - Phylum Anthocerophyta (hornworts) ⎭
  - Phylum Lycophyta (lycophytes) ⎫
  - Phylum Monilophyta (ferns, horsetails, whisk ferns) ⎬ Seedless vascular plants
  - Phylum Ginkgophyta (ginkgo) ⎫
  - Phylum Cycadophyta (cycads) ⎬ Gymnosperms ⎫
  - Phylum Gnetophyta (gnetophytes) ⎪ ⎬ Seed plants
  - Phylum Coniferophyta (conifers) ⎭ ⎪
  - Phylum Anthophyta (flowering plants) ⎬ Angiosperms ⎭

### Unikonta

- Amoebozoa (amoebozoans)
  - Dictyostelida (cellular slime molds)
  - Entamoeba (entamoebas)
- Nucleariida (nucleariids)
- Fungi
  - *Phylum Chytridiomycota (chytrids)
  - *Phylum Zygomycota (zygomycetes)
  - Phylum Glomeromycota (glomeromycetes)
  - Phylum Ascomycota (sac fungi)
  - Phylum Basidiomycota (club fungi)

- Choanoflagellata (choanoflagellates)
- Animalia
  - Phylum Porifera (sponges)
  - Phylum Ctenophora (comb jellies)
  - Phylum Cnidaria (cnidarians)
  - Lophotrochozoa (lophotrochozoans)
    - Phylum Platyhelminthes (flatworms)
    - Phylum Ectoprocta (ectoprocts)
    - Phylum Brachiopoda (brachiopods)
    - Phylum Rotifera (rotifers)
    - Phylum Mollusca (molluscs)
    - Phylum Annelida (segmented worms)

Ecdysozoa (ecdysozoans)
- Phylum Nematoda (roundworms)
- Phylum Arthropoda (This survey groups arthropods into a single phylum, but some zoologists now split the arthropods into multiple phyla.)
  - Subphylum Chelicerata (horseshoe crabs, arachnids)
  - Subphylum Myriapoda (millipedes, centipedes)
  - Subphylum Hexapoda (insects, springtails)
  - Subphylum Crustacea (crustaceans)
- Phylum Onychophora (velvet worms)

Deuterostomia (deuterostomes)
- Phylum Hemichordata (hemichordates)
- Phylum Echinodermata (echinoderms)
- Phylum Chordata (chordates)
  - Subphylum Cephalochordata (lancelets)
  - Subphylum Urochordata (tunicates)
  - Subphylum Craniata (craniates)
    - Myxini (hagfishes)
    - Petromyzontida (lampreys)
    - Chondrichthyes (sharks, rays, chimaeras)
    - Actinopterygii (ray-finned fishes)
    - Actinistia (coelacanths)
    - Dipnoi (lungfishes)
    - Amphibia (amphibians)
    - Reptilia (tuataras, lizards, snakes, turtles, crocodilians, birds)
    - Mammalia (mammals)

    } Vertebrates

## Graphs

Graphs provide a visual representation of numerical data. They may reveal patterns or trends in the data that are not easy to recognize in a table. A graph is a diagram that shows how one variable in a data set is related (or perhaps not related) to another variable. If one variable is dependent on the other, the dependent variable is typically plotted on the $y$-axis and the independent variable on the $x$-axis. Types of graphs that are frequently used in biology include scatter plots, line graphs, bar graphs, and histograms.

A **scatter plot** is used when the data for all variables are numerical and continuous. Each piece of data is represented by a point. In a **line graph**, each data point is connected to the next point in the data set with a straight line, as in the graph below.

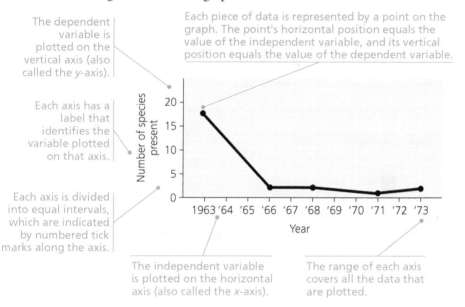

The dependent variable is plotted on the vertical axis (also called the $y$-axis).

Each axis has a label that identifies the variable plotted on that axis.

Each axis is divided into equal intervals, which are indicated by numbered tick marks along the axis.

Each piece of data is represented by a point on the graph. The point's horizontal position equals the value of the independent variable, and its vertical position equals the value of the dependent variable.

The independent variable is plotted on the horizontal axis (also called the $x$-axis).

The range of each axis covers all the data that are plotted.

Two or more data sets can be plotted on the same line graph to show how two dependent variables are related to the same independent variable.

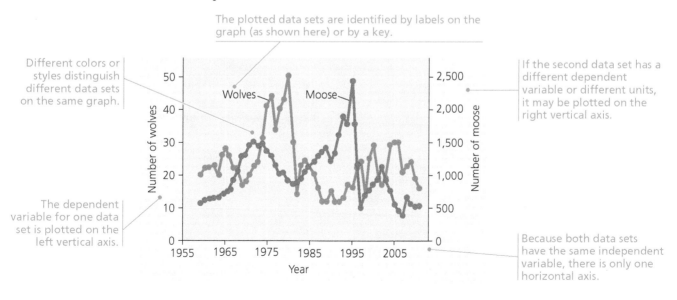

The plotted data sets are identified by labels on the graph (as shown here) or by a key.

Different colors or styles distinguish different data sets on the same graph.

The dependent variable for one data set is plotted on the left vertical axis.

If the second data set has a different dependent variable or different units, it may be plotted on the right vertical axis.

Because both data sets have the same independent variable, there is only one horizontal axis.

In some scatter-plot graphs, a straight or curved line is drawn through the entire data set to show the general trend in the data. A straight line that mathematically fits the data best is called a *regression line*. Alternatively, a mathematical function that best fits the data may describe a curved line, often termed a *best-fit curve*.

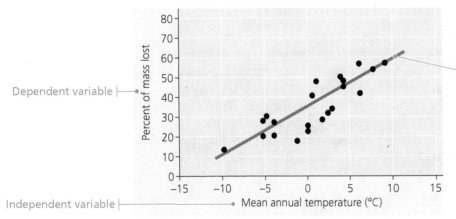

Dependent variable

Independent variable

The regression line can be expressed as a mathematical equation. It allows you to predict the value of the dependent variable for any value of the independent variable within the range of the data set and, less commonly, beyond the range of the data.

A **bar graph** is a kind of graph in which the independent variable represents groups or nonnumerical categories and the values of the dependent variable(s) are shown by bars.

As in a line graph or scatter plot, the vertical axis is usually used for the dependent variable.

The axis for the dependent variable is labeled and divided into equal intervals indicated by numbered tick marks.

Each piece of data is represented by a bar on the graph. The top of the bar aligns with the value of the dependent variable.

If multiple data sets are plotted on the same bar graph, they are distinguished by bars of different colors or styles and identified by labels or a key.

The groups or categories of the independent variable are usually spaced equally along the horizontal axis. (In some bar graphs, the horizontal axis is used for the dependent variable and the vertical axis for the independent variable.)

A variant of a bar graph called a **histogram** can be made for numeric data by first grouping, or "binning," the variable plotted on the $x$-axis into intervals of equal width. The "bins" may be integers or ranges of numbers. In the histogram below, the intervals are 25 mg/dL wide. The height of each bar shows the percent (or alternatively, the number) of experimental subjects whose characteristics can be described by one of the intervals plotted on the $x$-axis.

The height of this bar shows the percent of individuals (about 4%) whose plasma LDL cholesterol levels are in the range indicated on the $x$-axis.

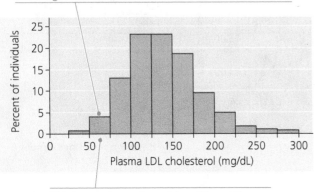

This interval runs from 50 to 74 mg/dL.

## Glossary of Scientific Inquiry Terms

See Concept 1.3 for more discussion of the process of scientific inquiry.

**control group** In a controlled experiment, a set of subjects that lacks (or does not receive) the specific factor being tested. Ideally, the control group should be identical to the experimental group in other respects.

**deductive reasoning** A type of logic in which specific results are predicted from a general premise.

**dependent variable** In an experiment, a variable whose value is influenced by changes in another variable (the independent variable).

**experimental group** A set of subjects that has (or receives) the specific factor being tested in a controlled experiment.

**hypothesis** A testable explanation for a set of observations based on the available data and guided by inductive reasoning. A hypothesis is narrower in scope than a theory.

**independent variable** A variable whose value is manipulated or changed during an experiment to reveal possible effects on another variable (the dependent variable).

**inductive reasoning** A type of logic in which generalizations are based on a large number of specific observations.

**model** A physical or conceptual representation of a natural phenomenon.

**prediction** In deductive reasoning, a forecast that follows logically from a hypothesis. By testing predictions, experiments may allow certain hypotheses to be rejected.

**theory** An explanation that is broader in scope than a hypothesis, generates new hypotheses, and is supported by a large body of evidence.

## Chi-Square ($\chi^2$) Distribution Table

To use the table, find the row that corresponds to the degrees of freedom in your data set. (The degrees of freedom is the number of categories of data minus 1.) Move along that row to the pair of values that your calculated $\chi^2$ value lies between. Move up from those numbers to the probabilities at the top of the columns to find the probability range for your $\chi^2$ value. A probability of 0.05 or less is generally considered significant. See the Scientific Skills Exercise in Chapter 12 for an example of how to use the chi-square test.

| Degrees of Freedom (df) | Probability | | | | | | | | | | |
|---|---|---|---|---|---|---|---|---|---|---|---|
| | 0.95 | 0.90 | 0.80 | 0.70 | 0.50 | 0.30 | 0.20 | 0.10 | 0.05 | 0.01 | 0.001 |
| 1 | 0.004 | 0.02 | 0.06 | 0.15 | 0.45 | 1.07 | 1.64 | 2.71 | 3.84 | 6.64 | 10.83 |
| 2 | 0.10 | 0.21 | 0.45 | 0.71 | 1.39 | 2.41 | 3.22 | 4.61 | 5.99 | 9.21 | 13.82 |
| 3 | 0.35 | 0.58 | 1.01 | 1.42 | 2.37 | 3.66 | 4.64 | 6.25 | 7.82 | 11.34 | 16.27 |
| 4 | 0.71 | 1.06 | 1.65 | 2.19 | 3.36 | 4.88 | 5.99 | 7.78 | 9.49 | 13.28 | 18.47 |
| 5 | 1.15 | 1.61 | 2.34 | 3.00 | 4.35 | 6.06 | 7.29 | 9.24 | 11.07 | 15.09 | 20.52 |
| 6 | 1.64 | 2.20 | 3.07 | 3.83 | 5.35 | 7.23 | 8.56 | 10.64 | 12.59 | 16.81 | 22.46 |
| 7 | 2.17 | 2.83 | 3.82 | 4.67 | 6.35 | 8.38 | 9.80 | 12.02 | 14.07 | 18.48 | 24.32 |
| 8 | 2.73 | 3.49 | 4.59 | 5.53 | 7.34 | 9.52 | 11.03 | 13.36 | 15.51 | 20.09 | 26.12 |
| 9 | 3.33 | 4.17 | 5.38 | 6.39 | 8.34 | 10.66 | 12.24 | 14.68 | 16.92 | 21.67 | 27.88 |
| 10 | 3.94 | 4.87 | 6.18 | 7.27 | 9.34 | 11.78 | 13.44 | 15.99 | 18.31 | 23.21 | 29.59 |

# Credits

structure of a collagen peptide, *Structure* 3:893-906 (1995); **2.19** Based on D.W. Heinz et al., How amino-acid insertions are allowed in an alpha-helix of T4 lysozyme, *Nature* 361:561-564 (1993); **2.21d** PDB ID 3GS0: S.K. Palaninathan, N.N. Mohamedmohaideen, E. Orlandini, G. Ortore, S. Nencetti, A. Lapucci, A. Rossello, J.S. Freundlich, J.C. Sacchettini. Novel transthyretin amyloid fibril formation inhibitors: Synthesis, biological evaluation, and X-ray structural analysis. *Public Library of Science ONE* 4:e6290-e6290 (2009); **2.21g**, PDB ID 2HHB: G. Fermi, M.F. Perutz, B. Shaanan, R. Fourme. The crystal structure of human deoxyhaemoglobin at 1.74 A resolution. *J.Mol.Biol.* 175:159-174 (1984). **p. 41** Data for human: S.M. Fullerton et al., Molecular and population genetic analysis of allelic sequence diversity at the human beta-globin locus, *Proc. Natl. Acad. Sci USA* 91:1805-1809 (1994). Data for rhesus monkey: G. Matsuda et al., The primary structure of the alpha and beta polypeptide chains of adult hemoglobin of the rhesus monkey (*Macaca mulafta*). Biochemical studies on hemoglobins and myoglobins. IV. *Int. J. Protein Research II* 2:99-108 (1970). Data for gibbon: S. Boyer et al., Primate hemoglobins: Some sequences and some proposals concerning the character of evolution and mutation. *Biochemical Genetics* 5:405-448 (1971).

**Chapter 3** **3.5b, 13.25, 14.12,** Adapted from *The World of the Cell*, 3rd Edition, by W.M. Becker, J.B. Reece and M.F. Poenie, 1996. Copyright © 1996 by Pearson Education, Inc. Reprinted and electronically reproduced by permission of Pearson Education, Inc. Upper Saddle River, NJ. **3.7a & b, 3.10, and 3.11** Adapted from illustrations by Tomo Narashima in *Human Anatomy and Physiology*, 5th ed. by E.N. Marieb, 2001. Copyright © 2001 by E.N. Marieb. Reprinted and electronically reproduced with permission by Pearson Education, Inc. Upper Saddle River, NJ. **3.8a** Adapted from *Human Anatomy and Physiology*, 5th ed. by E.N. Marieb, 2001. Copyright © 2001 by E.N. Marieb. Reprinted and electronically reproduced with permission by Pearson Education, Inc. Upper Saddle River, New Jersey. **Table 3.1** Adapted from *The World of the Cell*, 4th ed., by W.M. Becker, L.J. Kleinsmith, and J. Hardin, 2000. Copyright © 2000 by Pearson Education, Inc. Reprinted and electronically reproduced by permission of Pearson Education, Inc. Upper Saddle River, NJ.

**Chapter 4** **4.4** Source: Based on "The Rapid Intermixing of Cell Surface Antigens After Formation of Mouse-Human Heterokaryons" by L. D. Frye and M. Edidin, from *Journal of Cell Science*, September 1970, Volume 7; **4.6** Source: Protein Data Bank ID 3HAO: "Similar Energetic Contributions of Packing in the Core of Membrane and Water-Soluble Proteins" by Nathan H. Joh et al., from *Journal of the American Chemical Society*, Volume 131(31); **4 SSE** Adaptation of Figure 1 from "Developmental Changes in Glucose Transport of Guinea Pig Erythrocytes" by Takahito Kondo and Ernest Beutler, from *Journal of Clinical Investigation*, January 1980, Volume 65(1). Copyright © by American Society for Clinical Investigation. Permission to reprint conveyed through Copyright Clearance Center, Inc.

**Chapter 5** **p. 102** Data from S.R. Commerford et al., Diets enriched in sucrose or fat increase gluconeogenesis and G-6-Pase but not basal glucose production in rats, *American Journal of Physiology—Endocrinology and Metabolism* 283:E545–E555 (2002).

**Chapter 6** **6.5** Adapted from *Molecular Biology of the Cell*, 4th ed., by B. Alberts, et al. Copyright © 2002 by Garland Science/Taylor & Francis Books, LLC. Reprinted with permission. **6.9** Adapted from *Biochemistry*, 2nd ed., by C.K. Matthews and K.E. van Holde, 1996. Copyright © 1996 by Pearson Education, Inc. Reprinted and

electronically reproduced by permission of Pearson Education, Inc. Upper Saddle River, NJ. **p. 123** Data from M.E. Harper and M.D. Brand, The quantitative contributions of mitochondrial proton leak and ATP turnover reactions to the changed respiration rates of hepatocytes from rats of different thyroid status, *Journal of Biological Chemistry* 268:14850–14860 (1993).

**Chapter 7** **7.10** Source: Based on "*Bacterium photometricum. Ein Beitrag zur vergteiehenden Physiologie des Licht- und Farbensinnes*" by Theodore W. Engelmann, from *Archive Für Die Gesamte Physiologie Des Menschen Und Der Tiere*, 1883, Volume 30(1); **7.13b** Adaptation of figure 1a from "Architecture of the Photosynthetic Oxygen-Evolving Center" by Kristina N. Ferreira et al., from *Science*, March 2004, Volume 303(5665). Copyright © 2004 by AAAS. Reprinted with permission; **7.15** Adaptation of Figure 4.1 from *Energy, Plants, and Man*, by Richard Walker and David Alan Walker. Copyright © 1992 by Richard Walker and David Alan Walker. Reprinted with permission of Richard Walker; **7 SSE** Source: Data from "Potential Effects of Global Atmospheric $CO_2$ Enrichment on the Growth and Competitiveness of $C_3$ and $C_4$ Weed and Crop Plants" by D. T. Patterson and E. P. Flint, from *Weed Science*, 1980, Volume 28.

**Chapter 8** **8.8** *The World of the Cell*, 3rd Edition, by Wayne M. Becker, Jane B. Reece, and Martin F. Poenie. Copyright © 1996 by Pearson Education. Reprinted and electronically reproduced by permission of Pearson Education, Inc., Upper Saddle River, New Jersey; **8.12** Figure adapted from *The World of the Cell*, 3rd Edition, by Wayne M. Becker, Jane B. Reece, and Martin F. Poenie. Copyright © 1996 by Pearson Education, Inc. Adapted and electronically reproduced by permission of Pearson Education, Inc., Upper Saddle River, New Jersey; **p. 176 Quote** Source: Rudolf Virchow.

**Chapter 9** **9.9** Source: Based on "Chromosomes Move Poleward in Anaphase along Stationary Microtubules That Coordinately Disassemble from Their Kinetochore Ends" by Gary J. Gorbsky et al., from *Journal of Cell Biology*, January 1987, Volume 104(1); **9.13** Adaptation of figure 18.41 from *Molecular Biology of the Cell*, 4th Edition, by Bruce Alberts et al. Copyright © 2002 by Garland Science/Taylor & Francis LLC. Reprinted with permission; **9.14** Source: Based on "Mammalian Cell Fusion: Induction of Premature Chromosome Condensation in Interphase Nuclei" by R. T. Johnson and P. N. Rao, from *Nature*, May 1970, Volume 226(5247); **9 SSE** Adaptation of Figure 3A from "Regulation of Glioblastoma Progression by Cord Blood Stem Cells Is Mediated by Downregulation of Cyclin D1" by Kiran K. Velpula et al., from PLoS ONE, March 24, 2011, Volume 6(3). Copyright © 2011 by Kiran K. Velpula et al. Article is open-access and distributed under the terms of the Creative Commons Attribution License, which permits unrestricted use, distribution, and reproduction in any medium, provided the original author and source are credited.

**Chapter 14** **14.17b and c** Adapted from *Biochemistry*, 2nd ed., by C.K. Matthews and K.E. van Holde, 1996. Copyright © 1996 by Pearson Education, Inc. Reprinted and electronically reproduced by permission of Pearson Education, Inc. Upper Saddle River, NJ. **p. 234** Material provided courtesy of Dr. Thomas Schneider, National Cancer Institute, National Institutes of Health, 2012.

**Chapter 15** **p. 310** Adapted from "New Variants and Age Shift to High Fatality Groups Contribute to Severe Successive Waves in the 2009 Influenza Pandemic in Taiwan" by J.R. Yang et al., *Public Library of Science ONE*, 6(11), e28288 (11/30/11). Copyright © 2011 by Yang et al. Reprinted with permission.

## Pronunciation Key

| | |
|---|---|
| ā | ace |
| a/ah | ash |
| ch | chose |
| ē | meet |
| e/eh | bet. |
| g | game |
| ī | ice |
| i | hit |
| ks | box |
| kw | quick |
| ng | song |
| ō | robe |
| o | ox |
| oy | boy |
| s | say |
| sh | shell |
| th | thin |
| ū | boot |
| u/uh | up |
| z | zoo |

′ = primary accent
′ = secondary accent

**5′ cap** A modified form of guanine nucleotide added onto the 5′ end of a pre-mRNA molecule.

**ABC hypothesis** A model of flower formation identifying three classes of organ identity genes that direct formation of the four types of floral organs.

**abiotic** (ā′-bī-ot′-ik) Nonliving; referring to the physical and chemical properties of an environment.

**abortion** The termination of a pregnancy in progress.

**abscisic acid (ABA)** (ab-sis′-ik) A plant hormone that slows growth, often antagonizing the actions of growth hormones. Two of its many effects are to promote seed dormancy and facilitate drought tolerance.

**absorption** The third stage of food processing in animals: the uptake of small nutrient molecules by an organism's body.

**absorption spectrum** The range of a pigment's ability to absorb various wavelengths of light; also a graph of such a range.

**abyssal zone** (uh-bis′-ul) The part of the ocean's benthic zone between 2,000 and 6,000 m deep.

**acanthodian** (ak′-an-thō′-dē-un) Any of a group of ancient jawed aquatic vertebrates from the Silurian and Devonian periods.

**accessory fruit** A fruit, or assemblage of fruits, in which the fleshy parts are derived largely or entirely from tissues other than the ovary.

**acclimatization** (uh-klī′-muh-tī -zā′-shun) Physiological adjustment to a change in an environmental factor.

**acetyl CoA** Acetyl coenzyme A; the entry compound for the citric acid cycle in cellular respiration, formed from a two-carbon fragment of pyruvate attached to a coenzyme.

**acetylcholine** (as′-uh-til-kō′-lēn) One of the most common neurotransmitters; functions by binding to receptors and altering the permeability of the postsynaptic membrane to specific ions, either depolarizing or hyperpolarizing the membrane.

**acid** A substance that increases the hydrogen ion concentration of a solution.

**acoelomate** (uh-sē′-lō-māt) A solid-bodied animal lacking a cavity between the gut and outer body wall.

**acquired immunodeficiency syndrome (AIDS)** The symptoms and signs present during the late stages of HIV infection, defined by a specified reduction in the number of T cells and the appearance of characteristic secondary infections.

**acrosomal reaction** (ak′-ruh-sōm′-ul) The discharge of hydrolytic enzymes from the acrosome, a vesicle in the tip of a sperm, when the sperm approaches or contacts an egg.

**acrosome** (ak′-ruh-sōm) A vesicle in the tip of a sperm containing hydrolytic enzymes and other proteins that help the sperm reach the egg.

**actin** (ak′-tin) A globular protein that links into chains, two of which twist helically about each other, forming microfilaments (actin filaments) in muscle and other kinds of cells.

**action potential** An electrical signal that propagates (travels) along the membrane of a neuron or other excitable cell as a nongraded (all-or-none) depolarization.

**action spectrum** A graph that profiles the relative effectiveness of different wavelengths of radiation in driving a particular process.

**activation energy** The amount of energy that reactants must absorb before a chemical reaction will start; also called free energy of activation.

**activator** A protein that binds to DNA and stimulates gene transcription. In prokaryotes, activators bind in or near the promoter; in eukaryotes, activators generally bind to control elements in enhancers.

**active immunity** Long-lasting immunity conferred by the action of B cells and T cells and the resulting B and T memory cells specific for a pathogen. Active immunity can develop as a result of natural infection or immunization.

**active site** The specific region of an enzyme that binds the substrate and that forms the pocket in which catalysis occurs.

**active transport** The movement of a substance across a cell membrane against its concentration or electrochemical gradient, mediated by specific transport proteins and requiring an expenditure of energy.

**adaptation** Inherited characteristic of an organism that enhances its survival and reproduction in a specific environment.

**adaptive evolution** Evolution that results in a better match between organisms and their environment.

**adaptive immunity** A vertebrate-specific defense that is mediated by B lymphocytes (B cells) and T lymphocytes (T cells) and that exhibits specificity, memory, and self-nonself recognition; also called acquired immunity.

**adaptive radiation** Period of evolutionary change in which groups of organisms form many new species whose adaptations allow them to fill different ecological roles in their communities.

**addition rule** A rule of probability stating that the probability of any one of two or more mutually exclusive events occurring can be determined by adding their individual probabilities.

**adenosine triphosphate** *See* ATP (adenosine triphosphate).

**adenylyl cyclase** (uh-den′-uh-lil) An enzyme that converts ATP to cyclic AMP in response to an extracellular signal.

**adhesion** The clinging of one substance to another, such as water to plant cell walls by means of hydrogen bonds.

**adipose tissue** A connective tissue that insulates the body and serves as a fuel reserve; contains fat-storing cells called adipose cells.

**adrenal gland** (uh-drē′-nul) One of two endocrine glands located adjacent to the kidneys in mammals. Endocrine cells in the outer portion (cortex) respond to adrenocorticotropic hormone (ACTH) by secreting steroid hormones that help maintain homeostasis during long-term stress. Neurosecretory cells in the central portion (medulla) secrete epinephrine and norepinephrine in response to nerve signals triggered by short-term stress.

**aerobic respiration** A catabolic pathway for organic molecules, using oxygen ($O_2$) as the final electron acceptor in an electron transport chain and ultimately producing ATP. This is the most efficient catabolic pathway and is carried out in most eukaryotic cells and many prokaryotic organisms.

**age structure** The relative number of individuals of each age in a population.

**aggregate fruit** A fruit derived from a single flower that has more than one carpel.

**AIDS (acquired immunodeficiency syndrome)** The symptoms and signs present during the late stages of HIV infection, defined by a specified reduction in the number of T cells and the appearance of characteristic secondary infections.

**alcohol fermentation** Glycolysis followed by the reduction of pyruvate to ethyl alcohol, regenerating $NAD^+$ and releasing carbon dioxide.

**aldosterone** (al-dos'-tuh-rōn) A steroid hormone that acts on tubules of the kidney to regulate the transport of sodium ions ($Na^+$) and potassium ions ($K^+$).

**alga** (plural, **algae**) A member of a diverse collection of photosynthetic protists that includes both unicellular and multicellular forms. Algal species are included in three eukaryote supergroups (Excavata, "SAR" clade, and Archaeplastida).

**alimentary canal** (al'-uh-men'-tuh-rē) A complete digestive tract, consisting of a tube running between a mouth and an anus.

**alkaline vent** A deep-sea hydrothermal vent that releases water that is warm (40–90°C) rather than hot and that has a high pH (is basic). These vents consist of tiny pores lined with iron and other catalytic minerals that some scientists hypothesize might have been the location of the earliest abiotic synthesis of organic compounds.

**allele** (uh-lē'-ul) Any of the alternative versions of a gene that may produce distinguishable phenotypic effects.

**allopatric speciation** (al'-uh-pat'-rik) The formation of new species in populations that are geographically isolated from one another.

**allopolyploid** (al'-ō-pol'-ē-ployd) A fertile individual that has more than two chromosome sets as a result of two different species interbreeding and combining their chromosomes.

**allosteric regulation** The binding of a regulatory molecule to a protein at one site that affects the function of the protein at a different site.

**alpha (α) helix** (al'-fuh hē'-liks) A coiled region constituting one form of the secondary structure of proteins, arising from a specific pattern of hydrogen bonding between atoms of the polypeptide backbone (not the side chains).

**alternation of generations** A life cycle in which there is both a multicellular diploid form, the sporophyte, and a multicellular haploid form, the gametophyte; characteristic of plants and some algae.

**alternative RNA splicing** A type of eukaryotic gene regulation at the RNA-processing level in which different mRNA molecules are produced from the same primary transcript, depending on which RNA segments are treated as exons and which as introns.

**altruism** (al'-trū-iz-um) Selflessness; behavior that reduces an individual's fitness while increasing the fitness of another individual.

**alveolates** (al-vē'-uh-lets) One of the three major subgroups for which the "SAR" eukaryotic supergroup is named. This clade arose by secondary endosymbiosis; alveolate protists have membrane-enclosed sacs (alveoli) located just under the plasma membrane.

**alveolus** (al-vē'-uh-lus) (plural, **alveoli**) One of the dead-end air sacs where gas exchange occurs in a mammalian lung.

**Alzheimer's disease** (alts'-hī-merz) An age-related dementia (mental deterioration) characterized by confusion and memory loss.

**amino acid** (uh-mēn'-ō) An organic molecule possessing both a carboxyl and an amino group. Amino acids serve as the monomers of polypeptides.

**amino group** (uh-mēn'-ō) A chemical group consisting of a nitrogen atom bonded to two hydrogen atoms; can act as a base in solution, accepting a hydrogen ion and acquiring a charge of 1+.

**aminoacyl-tRNA synthetase** An enzyme that joins each amino acid to the appropriate tRNA.

**ammonia** A small, toxic molecule ($NH_3$) produced by nitrogen fixation or as a metabolic waste product of protein and nucleic acid metabolism.

**ammonite** A member of a group of shelled cephalopods that were important marine predators for hundreds of millions of years until their extinction at the end of the Cretaceous period (65.5 million years ago).

**amniocentesis** (am'-nē-ō-sen-tē'-sis) A technique associated with prenatal diagnosis in which amniotic fluid is obtained by aspiration from a needle inserted into the uterus. The fluid and the fetal cells it contains are analyzed to detect certain genetic and congenital defects in the fetus.

**amniote** (am'-nē-ōt) A member of a clade of tetrapods named for a key derived character, the amniotic egg, which contains specialized membranes, including the fluid-filled amnion, that protect the embryo. Amniotes include mammals as well as birds and other reptiles.

**amniotic egg** An egg that contains specialized membranes that function in protection, nourishment, and gas exchange. The amniotic egg was a major evolutionary innovation, allowing embryos to develop on land in a fluid-filled sac, thus reducing the dependence of tetrapods on water for reproduction.

**amoeba** (uh-mē'-buh) A protist characterized by the presence of pseudopodia.

**amoebocyte** (uh-mē'-buh-sīt') An amoeba-like cell that moves by pseudopodia and is found in most animals. Depending on the species, it may digest and distribute food, dispose of wastes, form skeletal fibers, fight infections, or change into other cell types.

**amoebozoan** (uh-mē'-buh-zō'-an) A protist in a clade that includes many species with lobe- or tube-shaped pseudopodia.

**amphibian** A member of the clade of tetrapods that includes salamanders, frogs, and caecilians.

**amphipathic** (am'-fē-path'-ik) Having both a hydrophilic region and a hydrophobic region.

**amplification** The strengthening of stimulus energy during transduction.

**amygdala** (uh-mig'-duh-luh) A structure in the temporal lobe of the vertebrate brain that has a major role in the processing of emotions.

**amylase** (am'-uh-lās') An enzyme that hydrolyzes starch (a glucose polymer from plants) and glycogen (a glucose polymer from animals) into smaller polysaccharides and the disaccharide maltose.

**anabolic pathway** (an'-uh-bol'-ik) A metabolic pathway that consumes energy to synthesize a complex molecule from simpler molecules.

**anaerobic respiration** (an-er-ō'-bik) A catabolic pathway in which inorganic molecules other than oxygen accept electrons at the "downhill" end of electron transport chains.

**analogous** Having characteristics that are similar because of convergent evolution, not homology.

**analogy** (an-al'-uh-jē) Similarity between two species that is due to convergent evolution rather than to descent from a common ancestor with the same trait.

**anaphase** The fourth stage of mitosis, in which the chromatids of each chromosome have separated and the daughter chromosomes are moving to the poles of the cell.

**anatomy** The structure of an organism.

**anchorage dependence** The requirement that a cell must be attached to a substratum in order to initiate cell division.

**androgen** (an'-drō-jen) Any steroid hormone, such as testosterone, that stimulates the development and maintenance of the male reproductive system and secondary sex characteristics.

**aneuploidy** (an'-yū-ploy'-dē) A chromosomal aberration in which one or more chromosomes are present in extra copies or are deficient in number.

**angiosperm** (an'-jē-ō-sperm) A flowering plant, which forms seeds inside a protective chamber called an ovary.

**angiotensin II** A peptide hormone that stimulates constriction of precapillary arterioles and increases reabsorption of NaCl and water by the proximal tubules of the kidney, increasing blood pressure and volume.

**anhydrobiosis** (an-hī'-drō-bī-ō'-sis) A dormant state involving loss of almost all body water.

**animal pole** The point at the end of an egg in the hemisphere where the least yolk is concentrated; opposite of vegetal pole.

**anion** (an'-ī-on) A negatively charged ion.

**anterior** Pertaining to the front, or head, of a bilaterally symmetrical animal.

**anterior pituitary** A portion of the pituitary gland that develops from nonneural tissue; consists of endocrine cells that synthesize and secrete several tropic and nontropic hormones.

**anther** In an angiosperm, the terminal pollen sac of a stamen, where pollen grains containing sperm-producing male gametophytes form.

**antheridium** (an-thuh-rid'-ē-um) (plural, **antheridia**) In plants, the male gametangium, a moist chamber in which gametes develop.

**anthropoid** (an'-thruh-poyd) A member of a primate group made up of the monkeys and the apes (gibbons, orangutans, gorillas, chimpanzees, bonobos, and humans).

**antibody** A protein secreted by plasma cells (differentiated B cells) that binds to a particular antigen; also called immunoglobulin. All antibodies have the same Y-shaped structure and in their monomer form consist of two identical heavy chains and two identical light chains.

**anticodon** (an'-tī-kō'-don) A nucleotide triplet at one end of a tRNA molecule that base-pairs with a particular complementary codon on an mRNA molecule.

**antidiuretic hormone (ADH)** (an'-tī-dī-yŭ-ret'-ik) A peptide hormone, also called vasopressin, that promotes water retention by the kidneys. Produced in the hypothalamus and released from the posterior pituitary, ADH also functions in the brain.

**antigen** (an'-ti-jen) A substance that elicits an immune response by binding to receptors of B or T cells.

**antigen presentation** (an'-ti-jen) The process by which an MHC molecule binds to a fragment of an intracellular protein antigen and carries it to the cell surface, where it is displayed and can be recognized by a T cell.

**antigen-presenting cell** (an'-ti-jen) A cell that upon ingesting pathogens or internalizing pathogen proteins generates peptide fragments that are bound by class II MHC molecules and subsequently displayed on the cell surface to T cells. Macrophages, dendritic cells, and B cells are the primary antigen-presenting cells.

**antigen receptor** (an'-ti-jen) The general term for a surface protein, located on B cells and T cells, that binds to antigens, initiating adaptive immune responses. The antigen receptors on B cells are called B cell receptors, and the antigen receptors on T cells are called T cell receptors.

**antiparallel** Referring to the arrangement of the sugar-phosphate backbones in a DNA double helix (they run in opposite $5' \rightarrow 3'$ directions).

**aphotic zone** (ā'-fō'-tik) The part of an ocean or lake beneath the photic zone, where light does not penetrate sufficiently for photosynthesis to occur.

**apical bud** (ā'-pik-ul) A bud at the tip of a plant stem; also called a terminal bud.

**apical dominance** (ā'-pik-ul) Tendency for growth to be concentrated at the tip of a plant shoot, because the apical bud partially inhibits axillary bud growth.

**apical ectodermal ridge (AER)** (ā'-pik-ul) A thickened area of ectoderm at the tip of a limb bud that promotes outgrowth of the limb bud.

**apical meristem** (ā'-pik-ul mār'-uh-stem) Embryonic plant tissue in the tips of roots and buds of shoots. The dividing cells of an apical meristem enable the plant to grow in length.

**apicomplexan** (ap'-ē-kom-pleks'-un) A protist in a clade that includes many species that parasitize animals. Some apicomplexans cause human disease.

**apomixis** (ap'-uh-mik'-sis) The ability of some plant species to reproduce asexually through seeds without fertilization by a male gamete.

**apoplast** (ap'-ō-plast) Everything external to the plasma membrane of a plant cell, including cell walls, intercellular spaces, and the space within dead structures such as xylem vessels and tracheids.

**apoptosis** (ā-puh-tō'-sus) A type of programmed cell death, which is brought about by activation of enzymes that break down many chemical components in the cell.

**aposematic coloration** (ap'-ō-si-mat'-ik) The bright warning coloration of many animals with effective physical or chemical defenses.

**appendix** A small, finger-like extension of the vertebrate cecum; contains a mass of white blood cells that contribute to immunity.

**aquaporin** A channel protein in a cellular membrane that specifically facilitates osmosis, the diffusion of free water across the membrane.

**aqueous solution** (ā'-kwē-us) A solution in which water is the solvent.

**arachnid** A member of a subgroup of the major arthropod clade Chelicerata. Arachnids have six pairs of appendages, including four pairs of walking legs, and include spiders, scorpions, ticks, and mites.

**arbuscular mycorrhiza** (ar-bus'-kyŭ-lur mī'-kō-rī'-zuh) Association of a fungus with a plant root system in which the fungus causes the invagination of the host (plant) cells' plasma membranes.

**arbuscular mycorrhizal fungus** (ar-bus'-kyŭ-lur) A symbiotic fungus whose hyphae grow through the cell wall of plant roots and extend into the root cell (enclosed in tubes formed by invagination of the root cell plasma membrane).

**Archaea** (ar'-kē'-uh) One of two prokaryotic domains, the other being Bacteria.

**Archaeplastida** (ar'-kē-plas'-tid-uh) One of four supergroups of eukaryotes proposed in a current hypothesis of the evolutionary history of eukaryotes. This monophyletic group, which includes red algae, green algae, and land plants, descended from an ancient protist ancestor that engulfed a cyanobacterium. *See also* Excavata, "SAR" clade, and Unikonta.

**archegonium** (ar-ki-gō'-nē-um) (plural, **archegonia**) In plants, the female gametangium, a moist chamber in which gametes develop.

**archenteron** (ar-ken'-tuh-ron) The endoderm-lined cavity, formed during gastrulation, that develops into the digestive tract of an animal.

**archosaur** (ar'-kō-sōr) A member of the reptilian group that includes crocodiles, alligators and dinosaurs, including birds.

**arteriole** (ar-ter'-ē-ōl) A vessel that conveys blood between an artery and a capillary bed.

**artery** A vessel that carries blood away from the heart to organs throughout the body.

**arthropod** A segmented ecdysozoan with a hard exoskeleton and jointed appendages. Familiar examples include insects, spiders, millipedes, and crabs.

**artificial selection** The selective breeding of domesticated plants and animals to encourage the occurrence of desirable traits.

**ascocarp** The fruiting body of a sac fungus (ascomycete).

**ascomycete** (as'-kuh-mī-sēt) A member of the fungal phylum Ascomycota, commonly called sac fungus. The name comes from the saclike structure in which the spores develop.

**ascus** (plural, **asci**) A saclike spore capsule located at the tip of a dikaryotic hypha of a sac fungus.

**asexual reproduction** The generation of offspring from a single parent that occurs without the fusion of gametes (by budding, division of a single cell, or division of the entire organism into two or more parts). In most

cases, the offspring are genetically identical to the parent.

**A site** One of a ribosome's three binding sites for tRNA during translation. The A site holds the tRNA carrying the next amino acid to be added to the polypeptide chain. (A stands for aminoacyl tRNA.)

**assisted migration** The translocation of a species to a favorable habitat beyond its native range for the purpose of protecting the species from human-caused threats.

**associative learning** The acquired ability to associate one environmental feature (such as a color) with another (such as danger).

**aster** A radial array of short microtubules that extends from each centrosome toward the plasma membrane in an animal cell undergoing mitosis.

**astrocyte** A glial cell with diverse functions, including providing structural support for neurons, regulating the interstitial environment, facilitating synaptic transmission, and assisting in regulating the blood supply to the brain.

**atherosclerosis** A cardiovascular disease in which fatty deposits called plaques develop in the inner walls of the arteries, obstructing the arteries and causing them to harden.

**atom** The smallest unit of matter that retains the properties of an element.

**atomic mass** The total mass of an atom, numerically equivalent to the mass in grams of 1 mole of the atom. (For an element with more than one isotope, the atomic mass is the average mass of the naturally occurring isotopes, weighted by their abundance.)

**atomic nucleus** An atom's dense central core, containing protons and neutrons.

**atomic number** The number of protons in the nucleus of an atom, unique for each element and designated by a subscript.

**ATP (adenosine triphosphate)** (a-den'-ō-sēn trī-fos'-fāt) An adenine-containing nucleoside triphosphate that releases free energy when its phosphate bonds are hydrolyzed. This energy is used to drive endergonic reactions in cells.

**ATP synthase** A complex of several membrane proteins that functions in chemiosmosis with adjacent electron transport chains, using the energy of a hydrogen ion (proton) concentration gradient to make ATP. ATP synthases are found in the inner mitochondrial membranes of eukaryotic cells and in the plasma membranes of prokaryotes.

**atrial natriuretic peptide (ANP)** (ā'-trē-ul na'-trē-yŭ-ret'-ik) A peptide hormone secreted by cells of the atria of the heart in response to high blood pressure. ANP's effects on the kidney alter ion and water movement and reduce blood pressure.

**atrioventricular (AV) node** A region of specialized heart muscle tissue between the left and right atria where electrical impulses are delayed for about 0.1 second before spreading to both ventricles and causing them to contract.

**atrioventricular (AV) valve** A heart valve located between each atrium and ventricle that prevents a backflow of blood when the ventricle contracts.

**atrium** (ā′-trē-um) (plural, **atria**) A chamber of the vertebrate heart that receives blood from the veins and transfers blood to a ventricle.

**autocrine** Referring to a secreted molecule that acts on the cell that secreted it.

**autoimmune disease** An immunological disorder in which the immune system turns against self.

**autonomic nervous system** (ot′-ō-nom′-ik) An efferent branch of the vertebrate peripheral nervous system that regulates the internal environment; consists of the sympathetic, parasympathetic, and enteric divisions.

**autopolyploid** (ot′-ō-pol′-ē-ployd) An individual that has more than two chromosome sets that are all derived from a single species.

**autosome** (ot′-ō-sōm) A chromosome that is not directly involved in determining sex; not a sex chromosome.

**autotroph** (ot′-ō-trōf) An organism that obtains organic food molecules without eating other organisms or substances derived from other organisms. Autotrophs use energy from the sun or from oxidation of inorganic substances to make organic molecules from inorganic ones.

**auxin** (ôk′-sin) A term that primarily refers to indoleacetic acid (IAA), a natural plant hormone that has a variety of effects, including cell elongation, root formation, secondary growth, and fruit growth.

**axillary bud** (ak′-sil-ār-ē) A structure that has the potential to form a lateral shoot, or branch. The bud appears in the angle formed between a leaf and a stem.

**axon** (ak′-son) A typically long extension, or process, of a neuron that carries nerve impulses away from the cell body toward target cells.

**B cells** The lymphocytes that complete their development in the bone marrow and become effector cells for the humoral immune response.

**Bacteria** One of two prokaryotic domains, the other being Archaea.

**bacteriophage** (bak-tēr′-ē-ō-fāj) A virus that infects bacteria; also called a phage.

**bacteroid** A form of the bacterium *Rhizobium* contained within the vesicles formed by the root cells of a root nodule.

**balancing selection** Natural selection that maintains two or more phenotypic forms in a population.

**bar graph** A graph in which the independent variable represents groups or nonnumerical categories and the values of the dependent variable(s) are shown by bars.

**bark** All tissues external to the vascular cambium, consisting mainly of the secondary phloem and layers of periderm.

**Barr body** A dense object lying along the inside of the nuclear envelope in cells of female mammals, representing a highly condensed, inactivated X chromosome.

**basal angiosperm** A member of one of three clades of early-diverging lineages of extant flowering plants. Examples are *Amborella*, water lilies, and star anise and its relatives.

**basal body** (bā′-sul) A eukaryotic cell structure consisting of a "9 + 0" arrangement of microtubule triplets. The basal body may organize the microtubule assembly of a cilium or flagellum and is structurally very similar to a centriole.

**basal metabolic rate (BMR)** The metabolic rate of a resting, fasting, and nonstressed endotherm at a comfortable temperature.

**basal taxon** In a specified group of organisms, a taxon whose evolutionary lineage diverged early in the history of the group.

**base** A substance that reduces the hydrogen ion concentration of a solution.

**basidiocarp** Elaborate fruiting body of a dikaryotic mycelium of a club fungus.

**basidiomycete** (buh-sid′-ē-ō-mī′-sēt) A member of the fungal phylum Basidiomycota, commonly called club fungus. The name comes from the club-like shape of the basidium.

**basidium** (plural, **basidia**) (buh-sid′-ē-um, buh-sid′-ē-ah) A reproductive appendage that produces sexual spores on the gills of mushrooms (club fungi).

**Batesian mimicry** (bāt′-zē-un mim′-uh-krē) A type of mimicry in which a harmless species looks like a species that is poisonous or otherwise harmful to predators.

**behavior** Individually, an action carried out by muscles or glands under control of the nervous system in response to a stimulus; collectively, the sum of an animal's responses to external and internal stimuli.

**behavioral ecology** The study of the evolution of and ecological basis for animal behavior.

**benign tumor** A mass of abnormal cells with specific genetic and cellular changes such that the cells are not capable of surviving at a new site and generally remain at the site of the tumor's origin.

**benthic zone** The bottom surface of an aquatic environment.

**benthos** (ben′-thōz) The communities of organisms living in the benthic zone of an aquatic biome.

**beta (β) pleated sheet** One form of the secondary structure of proteins in which the polypeptide chain folds back and forth. Two regions of the chain lie parallel to each other and are held together by hydrogen bonds between atoms of the polypeptide backbone (not the side chains).

**beta oxidation** A metabolic sequence that breaks fatty acids down to two-carbon fragments that enter the citric acid cycle as acetyl CoA.

**bicoid** A maternal effect gene that codes for a protein responsible for specifying the anterior end in *Drosophila melanogaster*.

**bilateral symmetry** Body symmetry in which a central longitudinal plane divides the body into two equal but opposite halves.

**bilaterian** (bī′-luh-ter′-ē-uhn) A member of a clade of animals with bilateral symmetry and three germ layers.

**bile** A mixture of substances that is produced in the liver and stored in the gallbladder; enables formation of fat droplets in water as an aid in the digestion and absorption of fats.

**binary fission** A method of asexual reproduction by "division in half." In prokaryotes, binary fission does not involve mitosis, but in single-celled eukaryotes that undergo binary fission, mitosis is part of the process.

**binomial** A common term for the two-part, latinized format for naming a species, consisting of the genus and specific epithet; also called a binomen.

**biodiversity hot spot** A relatively small area with numerous endemic species and a large number of endangered and threatened species.

**bioenergetics** (1) The overall flow and transformation of energy in an organism. (2) The study of how energy flows through organisms.

**biofilm** A surface-coating colony of one or more species of prokaryotes that engage in metabolic cooperation.

**biofuel** A fuel produced from biomass.

**biogenic amine** A neurotransmitter derived from an amino acid.

**biogeochemical cycle** Any of the various chemical cycles, which involve both biotic and abiotic components of ecosystems.

**biogeography** The scientific study of the past and present geographic distributions of species.

**bioinformatics** The use of computers, software, and mathematical models to process and integrate biological information from large data sets.

**biological augmentation** An approach to restoration ecology that uses organisms to add essential materials to a degraded ecosystem.

**biological clock** An internal timekeeper that controls an organism's biological rhythms. The biological clock marks time with or without environmental cues but often requires signals from the environment to remain tuned to an appropriate period. *See also* circadian rhythm.

**biological magnification** A process in which retained substances become more concentrated at each higher trophic level in a food chain.

**biological species concept** Definition of a species as a group of populations whose members have the potential to interbreed in nature and produce viable, fertile offspring but do not produce viable, fertile offspring with members of other such groups.

**biology** The scientific study of life.

**biomanipulation** An approach that applies the top-down model of community organization to alter ecosystem characteristics. For example, ecologists can prevent algal blooms and eutrophication by altering the density of higher-level consumers in lakes instead of by using chemical treatments.

**biomass** The total mass of organic matter comprising a group of organisms in a particular habitat.

**biome** (bī′-ōm) Any of the world's major ecosystem types, often classified according to the predominant vegetation for terrestrial biomes and the physical environment for aquatic biomes and characterized by adaptations of organisms to that particular environment.

**bioremediation** The use of organisms to detoxify and restore polluted and degraded ecosystems.

**biosphere** The entire portion of Earth inhabited by life; the sum of all the planet's ecosystems.

**biotechnology** The manipulation of organisms or their components to produce useful products.

**biotic** (bī-ot′-ik) Pertaining to the living factors—the organisms—in an environment.

**bipolar disorder** A depressive mental illness characterized by swings of mood from high to low; also called manic-depressive disorder.

**birth control pill** A hormonal contraceptive that inhibits ovulation, retards follicular development, or alters a woman's cervical mucus to prevent sperm from entering the uterus.

**blade** (1) A leaflike structure of a seaweed that provides most of the surface area for photosynthesis. (2) The flattened portion of a typical leaf.

**blastocoel** (blas′-tuh-sēl) The fluid-filled cavity that forms in the center of a blastula.

**blastocyst** (blas′-tuh-sist) The blastula stage of mammalian embryonic development, consisting of an inner cell mass, a cavity, and an outer layer, the trophoblast. In humans, the blastocyst forms 1 week after fertilization.

**blastomere** An early embryonic cell arising during the cleavage stage of an early embryo.

**blastopore** (blas′-tō-pōr) In a gastrula, the opening of the archenteron that typically develops into the anus in deuterostomes and the mouth in protostomes.

**blastula** (blas′-tyū-luh) A hollow ball of cells that marks the end of the cleavage stage during early embryonic development in animals.

**blood** A connective tissue with a fluid matrix called plasma in which red blood cells, white blood cells, and cell fragments called platelets are suspended.

**blue-light photoreceptor** A type of light receptor in plants that initiates a variety of responses, such as phototropism and slowing of hypocotyl elongation.

**body cavity** A fluid- or air-filled space between the digestive tract and the body wall.

**body plan** In multicellular eukaryotes, a set of morphological and developmental traits that are integrated into a functional whole—the living organism.

**Bohr shift** A lowering of the affinity of hemoglobin for oxygen, caused by a drop in pH. It facilitates the release of oxygen from hemoglobin in the vicinity of active tissues.

**bolus** A lubricated ball of chewed food.

**bone** A connective tissue consisting of living cells held in a rigid matrix of collagen fibers embedded in calcium salts.

**book lung** An organ of gas exchange in spiders, consisting of stacked plates contained in an internal chamber.

**bottleneck effect** Genetic drift that occurs when the size of a population is reduced, as by a natural disaster or human actions. Typically, the surviving population is no longer genetically representative of the original population.

**bottom-up model** A model of community organization in which mineral nutrients influence community organization by controlling plant or phytoplankton numbers, which in turn control herbivore numbers, which in turn control predator numbers.

**Bowman's capsule** (bō′-munz) A cup-shaped receptacle in the vertebrate kidney that is the initial, expanded segment of the nephron, where filtrate enters from the blood.

**brachiopod** (bra′-kē-uh-pod′) A marine lophophorate with a shell divided into dorsal and ventral halves; also called lamp shells.

**brain** Organ of the central nervous system where information is processed and integrated.

**brainstem** A collection of structures in the vertebrate brain, including the midbrain, the pons, and the medulla oblongata; functions in homeostasis, coordination of movement, and conduction of information to higher brain centers.

**branch point** The representation on a phylogenetic tree of the divergence of two or more taxa from a common ancestor. A branch point is usually shown as a dichotomy in which a branch representing the ancestral lineage splits (at the branch point) into two branches, one for each of the two descendant lineages.

**brassinosteroid** A steroid hormone in plants that has a variety of effects, including inducing cell elongation, retarding leaf abscission, and promoting xylem differentiation.

**breathing** Ventilation of the lungs through alternating inhalation and exhalation.

**bronchiole** (brong′-kē-ōl′) A fine branch of the bronchi that transports air to alveoli.

**bronchus** (brong′-kus) (plural, **bronchi**) One of a pair of breathing tubes that branch from the trachea into the lungs.

**brown alga** A multicellular, photosynthetic protist with a characteristic brown or olive color that results from carotenoids in its plastids. Most brown algae are marine, and some have a plantlike body.

**bryophyte** (brī′-uh-fīt) An informal name for a moss, liverwort, or hornwort; a nonvascular plant that lives on land but lacks some of the terrestrial adaptations of vascular plants.

**buffer** A solution that contains a weak acid and its corresponding base. A buffer minimizes changes in pH when acids or bases are added to the solution.

**bulk feeder** An animal that eats relatively large pieces of food.

**bulk flow** The movement of a fluid due to a difference in pressure between two locations.

**bundle-sheath cell** In $C_4$ plants, a type of photosynthetic cell arranged into tightly packed sheaths around the veins of a leaf.

**$C_3$ plant** A plant that uses the Calvin cycle for the initial steps that incorporate $CO_2$ into organic material, forming a three-carbon compound as the first stable intermediate.

**$C_4$ plant** A plant in which the Calvin cycle is preceded by reactions that incorporate $CO_2$ into a four-carbon compound, the end product of which supplies $CO_2$ for the Calvin cycle.

**calcitonin** (kal′-si-tō′-nin) A hormone secreted by the thyroid gland that lowers blood calcium levels by promoting calcium deposition in bone and calcium excretion from the kidneys; nonessential in adult humans.

**callus** A mass of dividing, undifferentiated cells growing in culture.

**calorie (cal)** The amount of heat energy required to raise the temperature of 1 g of water by 1°C; also the amount of heat energy that 1 g of water releases when it cools by 1°C. The Calorie (with a capital C), usually used to indicate the energy content of food, is a kilocalorie.

**Calvin cycle** The second of two major stages in photosynthesis (following the light reactions), involving fixation of atmospheric $CO_2$ and reduction of the fixed carbon into carbohydrate.

**Cambrian explosion** A relatively brief time in geologic history when many present-day phyla of animals first appeared in the fossil record. This burst of evolutionary change occurred about 535–525 million years ago and saw the emergence of the first large, hard-bodied animals.

**CAM plant** A plant that uses crassulacean acid metabolism, an adaptation for photosynthesis in arid conditions. In this process, $CO_2$ entering open stomata during the night is converted to organic acids, which release $CO_2$ for the Calvin cycle during the day, when stomata are closed.

**canopy** The uppermost layer of vegetation in a terrestrial biome.

**capillary** (kap′-il-ār′-ē) A microscopic blood vessel that penetrates the tissues and consists of a single layer of endothelial cells that allows exchange between the blood and interstitial fluid.

**capillary bed** (kap′-il-ār′-ē) A network of capillaries in a tissue or organ.

**capsid** The protein shell that encloses a viral genome. It may be rod-shaped, polyhedral, or more complex in shape.

**capsule** (1) In many prokaryotes, a dense and well-defined layer of polysaccharide or protein that surrounds the cell wall and is sticky, protecting the cell and enabling it to adhere to substrates or other cells. (2) The sporangium of a bryophyte (moss, liverwort, or hornwort).

**carbohydrate** (kar′-bō-hī′-drāt) A sugar (monosaccharide) or one of its dimers (disaccharides) or polymers (polysaccharides).

**carbon fixation** The initial incorporation of carbon from $CO_2$ into an organic compound by an autotrophic organism (a plant, another photosynthetic organism, or a chemoautotrophic prokaryote).

**carbonyl group** (kar-buh-nēl′) A chemical group present in aldehydes and ketones and consisting of a carbon atom double-bonded to an oxygen atom.

**carboxyl group** (kar-bok′-sil) A chemical group present in organic acids and consisting of a single carbon atom double-bonded to an oxygen atom and also bonded to a hydroxyl group.

**cardiac cycle** (kar′-dē-ak) The alternating contractions and relaxations of the heart.

**cardiac muscle** (kar'-dē-ak) A type of striated muscle that forms the contractile wall of the heart. Its cells are joined by intercalated disks that relay the electrical signals underlying each heartbeat.

**cardiac output** (kar'-dē-ak) The volume of blood pumped per minute by each ventricle of the heart.

**cardiovascular system** A closed circulatory system with a heart and branching network of arteries, capillaries, and veins. The system is characteristic of vertebrates.

**carnivore** An animal that mainly eats other animals.

**carotenoid** (kuh-rot'-uh-noyd') An accessory pigment, either yellow or orange, in the chloroplasts of plants and in some prokaryotes. By absorbing wavelengths of light that chlorophyll cannot, carotenoids broaden the spectrum of colors that can drive photosynthesis.

**carpel** (kar'-pul) The ovule-producing reproductive organ of a flower, consisting of the stigma, style, and ovary.

**carrier** In genetics, an individual who is heterozygous at a given genetic locus for a recessively inherited disorder. The heterozygote is generally phenotypically normal for the disorder but can pass on the recessive allele to offspring.

**carrying capacity** The maximum population size that can be supported by the available resources, symbolized as $K$.

**cartilage** (kar'-til-ij) A flexible connective tissue with an abundance of collagenous fibers embedded in chondroitin sulfate.

**Casparian strip** (ka-spär'-ē-un) A water-impermeable ring of wax in the endodermal cells of plants that blocks the passive flow of water and solutes into the stele by way of cell walls.

**catabolic pathway** (kat'-uh-bol'-ik) A metabolic pathway that releases energy by breaking down complex molecules to simpler molecules.

**catalyst** (kat'-uh-list) A chemical agent that selectively increases the rate of a reaction without being consumed by the reaction.

**catecholamine** (kat'-uh-kōl'-uh-mēn) Any of a class of neurotransmitters and hormones, including the hormones epinephrine and norepinephrine, that are synthesized from the amino acid tyrosine.

**cation** (cat'-ī'-on) A positively charged ion.

**cation exchange** (cat'-ī'-on) A process in which positively charged minerals are made available to a plant when hydrogen ions in the soil displace mineral ions from the clay particles.

**cecum** (sē'-kum) (plural, **ceca**) The blind pouch forming one branch of the large intestine.

**cell body** The part of a neuron that houses the nucleus and most other organelles.

**cell cycle** An ordered sequence of events in the life of a cell, from its origin in the division of a parent cell until its own division into two. The eukaryotic cell cycle is composed of interphase (including $G_1$, S, and $G_2$ subphases) and M phase (including mitosis and cytokinesis).

**cell cycle control system** A cyclically operating set of molecules in the eukaryotic cell that both triggers and coordinates key events in the cell cycle.

**cell division** The reproduction of cells.

**cell fractionation** The disruption of a cell and separation of its parts by centrifugation at successively higher speeds.

**cell-mediated immune response** The branch of adaptive immunity that involves the activation of cytotoxic T cells, which defend against infected cells.

**cell plate** A membrane-bounded, flattened sac located at the midline of a dividing plant cell, inside which the new cell wall forms during cytokinesis.

**cellular respiration** The catabolic pathways of aerobic and anaerobic respiration, which break down organic molecules and use an electron transport chain for the production of ATP.

**cellulose** (sel'-yū-lōs) A structural polysaccharide of plant cell walls, consisting of glucose monomers joined by β glycosidic linkages.

**cell wall** A protective layer external to the plasma membrane in the cells of plants, prokaryotes, fungi, and some protists. Polysaccharides such as cellulose (in plants and some protists), chitin (in fungi), and peptidoglycan (in bacteria) are important structural components of cell walls.

**central nervous system (CNS)** The portion of the nervous system where signal integration occurs; in vertebrate animals, the brain and spinal cord.

**central vacuole** In a mature plant cell, a large membranous sac with diverse roles in growth, storage, and sequestration of toxic substances.

**centriole** (sen'-trē-ōl) A structure in the centrosome of an animal cell composed of a cylinder of microtubule triplets arranged in a "9 + 0" pattern. A centrosome has a pair of centrioles.

**centromere** (sen'-trō-mēr) In a duplicated chromosome, the region on each sister chromatid where it is most closely attached to the other chromatid by proteins that bind to the centromeric DNA. Other proteins condense the chromatin in that region, so it appears as a narrow "waist" on the duplicated chromosome. (An unduplicated chromosome has a single centromere, identified by the proteins bound there.)

**centrosome** (sen'-trō-sōm) A structure present in the cytoplasm of animal cells that functions as a microtubule-organizing center and is important during cell division. A centrosome has two centrioles.

**cercozoan** An amoeboid or flagellated protist that feeds with threadlike pseudopodia.

**cerebellum** (sār'-ruh-bel'-um) Part of the vertebrate hindbrain located dorsally; functions in unconscious coordination of movement and balance.

**cerebral cortex** (suh-rē'-brul) The surface of the cerebrum; the largest and most complex part of the mammalian brain, containing nerve cell bodies of the cerebrum; the part of the vertebrate brain most changed through evolution.

**cerebral hemisphere** (suh-rē'-brul) The right or left side of the cerebrum.

**cerebrum** (suh-rē'-brum) The dorsal portion of the vertebrate forebrain, composed of right and left hemispheres; the integrating center for memory, learning, emotions, and other highly complex functions of the central nervous system.

**cervix** (ser'-viks) The neck of the uterus, which opens into the vagina.

**chaparral** A scrubland biome of dense, spiny evergreen shrubs found at midlatitudes along coasts where cold ocean currents circulate offshore; characterized by mild, rainy winters and long, hot, dry summers.

**chaperonin** (shap'-er-ō'-nin) A protein complex that assists in the proper folding of other proteins.

**character** An observable heritable feature that may vary among individuals.

**character displacement** The tendency for characteristics to be more divergent in sympatric populations of two species than in allopatric populations of the same two species.

**checkpoint** A control point in the cell cycle where stop and go-ahead signals can regulate the cycle.

**chelicera** (kē-lih'-suh-ruh) (plural, **chelicerae**) One of a pair of clawlike feeding appendages characteristic of chelicerates.

**chelicerate** (kē-lih-suh'-rāte) An arthropod that has chelicerae and a body divided into a cephalothorax and an abdomen. Living chelicerates include sea spiders, horseshoe crabs, scorpions, ticks, and spiders.

**chemical bond** An attraction between two atoms, resulting from a sharing of outer-shell electrons or the presence of opposite charges on the atoms. The bonded atoms gain complete outer electron shells.

**chemical energy** Energy available in molecules for release in a chemical reaction; a form of potential energy.

**chemical equilibrium** In a chemical reaction, the state in which the rate of the forward reaction equals the rate of the reverse reaction, so that the relative concentrations of the reactants and products do not change with time.

**chemical reaction** The making and breaking of chemical bonds, leading to changes in the composition of matter.

**chemiosmosis** (kem'-ē-oz-mō'-sis) An energy-coupling mechanism that uses energy stored in the form of a hydrogen ion gradient across a membrane to drive cellular work, such as the synthesis of ATP. Under aerobic conditions, most ATP synthesis in cells occurs by chemiosmosis.

**chemoautotroph** (kē'-mō-ot'-ō-trōf) An organism that obtains energy by oxidizing inorganic substances and needs only carbon dioxide as a carbon source.

**chemoheterotroph** (kē'-mō-het'-er-ō-trōf) An organism that requires organic molecules for both energy and carbon.

**chemoreceptor** A sensory receptor that responds to a chemical stimulus, such as a solute or an odorant.

**chiasma** (plural, **chiasmata**) (kī-az'-muh, kī-az'-muh-tuh) The X-shaped, microscopically visible region where crossing over has occurred earlier in prophase I between homologous nonsister chromatids. Chiasmata become visible after synapsis ends, with the two homologs remaining associated due to sister chromatid cohesion.

**chitin** (kī'-tin) A structural polysaccharide, consisting of amino sugar monomers, found in many fungal cell walls and in the exoskeletons of all arthropods.

**chlorophyll** (klōr'-ō-fil) A green pigment located in membranes within the chloroplasts of plants and algae and in the membranes of certain prokaryotes. Chlorophyll *a* participates directly in the light reactions, which convert solar energy to chemical energy.

**chlorophyll *a*** (klōr'-ō-fil) A photosynthetic pigment that participates directly in the light reactions, which convert solar energy to chemical energy.

**chlorophyll *b*** (klōr'-ō-fil) An accessory photosynthetic pigment that transfers energy to chlorophyll *a*.

**chloroplast** (klōr'-ō-plast) An organelle found in plants and photosynthetic protists that absorbs sunlight and uses it to drive the synthesis of organic compounds from carbon dioxide and water.

**choanocyte** (kō-an'-uh-sīt) A flagellated feeding cell found in sponges. Also called a collar cell, it has a collar-like ring that traps food particles around the base of its flagellum.

**cholesterol** (kō-les'-tuh-rol) A steroid that forms an essential component of animal cell membranes and acts as a precursor molecule for the synthesis of other biologically important steroids, such as many hormones.

**chondrichthyan** (kon-drik'-thē-an) A member of the clade Chondrichthyes, vertebrates with skeletons made mostly of cartilage, such as sharks and rays.

**chordate** A member of the phylum Chordata, animals that at some point during their development have a notochord; a dorsal, hollow nerve cord; pharyngeal slits or clefts; and a muscular, post-anal tail.

**chorionic villus sampling (CVS)** (kōr'-ē-on'-ik vil'-us) A technique associated with prenatal diagnosis in which a small sample of the fetal portion of the placenta is removed for analysis to detect certain genetic and congenital defects in the fetus.

**chromatin** (krō'-muh-tin) The complex of DNA and proteins that makes up eukaryotic chromosomes. When the cell is not dividing, chromatin exists in its dispersed form, as a mass of very long, thin fibers that are not visible with a light microscope.

**chromosome** (krō'-muh-sōm) A cellular structure consisting of one DNA molecule and associated protein molecules. (In some contexts, such as genome sequencing, the term may refer to the DNA alone.) A eukaryotic cell typically has multiple, linear chromosomes, which are located in the nucleus. A prokaryotic cell often has a single, circular chromosome, which is found in the nucleoid, a region that is not enclosed by a membrane. *See also* chromatin.

**chromosome theory of inheritance** (krō'-muh-sōm) A basic principle in biology stating that genes are located at specific positions (loci) on chromosomes and that the behavior of chromosomes during meiosis accounts for inheritance patterns.

**chylomicron** (kī'-lō-mī'-kron) A lipid transport globule composed of fats mixed with cholesterol and coated with proteins.

**chyme** (kīm) The mixture of partially digested food and digestive juices formed in the stomach.

**chytrid** (kī'-trid) A member of the fungal phylum Chytridiomycota, mostly aquatic fungi with flagellated zoospores that represent an early-diverging fungal lineage.

**ciliate** (sil'-ē-it) A type of protist that moves by means of cilia.

**cilium** (sil'-ē-um) (plural, **cilia**) A short appendage containing microtubules in eukaryotic cells. A motile cilium is specialized for locomotion or moving fluid past the cell; it is formed from a core of nine outer doublet microtubules and two inner single microtubules (the "9 + 2" arrangement) ensheathed in an extension of the plasma membrane. A primary cilium is usually nonmotile and plays a sensory and signaling role; it lacks the two inner microtubules (the "9 + 0" arrangement).

**circadian rhythm** (ser-kā'-dē-un) A physiological cycle of about 24 hours that persists even in the absence of external cues.

***cis-trans* isomer** One of several compounds that have the same molecular formula and covalent bonds between atoms but differ in the spatial arrangements of their atoms owing to the inflexibility of double bonds; formerly called a geometric isomer.

**citric acid cycle** A chemical cycle involving eight steps that completes the metabolic breakdown of glucose molecules begun in glycolysis by oxidizing acetyl CoA (derived from pyruvate) to carbon dioxide; occurs within the mitochondrion in eukaryotic cells and in the cytosol of prokaryotes; together with pyruvate oxidation, the second major stage in cellular respiration.

**clade** (klayd) A group of species that includes an ancestral species and all of its descendants. A clade is equivalent to a monophyletic group.

**cladistics** (kluh-dis'-tiks) An approach to systematics in which organisms are placed into groups called clades based primarily on common descent.

**class** In Linnaean classification, the taxonomic category above the level of order.

**cleavage** (1) The process of cytokinesis in animal cells, characterized by pinching of the plasma membrane. (2) The succession of rapid cell divisions without significant growth during early embryonic development that converts the zygote to a ball of cells.

**cleavage furrow** The first sign of cleavage in an animal cell; a shallow groove around the cell in the cell surface near the old metaphase plate.

**climate** The long-term prevailing weather conditions at a given place.

**climograph** A plot of the temperature and precipitation in a particular region.

**clitoris** (klit'-uh-ris) An organ at the upper intersection of the labia minora that engorges with blood and becomes erect during sexual arousal.

**cloaca** (klō-ā'-kuh) A common opening for the digestive, urinary, and reproductive tracts found in many nonmammalian vertebrates but in few mammals.

**clonal selection** The process by which an antigen selectively binds to and activates only those lymphocytes bearing receptors specific for the antigen. The selected lymphocytes proliferate and differentiate into a clone of effector cells and a clone of memory cells specific for the stimulating antigen.

**clone** (1) A lineage of genetically identical individuals or cells. (2) In popular usage, an individual that is genetically identical to another individual. (3) As a verb, to make one or more genetic replicas of an individual or cell. *See also* gene cloning.

**cloning vector** In genetic engineering, a DNA molecule that can carry foreign DNA into a host cell and replicate there. Cloning vectors include plasmids and bacterial artificial chromosomes (BACs), which move recombinant DNA from a test tube back into a cell, and viruses that transfer recombinant DNA by infection.

**closed circulatory system** A circulatory system in which blood is confined to vessels and is kept separate from the interstitial fluid.

**cnidocyte** (nī'-duh-sīt) A specialized cell unique to the phylum Cnidaria; contains a capsule-like organelle housing a coiled thread that, when discharged, explodes outward and functions in prey capture or defense.

**cochlea** (kok'-lē-uh) The complex, coiled organ of hearing that contains the organ of Corti.

**codominance** The situation in which the phenotypes of both alleles are exhibited in the heterozygote because both alleles affect the phenotype in separate, distinguishable ways.

**codon** (kō'-don) A three-nucleotide sequence of DNA or mRNA that specifies a particular amino acid or termination signal; the basic unit of the genetic code.

**coefficient of relatedness** The fraction of genes that, on average, are shared by two individuals.

**coelom** (sē'-lōm) A body cavity lined by tissue derived only from mesoderm.

**coelomate** (sē'-lō-māt) An animal that possesses a true coelom (a body cavity lined by tissue completely derived from mesoderm).

**coenocytic fungus** (sē'-no-si'-tic) A fungus that lacks septa and hence whose body is made up of a continuous cytoplasmic mass that may contain hundreds or thousands of nuclei.

**coenzyme** (kō-en'-zīm) An organic molecule serving as a cofactor. Most vitamins function as coenzymes in metabolic reactions.

**coevolution** The joint evolution of two interacting species, each in response to selection imposed by the other.

**cofactor** Any nonprotein molecule or ion that is required for the proper functioning of an enzyme. Cofactors can be permanently bound to the active site or may bind loosely and reversibly, along with the substrate, during catalysis.

**cognition** The process of knowing that may include awareness, reasoning, recollection, and judgment.

**cognitive map** A neural representation of the abstract spatial relationships between objects in an animal's surroundings.

**cohesion** The linking together of like molecules, often by hydrogen bonds.

**cohesion-tension hypothesis** The leading explanation of the ascent of xylem sap. It states that transpiration exerts pull on xylem sap, putting the sap under negative pressure, or tension, and that the cohesion of water molecules transmits this pull along the entire length of the xylem from shoots to roots.

**cohort** A group of individuals of the same age in a population.

**coleoptile** (kō′-lē-op′-tul) The covering of the young shoot of the embryo of a grass seed.

**coleorhiza** (kō′-lē-uh-rī′-zuh) The covering of the young root of the embryo of a grass seed.

**collagen** A glycoprotein in the extracellular matrix of animal cells that forms strong fibers, found extensively in connective tissue and bone; the most abundant protein in the animal kingdom.

**collecting duct** The location in the kidney where processed filtrate, called urine, is collected from the renal tubules.

**collenchyma cell** (kō-len′-kim-uh) A flexible plant cell type that occurs in strands or cylinders that support young parts of the plant without restraining growth.

**colon** (kō′-len) The largest section of the vertebrate large intestine; functions in water absorption and formation of feces.

**commensalism** (kuh-men′-suh-lizm) A symbiotic relationship in which one organism benefits but the other is neither helped nor harmed.

**communication** In animal behavior, a process involving transmission of, reception of, and response to signals. The term is also used in connection with other organisms, as well as individual cells of multicellular organisms.

**community** All the organisms that inhabit a particular area; an assemblage of populations of different species living close enough together for potential interaction.

**community ecology** The study of how interactions between species affect community structure and organization.

**companion cell** A type of plant cell that is connected to a sieve-tube element by many plasmodesmata and whose nucleus and ribosomes may serve one or more adjacent sieve-tube elements.

**competitive exclusion** The concept that when populations of two similar species compete for the same limited resources, one population will use the resources more efficiently and have a reproductive advantage that will eventually lead to the elimination of the other population.

**competitive inhibitor** A substance that reduces the activity of an enzyme by entering the active site in place of the substrate, whose structure it mimics.

**complement system** A group of about 30 blood proteins that may amplify the inflammatory response, enhance phagocytosis, or directly lyse extracellular pathogens.

**complementary DNA (cDNA)** A double-stranded DNA molecule made *in vitro* using mRNA as a template and the enzymes reverse transcriptase and DNA polymerase. A cDNA molecule corresponds to the exons of a gene.

**complete dominance** The situation in which the phenotypes of the heterozygote and dominant homozygote are indistinguishable.

**complete flower** A flower that has all four basic floral organs: sepals, petals, stamens, and carpels.

**complete metamorphosis** The transformation of a larva into an adult that looks very different, and often functions very differently in its environment, than the larva.

**compound** A substance consisting of two or more different elements combined in a fixed ratio.

**compound eye** A type of multifaceted eye in insects and crustaceans consisting of up to several thousand light-detecting, focusing ommatidia.

**concentration gradient** A region along which the density of a chemical substance increases or decreases.

**conception** The fertilization of an egg by a sperm in humans.

**cone** A cone-shaped cell in the retina of the vertebrate eye, sensitive to color.

**conformer** An animal for which an internal condition conforms to (changes in accordance with) changes in an environmental variable.

**conidium** (plural, **conidia**) A haploid spore produced at the tip of a specialized hypha in ascomycetes during asexual reproduction.

**conifer** A member of the largest gymnosperm phylum. Most conifers are cone-bearing trees, such as pines and firs.

**conjugation** (kon′-jū-gā′-shun) (1) In prokaryotes, the direct transfer of DNA between two cells that are temporarily joined. When the two cells are members of different species, conjugation results in horizontal gene transfer. (2) In ciliates, a sexual process in which two cells exchange haploid micronuclei but do not reproduce.

**connective tissue** Animal tissue that functions mainly to bind and support other tissues, having a sparse population of cells scattered through an extracellular matrix.

**conodont** An early, soft-bodied vertebrate with prominent eyes and dental elements.

**conservation biology** The integrated study of ecology, evolutionary biology, physiology, molecular biology, and genetics to sustain biological diversity at all levels.

**consumer** An organism that feeds on producers, other consumers, or nonliving organic material.

**contraception** The deliberate prevention of pregnancy.

**contractile vacuole** A membranous sac that helps move excess water out of certain freshwater protists.

**control element** A segment of noncoding DNA that helps regulate transcription of a gene by serving as a binding site for a transcription factor. Multiple control elements are present in a eukaryotic gene's enhancer.

**control group** In a controlled experiment, a set of subjects that lacks (or does not receive) the specific factor being tested. Ideally, the control group should be identical to the experimental group in other respects.

**controlled experiment** An experiment in which an experimental group is compared with a control group that varies only in the factor being tested.

**convergent evolution** The evolution of similar features in independent evolutionary lineages.

**convergent extension** A process in which the cells of a tissue layer rearrange themselves in such a way that the sheet of cells becomes narrower (converges) and longer (extends).

**cooperativity** A kind of allosteric regulation whereby a shape change in one subunit of a protein caused by substrate binding is transmitted to all the other subunits, facilitating binding of additional substrate molecules to those subunits.

**coral reef** Typically a warm-water, tropical ecosystem dominated by the hard skeletal structures secreted primarily by corals. Some coral reefs also exist in cold, deep waters.

**corepressor** A small molecule that binds to a bacterial repressor protein and changes the protein's shape, allowing it to bind to the operator and switch an operon off.

**cork cambium** (kam′-bē-um) A cylinder of meristematic tissue in woody plants that replaces the epidermis with thicker, tougher cork cells.

**corpus callosum** (kor′-pus kuh-lō′-sum) The thick band of nerve fibers that connects the right and left cerebral hemispheres in mammals, enabling the hemispheres to process information together.

**corpus luteum** (kor′-pus lū′-tē-um) A secreting tissue in the ovary that forms from the collapsed follicle after ovulation and produces progesterone.

**cortex** (1) The outer region of cytoplasm in a eukaryotic cell, lying just under the plasma membrane, that has a more gel-like consistency than the inner regions due to the presence of multiple microfilaments. (2) In plants, ground tissue that is between the vascular tissue and dermal tissue in a root or eudicot stem.

**cortical nephron** In mammals and birds, a nephron with a loop of Henle located almost entirely in the renal cortex.

**cotransport** The coupling of the "downhill" diffusion of one substance to the "uphill" transport of another against its own concentration gradient.

**cotyledon** (kot′-uh-lē′-dun) A seed leaf of an angiosperm embryo. Some species have one cotyledon, others two.

**countercurrent exchange** The exchange of a substance or heat between two fluids flowing in opposite directions. For example, blood in a fish gill flows in the opposite direction of water passing over the gill, maximizing diffusion of oxygen into and carbon dioxide out of the blood.

**countercurrent multiplier system** A countercurrent system in which energy is expended in active transport to facilitate exchange of materials and generate concentration gradients.

**covalent bond** (kō-vā´-lent) A type of strong chemical bond in which two atoms share one or more pairs of valence electrons.

**crassulacean acid metabolism (CAM)** An adaptation for photosynthesis in arid conditions, first discovered in the family Crassulaceae. In this process, a plant takes up $CO_2$ and incorporates it into a variety of organic acids at night; during the day, $CO_2$ is released from organic acids for use in the Calvin cycle.

**crista** (plural, **cristae**) (kris´-tuh, kris´-tē) An infolding of the inner membrane of a mitochondrion. The inner membrane houses electron transport chains and molecules of the enzyme catalyzing the synthesis of ATP (ATP synthase).

**critical load** The amount of added nutrient, usually nitrogen or phosphorus, that can be absorbed by plants without damaging ecosystem integrity.

**crop rotation** The practice of growing different crops in succession on the same land chiefly to preserve the productive capacity of the soil.

**cross-fostering study** A behavioral study in which the young of one species are placed in the care of adults from another species.

**crossing over** The reciprocal exchange of genetic material between nonsister chromatids during prophase I of meiosis.

**cross-pollination** In angiosperms, the transfer of pollen from an anther of a flower on one plant to the stigma of a flower on another plant of the same species.

**cryptic coloration** Camouflage that makes a potential prey difficult to spot against its background.

**culture** A system of information transfer through social learning or teaching that influences the behavior of individuals in a population.

**cuticle** (kyū´-tuh-kul) (1) A waxy covering on the surface of stems and leaves that prevents desiccation in terrestrial plants. (2) The exoskeleton of an arthropod, consisting of layers of protein and chitin that are variously modified for different functions. (3) A tough coat that covers the body of a nematode.

**cyclic AMP (cAMP)** Cyclic adenosine monophosphate, a ring-shaped molecule made from ATP that is a common intracellular signaling molecule (second messenger) in eukaryotic cells. It is also a regulator of some bacterial operons.

**cyclic electron flow** A route of electron flow during the light reactions of photosynthesis that involves only one photosystem and that produces ATP but not NADPH or $O_2$.

**cyclin** (sī´-klin) A cellular protein that occurs in a cyclically fluctuating concentration and that plays an important role in regulating the cell cycle.

**cyclin-dependent kinase (Cdk)** (sī´-klin) A protein kinase that is active only when attached to a particular cyclin.

**cyclostome** A member of the vertebrate subgroup lacking jaws. Cyclostomes include hagfishes and lampreys.

**cystic fibrosis** (sis´-tik fī-brō´-sis) A human genetic disorder caused by a recessive allele for a chloride channel protein; characterized by an excessive secretion of mucus and consequent vulnerability to infection; fatal if untreated.

**cytochrome** (sī´-tō-krōm) An iron-containing protein that is a component of electron transport chains in the mitochondria and chloroplasts of eukaryotic cells and the plasma membranes of prokaryotic cells.

**cytokinesis** (sī´-tō-kuh-nē´-sis) The division of the cytoplasm to form two separate daughter cells immediately after mitosis, meiosis I, or meiosis II.

**cytokinin** (sī´-tō-kī´-nin) Any of a class of related plant hormones that retard aging and act in concert with auxin to stimulate cell division, influence the pathway of differentiation, and control apical dominance.

**cytoplasm** (sī´-tō-plaz-um) The contents of the cell bounded by the plasma membrane; in eukaryotes, the portion exclusive of the nucleus.

**cytoplasmic determinant** A maternal substance, such as a protein or RNA, that when placed into an egg influences the course of early development by regulating the expression of genes that affect the developmental fate of cells.

**cytoplasmic streaming** A circular flow of cytoplasm, involving interactions of myosin and actin filaments, that speeds the distribution of materials within cells.

**cytoskeleton** A network of microtubules, microfilaments, and intermediate filaments that extend throughout the cytoplasm and serve a variety of mechanical, transport, and signaling functions.

**cytosol** (sī´-tō-sol) The semifluid portion of the cytoplasm.

**cytotoxic T cell** A type of lymphocyte that, when activated, kills infected cells as well as certain cancer cells and transplanted cells.

**dalton** A measure of mass for atoms and subatomic particles; the same as the atomic mass unit, or amu.

**data** Recorded observations.

**day-neutral plant** A plant in which flower formation is not controlled by photoperiod or day length.

**decomposer** An organism that absorbs nutrients from nonliving organic material such as corpses, fallen plant material, and the wastes of living organisms and converts them to inorganic forms; a detritivore.

**deductive reasoning** A type of logic in which specific results are predicted from a general premise.

**deep-sea hydrothermal vent** A dark, hot, oxygen-deficient environment associated with volcanic activity on or near the seafloor. The producers in a vent community are chemoautotrophic prokaryotes.

**de-etiolation** The changes a plant shoot undergoes in response to sunlight; also known informally as greening.

**dehydration reaction** A chemical reaction in which two molecules become covalently bonded to each other with the removal of a water molecule.

**deletion** (1) A deficiency in a chromosome resulting from the loss of a fragment through breakage. (2) A mutational loss of one or more nucleotide pairs from a gene.

**demographic transition** In a stable population, a shift from high birth and death rates to low birth and death rates.

**demography** The study of changes over time in the vital statistics of populations, especially birth rates and death rates.

**denaturation** (dē-nā´-chur-ā´-shun) In proteins, a process in which a protein loses its native shape due to the disruption of weak chemical bonds and interactions, thereby becoming biologically inactive; in DNA, the separation of the two strands of the double helix. Denaturation occurs under extreme (noncellular) conditions of pH, salt concentration, or temperature.

**dendrite** (den´-drīt) One of usually numerous, short, highly branched extensions of a neuron that receive signals from other neurons.

**dendritic cell** An antigen-presenting cell, located mainly in lymphatic tissues and skin, that is particularly efficient in presenting antigens to helper T cells, thereby initiating a primary immune response.

**density** The number of individuals per unit area or volume.

**density dependent** Referring to any characteristic that varies with population density.

**density-dependent inhibition** The phenomenon observed in normal animal cells that causes them to stop dividing when they come into contact with one another.

**density independent** Referring to any characteristic that is not affected by population density.

**deoxyribonucleic acid (DNA)** (dē-ok´-sē-rī´-bō-nū-klā´-ik) A nucleic acid molecule, usually a double-stranded helix, in which each polynucleotide strand consists of nucleotide monomers with a deoxyribose sugar and the nitrogenous bases adenine (A), cytosine (C), guanine (G), and thymine (T); capable of being replicated and determining the inherited structure of a cell's proteins.

**deoxyribose** (dē-ok´-si-rī´-bōs) The sugar component of DNA nucleotides, having one fewer hydroxyl group than ribose, the sugar component of RNA nucleotides.

**dependent variable** A variable whose value is measured during an experiment or other test to see whether it is influenced by changes in another variable (the independent variable).

**depolarization** A change in a cell's membrane potential such that the inside of the membrane is made less negative relative to the outside. For example, a neuron membrane is depolarized if a stimulus decreases its voltage from the resting potential of $-70$ mV in the direction of zero voltage.

**dermal tissue system** The outer protective covering of plants.

**desert** A terrestrial biome characterized by very low precipitation.

**desmosome** A type of intercellular junction in animal cells that functions as a rivet, fastening cells together.

**determinate cleavage** A type of embryonic development in protostomes that rigidly casts the developmental fate of each embryonic cell very early.

**determinate growth** A type of growth characteristic of most animals and some plant organs, in which growth stops after a certain size is reached.

**determination** The progressive restriction of developmental potential in which the possible fate of each cell becomes more limited as an embryo develops. At the end of determination, a cell is committed to its fate.

**detritivore** (deh-trī'-tuh-vōr) A consumer that derives its energy and nutrients from nonliving organic material such as corpses, fallen plant material, and the wastes of living organisms; a decomposer.

**detritus** (di-trī'-tus) Dead organic matter.

**deuteromycete** (dū'-tuh-rō-mī'-sēt) Traditional classification for a fungus with no known sexual stage.

**deuterostome development** (dū'-tuh-rō-stōm') In animals, a developmental mode distinguished by the development of the anus from the blastopore; often also characterized by radial cleavage and by the body cavity forming as outpockets of mesodermal tissue.

**Deuterostomia** (dū'-tuh-rō-stōm'-ē-uh) One of the three main lineages of bilaterian animals. *See also* Ecdysozoa and Lophotrochozoa.

**development** The events involved in an organism's changing gradually from a simple to a more complex or specialized form.

**diabetes mellitus** (dī'-uh-bē'-tis mel'-uh-tus) An endocrine disorder marked by an inability to maintain glucose homeostasis. The type 1 form results from autoimmune destruction of insulin-secreting cells; treatment usually requires daily insulin injections. The type 2 form most commonly results from reduced responsiveness of target cells to insulin; obesity and lack of exercise are risk factors.

**diacylglycerol (DAG)** (dī-a'-sil-glis'-er-ol) A second messenger produced by the cleavage of the phospholipid $PIP_2$ in the plasma membrane.

**diaphragm** (dī'-uh-fram') (1) A sheet of muscle that forms the bottom wall of the thoracic cavity in mammals. Contraction of the diaphragm pulls air into the lungs. (2) A dome-shaped rubber cup fitted into the upper portion of the vagina before sexual intercourse. It serves as a physical barrier to the passage of sperm into the uterus.

**diapsid** (dī-ap'-sid) A member of an amniote clade distinguished by a pair of holes on each side of the skull. Diapsids include the lepidosaurs and archosaurs.

**diastole** (dī-as'-tō-lē) The stage of the cardiac cycle in which a heart chamber is relaxed and fills with blood.

**diastolic pressure** Blood pressure in the arteries when the ventricles are relaxed.

**diatom** Photosynthetic protist in the stramenopile clade; diatoms have a unique glass-like wall made of silicon dioxide embedded in an organic matrix.

**dicot** A term traditionally used to refer to flowering plants that have two embryonic seed leaves, or cotyledons. Recent molecular evidence indicates that dicots do not form a clade; species once classified as dicots are now grouped into eudicots, magnoliids, and several lineages of basal angiosperms.

**differential gene expression** The expression of different sets of genes by cells with the same genome.

**differentiation** The process by which a cell or group of cells becomes specialized in structure and function.

**diffusion** The random thermal motion of particles of liquids, gases, or solids. In the presence of a concentration or electrochemical gradient, diffusion results in the net movement of a substance from a region where it is more concentrated to a region where it is less concentrated.

**digestion** The second stage of food processing in animals: the breaking down of food into molecules small enough for the body to absorb.

**dihybrid** (dī'-hī'-brid) An organism that is heterozygous with respect to two genes of interest. All the offspring from a cross between parents doubly homozygous for different alleles are dihybrids. For example, parents of genotypes *AABB* and *aabb* produce a dihybrid of genotype *AaBb*.

**dihybrid cross** (dī'-hī'-brid) A cross between two organisms that are each heterozygous for both of the characters being followed (or the self-pollination of a plant that is heterozygous for both characters).

**dikaryotic** (dī'-kār-ē-ot'-ik) Referring to a fungal mycelium with two haploid nuclei per cell, one from each parent.

**dinoflagellate** (dī'-nō-flaj'-uh-let) A member of a group of mostly unicellular photosynthetic algae with two flagella situated in perpendicular grooves in cellulose plates covering the cell.

**dinosaur** A member of an extremely diverse clade of reptiles varying in body shape, size, and habitat. Birds are the only extant dinosaurs.

**dioecious** (dī-ē'-shus) In plant biology, having the male and female reproductive parts on different individuals of the same species.

**diploblastic** Having two germ layers.

**diploid cell** (dip'-loyd) A cell containing two sets of chromosomes ($2n$), one set inherited from each parent.

**diplomonad** A protist that has modified mitochondria, two equal-sized nuclei, and multiple flagella.

**directional selection** Natural selection in which individuals at one end of the phenotypic range survive or reproduce more successfully than do other individuals.

**disaccharide** (dī-sak'-uh-rīd) A double sugar, consisting of two monosaccharides joined by a glycosidic linkage formed by a dehydration reaction.

**dispersal** The movement of individuals or gametes away from their parent location. This movement sometimes expands the geographic range of a population or species.

**dispersion** The pattern of spacing among individuals within the boundaries of a population.

**disruptive selection** Natural selection in which individuals on both extremes of a phenotypic range survive or reproduce more successfully than do individuals with intermediate phenotypes.

**distal tubule** In the vertebrate kidney, the portion of a nephron that helps refine filtrate and empties it into a collecting duct.

**disturbance** A natural or human-caused event that changes a biological community and usually removes organisms from it. Disturbances, such as fires and storms, play a pivotal role in structuring many communities.

**disulfide bridge** A strong covalent bond formed when the sulfur of one cysteine monomer bonds to the sulfur of another cysteine monomer.

**DNA (deoxyribonucleic acid)** (dē-ok'-sē-rī'-bō-nū-klā'-ik) A nucleic acid molecule, usually a double-stranded helix, in which each polynucleotide strand consists of nucleotide monomers with a deoxyribose sugar and the nitrogenous bases adenine (A), cytosine (C), guanine (G), and thymine (T); capable of being replicated and determining the inherited structure of a cell's proteins.

**DNA cloning** The production of multiple copies of a specific DNA segment.

**DNA ligase** (lī'-gās) A linking enzyme essential for DNA replication; catalyzes the covalent bonding of the 3' end of one DNA fragment (such as an Okazaki fragment) to the 5' end of another DNA fragment (such as a growing DNA chain).

**DNA methylation** The presence of methyl groups on the DNA bases (usually cytosine) of plants, animals, and fungi. (The term also refers to the process of adding methyl groups to DNA bases.)

**DNA microarray assay** A method to detect and measure the expression of thousands of genes at one time. Tiny amounts of a large number of single-stranded DNA fragments representing different genes are fixed to a glass slide and tested for hybridization with samples of labeled cDNA.

**DNA polymerase** (puh-lim'-er-ās) An enzyme that catalyzes the elongation of new DNA (for example, at a replication fork) by the addition of nucleotides to the 3' end of an existing chain. There are several different DNA polymerases; DNA polymerase III and DNA polymerase I play major roles in DNA replication in *E. coli*.

**DNA replication** The process by which a DNA molecule is copied; also called DNA synthesis.

**DNA sequencing** Determining the complete nucleotide sequence of a gene or DNA segment.

**DNA technology** Techniques for sequencing and manipulating DNA.

**domain** (1) A taxonomic category above the kingdom level. The three domains are

Archaea, Bacteria, and Eukarya. (2) A discrete structural and functional region of a protein.

**dominant allele** An allele that is fully expressed in the phenotype of a heterozygote.

**dominant species** A species with substantially higher abundance or biomass than other species in a community. Dominant species exert a powerful control over the occurrence and distribution of other species.

**dopamine** A neurotransmitter that is a catecholamine, like epinephrine and norepinephrine.

**dormancy** A condition typified by extremely low metabolic rate and a suspension of growth and development.

**dorsal** Pertaining to the top of an animal with radial or bilateral symmetry.

**dorsal lip** The region above the blastopore on the dorsal side of the amphibian embryo.

**double bond** A double covalent bond; the sharing of two pairs of valence electrons by two atoms.

**double circulation** A circulatory system consisting of separate pulmonary and systemic circuits, in which blood passes through the heart after completing each circuit.

**double fertilization** A mechanism of fertilization in angiosperms in which two sperm cells unite with two cells in the female gametophyte (embryo sac) to form the zygote and endosperm.

**double helix** The form of native DNA, referring to its two adjacent antiparallel polynucleotide strands wound around an imaginary axis into a spiral shape.

**Down syndrome** A human genetic disease usually caused by the presence of an extra chromosome 21; characterized by developmental delays and heart and other defects that are generally treatable or non-life-threatening.

**Duchenne muscular dystrophy** (duh-shen′) A human genetic disease caused by a sex-linked recessive allele; characterized by progressive weakening and a loss of muscle tissue.

**duodenum** (dū′-uh-dēn′-um) The first section of the small intestine, where chyme from the stomach mixes with digestive juices from the pancreas, liver, and gallbladder as well as from gland cells of the intestinal wall.

**duplication** An aberration in chromosome structure due to fusion with a fragment from a homologous chromosome, such that a portion of a chromosome is duplicated.

**dynein** (dī′-nē-un) In cilia and flagella, a large motor protein extending from one microtubule doublet to the adjacent doublet. ATP hydrolysis drives changes in dynein shape that lead to bending of cilia and flagella.

**E site** One of a ribosome's three binding sites for tRNA during translation. The E site is the place where discharged tRNAs leave the ribosome. (E stands for exit.)

**Ecdysozoa** (ek′-dē-sō-zō′-uh) One of the three main lineages of bilaterian animals; many ecdysozoans are molting animals. *See also* Deuterostomia and Lophotrochozoa.

**echinoderm** (i-kī′-nō-derm) A slow-moving or sessile marine deuterostome with a water vascular system and, in larvae, bilateral symmetry. Echinoderms include sea stars, brittle stars, sea urchins, feather stars, and sea cucumbers.

**ecological footprint** The aggregate land and water area required by a person, city, or nation to produce all of the resources it consumes and to absorb all of the wastes it generates.

**ecological niche** (nich) The sum of a species' use of the biotic and abiotic resources in its environment.

**ecological species concept** Definition of a species in terms of ecological niche, the sum of how members of the species interact with the nonliving and living parts of their environment.

**ecological succession** Transition in the species composition of a community following a disturbance; establishment of a community in an area virtually barren of life.

**ecology** The study of how organisms interact with each other and their environment.

**ecosystem** All the organisms in a given area as well as the abiotic factors with which they interact; one or more communities and the physical environment around them.

**ecosystem ecology** The study of energy flow and the cycling of chemicals among the various biotic and abiotic components in an ecosystem.

**ecosystem engineer** An organism that influences community structure by causing physical changes in the environment.

**ecosystem service** A function performed by an ecosystem that directly or indirectly benefits humans.

**ecotone** The transition from one type of habitat or ecosystem to another, such as the transition from a forest to a grassland.

**ectoderm** (ek′-tō-durm) The outermost of the three primary germ layers in animal embryos; gives rise to the outer covering and, in some phyla, the nervous system, inner ear, and lens of the eye.

**ectomycorrhiza** (plural, **ectomycorrhizae**) (ek′-tō-mī′-kō-rī′-zuh, ek′-tō-mī′-kō-rī′-zē) Association of a fungus with a plant root system in which the fungus surrounds the roots but does not cause invagination of the host (plant) cell's plasma membrane.

**ectomycorrhizal fungus** A symbiotic fungus that forms sheaths of hyphae over the surface of plant roots and also grows into extracellular spaces of the root cortex.

**ectoparasite** A parasite that feeds on the external surface of a host.

**ectopic** Occurring in an abnormal location.

**ectoproct** A sessile, colonial lophophorate; also called a bryozoan.

**ectothermic** Referring to organisms for which external sources provide most of the heat for temperature regulation.

**Ediacaran biota** (ē′-dē-uh-keh′-run bī-ō′-tuh) An early group of macroscopic, soft-bodied, multicellular eukaryotes known from fossils that range in age from 635 million to 535 million years old.

**effective population size** An estimate of the size of a population based on the numbers of females and males that successfully breed; generally smaller than the total population.

**effector** Pathogen-encoded protein that cripples the host's innate immune system.

**effector cell** (1) A muscle cell or gland cell that carries out the body's response to stimuli as directed by signals from the brain or other processing center of the nervous system. (2) A lymphocyte that has undergone clonal selection and is capable of mediating an adaptive immune response.

**egg** The female gamete.

**egg-polarity gene** A gene that helps control the orientation (polarity) of the egg; also called a maternal effect gene.

**ejaculation** The propulsion of sperm from the epididymis through the muscular vas deferens, ejaculatory duct, and urethra.

**electrocardiogram (ECG or EKG)** A record of the electrical impulses that travel through heart muscle during the cardiac cycle.

**electrochemical gradient** The diffusion gradient of an ion, which is affected by both the concentration difference of an ion across a membrane (a chemical force) and the ion's tendency to move relative to the membrane potential (an electrical force).

**electrogenic pump** An active transport protein that generates voltage across a membrane while pumping ions.

**electromagnetic receptor** A receptor of electromagnetic energy, such as visible light, electricity, or magnetism.

**electromagnetic spectrum** The entire spectrum of electromagnetic radiation, ranging in wavelength from less than a nanometer to more than a kilometer.

**electron** A subatomic particle with a single negative electrical charge and a mass about 1/2,000 that of a neutron or proton. One or more electrons move around the nucleus of an atom.

**electron microscope (EM)** A microscope that uses magnets to focus an electron beam on or through a specimen, resulting in a practical resolution that is 100-fold greater than that of a light microscope using standard techniques. A transmission electron microscope (TEM) is used to study the internal structure of thin sections of cells. A scanning electron microscope (SEM) is used to study the fine details of cell surfaces.

**electron shell** An energy level of electrons at a characteristic average distance from the nucleus of an atom.

**electron transport chain** A sequence of electron carrier molecules (membrane proteins) that shuttle electrons down a series of redox reactions that release energy used to make ATP.

**electronegativity** The attraction of a given atom for the electrons of a covalent bond.

**electroporation** A technique to introduce recombinant DNA into cells by applying a brief electrical pulse to a solution containing the cells. The pulse creates temporary holes in the cells' plasma membranes, through which DNA can enter.

**element** Any substance that cannot be broken down to any other substance by chemical reactions.

**elimination** The fourth and final stage of food processing in animals: the passing of undigested material out of the body.

**embryo sac** (em'-brē-ō) The female gametophyte of angiosperms, formed from the growth and division of the megaspore into a multicellular structure that typically has eight haploid nuclei.

**embryonic lethal** A mutation with a phenotype leading to death of an embryo or larva.

**embryophyte** Alternate name for land plants that refers to their shared derived trait of multicellular, dependent embryos.

**emergent properties** New properties that arise with each step upward in the hierarchy of life, owing to the arrangement and interactions of parts as complexity increases.

**emigration** The movement of individuals out of a population.

**enantiomer** (en-an'-tē-ō-mer) One of two compounds that are mirror images of each other and that differ in shape due to the presence of an asymmetric carbon.

**endangered species** A species that is in danger of extinction throughout all or a significant portion of its range.

**endemic** (en-dem'-ik) Referring to a species that is confined to a specific geographic area.

**endergonic reaction** (en'-der-gon'-ik) A nonspontaneous chemical reaction in which free energy is absorbed from the surroundings.

**endocrine gland** (en'-dō-krin) A ductless gland that secretes hormones directly into the interstitial fluid, from which they diffuse into the bloodstream.

**endocrine system** (en'-dō-krin) In animals, the internal system of communication involving hormones, the ductless glands that secrete hormones, and the molecular receptors on or in target cells that respond to hormones; functions in concert with the nervous system to effect internal regulation and maintain homeostasis.

**endocytosis** (en'-dō-sī-tō'-sis) Cellular uptake of biological molecules and particulate matter via formation of vesicles from the plasma membrane.

**endoderm** (en'-dō-durm) The innermost of the three primary germ layers in animal embryos; lines the archenteron and gives rise to the liver, pancreas, lungs, and the lining of the digestive tract in species that have these structures.

**endodermis** In plant roots, the innermost layer of the cortex that surrounds the vascular cylinder.

**endomembrane system** The collection of membranes inside and surrounding a eukaryotic cell, related either through direct physical contact or by the transfer of membranous vesicles; includes the plasma membrane, the nuclear envelope, the smooth and rough endoplasmic reticulum, the Golgi apparatus, lysosomes, vesicles, and vacuoles.

**endometriosis** (en'-dō-mē-trē-ō'-sis) The condition resulting from the presence of endometrial tissue outside of the uterus.

**endometrium** (en'-dō-mē'-trē-um) The inner lining of the uterus, which is richly supplied with blood vessels.

**endoparasite** A parasite that lives within a host.

**endophyte** A harmless fungus, or occasionally another organism, that lives between cells of a plant part or multicellular alga.

**endoplasmic reticulum (ER)** (en'-dō-plaz'-mik ruh-tik'-yū-lum) An extensive membranous network in eukaryotic cells, continuous with the outer nuclear membrane and composed of ribosome-studded (rough) and ribosome-free (smooth) regions.

**endorphin** (en-dōr'-fin) Any of several hormones produced in the brain and anterior pituitary that inhibit pain perception.

**endoskeleton** A hard skeleton buried within the soft tissues of an animal.

**endosperm** In angiosperms, a nutrient-rich tissue formed by the union of a sperm with two polar nuclei during double fertilization. The endosperm provides nourishment to the developing embryo in angiosperm seeds.

**endospore** A thick-coated, resistant cell produced by some bacterial cells when they are exposed to harsh conditions.

**endosymbiont theory** The theory that mitochondria and plastids, including chloroplasts, originated as prokaryotic cells engulfed by a host cell. The engulfed cell and its host cell then evolved into a single organism. *See also* endosymbiosis.

**endosymbiosis** A relationship between two species in which one organism lives inside the cell or cells of another organism. *See also* endosymbiont theory.

**endothelium** (en'-dō-thē'-lē-um) The simple squamous layer of cells lining the lumen of blood vessels.

**endothermic** Referring to organisms that are warmed by heat generated by their own metabolism. This heat usually maintains a relatively stable body temperature higher than that of the external environment.

**endotoxin** A toxic component of the outer membrane of certain gram-negative bacteria that is released only when the bacteria die.

**energetic hypothesis** The concept that the length of a food chain is limited by the inefficiency of energy transfer along the chain.

**energy** The capacity to cause change, especially to do work (to move matter against an opposing force).

**energy coupling** In cellular metabolism, the use of energy released from an exergonic reaction to drive an endergonic reaction.

**enhancer** A segment of eukaryotic DNA containing multiple control elements, usually located far from the gene whose transcription it regulates.

**enteric division** One of three divisions of the autonomic nervous system; consists of networks of neurons in the digestive tract, pancreas, and gallbladder; normally regulated by the sympathetic and parasympathetic divisions of the autonomic nervous system.

**entropy** A measure of disorder, or randomness.

**enzyme** (en'-zīm) A macromolecule serving as a catalyst, a chemical agent that increases the rate of a reaction without being consumed by the reaction. Most enzymes are proteins.

**enzyme-substrate complex** (en'-zīm) A temporary complex formed when an enzyme binds to its substrate molecule(s).

**epicotyl** (ep'-uh-kot'-ul) In an angiosperm embryo, the embryonic axis above the point of attachment of the cotyledon(s) and below the first pair of miniature leaves.

**epidemic** A widespread outbreak of a disease.

**epidermis** (1) The dermal tissue system of nonwoody plants, usually consisting of a single layer of tightly packed cells. (2) The outermost layer of cells in an animal.

**epididymis** (ep'-uh-did'-uh-mus) A coiled tubule located adjacent to the mammalian testis where sperm are stored.

**epigenetic inheritance** Inheritance of traits transmitted by mechanisms that do not involve the nucleotide sequence.

**epinephrine** (ep'-i-nef'-rin) A catecholamine that, when secreted as a hormone by the adrenal medulla, mediates "fight-or-flight" responses to short-term stresses; also released by some neurons as a neurotransmitter; also called adrenaline.

**epiphyte** (ep'-uh-fīt) A plant that nourishes itself but grows on the surface of another plant for support, usually on the branches or trunks of trees.

**epistasis** (ep'-i-stā'-sis) A type of gene interaction in which the phenotypic expression of one gene alters that of another independently inherited gene.

**epithelial tissue** (ep'-uh-thē'-lē-ul) Sheets of tightly packed cells that line organs and body cavities as well as external surfaces.

**epithelium** An epithelial tissue.

**epitope** A small, accessible region of an antigen to which an antigen receptor or antibody binds.

**equilibrium potential** ($E_{ion}$) The magnitude of a cell's membrane voltage at equilibrium; calculated using the Nernst equation.

**erythrocyte** (eh-rith'-ruh-sīt) A blood cell that contains hemoglobin, which transports oxygen; also called a red blood cell.

**erythropoietin (EPO)** (eh-rith'-rō-poy'-uh-tin) A hormone that stimulates the production of erythrocytes. It is secreted by the kidney when body tissues do not receive enough oxygen.

**esophagus** (eh-sof'-uh-gus) A muscular tube that conducts food, by peristalsis, from the pharynx to the stomach.

**essential amino acid** An amino acid that an animal cannot synthesize itself and must be obtained from food in prefabricated form.

**essential element** A chemical element required for an organism to survive, grow, and reproduce.

**essential fatty acid** An unsaturated fatty acid that an animal needs but cannot make.

**essential nutrient** A substance that an organism cannot synthesize from any other material and therefore must absorb in preassembled form.

**estradiol** (es'-truh-dī'-ol) A steroid hormone that stimulates the development and maintenance of the female reproductive system and secondary sex characteristics; the major estrogen in mammals.

**estrogen** (es′-trō-jen) Any steroid hormone, such as estradiol, that stimulates the development and maintenance of the female reproductive system and secondary sex characteristics.

**estrous cycle** (es′-trus) A reproductive cycle characteristic of female mammals except humans and certain other primates, in which the nonpregnant endometrium is reabsorbed rather than shed, and sexual response occurs only during mid-cycle at estrus.

**estuary** The area where a freshwater stream or river merges with the ocean.

**ethylene** (eth′-uh-lēn) A gaseous plant hormone involved in responses to mechanical stress, programmed cell death, leaf abscission, and fruit ripening.

**etiolation** Plant morphological adaptations for growing in darkness.

**euchromatin** (yū-krō′-muh-tin) The less condensed form of eukaryotic chromatin that is available for transcription.

**eudicot** (yū-dī′-kot) A member of a clade that contains the vast majority of flowering plants that have two embryonic seed leaves, or cotyledons.

**euglenid** (yū′-glen-id) A protist, such as *Euglena* or its relatives, characterized by an anterior pocket from which one or two flagella emerge.

**euglenozoan** A member of a diverse clade of flagellated protists that includes predatory heterotrophs, photosynthetic autotrophs, and pathogenic parasites.

**Eukarya** (yū-kar′-ē-uh) The domain that includes all eukaryotic organisms.

**eukaryotic cell** (yū′-ker-ē-ot′-ik) A type of cell with a membrane-enclosed nucleus and membrane-enclosed organelles. Organisms with eukaryotic cells (protists, plants, fungi, and animals) are called eukaryotes.

**eumetazoan** (yū′-met-uh-zō′-un) A member of a clade of animals with true tissues. All animals except sponges and a few other groups are eumetazoans.

**eurypterid** (yur-ip′-tuh-rid) An extinct carnivorous chelicerate; also called a water scorpion.

**Eustachian tube** (yū-stā′-shun) The tube that connects the middle ear to the pharynx.

**eutherian** (yū-thēr′-ē-un) Placental mammal; mammal whose young complete their embryonic development within the uterus, joined to the mother by the placenta.

**eutrophic lake** (yū-trōf′-ik) A lake that has a high rate of biological productivity supported by a high rate of nutrient cycling.

**eutrophication** A process by which nutrients, particularly phosphorus and nitrogen, become highly concentrated in a body of water, leading to increased growth of organisms such as algae or cyanobacteria.

**evaporative cooling** The process in which the surface of an object becomes cooler during evaporation, a result of the molecules with the greatest kinetic energy changing from the liquid to the gaseous state.

**evapotranspiration** The total evaporation of water from an ecosystem, including water transpired by plants and evaporated from a landscape, usually measured in millimeters and estimated for a year.

**evo-devo** Evolutionary developmental biology; a field of biology that compares developmental processes of different multicellular organisms to understand how these processes have evolved and how changes can modify existing organismal features or lead to new ones.

**evolution** Descent with modification; the idea that living species are descendants of ancestral species that were different from the present-day ones; also defined more narrowly as the change in the genetic composition of a population from generation to generation.

**evolutionary tree** A branching diagram that reflects a hypothesis about evolutionary relationships among groups of organisms.

**Excavata** (ex′-kuh-vah′-tuh) One of four supergroups of eukaryotes proposed in a current hypothesis of the evolutionary history of eukaryotes. Excavates have unique cytoskeletal features, and some species have an "excavated" feeding groove on one side of the cell body. *See also* "SAR" clade, Archaeplastida, and Unikonta.

**excitatory postsynaptic potential (EPSP)** An electrical change (depolarization) in the membrane of a postsynaptic cell caused by the binding of an excitatory neurotransmitter from a presynaptic cell to a postsynaptic receptor; makes it more likely for a postsynaptic cell to generate an action potential.

**excretion** The disposal of nitrogen-containing metabolites and other waste products.

**exergonic reaction** (ek′-ser-gon′-ik) A spontaneous chemical reaction in which there is a net release of free energy.

**exocytosis** (ek′-sō-sī-tō′-sis) The cellular secretion of biological molecules by the fusion of vesicles containing them with the plasma membrane.

**exon** A sequence within a primary transcript that remains in the RNA after RNA processing; also refers to the region of DNA from which this sequence was transcribed.

**exoskeleton** A hard encasement on the surface of an animal, such as the shell of a mollusc or the cuticle of an arthropod, that provides protection and points of attachment for muscles.

**exotoxin** (ek′-sō-tok′-sin) A toxic protein that is secreted by a prokaryote or other pathogen and that produces specific symptoms, even if the pathogen is no longer present.

**expansin** Plant enzyme that breaks the cross-links (hydrogen bonds) between cellulose microfibrils and other cell wall constituents, loosening the wall's fabric.

**experiment** A scientific test, carried out under controlled conditions, involving manipulation of one or more factors in a system in order to see the effects of those changes.

**experimental group** A set of subjects that has (or receives) the specific factor being tested in a controlled experiment.

**exponential population growth** Growth of a population in an ideal, unlimited environment, represented by a J-shaped curve when population size is plotted over time.

**expression vector** A cloning vector that contains a highly active bacterial promoter just upstream of a restriction site where a eukaryotic gene can be inserted, allowing the gene to be expressed in a bacterial cell. Expression vectors are also available that have been genetically engineered for use in specific types of eukaryotic cells.

**extinction vortex** A downward population spiral in which inbreeding and genetic drift combine to cause a small population to shrink and, unless the spiral is reversed, become extinct.

**extracellular matrix (ECM)** The meshwork surrounding animal cells, consisting of glycoproteins, polysaccharides, and proteoglycans synthesized and secreted by cells.

**extraembryonic membrane** One of four membranes (yolk sac, amnion, chorion, and allantois) located outside the embryo that support the developing embryo in reptiles and mammals.

**extreme halophile** An organism that lives in a highly saline environment, such as the Great Salt Lake or the Dead Sea.

**extreme thermophile** An organism that thrives in hot environments (often 60–80°C or hotter).

**extremophile** An organism that lives in environmental conditions so extreme that few other species can survive there. Extremophiles include extreme halophiles ("salt lovers") and extreme thermophiles ("heat lovers").

**$F_1$ generation** The first filial, hybrid (heterozygous) offspring arising from a parental (P generation) cross.

**$F_2$ generation** The offspring resulting from interbreeding (or self-pollination) of the hybrid $F_1$ generation.

**facilitated diffusion** The passage of molecules or ions down their electrochemical gradient across a biological membrane with the assistance of specific transmembrane transport proteins, requiring no energy expenditure.

**facilitation** An interaction in which one species has a positive effect on the survival and reproduction of another species without the intimate association of a symbiosis.

**facultative anaerobe** (fak′-ul-tā′-tiv an′-uh-rōb) An organism that makes ATP by aerobic respiration if oxygen is present but that switches to anaerobic respiration or fermentation if oxygen is not present.

**family** In Linnaean classification, the taxonomic category above genus.

**fast block to polyspermy** The depolarization of the egg plasma membrane that begins within 1–3 seconds after a sperm binds to an egg membrane protein. The depolarization lasts about 1 minute and prevents additional sperm from fusing with the egg during that time.

**fast-twitch fiber** A muscle fiber used for rapid, powerful contractions.

**fat** A lipid consisting of three fatty acids linked to one glycerol molecule; also called a triacylglycerol or triglyceride.

**fate map** A territorial diagram of embryonic development that displays the future derivatives of individual cells and tissues.

**fatty acid** A carboxylic acid with a long carbon chain. Fatty acids vary in length and in the number and location of double bonds; three fatty acids linked to a glycerol molecule form a fat molecule, also called triacylglycerol or triglyceride.

**feces** (fē'-sēz) The wastes of the digestive tract.

**feedback inhibition** A method of metabolic control in which the end product of a metabolic pathway acts as an inhibitor of an enzyme within that pathway.

**feedback regulation** The regulation of a process by its output or end product.

**fermentation** A catabolic process that makes a limited amount of ATP from glucose (or other organic molecules) without an electron transport chain and that produces a characteristic end product, such as ethyl alcohol or lactic acid.

**fertilization** (1) The union of haploid gametes to produce a diploid zygote. (2) The addition of mineral nutrients to the soil.

**fetus** (fē'-tus) A developing mammal that has all the major structures of an adult. In humans, the fetal stage lasts from the 9th week of gestation until birth.

**F factor** In bacteria, the DNA segment that confers the ability to form pili for conjugation and associated functions required for the transfer of DNA from donor to recipient. The F factor may exist as a plasmid or be integrated into the bacterial chromosome.

**fiber** A lignified cell type that reinforces the xylem of angiosperms and functions in mechanical support; a slender, tapered sclerenchyma cell that usually occurs in bundles.

**fibroblast** (fī'-brō-blast) A type of cell in loose connective tissue that secretes the protein ingredients of the extracellular fibers.

**fibronectin** An extracellular glycoprotein secreted by animal cells that helps them attach to the extracellular matrix.

**filament** In an angiosperm, the stalk portion of the stamen, the pollen-producing reproductive organ of a flower.

**filter feeder** An animal that feeds by using a filtration mechanism to strain small organisms or food particles from its surroundings.

**filtrate** Cell-free fluid extracted from the body fluid by the excretory system.

**filtration** In excretory systems, the extraction of water and small solutes, including metabolic wastes, from the body fluid.

**fimbria** (plural, **fimbriae**) A short, hairlike appendage of a prokaryotic cell that helps it adhere to the substrate or to other cells.

**first law of thermodynamics** The principle of conservation of energy: Energy can be transferred and transformed, but it cannot be created or destroyed.

**fission** The separation of an organism into two or more individuals of approximately equal size.

**fixed action pattern** In animal behavior, a sequence of unlearned acts that is essentially unchangeable and, once initiated, usually carried to completion.

**flaccid** (flas'-id) Limp. Lacking turgor (stiffness or firmness), as in a plant cell in surroundings where there is a tendency for water to leave the cell. (A walled cell becomes flaccid if it has a higher water potential than its surroundings, resulting in the loss of water.)

**flagellum** (fluh-jel'-um) (plural, **flagella**) A long cellular appendage specialized for locomotion. Like motile cilia, eukaryotic flagella have a core with nine outer doublet microtubules and two inner single microtubules (the "9 + 2" arrangement) ensheathed in an extension of the plasma membrane. Prokaryotic flagella have a different structure.

**florigen** A flowering signal, probably a protein, that is made in leaves under certain conditions and that travels to the shoot apical meristems, inducing them to switch from vegetative to reproductive growth.

**flower** In an angiosperm, a specialized shoot with up to four sets of modified leaves, bearing structures that function in sexual reproduction.

**fluid feeder** An animal that lives by sucking nutrient-rich fluids from another living organism.

**fluid mosaic model** The currently accepted model of cell membrane structure, which envisions the membrane as a mosaic of protein molecules drifting laterally in a fluid bilayer of phospholipids.

**follicle** (fol'-uh-kul) A microscopic structure in the ovary that contains the developing oocyte and secretes estrogens.

**follicle-stimulating hormone (FSH)** (fol'-uh-kul) A tropic hormone that is produced and secreted by the anterior pituitary and that stimulates the production of eggs by the ovaries and sperm by the testes.

**food chain** The pathway along which food energy is transferred from trophic level to trophic level, beginning with producers.

**food vacuole** A membranous sac formed by phagocytosis of microorganisms or particles to be used as food by the cell.

**food web** The interconnected feeding relationships in an ecosystem.

**foot** (1) The portion of a bryophyte sporophyte that gathers sugars, amino acids, water, and minerals from the parent gametophyte via transfer cells. (2) One of the three main parts of a mollusc; a muscular structure usually used for movement. *See also* mantle and visceral mass.

**foraging** The seeking and obtaining of food.

**foram (foraminiferan)** An aquatic protist that secretes a hardened shell containing calcium carbonate and extends pseudopodia through pores in the shell.

**forebrain** One of three ancestral and embryonic regions of the vertebrate brain; develops into the thalamus, hypothalamus, and cerebrum.

**fossil** A preserved remnant or impression of an organism that lived in the past.

**founder effect** Genetic drift that occurs when a few individuals become isolated from a larger population and form a new population whose gene pool composition is not reflective of that of the original population.

**fovea** (fō'-vē-uh) The place on the retina at the eye's center of focus, where cones are highly concentrated.

**F plasmid** The plasmid form of the F factor.

**fragmentation** A means of asexual reproduction whereby a single parent breaks into parts that regenerate into whole new individuals.

**frameshift mutation** A mutation occurring when nucleotides are inserted in or deleted from a gene and the number inserted or deleted is not a multiple of three, resulting in the improper grouping of the subsequent nucleotides into codons.

**free energy** The portion of a biological system's energy that can perform work when temperature and pressure are uniform throughout the system. The change in free energy of a system ($\Delta G$) is calculated by the equation $\Delta G = \Delta H - T\Delta S$, where $\Delta H$ is the change in enthalpy (in biological systems, equivalent to total energy), $\Delta T$ is the absolute temperature, and $\Delta S$ is the change in entropy.

**frequency-dependent selection** Selection in which the fitness of a phenotype depends on how common the phenotype is in a population.

**fruit** A mature ovary of a flower. The fruit protects dormant seeds and often functions in their dispersal.

**functional group** A specific configuration of atoms commonly attached to the carbon skeletons of organic molecules and involved in chemical reactions.

**G₀ phase** A nondividing state occupied by cells that have left the cell cycle, sometimes reversibly.

**G₁ phase** The first gap, or growth phase, of the cell cycle, consisting of the portion of interphase before DNA synthesis begins.

**G₂ phase** The second gap, or growth phase, of the cell cycle, consisting of the portion of interphase after DNA synthesis occurs.

**gallbladder** An organ that stores bile and releases it as needed into the small intestine.

**game theory** An approach to evaluating alternative strategies in situations where the outcome of a particular strategy depends on the strategies used by other individuals.

**gametangium** (gam'-uh-tan'-jē-um) (plural, **gametangia**) Multicellular plant structure in which gametes are formed. Female gametangia are called archegonia, and male gametangia are called antheridia.

**gamete** (gam'-ēt) A haploid reproductive cell, such as an egg or sperm. Gametes unite during sexual reproduction to produce a diploid zygote.

**gametogenesis** (guh-mē'-tō-gen'-uh-sis) The process by which gametes are produced.

**gametophore** (guh-mē'-tō-fōr) The mature gamete-producing structure of a moss gametophyte.

**gametophyte** (guh-mē'-tō-fīt) In organisms (plants and some algae) that have alternation of generations, the multicellular haploid form that produces haploid gametes by mitosis. The haploid gametes unite and develop into sporophytes.

**gamma-aminobutyric acid (GABA)** An amino acid that functions as a CNS neurotransmitter in the central nervous system of vertebrates.

**ganglion** (gang'-glē-uhn) (plural, **ganglia**) A cluster (functional group) of nerve cell bodies in a centralized nervous system.

**gap junction** A type of intercellular junction in animal cells, consisting of proteins surrounding a pore that allows the passage of materials between cells.

**gas exchange** The uptake of molecular oxygen from the environment and the discharge of carbon dioxide to the environment.

**gastric juice** A digestive fluid secreted by the stomach.

**gastrovascular cavity** A central cavity with a single opening in the body of certain animals, including cnidarians and flatworms, that functions in both the digestion and distribution of nutrients.

**gastrula** (gas'-trū-luh) An embryonic stage in animal development encompassing the formation of three layers: ectoderm, mesoderm, and endoderm.

**gastrulation** (gas'-trū-lā'-shun) In animal development, a series of cell and tissue movements in which the blastula-stage embryo folds inward, producing a three-layered embryo, the gastrula.

**gated channel** A transmembrane protein channel that opens or closes in response to a particular stimulus.

**gated ion channel** A gated channel for a specific ion. The opening or closing of such channels may alter a cell's membrane potential.

**gel electrophoresis** (ē-lek'-trō-fōr-ē'-sis) A technique for separating nucleic acids or proteins on the basis of their size and electrical charge, both of which affect their rate of movement through an electric field in a gel made of agarose or another polymer.

**gene** A discrete unit of hereditary information consisting of a specific nucleotide sequence in DNA (or RNA, in some viruses).

**gene annotation** Analysis of genomic sequences to identify protein-coding genes and determine the function of their products.

**gene cloning** The production of multiple copies of a gene.

**gene expression** The process by which information encoded in DNA directs the synthesis of proteins or, in some cases, RNAs that are not translated into proteins and instead function as RNAs.

**gene flow** The transfer of alleles from one population to another, resulting from the movement of fertile individuals or their gametes.

**gene pool** The aggregate of all copies of every type of allele at all loci in every individual in a population. The term is also used in a more restricted sense as the aggregate of alleles for just one or a few loci in a population.

**gene therapy** The introduction of genes into an afflicted individual for therapeutic purposes.

**genetic drift** A process in which chance events cause unpredictable fluctuations in allele frequencies from one generation to the next. Effects of genetic drift are most pronounced in small populations.

**genetic engineering** The direct manipulation of genes for practical purposes.

**genetic map** An ordered list of genetic loci (genes or other genetic markers) along a chromosome.

**genetic profile** An individual's unique set of genetic markers, detected most often today by PCR or, previously, by electrophoresis and nucleic acid probes.

**genetic recombination** General term for the production of offspring with combinations of traits that differ from those found in either parent.

**genetic variation** Differences among individuals in the composition of their genes or other DNA segments.

**genetically modified (GM) organism** An organism that has acquired one or more genes by artificial means; also called a transgenic organism.

**genetics** The scientific study of heredity and hereditary variation.

**genome** (jē'-nōm) The genetic material of an organism or virus; the complete complement of an organism's or virus's genes along with its noncoding nucleic acid sequences.

**genome-wide association study** (jē'-nōm) A large-scale analysis of the genomes of many people having a certain phenotype or disease, with the aim of finding genetic markers that correlate with that phenotype or disease.

**genomic imprinting** (juh-nō'-mik) A phenomenon in which expression of an allele in offspring depends on whether the allele is inherited from the male or female parent.

**genomics** (juh-nō'-miks) The systematic study of whole sets of genes (or other DNA) and their interactions within a species, as well as genome comparisons between species.

**genotype** (jē'-nō-tīp) The genetic makeup, or set of alleles, of an organism.

**genus** (jē'-nus) (plural, **genera**) A taxonomic category above the species level, designated by the first word of a species' two-part scientific name.

**geologic record** A standard time scale dividing Earth's history into time periods, grouped into four eons—Hadean, Archaean, Proterozoic, and Phanerozoic—and further subdivided into eras, periods, and epochs.

**germ layer** One of the three main layers in a gastrula that will form the various tissues and organs of an animal body.

**gestation** (jes-tā'-shun) See pregnancy.

**gibberellin** (jib'-uh-rel'-in) Any of a class of related plant hormones that stimulate growth in the stem and leaves, trigger the germination of seeds and breaking of bud dormancy, and (with auxin) stimulate fruit development.

**glans** The rounded structure at the tip of the clitoris or penis that is involved in sexual arousal.

**glia (glial cells)** Cells of the nervous system that support, regulate, and augment the functions of neurons.

**global ecology** The study of the functioning and distribution of organisms across the biosphere and how the regional exchange of energy and materials affects them.

**glomeromycete** (glō'-mer-ō-mī'-sēt) A member of the fungal phylum Glomeromycota, characterized by a distinct branching form of mycorrhizae called arbuscular mycorrhizae.

**glomerulus** (glō-măr'-yū-lus) A ball of capillaries surrounded by Bowman's capsule in the nephron and serving as the site of filtration in the vertebrate kidney.

**glucocorticoid** A steroid hormone that is secreted by the adrenal cortex and that influences glucose metabolism and immune function.

**glucagon** (glū'-kuh-gon) A hormone secreted by pancreatic alpha cells that raises blood glucose levels. It promotes glycogen breakdown and release of glucose by the liver.

**glutamate** An amino acid that functions as a neurotransmitter in the central nervous system.

**glyceraldehyde 3-phosphate (G3P)** (glis'-er-al'-de-hīd) A three-carbon carbohydrate that is the direct product of the Calvin cycle; it is also an intermediate in glycolysis.

**glycogen** (glī'-kō-jen) An extensively branched glucose storage polysaccharide found in the liver and muscle of animals; the animal equivalent of starch.

**glycolipid** A lipid with one or more covalently attached carbohydrates.

**glycolysis** (glī-kol'-uh-sis) A series of reactions that ultimately splits glucose into pyruvate. Glycolysis occurs in almost all living cells, serving as the starting point for fermentation or cellular respiration.

**glycoprotein** A protein with one or more covalently attached carbohydrates.

**glycosidic linkage** A covalent bond formed between two monosaccharides by a dehydration reaction.

**gnathostome** (na'-thu-stōm) A member of the vertebrate subgroup possessing jaws. The gnathostomes include sharks and rays, ray-finned fishes, coelacanths, lungfishes, amphibians, reptiles, and mammals.

**golden alga** A biflagellated, photosynthetic protist named for its color, which results from its yellow and brown carotenoids.

**Golgi apparatus** (gol'-jē) An organelle in eukaryotic cells consisting of stacks of flat membranous sacs that modify, store, and route products of the endoplasmic reticulum and synthesize some products, notably noncellulose carbohydrates.

**gonad** (gō'-nad) A male or female gamete-producing organ.

**G protein** A GTP-binding protein that relays signals from a plasma membrane signal receptor, known as a G protein-coupled receptor, to other signal transduction proteins inside the cell.

**G protein-coupled receptor (GPCR)** A signal receptor protein in the plasma membrane that responds to the binding of a signaling molecule by activating a G protein. Also called a G protein-linked receptor.

**graded potential** In a neuron, a shift in the membrane potential that has an amplitude proportional to signal strength and that decays as it spreads.

**Gram stain** A staining method that distinguishes between two different kinds of bacterial cell walls; may be used to help determine medical response to an infection.

**gram-negative** Describing the group of bacteria that have a cell wall that is structurally more complex and contains less peptidoglycan than the cell wall of gram-positive bacteria. Gram-negative bacteria are often more toxic than gram-positive bacteria.

**gram-positive** Describing the group of bacteria that have a cell wall that is structurally less complex and contains more peptidoglycan than the cell wall of gram-negative bacteria. Gram-positive bacteria are usually less toxic than gram-negative bacteria.

**granum** (gran'-um) (plural, **grana**) A stack of membrane-bounded thylakoids in the chloroplast. Grana function in the light reactions of photosynthesis.

**gravitropism** (grav'-uh-trō'-pizm) A response of a plant or animal to gravity.

**gray matter** Regions of clustered neuron cell bodies within the CNS.

**green alga** A photosynthetic protist, named for green chloroplasts that are similar in structure and pigment composition to the chloroplasts of land plants. Green algae are a paraphyletic group; some members are more closely related to land plants than they are to other green algae.

**greenhouse effect** The warming of Earth due to the atmospheric accumulation of carbon dioxide and certain other gases, which absorb reflected infrared radiation and reradiate some of it back toward Earth.

**gross primary production (GPP)** The total primary production of an ecosystem.

**ground tissue system** Plant tissues that are neither vascular nor dermal, fulfilling a variety of functions, such as storage, photosynthesis, and support.

**growth factor** (1) A protein that must be present in the extracellular environment (culture medium or animal body) for the growth and normal development of certain types of cells. (2) A local regulator that acts on nearby cells to stimulate cell proliferation and differentiation.

**growth hormone (GH)** A hormone that is produced and secreted by the anterior pituitary and that has both direct (nontropic) and tropic effects on a wide variety of tissues.

**guard cells** The two cells that flank the stomatal pore and regulate the opening and closing of the pore.

**gustation** The sense of taste.

**guttation** The exudation of water droplets from leaves, caused by root pressure in certain plants.

**gymnosperm** (jim'-nō-sperm) A vascular plant that bears naked seeds—seeds not enclosed in protective chambers.

**hair cell** A mechanosensory cell that alters output to the nervous system when hairlike projections on the cell surface are displaced.

**half-life** The amount of time it takes for 50% of a sample of a radioactive isotope to decay.

**halophile** See extreme halophile.

**Hamilton's rule** The principle that for natural selection to favor an altruistic act, the benefit to the recipient, devalued by the coefficient of relatedness, must exceed the cost to the altruist.

**haploid cell** (hap'-loyd) A cell containing only one set of chromosomes ($n$).

**Hardy-Weinberg equilibrium** The state of a population in which frequencies of alleles and genotypes remain constant from generation to generation, provided that only Mendelian segregation and recombination of alleles are at work.

**haustorium** (plural, **haustoria**) (ho-stŏr'-ē-um, ho-stŏr'-ē-uh) In certain symbiotic fungi, a specialized hypha that can penetrate the tissues of host organisms.

**heart** A muscular pump that uses metabolic energy to elevate the hydrostatic pressure of the circulatory fluid (blood or hemolymph). The fluid then flows down a pressure gradient through the body and eventually returns to the heart.

**heart attack** The damage or death of cardiac muscle tissue resulting from prolonged blockage of one or more coronary arteries.

**heart murmur** A hissing sound that most often results from blood squirting backward through a leaky valve in the heart.

**heart rate** The frequency of heart contraction (in beats per minute).

**heat** Thermal energy in transfer from one body of matter to another.

**heat of vaporization** The quantity of heat a liquid must absorb for 1 g of it to be converted from the liquid to the gaseous state.

**heat-shock protein** A protein that helps protect other proteins during heat stress. Heat-shock proteins are found in plants, animals, and microorganisms.

**heavy chain** One of the two types of polypeptide chains that make up an antibody molecule and B cell receptor; consists of a variable region, which contributes to the antigen-binding site, and a constant region.

**helicase** An enzyme that untwists the double helix of DNA at replication forks, separating the two strands and making them available as template strands.

**helper T cell** A type of T cell that, when activated, secretes cytokines that promote the response of B cells (humoral response) and cytotoxic T cells (cell-mediated response) to antigens.

**hemoglobin** (hē'-mō-glō'-bin) An iron-containing protein in red blood cells that reversibly binds oxygen.

**hemolymph** (hē'-mō-limf') In invertebrates with an open circulatory system, the body fluid that bathes tissues.

**hemophilia** (hē'-muh-fil'-ē-uh) A human genetic disease caused by a sex-linked recessive allele resulting in the absence of one or more blood-clotting proteins; characterized by excessive bleeding following injury.

**hepatic portal vein** A large vessel that conveys nutrient-laden blood from the small intestine to the liver, which regulates the blood's nutrient content.

**herbivore** (hur'-bi-vōr') An animal that mainly eats plants or algae.

**herbivory** An interaction in which an organism eats part of a plant or alga.

**heredity** The transmission of traits from one generation to the next.

**hermaphrodite** (hur-maf'-ruh-dīt') An individual that functions as both male and female in sexual reproduction by producing both sperm and eggs.

**hermaphroditism** (hur-maf'-rō-dī-tizm) A condition in which an individual has both female and male gonads and functions as both a male and a female in sexual reproduction by producing both sperm and eggs.

**heterochromatin** (het'-er-ō-krō'-muh-tin) Eukaryotic chromatin that remains highly compacted during interphase and is generally not transcribed.

**heterochrony** (het'-uh-rok'-ruh-nē) Evolutionary change in the timing or rate of an organism's development.

**heterocyst** (het'-er-ō-sist) A specialized cell that engages in nitrogen fixation in some filamentous cyanobacteria; also called a heterocyte.

**heterokaryon** (het'-er-ō-kār'-ē-un) A fungal mycelium that contains two or more haploid nuclei per cell.

**heteromorphic** (het'-er-ō-mōr'-fik) Referring to a condition in the life cycle of plants and certain algae in which the sporophyte and gametophyte generations differ in morphology.

**heterosporous** (het-er-os'-pōr-us) Referring to a plant species that has two kinds of spores: microspores, which develop into male gametophytes, and megaspores, which develop into female gametophytes.

**heterotroph** (het'-er-ō-trōf) An organism that obtains organic food molecules by eating other organisms or substances derived from them.

**heterozygote advantage** Greater reproductive success of heterozygous individuals compared with homozygotes; tends to preserve variation in a gene pool.

**heterozygous** (het'-er-ō-zī'-gus) Having two different alleles for a given gene.

**hibernation** A long-term physiological state in which metabolism decreases, the heart and respiratory system slow down, and body temperature is maintained at a lower level than normal.

**high-density lipoprotein (HDL)** A particle in the blood made up of thousands of cholesterol molecules and other lipids bound to a protein. HDL scavenges excess cholesterol.

**hindbrain** One of three ancestral and embryonic regions of the vertebrate brain; develops into the medulla oblongata, pons, and cerebellum.

**histamine** (his'-tuh-mēn) A substance released by mast cells that causes blood vessels to dilate and become more permeable in inflammatory and allergic responses.

**histogram** A variant of a bar graph that is made for numeric data by first grouping, or "binning," the variable plotted on the $x$-axis into intervals of equal width. The "bins" may be integers or ranges of numbers. The height of each bar shows the percent or number of experimental subjects whose characteristics can be described by one of the intervals plotted on the *x*-axis.

**histone** (his'-tōn) A small protein with a high proportion of positively charged amino acids that binds to the negatively charged DNA and plays a key role in chromatin structure.

**histone acetylation** (his'-tōn) The attachment of acetyl groups to certain amino acids of histone proteins.

**HIV (human immunodeficiency virus)** The infectious agent that causes AIDS. HIV is a retrovirus.

**holdfast** A rootlike structure that anchors a seaweed.

**holoblastic** (hō'-lō-blas'-tik) Referring to a type of cleavage in which there is complete division of the egg; occurs in eggs that have little yolk (such as those of the sea urchin) or a moderate amount of yolk (such as those of the frog).

**homeobox** (hō'-mē-ō-boks') A 180-nucleotide sequence within homeotic genes and some other developmental genes that is widely conserved in animals. Related sequences occur in plants and yeasts.

**homeostasis** (hō'-mē-ō-stā'-sis) The steady-state physiological condition of the body.

**homeotic gene** (hō-mē-o'-tik) Any of the master regulatory genes that control placement and spatial organization of body parts in animals, plants, and fungi by controlling the developmental fate of groups of cells.

**hominin** (hō'-mi-nin) A member of the human branch of the evolutionary tree. Hominins include *Homo sapiens* and our ancestors, a group of extinct species that are more closely related to us than to chimpanzees.

**homologous chromosomes** (or **homologs**) (hō-mol'-uh-gus) A pair of chromosomes of the same length, centromere position, and staining pattern that possess genes for the same characters at corresponding loci. One homologous chromosome is inherited from the organism's father, the other from the mother. Also called a homologous pair.

**homologous structures** (hō-mol'-uh-gus) Structures in different species that are similar because of common ancestry.

**homology** (hō-mol'-ō-jē) Similarity in characteristics resulting from a shared ancestry.

**homoplasy** (hō'-muh-play'-zē) A similar (analogous) structure or molecular sequence that has evolved independently in two species.

**homosporous** (hō-mos'-puh-rus) Referring to a plant species that has a single kind of spore, which typically develops into a bisexual gametophyte.

**homozygous** (hō'-mō-zī'-gus) Having two identical alleles for a given gene.

**horizontal gene transfer** The transfer of genes from one genome to another through mechanisms such as transposable elements, plasmid exchange, viral activity, and perhaps fusions of different organisms.

**hormone** In multicellular organisms, one of many types of secreted chemicals that are formed in specialized cells, travel in body fluids, and act on specific target cells in other parts of the organism, changing the target cells' functioning.

**hornwort** A small, herbaceous, nonvascular plant that is a member of the phylum Anthocerophyta.

**host** The larger participant in a symbiotic relationship, often providing a home and food source for the smaller symbiont.

**host range** The limited number of species whose cells can be infected by a particular virus.

**Human Genome Project** An international collaborative effort to map and sequence the DNA of the entire human genome.

**human immunodeficiency virus (HIV)** The infectious agent that causes AIDS (acquired immunodeficiency syndrome). HIV is a retrovirus.

**humoral immune response** (hyū'-mer-ul) The branch of adaptive immunity that involves the activation of B cells and that leads to the production of antibodies, which defend against bacteria and viruses in body fluids.

**humus** (hyū'-mus) Decomposing organic material that is a component of topsoil.

**Huntington's disease** A human genetic disease caused by a dominant allele; characterized by uncontrollable body movements and degeneration of the nervous system; usually fatal 10 to 20 years after the onset of symptoms.

**hybrid** Offspring that results from the mating of individuals from two different species or from two true-breeding varieties of the same species.

**hybrid zone** A geographic region in which members of different species meet and mate, producing at least some offspring of mixed ancestry.

**hybridization** In genetics, the mating, or crossing, of two true-breeding varieties.

**hydration shell** The sphere of water molecules around a dissolved ion.

**hydrocarbon** An organic molecule consisting only of carbon and hydrogen.

**hydrogen bond** A type of weak chemical bond that is formed when the slightly positive hydrogen atom of a polar covalent bond in one molecule is attracted to the slightly negative atom of a polar covalent bond in another molecule or in another region of the same molecule.

**hydrogen ion** A single proton with a charge of $1+$. The dissociation of a water molecule ($H_2O$) leads to the generation of a hydroxide ion ($OH^-$) and a hydrogen ion ($H^+$); in water, $H^+$ is not found alone but associates with a water molecule to form a hydronium ion.

**hydrolysis** (hī-drol'-uh-sis) A chemical reaction that breaks bonds between two molecules by the addition of water; functions in disassembly of polymers to monomers.

**hydronium ion** A water molecule that has an extra proton bound to it; $H_3O^+$, commonly represented as $H^+$.

**hydrophilic** (hī'-drō-fil'-ik) Having an affinity for water.

**hydrophobic** (hī'-drō-fō'-bik) Having no affinity for water; tending to coalesce and form droplets in water.

**hydrophobic interaction** (hī'-drō-fō'-bik) A type of weak chemical interaction caused when molecules that do not mix with water coalesce to exclude water.

**hydroponic culture** A method in which plants are grown in mineral solutions rather than in soil.

**hydrostatic skeleton** A skeletal system composed of fluid held under pressure in a closed body compartment; the main skeleton of most cnidarians, flatworms, nematodes, and annelids.

**hydrothermal vent** An area on the deep sea-floor where heated water and minerals from Earth's interior gush into the seawater.

**hydroxide ion** A water molecule that has lost a proton; $OH^-$.

**hydroxyl group** (hī-drok'-sil) A chemical group consisting of an oxygen atom joined to a hydrogen atom. Molecules possessing this group are soluble in water and are called alcohols.

**hyperpolarization** A change in a cell's membrane potential such that the inside of the membrane becomes more negative relative to the outside. Hyperpolarization reduces the chance that a neuron will transmit a nerve impulse.

**hypersensitive response** A plant's localized defense response to a pathogen, involving the death of cells around the site of infection.

**hypertension** A disorder in which blood pressure remains abnormally high.

**hypertonic** Referring to a solution that, when surrounding a cell, will cause the cell to lose water.

**hypha** (plural, **hyphae**) (hī'-fuh, hī'-fē) One of many connected filaments that collectively make up the mycelium of a fungus.

**hypocotyl** (hī'-puh-cot'-ul) In an angiosperm embryo, the embryonic axis below the point of attachment of the cotyledon(s) and above the radicle.

**hypothalamus** (hī'-pō-thal'-uh-mus) The ventral part of the vertebrate forebrain; functions in maintaining homeostasis, especially in coordinating the endocrine and nervous systems; secretes hormones of the posterior pituitary and releasing factors that regulate the anterior pituitary.

**hypothesis** (hī-poth'-uh-sis) A testable explanation for a set of observations based on the available data and guided by inductive reasoning. A hypothesis is narrower in scope than a theory.

**hypotonic** Referring to a solution that, when surrounding a cell, will cause the cell to take up water.

**imbibition** The physical adsorption of water onto the internal surfaces of structures.

**immigration** The influx of new individuals into a population from other areas.

**immune system** An organism's system of defenses against agents that cause disease.

**immunization** The process of generating a state of immunity by artificial means. In vaccination, an inactive or weakened form of a pathogen is administered, inducing B and T cell responses and immunological memory. In passive immunization, antibodies specific for a particular pathogen are administered, conferring immediate but temporary protection.

**immunoglobulin (Ig)** (im'-yū-nō-glob'-yū-lin) *See* antibody.

**imprinting** In animal behavior, the formation at a specific stage in life of a long-lasting behavioral response to a specific individual or object. *See also* genomic imprinting.

**inclusive fitness** The total effect an individual has on proliferating its genes by producing its own offspring and by providing aid that enables other close relatives to increase production of their offspring.

**incomplete dominance** The situation in which the phenotype of heterozygotes is intermediate between the phenotypes of individuals homozygous for either allele.

**incomplete flower** A flower in which one or more of the four basic floral organs (sepals, petals, stamens, or carpels) are either absent or nonfunctional.

**incomplete metamorphosis** A type of development in certain insects, such as grasshoppers, in which the young (called nymphs) resemble adults but are smaller and have different body proportions. The nymph goes through a series of molts, each time looking more like an adult, until it reaches full size.

**independent variable** A variable whose value is manipulated or changed during an experiment or other test to reveal possible effects on another variable (the dependent variable).

**indeterminate cleavage** A type of embryonic development in deuterostomes in which each cell produced by early cleavage divisions retains the capacity to develop into a complete embryo.

**indeterminate growth** A type of growth characteristic of plants, in which the organism continues to grow as long as it lives.

**induced fit** Caused by entry of the substrate, the change in shape of the active site of an enzyme so that it binds more snugly to the substrate.

**inducer** A specific small molecule that binds to a bacterial repressor protein and changes the repressor's shape so that it cannot bind to an operator, thus switching an operon on.

**induction** A process in which a group of cells or tissues influences the development of another group through close-range interactions.

**inductive reasoning** A type of logic in which generalizations are based on a large number of specific observations.

**inflammatory response** An innate immune defense triggered by physical injury or infection of tissue involving the release of substances that promote swelling, enhance the infiltration of white blood cells, and aid in tissue repair and destruction of invading pathogens.

**inflorescence** A group of flowers tightly clustered together.

**ingestion** The first stage of food processing in animals: the act of eating.

**ingroup** A species or group of species whose evolutionary relationships are being examined in a given analysis.

**inhibitory postsynaptic potential (IPSP)** An electrical change (usually hyperpolarization) in the membrane of a postsynaptic neuron caused by the binding of an inhibitory neurotransmitter from a presynaptic cell to a postsynaptic receptor; makes it more difficult for a postsynaptic neuron to generate an action potential.

**innate behavior** Animal behavior that is developmentally fixed and under strong genetic control. Innate behavior is exhibited in virtually the same form by all individuals in a population despite internal and external environmental differences during development and throughout their lifetimes.

**innate immunity** A form of defense common to all animals that is active immediately upon exposure to a pathogen and that is the same whether or not the pathogen has been encountered previously.

**inner cell mass** An inner cluster of cells at one end of a mammalian blastocyst that subsequently develops into the embryo proper and some of the extraembryonic membranes.

**inositol trisphosphate (IP$_3$)** (in-ō'-suh-tol) A second messenger that functions as an intermediate between certain signaling molecules and a subsequent second messenger, $Ca^{2+}$, by causing a rise in cytoplasmic $Ca^{2+}$ concentration.

**inquiry** The search for information and explanation, often focusing on specific questions.

**insertion** A mutation involving the addition of one or more nucleotide pairs to a gene.

***in situ* hybridization** A technique using nucleic acid hybridization with a labeled probe to detect the location of a specific mRNA in an intact organism.

**insulin** (in'-suh-lin) A hormone secreted by pancreatic beta cells that lowers blood glucose levels. It promotes the uptake of glucose by most body cells and the synthesis and storage of glycogen in the liver and also stimulates protein and fat synthesis.

**integral protein** A transmembrane protein with hydrophobic regions that extend into and often completely span the hydrophobic interior of the membrane and with hydrophilic regions in contact with the aqueous solution on one or both sides of the membrane (or lining the channel in the case of a channel protein).

**integrin** (in'-tuh-grin) In animal cells, a transmembrane receptor protein with two subunits that interconnects the extracellular matrix and the cytoskeleton.

**integument** (in-teg'-yū-ment) Layer of sporophyte tissue that contributes to the structure of an ovule of a seed plant.

**integumentary system** The outer covering of a mammal's body, including skin, hair, and nails, claws, or hooves.

**intercalated disk** (in-ter'-kuh-lā'-ted) A specialized junction between cardiac muscle cells that provides direct electrical coupling between the cells.

**interferon** (in'-ter-fēr'-on) A protein that has antiviral or immune regulatory functions. Interferon-α and interferon-β, secreted by virus-infected cells, help nearby cells resist viral infection; interferon-γ, secreted by T cells, helps activate macrophages.

**intermediate disturbance hypothesis** The concept that moderate levels of disturbance can foster greater species diversity than low or high levels of disturbance.

**intermediate filament** A component of the cytoskeleton that includes filaments intermediate in size between microtubules and microfilaments.

**interneuron** An association neuron; a nerve cell within the central nervous system that forms synapses with sensory and/or motor neurons and integrates sensory input and motor output.

**internode** A segment of a plant stem between the points where leaves are attached.

**interphase** The period in the cell cycle when the cell is not dividing. During interphase, cellular metabolic activity is high, chromosomes and organelles are duplicated, and cell size may increase. Interphase often accounts for about 90% of the cell cycle.

**intersexual selection** A form of natural selection in which individuals of one sex (usually the females) are choosy in selecting their mates from the other sex; also called mate choice.

**interspecific competition** Competition for resources between individuals of two or more species when resources are in short supply.

**interspecific interaction** A relationship between individuals of two or more species in a community.

**interstitial fluid** The fluid filling the spaces between cells in most animals.

**intertidal zone** The shallow zone of the ocean adjacent to land and between the high- and low-tide lines.

**intrasexual selection** A form of natural selection in which there is direct competition among individuals of one sex for mates of the opposite sex.

**introduced species** A species moved by humans, either intentionally or accidentally, from its native location to a new geographic region; also called non-native or exotic species.

**intron** (in'-tron) A noncoding, intervening sequence within a primary transcript that is removed from the transcript during RNA processing; also refers to the region of DNA from which this sequence was transcribed.

**invasive species** A species, often introduced by humans, that takes hold outside its native range.

**inversion** An aberration in chromosome structure resulting from reattachment of a chromosomal fragment in a reverse orientation to the chromosome from which it originated.

**invertebrate** An animal without a backbone. Invertebrates make up 95% of animal species.

***in vitro* fertilization (IVF)** (vē'-trō) Fertilization of oocytes in laboratory containers followed by artificial implantation of the early embryo in the mother's uterus.

***in vitro* mutagenesis** A technique used to discover the function of a gene by cloning it, introducing specific changes into the cloned gene's sequence, reinserting the mutated gene into a cell, and studying the phenotype of the mutant.

**ion** (ī'-on) An atom or group of atoms that has gained or lost one or more electrons, thus acquiring a charge.

**ion channel** (ī'-on) A transmembrane protein channel that allows a specific ion to diffuse across the membrane down its concentration or electrochemical gradient.

**ionic bond** (ī-on'-ik) A chemical bond resulting from the attraction between oppositely charged ions.

**ionic compound** (ī-on'-ik) A compound resulting from the formation of an ionic bond; also called a salt.

**iris** The colored part of the vertebrate eye, formed by the anterior portion of the choroid.

**isomer** (ī'-sō-mer) One of several compounds with the same molecular formula but different structures and therefore different properties. The three types of isomers are structural isomers, *cis-trans* isomers, and enantiomers.

**isomorphic** Referring to alternating generations in plants and certain algae in which the sporophytes and gametophytes look alike, although they differ in chromosome number.

**isotonic** (ī'-sō-ton'-ik) Referring to a solution that, when surrounding a cell, causes no net movement of water into or out of the cell.

**isotope** (ī'-sō-tōp') One of several atomic forms of an element, each with the same number of protons but a different number of neutrons, thus differing in atomic mass.

**iteroparity** Reproduction in which adults produce offspring over many years; also called repeated reproduction.

**jasmonate** Any of a class of plant hormones that regulate a wide range of developmental processes in plants and play a key role in plant defense against herbivores.

**joule (J)** A unit of energy: 1 J = 0.239 cal; 1 cal = 4.184 J.

**juxtaglomerular apparatus (JGA)** (juks'-tuh-gluh-mār'-yū-ler) A specialized tissue in nephrons that releases the enzyme renin in response to a drop in blood pressure or volume.

**juxtamedullary nephron** In mammals and birds, a nephron with a loop of Henle that extends far into the renal medulla.

**karyogamy** (kār'-ē-og'-uh-mē) In fungi, the fusion of haploid nuclei contributed by the two parents; occurs as one stage of sexual reproduction, preceded by plasmogamy.

**karyotype** (kār'-ē-ō-tīp) A display of the chromosome pairs of a cell arranged by size and shape.

**keystone species** A species that is not necessarily abundant in a community yet exerts strong control on community structure by the nature of its ecological role or niche.

**kidney** In vertebrates, one of a pair of excretory organs where blood filtrate is formed and processed into urine.

**kilocalorie (kcal)** A thousand calories; the amount of heat energy required to raise the temperature of 1 kg of water by 1°C.

**kinetic energy** (kuh-net'-ik) The energy associated with the relative motion of objects.

Moving matter can perform work by imparting motion to other matter.

**kinetic energy** (kuh-net'-ik) The energy associated with the relative motion of objects. Moving matter can perform work by imparting motion to other matter.

**kinetochore** (kuh-net'-uh-kōr) A structure of proteins attached to the centromere that links each sister chromatid to the mitotic spindle.

**kinetoplastid** A protist, such as a trypanosome, that has a single large mitochondrion that houses an organized mass of DNA.

**kingdom** A taxonomic category, the second broadest after domain.

**kin selection** Natural selection that favors altruistic behavior by enhancing the reproductive success of relatives.

**K-selection** Selection for life history traits that are sensitive to population density; also called density-dependent selection.

**labia majora** A pair of thick, fatty ridges that encloses and protects the rest of the vulva.

**labia minora** A pair of slender skin folds that surrounds the openings of the vagina and urethra.

**lacteal** (lak'-tē-ul) A tiny lymph vessel extending into the core of an intestinal villus and serving as the destination for absorbed chylomicrons.

**lactic acid fermentation** Glycolysis followed by the reduction of pyruvate to lactate, regenerating $NAD^+$ with no release of carbon dioxide.

**lagging strand** A discontinuously synthesized DNA strand that elongates by means of Okazaki fragments, each synthesized in a $5' \rightarrow 3'$ direction away from the replication fork.

**lancelet** A member of the clade Cephalochordata, small blade-shaped marine chordates that lack a backbone.

**landscape** An area containing several different ecosystems linked by exchanges of energy, materials, and organisms.

**landscape ecology** The study of how the spatial arrangement of habitat types affects the distribution and abundance of organisms and ecosystem processes.

**large intestine** The portion of the vertebrate alimentary canal between the small intestine and the anus; functions mainly in water absorption and the formation of feces.

**larva** (lar'-vuh) (plural, **larvae**) A free-living, sexually immature form in some animal life cycles that may differ from the adult animal in morphology, nutrition, and habitat.

**larynx** (lār'-inks) The portion of the respiratory tract containing the vocal cords; also called the voice box.

**lateralization** Segregation of functions in the cortex of the left and right cerebral hemispheres.

**lateral line system** A mechanoreceptor system consisting of a series of pores and receptor units along the sides of the body in fishes and aquatic amphibians; detects water movements made by the animal itself and by other moving objects.

**lateral meristem** (mār'-uh-stem) A meristem that thickens the roots and shoots of woody

plants. The vascular cambium and cork cambium are lateral meristems.

**lateral root** A root that arises from the pericycle of an established root.

**law of conservation of mass** A physical law stating that matter can change form but cannot be created or destroyed. In a closed system, the mass of the system is constant.

**law of independent assortment** Mendel's second law, stating that each pair of alleles segregates, or assorts, independently of each other pair during gamete formation; applies when genes for two characters are located on different pairs of homologous chromosomes or when they are far enough apart on the same chromosome to behave as though they are on different chromosomes.

**law of segregation** Mendel's first law, stating that the two alleles in a pair segregate (separate from each other) into different gametes during gamete formation.

**leading strand** The new complementary DNA strand synthesized continuously along the template strand toward the replication fork in the mandatory $5' \rightarrow 3'$ direction.

**leaf** The main photosynthetic organ of vascular plants.

**leaf primordium** (plural, **primordia**) A fingerlike projection along the flank of a shoot apical meristem, from which a leaf arises.

**learning** The modification of behavior as a result of specific experiences.

**lens** The structure in an eye that focuses light rays onto the photoreceptors.

**lenticel** (len'-ti-sel) A small raised area in the bark of stems and roots that enables gas exchange between living cells and the outside air.

**lepidosaur** (leh-pid'-uh-sōr) A member of the reptilian group that includes lizards, snakes, and two species of New Zealand animals called tuataras.

**leukocyte** (lū'-kō-sīt') A blood cell that functions in fighting infections; also called a white blood cell.

**lichen** The mutualistic association between a fungus and a photosynthetic alga or cyanobacterium.

**life cycle** The generation-to-generation sequence of stages in the reproductive history of an organism.

**life history** The traits that affect an organism's schedule of reproduction and survival.

**life table** An age-specific summary of the survival pattern of a population.

**ligament** A fibrous connective tissue that joins bones together at joints.

**ligand** (lig'-und) A molecule that binds specifically to another molecule, usually a larger one.

**ligand-gated ion channel** (lig'-und) A transmembrane protein containing a pore that opens or closes as it changes shape in response to a signaling molecule (ligand), allowing or blocking the flow of specific ions; also called an ionotropic receptor.

**light chain** One of the two types of polypeptide chains that make up an antibody molecule and B cell receptor; consists of a variable region, which contributes to the antigen-binding site, and a constant region.

**light-harvesting complex** A complex of proteins associated with pigment molecules (including chlorophyll *a*, chlorophyll *b*, and carotenoids) that captures light energy and transfers it to reaction-center pigments in a photosystem.

**light microscope (LM)** An optical instrument with lenses that refract (bend) visible light to magnify images of specimens.

**light reactions** The first of two major stages in photosynthesis (preceding the Calvin cycle). These reactions, which occur on the thylakoid membranes of the chloroplast or on membranes of certain prokaryotes, convert solar energy to the chemical energy of ATP and NADPH, releasing oxygen in the process.

**lignin** (lig'-nin) A strong polymer embedded in the cellulose matrix of the secondary cell walls of vascular plants that provides structural support in terrestrial species.

**limiting nutrient** An element that must be added for production to increase in a particular area.

**limnetic zone** In a lake, the well-lit, open surface waters far from shore.

**linear electron flow** A route of electron flow during the light reactions of photosynthesis that involves both photosystems (I and II) and produces ATP, NADPH, and $O_2$. The net electron flow is from $H_2O$ to $NADP^+$.

**line graph** A graph in which each data point is connected to the next point in the data set with a straight line.

**linkage map** A genetic map based on the frequencies of recombination between markers during crossing over of homologous chromosomes.

**linked genes** Genes located close enough together on a chromosome that they tend to be inherited together.

**lipid** (lip'-id) Any of a group of large biological molecules, including fats, phospholipids, and steroids, that mix poorly, if at all, with water.

**littoral zone** In a lake, the shallow, well-lit waters close to shore.

**liver** A large internal organ in vertebrates that performs diverse functions, such as producing bile, maintaining blood glucose level, and detoxifying poisonous chemicals in the blood.

**liverwort** A small, herbaceous, nonvascular plant that is a member of the phylum Hepatophyta.

**loam** The most fertile soil type, made up of roughly equal amounts of sand, silt, and clay.

**lobe-fin** A member of the vertebrate clade Sarcopterygii, osteichthyans with rod-shaped muscular fins, including coelacanths, lungfishes, and tetrapods.

**local regulator** A secreted molecule that influences cells near where it is secreted.

**locomotion** Active motion from place to place.

**locus** (lō'-kus) (plural, **loci**) (lō'-sī) A specific place along the length of a chromosome where a given gene is located.

**logistic population growth** Population growth that levels off as population size approaches carrying capacity.

**long-day plant** A plant that flowers (usually in late spring or early summer) only when the light period is longer than a critical length.

**long-term memory** The ability to hold, associate, and recall information over one's lifetime.

**long-term potentiation (LTP)** An enhanced responsiveness to an action potential (nerve signal) by a receiving neuron.

**loop of Henle** (hen'-lē) The hairpin turn, with a descending and ascending limb, between the proximal and distal tubules of the vertebrate kidney; functions in water and salt reabsorption.

**lophophore** (lof'-uh-fōr) In some lophotrochozoan animals, including brachiopods, a crown of ciliated tentacles that surround the mouth and function in feeding.

**Lophotrochozoa** (lo-phah'-truh-kō-zō'-uh) One of the three main lineages of bilaterian animals; lophotrochozoans include organisms that have lophophores or trochophore larvae. *See also* Deuterostomia and Ecdysozoa.

**low-density lipoprotein (LDL)** A particle in the blood made up of thousands of cholesterol molecules and other lipids bound to a protein. LDL transports cholesterol from the liver for incorporation into cell membranes.

**lung** An infolded respiratory surface of a terrestrial vertebrate, land snail, or spider that connects to the atmosphere by narrow tubes.

**luteinizing hormone (LH)** (lū'-tē-uh-nī'-zing) A tropic hormone that is produced and secreted by the anterior pituitary and that stimulates ovulation in females and androgen production in males.

**lycophyte** (lī'-kuh-fīt) An informal name for a member of the phylum Lycophyta, which includes club mosses, spike mosses, and quillworts.

**lymph** The colorless fluid, derived from interstitial fluid, in the lymphatic system of vertebrates.

**lymph node** An organ located along a lymph vessel. Lymph nodes filter lymph and contain cells that attack viruses and bacteria.

**lymphatic system** A system of vessels and nodes, separate from the circulatory system, that returns fluid, proteins, and cells to the blood.

**lymphocyte** A type of white blood cell that mediates immune responses. The two main classes are B cells and T cells.

**lysogenic cycle** (lī'-sō-jen'-ik) A type of phage replicative cycle in which the viral genome becomes incorporated into the bacterial host chromosome as a prophage, is replicated along with the chromosome, and does not kill the host.

**lysosome** (lī'-suh-sōm) A membrane-enclosed sac of hydrolytic enzymes found in the cytoplasm of animal cells and some protists.

**lysozyme** (lī'-sō-zīm) An enzyme that destroys bacterial cell walls; in mammals, it is found in sweat, tears, and saliva.

**lytic cycle** (lit'-ik) A type of phage replicative cycle resulting in the release of new phages by lysis (and death) of the host cell.

**macroclimate** Large-scale patterns in climate; the climate of an entire region.

**macroevolution** Evolutionary change above the species level. Examples of macroevolutionary change include the origin of a new group of organisms through a series of speciation events and the impact of mass extinctions on the diversity of life and its subsequent recovery.

**macromolecule** A giant molecule formed by the joining of smaller molecules, usually by a dehydration reaction. Polysaccharides, proteins, and nucleic acids are macromolecules.

**macronutrient** An essential element that an organism must obtain in relatively large amounts. *See also* micronutrient.

**macrophage** (mak'-rō-fāj) A phagocytic cell present in many tissues that functions in innate immunity by destroying microbes and in acquired immunity as an antigen-presenting cell.

**magnoliid** A member of the angiosperm clade that is most closely related to the combined eudicot and monocot clades. Extant examples are magnolias, laurels, and black pepper plants.

**major depressive disorder** A mood disorder characterized by feelings of sadness, lack of self-worth, emptiness, or loss of interest in nearly all things.

**major histocompatibility complex (MHC) molecule** A host protein that functions in antigen presentation. Foreign MHC molecules on transplanted tissue can trigger T cell responses that may lead to rejection of the transplant.

**malignant tumor** A cancerous tumor containing cells that have significant genetic and cellular changes and are capable of invading and surviving in new sites. Malignant tumors can impair the functions of one or more organs.

**Malpighian tubule** (mal-pig'-ē-un) A unique excretory organ of insects that empties into the digestive tract, removes nitrogenous wastes from the hemolymph, and functions in osmoregulation.

**mammal** A member of the clade Mammalia, amniotes that have hair and mammary glands (glands that produce milk).

**mammary gland** An exocrine gland that secretes milk for nourishing the young. Mammary glands are characteristic of mammals.

**mantle** One of the three main parts of a mollusc; a fold of tissue that drapes over the mollusc's visceral mass and may secrete a shell. *See also* foot and visceral mass.

**mantle cavity** A water-filled chamber that houses the gills, anus, and excretory pores of a mollusc.

**map unit** A unit of measurement of the distance between genes. One map unit is equivalent to a 1% recombination frequency.

**marine benthic zone** The ocean floor.

**mark-recapture method** A sampling technique used to estimate the size of animal populations.

**marsupial** (mar-sū'-pē-ul) A mammal, such as a koala, kangaroo, or opossum, whose young complete their embryonic development inside a maternal pouch called the marsupium.

**mass extinction** The elimination of a large number of species throughout Earth, the result of global environmental changes.

**mass number** The sum of the number of protons and neutrons in an atom's nucleus.

**mast cell** A vertebrate body cell that produces histamine and other molecules that trigger inflammation in response to infection and in allergic reactions.

**mate-choice copying** Behavior in which individuals in a population copy the mate choice of others, apparently as a result of social learning.

**maternal effect gene** A gene that, when mutant in the mother, results in a mutant phenotype in the offspring, regardless of the offspring's genotype. Maternal effect genes, also called egg-polarity genes, were first identified in *Drosophila melanogaster*.

**matter** Anything that takes up space and has mass.

**maximum likelihood** As applied to DNA sequence data, a principle that states that when considering multiple phylogenetic hypotheses, one should take into account the hypothesis that reflects the most likely sequence of evolutionary events, given certain rules about how DNA changes over time.

**maximum parsimony** A principle that states that when considering multiple explanations for an observation, one should first investigate the simplest explanation that is consistent with the facts.

**mean** The sum of all data points in a data set divided by the number of data points.

**mechanoreceptor** A sensory receptor that detects physical deformation in the body's environment associated with pressure, touch, stretch, motion, or sound.

**medulla oblongata** (meh-dul′-uh ŏb′-long-go′-tuh) The lowest part of the vertebrate brain, commonly called the medulla; a swelling of the hindbrain anterior to the spinal cord that controls autonomic, homeostatic functions, including breathing, heart and blood vessel activity, swallowing, digestion, and vomiting.

**medusa** (plural, **medusae**) (muh-dū′-suh) The floating, flattened, mouth-down version of the cnidarian body plan. The alternate form is the polyp.

**megapascal (MPa)** (meg′-uh-pas-kal′) A unit of pressure equivalent to about 10 atmospheres of pressure.

**megaphyll** (meh′-guh-fil) A leaf with a highly branched vascular system, characteristic of the vast majority of vascular plants. *See also* microphyll.

**megaspore** A spore from a heterosporous plant species that develops into a female gametophyte.

**meiosis** (mī-ō′-sis) A modified type of cell division in sexually reproducing organisms consisting of two rounds of cell division but only one round of DNA replication. It results in cells with half the number of chromosome sets as the original cell.

**meiosis I** (mī-ō′-sis) The first division of a two-stage process of cell division in sexually reproducing organisms that results in cells with half the number of chromosome sets as the original cell.

**meiosis II** (mī-ō′-sis) The second division of a two-stage process of cell division in sexually reproducing organisms that results in cells with half the number of chromosome sets as the original cell.

**melanocyte-stimulating hormone (MSH)** A hormone produced and secreted by the anterior pituitary with multiple activities, including regulating the behavior of pigment-containing cells in the skin of some vertebrates.

**melatonin** A hormone that is secreted by the pineal gland and that is involved in the regulation of biological rhythms and sleep.

**membrane potential** The difference in electrical charge (voltage) across a cell's plasma membrane due to the differential distribution of ions. Membrane potential affects the activity of excitable cells and the transmembrane movement of all charged substances.

**memory cell** One of a clone of long-lived lymphocytes, formed during the primary immune response, that remains in a lymphoid organ until activated by exposure to the same antigen that triggered its formation. Activated memory cells mount the secondary immune response.

**menopause** The cessation of ovulation and menstruation marking the end of a human female's reproductive years.

**menstrual cycle** (men′-strū-ul) *See* uterine cycle.

**menstruation** The shedding of portions of the endometrium during a uterine (menstrual) cycle.

**meristem** (mãr′-uh-stem) Plant tissue that remains embryonic as long as the plant lives, allowing for indeterminate growth.

**meristem identity gene** (mãr′-uh-stem) A plant gene that promotes the switch from vegetative growth to flowering.

**meroblastic** (mãr′-ō-blas′-tik) Referring to a type of cleavage in which there is incomplete division of a yolk-rich egg, characteristic of avian development.

**mesoderm** (mez′-ō-derm) The middle primary germ layer in a triploblastic animal embryo; develops into the notochord, the lining of the coelom, muscles, skeleton, gonads, kidneys, and most of the circulatory system in species that have these structures.

**mesohyl** (mez′-ō-hīl) A gelatinous region between the two layers of cells of a sponge.

**mesophyll** (mez′-ō-fil) Leaf cells specialized for photosynthesis. In $C_3$ and CAM plants, mesophyll cells are located between the upper and lower epidermis; in $C_4$ plants, they are located between the bundle-sheath cells and the epidermis.

**messenger RNA (mRNA)** A type of RNA, synthesized using a DNA template, that attaches to ribosomes in the cytoplasm and specifies the primary structure of a protein. (In eukaryotes, the primary RNA transcript must undergo RNA processing to become mRNA.)

**metabolic pathway** A series of chemical reactions that either builds a complex molecule (anabolic pathway) or breaks down a complex molecule to simpler molecules (catabolic pathway).

**metabolic rate** The total amount of energy an animal uses in a unit of time.

**metabolism** (muh-tab′-uh-lizm) The totality of an organism's chemical reactions, consisting of catabolic and anabolic pathways, which manage the material and energy resources of the organism.

**metagenomics** The collection and sequencing of DNA from a group of species, usually an environmental sample of microorganisms. Computer software sorts partial sequences and assembles them into genome sequences of individual species making up the sample.

**metamorphosis** (met′-uh-mōr′-fuh-sis) A developmental transformation that turns an animal larva into either an adult or an adult-like stage that is not yet sexually mature.

**metanephridium** (met′-uh-nuh-frid′-ē-um) (plural, **metanephridia**) An excretory organ found in many invertebrates that typically consists of tubules connecting ciliated internal openings to external openings.

**metaphase** The third stage of mitosis, in which the spindle is complete and the chromosomes, attached to microtubules at their kinetochores, are all aligned at the metaphase plate.

**metaphase plate** An imaginary structure located at a plane midway between the two poles of a cell in metaphase on which the centromeres of all the duplicated chromosomes are located.

**metapopulation** A group of spatially separated populations of one species that interact through immigration and emigration.

**metastasis** (muh-tas′-tuh-sis) The spread of cancer cells to locations distant from their original site.

**methanogen** (meth-an′-ō-jen) An organism that produces methane as a waste product of the way it obtains energy. All known methanogens are in domain Archaea.

**methyl group** A chemical group consisting of a carbon bonded to three hydrogen atoms. The methyl group may be attached to a carbon or to a different atom.

**microclimate** Climate patterns on a very fine scale, such as the specific climatic conditions underneath a log.

**microevolution** Evolutionary change below the species level; change in the allele frequencies in a population over generations.

**microfilament** A cable composed of actin proteins in the cytoplasm of almost every eukaryotic cell, making up part of the cytoskeleton and acting alone or with myosin to cause cell contraction; also called an actin filament.

**micronutrient** An essential element that an organism needs in very small amounts. *See also* macronutrient.

**microphyll** (mī′-krō-fil) In lycophytes, a small leaf with a single unbranched vein. *See also* megaphyll.

**micropyle** A pore in the integuments of an ovule.

**microRNA (miRNA)** A small, single-stranded RNA molecule, generated from a double-stranded RNA precursor. The miRNA associates with one or more proteins in a complex that can degrade or prevent translation of an mRNA with a complementary sequence.

**microspore** A spore from a heterosporous plant species that develops into a male gametophyte.

**microtubule** A hollow rod composed of tubulin proteins that makes up part of the cytoskeleton in all eukaryotic cells and is found in cilia and flagella.

**microvillus** (plural, **microvilli**) One of many fine, finger-like projections of the epithelial cells in the lumen of the small intestine that increase its surface area.

**midbrain** One of three ancestral and embryonic regions of the vertebrate brain; develops into sensory integrating and relay centers that send sensory information to the cerebrum.

**middle lamella** (luh-mel'-uh) In plants, a thin layer of adhesive extracellular material, primarily pectins, found between the primary walls of adjacent young cells.

**migration** A regular, long-distance change in location.

**mineral** In nutrition, a simple nutrient that is inorganic and therefore cannot be synthesized in the body.

**mineralocorticoid** A steroid hormone secreted by the adrenal cortex that regulates salt and water homeostasis.

**minimum viable population (MVP)** The smallest population size at which a species is able to sustain its numbers and survive.

**mismatch repair** The cellular process that uses specific enzymes to remove and replace incorrectly paired nucleotides.

**missense mutation** A nucleotide-pair substitution that results in a codon that codes for a different amino acid.

**mitochondrial matrix** The compartment of the mitochondrion enclosed by the inner membrane and containing enzymes and substrates for the citric acid cycle, as well as ribosomes and DNA.

**mitochondrion** (mī'-tō-kon'-drē-un) (plural, **mitochondria**) An organelle in eukaryotic cells that serves as the site of cellular respiration; uses oxygen to break down organic molecules and synthesize ATP.

**mitosis** (mī-tō'-sis) A process of nuclear division in eukaryotic cells conventionally divided into five stages: prophase, prometaphase, metaphase, anaphase, and telophase. Mitosis conserves chromosome number by allocating replicated chromosomes equally to each of the daughter nuclei.

**mitotic (M) phase** The phase of the cell cycle that includes mitosis and cytokinesis.

**mitotic spindle** An assemblage of microtubules and associated proteins that is involved in the movement of chromosomes during mitosis.

**mixotroph** An organism that is capable of both photosynthesis and heterotrophy.

**model** A physical or conceptual representation of a natural phenomenon.

**model organism** A particular species chosen for research into broad biological principles because it is representative of a larger group and usually easy to grow in a lab.

**molarity** A common measure of solute concentration, referring to the number of moles of solute per liter of solution.

**mold** Informal term for a fungus that grows as a filamentous fungus, producing haploid spores by mitosis and forming a visible mycelium.

**mole (mol)** The number of grams of a substance that equals its molecular or atomic mass in daltons; a mole contains Avogadro's number of the molecules or atoms in question.

**molecular clock** A method for estimating the time required for a given amount of evolutionary change, based on the observation that some regions of genomes evolve at constant rates.

**molecular mass** The sum of the masses of all the atoms in a molecule; sometimes called molecular weight.

**molecule** Two or more atoms held together by covalent bonds.

**molting** A process in ecdysozoans in which the exoskeleton is shed at intervals, allowing growth by the production of a larger exoskeleton.

**monilophyte** An informal name for a member of the phylum Monilophyta, which includes ferns, horsetails, and whisk ferns and their relatives.

**monoclonal antibody** (mon'-ō-klōn'-ul) Any of a preparation of antibodies that have been produced by a single clone of cultured cells and thus are all specific for the same epitope.

**monocot** A member of a clade consisting of flowering plants that have one embryonic seed leaf, or cotyledon.

**monogamous** (muh-nog'-uh-mus) Referring to a type of relationship in which one male mates with just one female.

**monohybrid** An organism that is heterozygous with respect to a single gene of interest. All the offspring from a cross between parents homozygous for different alleles are monohybrids. For example, parents of genotypes *AA* and *aa* produce a monohybrid of genotype *Aa*.

**monohybrid cross** A cross between two organisms that are heterozygous for the character being followed (or the self-pollination of a heterozygous plant).

**monomer** (mon'-uh-mer) The subunit that serves as the building block of a polymer.

**monophyletic** (mon'-ō-fī-let'-ik) Pertaining to a group of taxa that consists of a common ancestor and all of its descendants. A monophyletic taxon is equivalent to a clade.

**monosaccharide** (mon'-ō-sak'-uh-rīd) The simplest carbohydrate, active alone or serving as a monomer for disaccharides and polysaccharides. Also called simple sugars, monosaccharides have molecular formulas that are generally some multiple of $CH_2O$.

**monosomic** Referring to a diploid cell that has only one copy of a particular chromosome instead of the normal two.

**monotreme** An egg-laying mammal, such as a platypus or echidna. Like all mammals, monotremes have hair and produce milk, but they lack nipples.

**morphogen** A substance, such as Bicoid protein in *Drosophila*, that provides positional information in the form of a concentration gradient along an embryonic axis.

**morphogenesis** (mōr'-fō-jen'-uh-sis) The development of the form of an organism and its structures.

**morphological species concept** Definition of a species in terms of measurable anatomical criteria.

**moss** A small, herbaceous, nonvascular plant that is a member of the phylum Bryophyta.

**motor neuron** A nerve cell that transmits signals from the brain or spinal cord to muscles or glands.

**motor protein** A protein that interacts with cytoskeletal elements and other cell components, producing movement of the whole cell or parts of the cell.

**motor system** An efferent branch of the vertebrate peripheral nervous system composed of motor neurons that carry signals to skeletal muscles in response to external stimuli.

**motor unit** A single motor neuron and all the muscle fibers it controls.

**movement corridor** A series of small clumps or a narrow strip of quality habitat (usable by organisms) that connects otherwise isolated patches of quality habitat.

**MPF** Maturation-promoting factor (or M-phase-promoting factor); a protein complex required for a cell to progress from late interphase to mitosis. The active form consists of cyclin and a protein kinase.

**mucus** A viscous and slippery mixture of glycoproteins, cells, salts, and water that moistens and protects the membranes lining body cavities that open to the exterior.

**Müllerian mimicry** (myū-lār'-ē-un mim'-uh-krē) Reciprocal mimicry by two unpalatable species.

**multifactorial** Referring to a phenotypic character that is influenced by multiple genes and environmental factors.

**multigene family** A collection of genes with similar or identical sequences, presumably of common origin.

**multiple fruit** A fruit derived from an entire inflorescence.

**multiplication rule** A rule of probability stating that the probability of two or more independent events occurring together can be determined by multiplying their individual probabilities.

**muscle tissue** Tissue consisting of long muscle cells that can contract, either on its own or when stimulated by nerve impulses.

**mutagen** (myū'-tuh-jen) A chemical or physical agent that interacts with DNA and can cause a mutation.

**mutation** (myū-tā'-shun) A change in the nucleotide sequence of an organism's DNA or in the DNA or RNA of a virus.

**mutualism** (myū'-chū-ul-izm) A symbiotic relationship in which both participants benefit.

**mycelium** (mī-sē'-lē-um) The densely branched network of hyphae in a fungus.

**mycorrhiza** (plural, **mycorrhizae**) (mī′-kō-rī′-zuh, mī′-kō-rī′-zē) A mutualistic association of plant roots and fungus.

**mycosis** (mī-kō′-sis) General term for a fungal infection.

**myelin sheath** (mī′-uh-lin) Wrapped around the axon of a neuron, an insulating coat of cell membranes from Schwann cells or oligodendrocytes. It is interrupted by nodes of Ranvier, where action potentials are generated.

**myofibril** (mī′-ō-fī′-bril) A longitudinal bundle in a muscle cell (fiber) that contains thin filaments of actin and regulatory proteins and thick filaments of myosin.

**myoglobin** (mī′-uh-glō′-bin) An oxygen-storing, pigmented protein in muscle cells.

**myosin** (mī′-uh-sin) A type of motor protein that associates into filaments that interact with actin filaments to cause cell contraction.

**myriapod** (mir′-ē-uh-pod′) A terrestrial arthropod with many body segments and one or two pairs of legs per segment. Millipedes and centipedes are the two major groups of living myriapods.

**NAD⁺** Nicotinamide adenine dinucleotide, a coenzyme that cycles easily between oxidized ($NAD^+$) and reduced (NADH) states, thus acting as an electron carrier.

**NADP⁺** Nicotinamide adenine dinucleotide phosphate, an electron acceptor that, as NADPH, temporarily stores energized electrons produced during the light reactions.

**natural killer cell** A type of white blood cell that can kill tumor cells and virus-infected cells as part of innate immunity.

**natural selection** A process in which individuals that have certain inherited traits tend to survive and reproduce at higher rates than other individuals because of those traits.

**negative feedback** A form of regulation in which accumulation of an end product of a process slows the process; in physiology, a primary mechanism of homeostasis, whereby a change in a variable triggers a response that counteracts the initial change.

**negative pressure breathing** A breathing system in which air is pulled into the lungs.

**nematocyst** (nem′-uh-tuh-sist′) In a cnidocyte of a cnidarian, a capsule-like organelle containing a coiled thread that when discharged can penetrate the body wall of the prey.

**nephron** (nef′-ron) The tubular excretory unit of the vertebrate kidney.

**neritic zone** The shallow region of the ocean overlying the continental shelf.

**nerve** A fiber composed primarily of the bundled axons of neurons.

**nervous system** In animals, the fast-acting internal system of communication involving sensory receptors, networks of nerve cells, and connections to muscles and glands that respond to nerve signals; functions in concert with the endocrine system to effect internal regulation and maintain homeostasis.

**nervous tissue** Tissue made up of neurons and supportive cells.

**net ecosystem production (NEP)** The gross primary production of an ecosystem minus the energy used by all autotrophs and heterotrophs for respiration.

**net primary production (NPP)** The gross primary production of an ecosystem minus the energy used by the producers for respiration.

**neural crest** In vertebrates, a region located along the sides of the neural tube where it pinches off from the ectoderm. Neural crest cells migrate to various parts of the embryo and form pigment cells in the skin and parts of the skull, teeth, adrenal glands, and peripheral nervous system.

**neural tube** A tube of infolded ectodermal cells that runs along the anterior-posterior axis of a vertebrate, just dorsal to the notochord. It will give rise to the central nervous system.

**neurohormone** A molecule that is secreted by a neuron, travels in body fluids, and acts on specific target cells, changing their functioning.

**neuron** (nyūr′-on) A nerve cell; the fundamental unit of the nervous system, having structure and properties that allow it to conduct signals by taking advantage of the electrical charge across its plasma membrane.

**neuronal plasticity** The capacity of a nervous system to change with experience.

**neuropeptide** A relatively short chain of amino acids that serves as a neurotransmitter.

**neurotransmitter** A molecule that is released from the synaptic terminal of a neuron at a chemical synapse, diffuses across the synaptic cleft, and binds to the postsynaptic cell, triggering a response.

**neutral variation** Genetic variation that does not provide a selective advantage or disadvantage.

**neutron** A subatomic particle having no electrical charge (electrically neutral), with a mass of about $1.7 \times 10^{-24}$ g, found in the nucleus of an atom.

**neutrophil** The most abundant type of white blood cell. Neutrophils are phagocytic and tend to self-destruct as they destroy foreign invaders, limiting their life span to a few days.

**nitric oxide (NO)** A gas produced by many types of cells that functions as a local regulator and as a neurotransmitter.

**nitrogen cycle** The natural process by which nitrogen, either from the atmosphere or from decomposed organic material, is converted by soil bacteria to compounds assimilated by plants. This incorporated nitrogen is then taken in by other organisms and subsequently released, acted on by bacteria, and made available again to the nonliving environment.

**nitrogen fixation** The conversion of atmospheric nitrogen ($N_2$) to ammonia ($NH_3$). Biological nitrogen fixation is carried out by certain prokaryotes, some of which have mutualistic relationships with plants.

**nociceptor** (nō′-si-sep′-tur) A sensory receptor that responds to noxious or painful stimuli; also called a pain receptor.

**node** A point along the stem of a plant at which leaves are attached.

**node of Ranvier** (ron′-vē-ā′) Gap in the myelin sheath of certain axons where an action potential may be generated. In saltatory conduction, an action potential is regenerated at each node, appearing to "jump" along the axon from node to node.

**nodule** A swelling on the root of a legume. Nodules are composed of plant cells that contain nitrogen-fixing bacteria of the genus *Rhizobium*.

**noncompetitive inhibitor** A substance that reduces the activity of an enzyme by binding to a location remote from the active site, changing the enzyme's shape so that the active site no longer effectively catalyzes the conversion of substrate to product.

**nondisjunction** An error in meiosis or mitosis in which members of a pair of homologous chromosomes or a pair of sister chromatids fail to separate properly from each other.

**nonequilibrium model** A model that maintains that communities change constantly after being buffeted by disturbances.

**nonpolar covalent bond** A type of covalent bond in which electrons are shared equally between two atoms of similar electronegativity.

**nonsense mutation** A mutation that changes an amino acid codon to one of the three stop codons, resulting in a shorter and usually nonfunctional protein.

**norepinephrine** A catecholamine that is chemically and functionally similar to epinephrine and acts as a hormone or neurotransmitter; also called noradrenaline.

**northern coniferous forest** A terrestrial biome characterized by long, cold winters and dominated by cone-bearing trees.

**no-till agriculture** A plowing technique that minimally disturbs the soil, thereby reducing soil loss.

**notochord** (nō′-tuh-kord′) A longitudinal, flexible rod made of tightly packed mesodermal cells that runs along the anterior-posterior axis of a chordate in the dorsal part of the body.

**nuclear envelope** In a eukaryotic cell, the double membrane that surrounds the nucleus, perforated with pores that regulate traffic with the cytoplasm. The outer membrane is continuous with the endoplasmic reticulum.

**nuclear lamina** A netlike array of protein filaments that lines the inner surface of the nuclear envelope and helps maintain the shape of the nucleus.

**nucleariid** A member of a group of unicellular, amoeboid protists that are more closely related to fungi than they are to other protists.

**nuclease** An enzyme that cuts DNA or RNA, either removing one or a few bases or hydrolyzing the DNA or RNA completely into its component nucleotides.

**nucleic acid** (nū-klā′-ik) A polymer (polynucleotide) consisting of many nucleotide monomers; serves as a blueprint for proteins and, through the actions of proteins, for all cellular activities. The two types are DNA and RNA.

**nucleic acid hybridization** (nū-klā′-ik) The base pairing of one strand of a nucleic acid to the complementary sequence on a strand from *another* nucleic acid molecule.

**nucleic acid probe** (nū-klā′-ik) In DNA technology, a labeled single-stranded nucleic acid molecule used to locate a specific nucleotide sequence in a nucleic acid sample. Molecules of the probe hydrogen-bond to the complementary sequence wherever it occurs; radioactive, fluorescent, or other labeling of the probe allows its location to be detected.

**nucleoid** (nū'-klē-oyd) A non-membrane-enclosed region in a prokaryotic cell where its chromosome is located.

**nucleolus** (nū-klē'-ō-lus) (plural, **nucleoli**) A specialized structure in the nucleus, consisting of chromosomal regions containing ribosomal RNA (rRNA) genes along with ribosomal proteins imported from the cytoplasm; site of rRNA synthesis and ribosomal subunit assembly. *See also* ribosome.

**nucleosome** (nū'-klē-ō-sōm') The basic, bead-like unit of DNA packing in eukaryotes, consisting of a segment of DNA wound around a protein core composed of two copies of each of four types of histone.

**nucleotide** (nū'-klē-ō-tīd') The building block of a nucleic acid, consisting of a five-carbon sugar covalently bonded to a nitrogenous base and one or more phosphate groups.

**nucleotide excision repair** (nū'-klē-ō-tīd') A repair system that removes and then correctly replaces a damaged segment of DNA using the undamaged strand as a guide.

**nucleotide-pair substitution** (nū'-klē-ō-tīd') A type of point mutation in which one nucleotide in a DNA strand and its partner in the complementary strand are replaced by another pair of nucleotides.

**nucleus** (1) An atom's central core, containing protons and neutrons. (2) The organelle of a eukaryotic cell that contains the genetic material in the form of chromosomes, made up of chromatin. (3) A cluster of neurons.

**nutrition** The process by which an organism takes in and makes use of food substances.

**obligate aerobe** (ob'-lig-et âr'-ōb) An organism that requires oxygen for cellular respiration and cannot live without it.

**obligate anaerobe** (ob'-lig-et an'-uh-rōb) An organism that carries out only fermentation or anaerobic respiration. Such organisms cannot use oxygen and in fact may be poisoned by it.

**ocean acidification** Decreasing pH of ocean waters due to absorption of excess atmospheric $CO_2$ from the burning of fossil fuels.

**oceanic pelagic zone** Most of the ocean's waters far from shore, constantly mixed by ocean currents.

**odorant** A molecule that can be detected by sensory receptors of the olfactory system.

**Okazaki fragment** (ō'-kah-zah'-kē) A short segment of DNA synthesized away from the replication fork on a template strand during DNA replication. Many such segments are joined together to make up the lagging strand of newly synthesized DNA.

**olfaction** The sense of smell.

**oligodendrocyte** A type of glial cell that forms insulating myelin sheaths around the axons of neurons in the central nervous system.

**oligotrophic lake** A nutrient-poor, clear lake with few phytoplankton.

**ommatidium** (ōm'-uh-tid'-ē-um) (plural, **ommatidia**) One of the facets of the compound eye of arthropods and some polychaete worms.

**omnivore** An animal that regularly eats animals as well as plants or algae.

**oncogene** (on'-kō-jēn) A gene found in viral or cellular genomes that is involved in triggering molecular events that can lead to cancer.

**oocyte** (ō'-uh-sīt) A cell in the female reproductive system that differentiates to form an egg.

**oogenesis** (ō'-uh-jen'-uh-sis) The process in the ovary that results in the production of female gametes.

**oogonium** (ō'-uh-gō'-nē-em) (plural, **oogonia**) A cell that divides mitotically to form oocytes.

**open circulatory system** A circulatory system in which fluid called hemolymph bathes the tissues and organs directly and there is no distinction between the circulating fluid and the interstitial fluid.

**operator** In bacterial and phage DNA, a sequence of nucleotides near the start of an operon to which an active repressor can attach. The binding of the repressor prevents RNA polymerase from attaching to the promoter and transcribing the genes of the operon.

**operculum** (ō-per'-kyuh-lum) In aquatic osteichthyans, a protective bony flap that covers and protects the gills.

**operon** (op'-er-on) A unit of genetic function found in bacteria and phages, consisting of a promoter, an operator, and a coordinately regulated cluster of genes whose products function in a common pathway.

**opisthokont** (uh-pis'-thuh-kont') A member of an extremely diverse clade of eukaryotes that includes fungi, animals, and several closely-related groups of protists.

**opposable thumb** A thumb that can touch the ventral surface of the fingertips of all four fingers.

**opsin** A membrane protein bound to a light-absorbing pigment molecule.

**optimal foraging model** The basis for analyzing behavior as a compromise between feeding costs and feeding benefits.

**oral cavity** The mouth of an animal.

**orbital** The three-dimensional space where an electron is found 90% of the time.

**order** In Linnaean classification, the taxonomic category above the level of family.

**organ** A specialized center of body function composed of several different types of tissues.

**organ identity gene** A plant homeotic gene that uses positional information to determine which emerging leaves develop into which types of floral organs.

**organ of Corti** (kor'-tē) The actual hearing organ of the vertebrate ear, located in the floor of the cochlear duct in the inner ear; contains the receptor cells (hair cells) of the ear.

**organ system** A group of organs that work together in performing vital body functions.

**organelle** (ōr-guh-nel') Any of several membrane-enclosed structures with specialized functions, suspended in the cytosol of eukaryotic cells.

**organic chemistry** The study of carbon compounds (organic compounds).

**organismal ecology** The branch of ecology concerned with the morphological, physiological, and behavioral ways in which individual organisms meet the challenges posed by their biotic and abiotic environments.

**organogenesis** (ōr-gan'-ō-jen'-uh-sis) The process in which organ rudiments develop from the three germ layers after gastrulation.

**origin of replication** Site where the replication of a DNA molecule begins, consisting of a specific sequence of nucleotides.

**orthologous genes** Homologous genes that are found in different species because of speciation.

**osculum** (os'-kyuh-lum) A large opening in a sponge that connects the spongocoel to the environment.

**osmoconformer** An animal that is isoosmotic with its environment.

**osmolarity** (oz'-mō-lâr'-uh-tē) Solute concentration expressed as molarity.

**osmoregulation** Regulation of solute concentrations and water balance by a cell or organism.

**osmoregulator** An animal that controls its internal osmolarity independent of the external environment.

**osmosis** (oz-mō'-sis) The diffusion of free water across a selectively permeable membrane.

**osteichthyan** (os'-tē-ik'-thē-an) A member of a vertebrate clade with jaws and mostly bony skeletons.

**outgroup** A species or group of species from an evolutionary lineage that is known to have diverged before the lineage that contains the group of species being studied. An outgroup is selected so that its members are closely related to the group of species being studied, but not as closely related as any study-group members are to each other.

**oval window** In the vertebrate ear, a membrane-covered gap in the skull bone, through which sound waves pass from the middle ear to the inner ear.

**ovarian cycle** (ō-vâr'-ē-un) The cyclic recurrence of the follicular phase, ovulation, and the luteal phase in the mammalian ovary, regulated by hormones.

**ovary** (ō'-vuh-rē) (1) In flowers, the portion of a carpel in which the egg-containing ovules develop. (2) In animals, the structure that produces female gametes and reproductive hormones.

**oviduct** (ō'-vuh-duct) A tube passing from the ovary to the vagina in invertebrates or to the uterus in vertebrates, where it is also called a fallopian tube.

**oviparous** (ō-vip'-uh-rus) Referring to a type of development in which young hatch from eggs laid outside the mother's body.

**ovoviviparous** (ō'-vō-vī-vip'-uh-rus) Referring to a type of development in which young hatch from eggs that are retained in the mother's uterus.

**ovulation** The release of an egg from an ovary. In humans, an ovarian follicle releases an egg during each uterine (menstrual) cycle.

**ovule** (o'-vyūl) A structure that develops within the ovary of a seed plant and contains the female gametophyte.

**oxidation** The complete or partial loss of electrons from a substance involved in a redox reaction.

**oxidative phosphorylation** (fos′-fōr-uh-lā′-shun) The production of ATP using energy derived from the redox reactions of an electron transport chain; the third major stage of cellular respiration.

**oxidizing agent** The electron acceptor in a redox reaction.

**oxytocin** (ok′-si-tō′-sen) A hormone produced by the hypothalamus and released from the posterior pituitary. It induces contractions of the uterine muscles during labor and causes the mammary glands to eject milk during nursing.

*p53* **gene** A tumor-suppressor gene that codes for a specific transcription factor that promotes the synthesis of proteins that inhibit the cell cycle.

**paedomorphosis** (pē′-duh-mōr′-fuh-sis) The retention in an adult organism of the juvenile features of its evolutionary ancestors.

**pain receptor** A sensory receptor that responds to noxious or painful stimuli; also called a nociceptor.

**paleoanthropology** The study of human origins and evolution.

**paleontology** (pā′-lē-un-tol′-ō-jē) The scientific study of fossils.

**pancreas** (pan′-krē-us) A gland with exocrine and endocrine tissues. The exocrine portion functions in digestion, secreting enzymes and an alkaline solution into the small intestine via a duct; the ductless endocrine portion functions in homeostasis, secreting the hormones insulin and glucagon into the blood.

**pancrustacean** A member of a diverse arthropod clade that includes lobsters, crabs, barnacles and other crustaceans, as well as insects and their six-legged terrestrial relatives.

**pandemic** A global epidemic.

**Pangaea** (pan-jē′-uh) The supercontinent that formed near the end of the Paleozoic era, when plate movements brought all the landmasses of Earth together.

**parabasalid** A protist, such as a trichomonad, with modified mitochondria.

**paracrine** Referring to a secreted molecule that acts on a neighboring cell.

**paralogous genes** Homologous genes that are found in the same genome as a result of gene duplication.

**paraphyletic** (pār′-uh-fī-let′-ik) Pertaining to a group of taxa that consists of a common ancestor and some, but not all, of its descendants.

**parareptile** A basal group of reptiles, consisting mostly of large, stocky quadrupedal herbivores. Parareptiles died out in the late Triassic period.

**parasite** (pār′-uh-sīt) An organism that feeds on the cell contents, tissues, or body fluids of another species (the host) while in or on the host organism. Parasites harm but usually do not kill their host.

**parasitism** (pār′-uh-sit-izm) A symbiotic relationship in which one organism, the parasite, benefits at the expense of another, the host, by living either within or on the host.

**parasympathetic division** One of three divisions of the autonomic nervous system; generally enhances body activities that gain and conserve energy, such as digestion and reduced heart rate.

**parathyroid gland** One of four small endocrine glands, embedded in the surface of the thyroid gland, that secrete parathyroid hormone.

**parathyroid hormone (PTH)** A hormone secreted by the parathyroid glands that raises blood calcium level by promoting calcium release from bone and calcium retention by the kidneys.

**parenchyma cell** (puh-ren′-ki-muh) A relatively unspecialized plant cell type that carries out most of the metabolism, synthesizes and stores organic products, and develops into a more differentiated cell type.

**parental type** An offspring with a phenotype that matches one of the true-breeding parental (P generation) phenotypes; also refers to the phenotype itself.

**Parkinson's disease** A progressive brain disease characterized by difficulty in initiating movements, slowness of movement, and rigidity.

**parthenogenesis** (par′-thuh-nō′-jen′-uh-sis) A form of asexual reproduction in which females produce offspring from unfertilized eggs.

**partial pressure** The pressure exerted by a particular gas in a mixture of gases (for instance, the pressure exerted by oxygen in air).

**passive immunity** Short-term immunity conferred by the transfer of antibodies, as occurs in the transfer of maternal antibodies to a fetus or nursing infant.

**passive transport** The diffusion of a substance across a biological membrane with no expenditure of energy.

**pathogen** An organism or virus that causes disease.

**pathogen-associated molecular patterns (PAMPs)** Short molecular sequences that typify certain groups of pathogens and that are recognized by cells of the innate immune system.

**pattern formation** The development of a multicellular organism's spatial organization, the arrangement of organs and tissues in their characteristic places in three-dimensional space.

**peat** Extensive deposits of partially decayed organic material often formed primarily from the wetland moss *Sphagnum*.

**pedigree** A diagram of a family tree with conventional symbols, showing the occurrence of heritable characters in parents and offspring over multiple generations.

**pelagic zone** The open-water component of aquatic biomes.

**penis** The copulatory structure of male mammals.

**PEP carboxylase** An enzyme that adds $CO_2$ to phosphoenolpyruvate (PEP) to form oxaloacetate in mesophyll cells of $C_4$ plants. It acts prior to photosynthesis.

**pepsin** An enzyme present in gastric juice that begins the hydrolysis of proteins.

**pepsinogen** The inactive form of pepsin secreted by chief cells located in gastric pits of the stomach.

**peptide bond** The covalent bond between the carboxyl group on one amino acid and the amino group on another, formed by a dehydration reaction.

**peptidoglycan** (pep′-tid-ō-glī′-kan) A type of polymer in bacterial cell walls consisting of modified sugars cross-linked by short polypeptides.

**perception** The interpretation of sensory system input by the brain.

**pericycle** The outermost layer in the vascular cylinder, from which lateral roots arise.

**periderm** (par′-uh-derm′) The protective coat that replaces the epidermis in woody plants during secondary growth, formed of the cork and cork cambium.

**peripheral nervous system (PNS)** The sensory and motor neurons that connect to the central nervous system.

**peripheral protein** A protein loosely bound to the surface of a membrane or to part of an integral protein and not embedded in the lipid bilayer.

**peristalsis** (par′-uh-stal′-sis) (1) Alternating waves of contraction and relaxation in the smooth muscles lining the alimentary canal that push food along the canal. (2) A type of movement on land produced by rhythmic waves of muscle contractions passing from front to back, as in many annelids.

**peristome** (par′-uh-stōm′) A ring of interlocking, tooth-like structures on the upper part of a moss capsule (sporangium), often specialized for gradual spore discharge.

**peritubular capillary** One of the tiny blood vessels that form a network surrounding the proximal and distal tubules in the kidney.

**peroxisome** (puh-rok′-suh-sōm′) An organelle containing enzymes that transfer hydrogen atoms from various substrates to oxygen ($O_2$), producing and then degrading hydrogen peroxide ($H_2O_2$).

**petal** A modified leaf of a flowering plant. Petals are the often colorful parts of a flower that advertise it to insects and other pollinators.

**petiole** (pet′-ē-ōl) The stalk of a leaf, which joins the leaf to a node of the stem.

**P generation** The true-breeding (homozygous) parent individuals from which $F_1$ hybrid offspring are derived in studies of inheritance; P stands for "parental."

**pH** A measure of hydrogen ion concentration equal to $-\log [H^+]$ and ranging in value from 0 to 14.

**phage** (fāj) A virus that infects bacteria; also called a bacteriophage.

**phagocytosis** (fag′-ō-sī-tō′-sis) A type of endocytosis in which large particulate substances or small organisms are taken up by a cell. It is carried out by some protists and by certain immune cells of animals (in mammals, mainly macrophages, neutrophils, and dendritic cells).

**pharyngeal cleft** (fuh-rin′-jē-ul) In chordate embryos, one of the grooves that separate a series of arches along the outer surface of the pharynx and may develop into a pharyngeal slit.

**pharyngeal slit** (fuh-rin′-jē-ul) In chordate embryos, one of the slits that form from the pharyngeal clefts and open into the pharynx, later developing into gill slits in many vertebrates.

**pharynx** (fār′-inks) (1) An area in the vertebrate throat where air and food passages cross. (2) In flatworms, the muscular tube that protrudes from the ventral side of the worm and ends in the mouth.

**phase change** (1) A shift from one developmental phase to another. (2) In plants, a morphological change that arises from a transition in shoot apical meristem activity.

**phenotype** (fē′-nō-tīp) The observable physical and physiological traits of an organism, which are determined by its genetic makeup.

**pheromone** (fār′-uh-mōn) In animals and fungi, a small molecule released into the environment that functions in communication between members of the same species. In animals, it acts much like a hormone in influencing physiology and behavior.

**phloem** (flō′-em) Vascular plant tissue consisting of living cells arranged into elongated tubes that transport sugar and other organic nutrients throughout the plant.

**phloem sap** (flō′-em) The sugar-rich solution carried through a plant's sieve tubes.

**phosphate group** A chemical group consisting of a phosphorus atom bonded to four oxygen atoms; important in energy transfer.

**phospholipid** (fos′-fō-lip′-id) A lipid made up of glycerol joined to two fatty acids and a phosphate group. The hydrocarbon chains of the fatty acids act as nonpolar, hydrophobic tails, while the rest of the molecule acts as a polar, hydrophilic head. Phospholipids form bilayers that function as biological membranes.

**phosphorylated intermediate** (fos′-fōr-uh-lā′-ted) A molecule (often a reactant) with a phosphate group covalently bound to it, making it more reactive (less stable) than the unphosphorylated molecule.

**phosphorylation cascade** (fos′-fōr-uh-lā′-shun) A series of protein phosphorylations occurring sequentially in which each protein kinase phosphorylates the next, activating it; often found in signaling pathways.

**photic zone** (fō′-tic) The narrow top layer of an ocean or lake, where light penetrates sufficiently for photosynthesis to occur.

**photoautotroph** (fō′-tō-ot′-ō-trōf) An organism that harnesses light energy to drive the synthesis of organic compounds from carbon dioxide.

**photoheterotroph** (fō′-tō-het′-er-ō-trōf) An organism that uses light to generate ATP but must obtain carbon in organic form.

**photomorphogenesis** Effects of light on plant morphology.

**photon** (fō′-ton) A quantum, or discrete quantity, of light energy that behaves as if it were a particle.

**photoperiodism** (fō′-tō-pēr′-ē-ō-dizm) A physiological response to photoperiod, the interval in a 24-hour period during which an organism is exposed to light. An example of photoperiodism is flowering.

**photophosphorylation** (fō′-tō-fos′-fōr-uh-lā′-shun) The process of generating ATP from ADP and phosphate by means of chemiosmosis, using a proton-motive force generated across the thylakoid membrane of the chloroplast or the membrane of certain prokaryotes during the light reactions of photosynthesis.

**photoreceptor** An electromagnetic receptor that detects the radiation known as visible light.

**photorespiration** A metabolic pathway that consumes oxygen and ATP, releases carbon dioxide, and decreases photosynthetic output. Photorespiration generally occurs on hot, dry, bright days, when stomata close and the $O_2/CO_2$ ratio in the leaf increases, favoring the binding of $O_2$ rather than $CO_2$ by rubisco.

**photosynthesis** (fō′-tō-sin′-thi-sis) The conversion of light energy to chemical energy that is stored in sugars or other organic compounds; occurs in plants, algae, and certain prokaryotes.

**photosystem** A light-capturing unit located in the thylakoid membrane of the chloroplast or in the membrane of some prokaryotes, consisting of a reaction-center complex surrounded by numerous light-harvesting complexes. There are two types of photosystems, I and II; they absorb light best at different wavelengths.

**photosystem I (PS I)** A light-capturing unit in a chloroplast's thylakoid membrane or in the membrane of some prokaryotes; it has two molecules of P700 chlorophyll *a* at its reaction center.

**photosystem II (PS II)** One of two light-capturing units in a chloroplast's thylakoid membrane or in the membrane of some prokaryotes; it has two molecules of P680 chlorophyll *a* at its reaction center.

**phototropism** (fō′-tō-trō′-pizm) Growth of a plant shoot toward or away from light.

**phyllotaxy** (fil′-uh-tak′-sē) The pattern of leaf attachment to the stem of a plant.

**phylogenetic species concept** Definition of a species as the smallest group of individuals that share a common ancestor, forming one branch on the tree of life.

**phylogenetic tree** A branching diagram that represents a hypothesis about the evolutionary history of a group of organisms.

**phylogeny** (fī-loj′-uh-nē) The evolutionary history of a species or group of related species.

**phylum** (fī′-lum) (plural, **phyla**) In Linnaean classification, the taxonomic category above class.

**physiology** The processes and functions of an organism.

**phytochrome** (fī′-tuh-krōm) A type of light receptor in plants that mostly absorbs red light and regulates many plant responses, such as seed germination and shade avoidance.

**phytoremediation** An emerging technology that seeks to reclaim contaminated areas by taking advantage of some plant species' ability to extract heavy metals and other pollutants from the soil and to concentrate them in easily harvested portions of the plant.

**pilus** (plural, **pili**) (pī′-lus, pī′-lī) In bacteria, a structure that links one cell to another at the start of conjugation; also called a sex pilus or conjugation pilus.

**pineal gland** (pī′-nē-ul) A small gland on the dorsal surface of the vertebrate forebrain that secretes the hormone melatonin.

**pinocytosis** (pī′-nō-sī-tō′-sis) A type of endocytosis in which the cell ingests extracellular fluid and its dissolved solutes.

**pistil** A single carpel or a group of fused carpels.

**pith** Ground tissue that is internal to the vascular tissue in a stem; in many monocot roots, parenchyma cells that form the central core of the vascular cylinder.

**pituitary gland** (puh-tū′-uh-tār′-ē) An endocrine gland at the base of the hypothalamus; consists of a posterior lobe, which stores and releases two hormones produced by the hypothalamus, and an anterior lobe, which produces and secretes many hormones that regulate diverse body functions.

**placenta** (pluh-sen′-tuh) A structure in the uterus of a pregnant eutherian mammal that nourishes the fetus with the mother's blood supply; formed from the uterine lining and embryonic membranes.

**placoderm** A member of an extinct group of fishlike vertebrates that had jaws and were enclosed in a tough outer armor.

**planarian** A free-living flatworm found in ponds and streams.

**plasma** (plaz′-muh) The liquid matrix of blood in which the blood cells are suspended.

**plasma cell** (plaz′-muh) The antibody-secreting effector cell of humoral immunity. Plasma cells arise from antigen-stimulated B cells.

**plasma membrane** (plaz′-muh) The membrane at the boundary of every cell that acts as a selective barrier, regulating the cell's chemical composition.

**plasmid** (plaz′-mid) A small, circular, double-stranded DNA molecule that carries accessory genes separate from those of a bacterial chromosome; in DNA cloning, plasmids are used as vectors carrying up to about 10,000 base pairs (10 kb) of DNA. Plasmids are also found in some eukaryotes, such as yeasts.

**plasmodesma** (plaz′-mō-dez′-muh) (plural, **plasmodesmata**) An open channel through the cell wall that connects the cytoplasm of adjacent plant cells, allowing water, small solutes, and some larger molecules to pass between the cells.

**plasmogamy** (plaz-moh′-guh-mē) In fungi, the fusion of the cytoplasm of cells from two individuals; occurs as one stage of sexual reproduction, followed later by karyogamy.

**plasmolysis** (plaz-mol′-uh-sis) A phenomenon in walled cells in which the cytoplasm shrivels and the plasma membrane pulls away from the cell wall; occurs when the cell loses water to a hypertonic environment.

**plastid** One of a family of closely related organelles that includes chloroplasts, chromoplasts, and amyloplasts. Plastids are found in cells of photosynthetic eukaryotes.

**plate tectonics** The theory that the continents are part of great plates of Earth's crust that float on the hot, underlying portion of the mantle. Movements in the mantle cause the continents to move slowly over time.

**platelet** A pinched-off cytoplasmic fragment of a specialized bone marrow cell. Platelets circulate in the blood and are important in blood clotting.

**pleiotropy** (pli'-o-truh-pē) The ability of a single gene to have multiple effects.

**pluripotent** Describing a cell that can give rise to many, but not all, parts of an organism.

**point mutation** A change in a single nucleotide pair of a gene.

**polar covalent bond** A covalent bond between atoms that differ in electronegativity. The shared electrons are pulled closer to the more electronegative atom, making it slightly negative and the other atom slightly positive.

**polar molecule** A molecule (such as water) with an uneven distribution of charges in different regions of the molecule.

**polarity** A lack of symmetry; structural differences in opposite ends of an organism or structure, such as the root end and shoot end of a plant.

**pollen grain** In seed plants, a structure consisting of the male gametophyte enclosed within a pollen wall.

**pollen tube** A tube that forms after germination of the pollen grain and that functions in the delivery of sperm to the ovule.

**pollination** (pol'-uh-nā'-shun) The transfer of pollen to the part of a seed plant containing the ovules, a process required for fertilization.

**poly-A tail** A sequence of 50–250 adenine nucleotides added onto the 3' end of a premRNA molecule.

**polygamous** Referring to a type of relationship in which an individual of one sex mates with several of the other.

**polygenic inheritance** (pol'-ē-jen'-ik) An additive effect of two or more genes on a single phenotypic character.

**polymer** (pol'-uh-mer) A long molecule consisting of many similar or identical monomers linked together by covalent bonds.

**polymerase chain reaction (PCR)** (puh-lim'-uh-rās) A technique for amplifying DNA *in vitro* by incubating it with specific primers, a heat-resistant DNA polymerase, and nucleotides.

**polynucleotide** (pol'-ē-nū'-klē-ō-tīd) A polymer consisting of many nucleotide monomers in a chain. The nucleotides can be those of DNA or RNA.

**polyp** The sessile variant of the cnidarian body plan. The alternate form is the medusa.

**polypeptide** (pol'-ē-pep'-tīd) A polymer of many amino acids linked together by peptide bonds.

**polyphyletic** (pol'-ē-fī-let'-ik) Pertaining to a group of taxa that includes distantly related organisms but does not include their most recent common ancestor.

**polyploidy** (pol'-ē-ploy'-dē) A chromosomal alteration in which the organism possesses more than two complete chromosome sets. It is the result of an accident of cell division.

**polyribosome (polysome)** (pol'-ē-rī'-buh-sōm') A group of several ribosomes attached to, and translating, the same messenger RNA molecule.

**polysaccharide** (pol'-ē-sak'-uh-rīd) A polymer of many monosaccharides, formed by dehydration reactions.

**polytomy** (puh-lit'-uh-mē) In a phylogenetic tree, a branch point from which more than two descendant taxa emerge. A polytomy indicates that the evolutionary relationships between the descendant taxa are not yet clear.

**pons** A portion of the brain that participates in certain automatic, homeostatic functions, such as regulating the breathing centers in the medulla.

**population** A group of individuals of the same species that live in the same area and interbreed, producing fertile offspring.

**population dynamics** The study of how complex interactions between biotic and abiotic factors influence variations in population size.

**population ecology** The study of populations in relation to their environment, including environmental influences on population density and distribution, age structure, and variations in population size.

**positional information** Molecular cues that control pattern formation in an animal or plant embryonic structure by indicating a cell's location relative to the organism's body axes. These cues elicit a response by genes that regulate development.

**positive feedback** A form of regulation in which an end product of a process speeds up that process; in physiology, a control mechanism in which a change in a variable triggers a response that reinforces or amplifies the change.

**positive pressure breathing** A breathing system in which air is forced into the lungs.

**posterior** Pertaining to the rear, or tail end, of a bilaterally symmetrical animal.

**posterior pituitary** An extension of the hypothalamus composed of nervous tissue that secretes oxytocin and antidiuretic hormone made in the hypothalamus; a temporary storage site for these hormones.

**postzygotic barrier** (pōst'-zī-got'-ik) A reproductive barrier that prevents hybrid zygotes produced by two different species from developing into viable, fertile adults.

**potential energy** The energy that matter possesses as a result of its location or spatial arrangement (structure).

**predation** An interaction between species in which one species, the predator, eats the other, the prey.

**prediction** In deductive reasoning, a forecast that follows logically from a hypothesis. By testing predictions, experiments may allow certain hypotheses to be rejected.

**pregnancy** The condition of carrying one or more embryos in the uterus; also called gestation.

**prepuce** (prē'-pyūs) A fold of skin covering the head of the clitoris or penis.

**pressure potential ($\Psi_p$)** A component of water potential that consists of the physical pressure on a solution, which can be positive, zero, or negative.

**prezygotic barrier** (prē'-zī-got'-ik) A reproductive barrier that impedes mating between species or hinders fertilization if interspecific mating is attempted.

**primary cell wall** In plants, a relatively thin and flexible layer that surrounds the plasma membrane of a young cell.

**primary consumer** An herbivore; an organism that eats plants or other autotrophs.

**primary electron acceptor** In the thylakoid membrane of a chloroplast or in the membrane of some prokaryotes, a specialized molecule that shares the reaction-center complex with a pair of chlorophyll *a* molecules and that accepts an electron from them.

**primary growth** Growth produced by apical meristems, lengthening stems and roots.

**primary immune response** The initial adaptive immune response to an antigen, which appears after a lag of about 10–17 days.

**primary oocyte** (ō'-uh-sīt) An oocyte prior to completion of meiosis I.

**primary producer** An autotroph, usually a photosynthetic organism. Collectively, autotrophs make up the trophic level of an ecosystem that ultimately supports all other levels.

**primary production** The amount of light energy converted to chemical energy (organic compounds) by the autotrophs in an ecosystem during a given time period.

**primary structure** The level of protein structure referring to the specific linear sequence of amino acids.

**primary succession** A type of ecological succession that occurs in an area where there were originally no organisms present and where soil has not yet formed.

**primary transcript** An initial RNA transcript from any gene; also called pre-mRNA when transcribed from a protein-coding gene.

**primase** An enzyme that joins RNA nucleotides to make a primer during DNA replication, using the parental DNA strand as a template.

**primer** A short stretch of RNA with a free 3' end, bound by complementary base pairing to the template strand and elongated with DNA nucleotides during DNA replication.

**primitive streak** A thickening along the future anterior-posterior axis on the surface of an early avian or mammalian embryo, caused by a piling up of cells as they congregate at the midline before moving into the embryo.

**prion** An infectious agent that is a misfolded version of a normal cellular protein. Prions appear to increase in number by converting correctly folded versions of the protein to more prions.

**problem solving** The cognitive activity of devising a method to proceed from one state to another in the face of real or apparent obstacles.

**producer** An organism that produces organic compounds from $CO_2$ by harnessing light energy (in photosynthesis) or by oxidizing inorganic chemicals (in chemosynthetic reactions carried out by some prokaryotes).

**product** A material resulting from a chemical reaction.

**production efficiency** The percentage of energy stored in assimilated food that is not used for respiration or eliminated as waste.

**progesterone** A steroid hormone that prepares the uterus for pregnancy; the major progestin in mammals.

**progestin** Any steroid hormone with progesterone-like activity.

**prokaryotic cell** (prō′-kär′-ē-ot′-ik) A type of cell lacking a membrane-enclosed nucleus and membrane-enclosed organelles. Organisms with prokaryotic cells (bacteria and archaea) are called prokaryotes.

**prolactin** A hormone produced and secreted by the anterior pituitary with a great diversity of effects in different vertebrate species. In mammals, it stimulates growth of and milk production by the mammary glands.

**prometaphase** The second stage of mitosis, in which the nuclear envelope fragments and the spindle microtubules attach to the kinetochores of the chromosomes.

**promoter** A specific nucleotide sequence in the DNA of a gene that binds RNA polymerase, positioning it to start transcribing RNA at the appropriate place.

**prophage** (prō′-fāj) A phage genome that has been inserted into a specific site on a bacterial chromosome.

**prophase** The first stage of mitosis, in which the chromatin condenses into discrete chromosomes visible with a light microscope, the mitotic spindle begins to form, and the nucleolus disappears but the nucleus remains intact.

**prostaglandin** (pros′-tuh-glan′-din) One of a group of modified fatty acids that are secreted by virtually all tissues and that perform a wide variety of functions as local regulators.

**prostate gland** (pros′-tāt) A gland in human males that secretes an acid-neutralizing component of semen.

**protease** (prō′-tē-āz) An enzyme that digests proteins by hydrolysis.

**protein** (prō′-tēn) A biologically functional molecule consisting of one or more polypeptides folded and coiled into a specific three-dimensional structure.

**protein kinase** (prō′-tēn) An enzyme that transfers phosphate groups from ATP to a protein, thus phosphorylating the protein.

**protein phosphatase** (prō′-tēn) An enzyme that removes phosphate groups from (dephosphorylates) proteins, often functioning to reverse the effect of a protein kinase.

**proteoglycan** (prō′-tē-ō-glī′-kan) A large molecule consisting of a small core protein with many carbohydrate chains attached, found in the extracellular matrix of animal cells. A proteoglycan may consist of up to 95% carbohydrate.

**proteome** The entire set of proteins expressed by a given cell or group of cells.

**proteomics** (prō′-tē-ō′-miks) The systematic study of sets of proteins and their properties, including their abundance, chemical modifications, and interactions.

**protist** An informal term applied to any eukaryote that is not a plant, animal, or fungus. Most protists are unicellular, though some are colonial or multicellular.

**protocell** An abiotic precursor of a living cell that had a membrane-like structure and that maintained an internal chemistry different from that of its surroundings.

**proton** (prō′-ton) A subatomic particle with a single positive electrical charge, with a mass of about $1.7 \times 10^{-24}$ g, found in the nucleus of an atom.

**protonema** (prō′-tuh-nē′-muh) (plural, **protonemata**) A mass of green, branched, one-cell-thick filaments produced by germinating moss spores.

**protonephridium** (prō′-tō-nuh-frid′-ē-um) (plural, **protonephridia**) An excretory system, such as the flame bulb system of flatworms, consisting of a network of tubules lacking internal openings.

**proton-motive force** (prō′-ton) The potential energy stored in the form of a proton electrochemical gradient, generated by the pumping of hydrogen ions ($H^+$) across a biological membrane during chemiosmosis.

**proton pump** (prō′-ton) An active transport protein in a cell membrane that uses ATP to transport hydrogen ions out of a cell against their concentration gradient, generating a membrane potential in the process.

**proto-oncogene** (prō′-tō-on′-kō-jēn) A normal cellular gene that has the potential to become an oncogene.

**protoplast** The living part of a plant cell, which also includes the plasma membrane.

**protostome development** In animals, a developmental mode distinguished by the development of the mouth from the blastopore; often also characterized by spiral cleavage and by the body cavity forming when solid masses of mesoderm split.

**provirus** A viral genome that is permanently inserted into a host genome.

**proximal tubule** In the vertebrate kidney, the portion of a nephron immediately downstream from Bowman's capsule that conveys and helps refine filtrate.

**pseudocoelomate** (sū′-dō-sē′-lō-māt) An animal whose body cavity is lined by tissue derived from mesoderm and endoderm.

**pseudogene** (sū′-dō-jēn) A DNA segment that is very similar to a real gene but does not yield a functional product; a DNA segment that formerly functioned as a gene but has become inactivated in a particular species because of mutation.

**pseudopodium** (sū′-dō-pō′-dē-um) (plural, **pseudopodia**) A cellular extension of amoeboid cells used in moving and feeding.

**P site** One of a ribosome's three binding sites for tRNA during translation. The P site holds the tRNA carrying the growing polypeptide chain. (P stands for peptidyl tRNA.)

**pterosaur** Winged reptile that lived during the Mesozoic era.

**pulse** The rhythmic bulging of the artery walls with each heartbeat.

**punctuated equilibria** In the fossil record, long periods of apparent stasis, in which a species undergoes little or no morphological change, interrupted by relatively brief periods of sudden change.

**Punnett square** A diagram used in the study of inheritance to show the predicted genotypic results of random fertilization in genetic crosses between individuals of known genotype.

**pupil** The opening in the iris, which admits light into the interior of the vertebrate eye. Muscles in the iris regulate its size.

**purine** (pyū′-rēn) One of two types of nitrogenous bases found in nucleotides, characterized by a six-membered ring fused to a five-membered ring. Adenine (A) and guanine (G) are purines.

**pyrimidine** (puh-rim′-uh-dēn) One of two types of nitrogenous bases found in nucleotides, characterized by a six-membered ring. Cytosine (C), thymine (T), and uracil (U) are pyrimidines.

**quantitative character** A heritable feature that varies continuously over a range rather than in an either-or fashion.

**quaternary structure** (kwot′-er-när′-ē) The particular shape of a complex, aggregate protein, defined by the characteristic three-dimensional arrangement of its constituent subunits, each a polypeptide.

**radial cleavage** A type of embryonic development in deuterostomes in which the planes of cell division that transform the zygote into a ball of cells are either parallel or perpendicular to the vertical axis of the embryo, thereby aligning tiers of cells one above the other.

**radial symmetry** Symmetry in which the body is shaped like a pie or barrel (lacking a left side and a right side) and can be divided into mirror-imaged halves by any plane through its central axis.

**radicle** An embryonic root of a plant.

**radioactive isotope** An isotope (an atomic form of a chemical element) that is unstable; the nucleus decays spontaneously, giving off detectable particles and energy.

**radiolarian** A protist, usually marine, with a shell generally made of silica and pseudopodia that radiate from the central body.

**radiometric dating** A method for determining the absolute age of rocks and fossils, based on the half-life of radioactive isotopes.

**radula** A straplike scraping organ used by many molluscs during feeding.

*ras* **gene** A gene that codes for Ras, a G protein that relays a growth signal from a growth factor receptor on the plasma membrane to a cascade of protein kinases, ultimately resulting in stimulation of the cell cycle.

**ratite** (rat′-īt) A member of the group of flightless birds.

**ray-finned fish** A member of the clade Actinopterygii, aquatic osteichthyans with fins supported by long, flexible rays, including tuna, bass, and herring.

**reabsorption** In excretory systems, the recovery of solutes and water from filtrate.

**reactant** A starting material in a chemical reaction.

**reaction-center complex** A complex of proteins associated with a special pair of chlorophyll *a* molecules and a primary electron acceptor. Located centrally in a photosystem, this complex triggers the light reactions of photosynthesis. Excited by light energy, the pair of chlorophylls donates an electron to the primary electron acceptor, which passes an electron to an electron transport chain.

**reading frame** On an mRNA, the triplet grouping of ribonucleotides used by the translation machinery during polypeptide synthesis.

**receptacle** The base of a flower; the part of the stem that is the site of attachment of the floral organs.

**reception** In cellular communication, the first step of a signaling pathway in which a signaling molecule is detected by a receptor molecule on or in the cell.

**receptor-mediated endocytosis** (en′-dō-sī-tō′-sis) The movement of specific molecules into a cell by the infolding of vesicles containing proteins with receptor sites specific to the molecules being taken in; enables a cell to acquire bulk quantities of specific substances.

**receptor potential** An initial response of a receptor cell to a stimulus, consisting of a change in voltage across the receptor membrane proportional to the stimulus strength.

**receptor tyrosine kinase (RTK)** A receptor protein spanning the plasma membrane, the cytoplasmic (intracellular) part of which can catalyze the transfer of a phosphate group from ATP to a tyrosine on another protein. Receptor tyrosine kinases often respond to the binding of a signaling molecule by dimerizing and then phosphorylating a tyrosine on the cytoplasmic portion of the other receptor in the dimer.

**recessive allele** An allele whose phenotypic effect is not observed in a heterozygote.

**reciprocal altruism** Altruistic behavior between unrelated individuals, whereby the altruistic individual benefits in the future when the beneficiary reciprocates.

**recombinant chromosome** A chromosome created when crossing over combines DNA from two parents into a single chromosome.

**recombinant DNA** A DNA molecule made *in vitro* with segments from different sources.

**recombinant type (recombinant)** An offspring whose phenotype differs from that of the true-breeding P generation parents; also refers to the phenotype itself.

**rectum** The terminal portion of the large intestine, where the feces are stored prior to elimination.

**red alga** A photosynthetic protist, named for its color, which results from a red pigment that masks the green of chlorophyll. Most red algae are multicellular and marine.

**redox reaction** (rē′-doks) A chemical reaction involving the complete or partial transfer of one or more electrons from one reactant to another; short for **red**uction-**ox**idation reaction.

**reducing agent** The electron donor in a redox reaction.

**reduction** The complete or partial addition of electrons to a substance involved in a redox reaction.

**reflex** An automatic reaction to a stimulus, mediated by the spinal cord or lower brain.

**refractory period** (rē-frakt′-ōr-ē) The short time immediately after an action potential in which the neuron cannot respond to another stimulus, owing to the inactivation of voltage-gated sodium channels.

**regulator** An animal for which mechanisms of homeostasis moderate internal changes in a particular variable in the face of external fluctuation of that variable.

**regulatory gene** A gene that codes for a protein, such as a repressor, that controls the transcription of another gene or group of genes.

**reinforcement** In evolutionary biology, a process in which natural selection strengthens prezygotic barriers to reproduction, thus reducing the chances of hybrid formation. Such a process is likely to occur only if hybrid offspring are less fit than members of the parent species.

**relative abundance** The proportional abundance of different species in a community.

**relative fitness** The contribution an individual makes to the gene pool of the next generation, relative to the contributions of other individuals in the population.

**renal cortex** The outer portion of the vertebrate kidney.

**renal medulla** The inner portion of the vertebrate kidney, beneath the renal cortex.

**renal pelvis** The funnel-shaped chamber that receives processed filtrate from the vertebrate kidney's collecting ducts and is drained by the ureter.

**renin-angiotensin-aldosterone system (RAAS)** A hormone cascade pathway that helps regulate blood pressure and blood volume.

**repetitive DNA** Nucleotide sequences, usually noncoding, that are present in many copies in a eukaryotic genome. The repeated units may be short and arranged tandemly (in series) or long and dispersed in the genome.

**replication fork** A Y-shaped region on a replicating DNA molecule where the parental strands are being unwound and new strands are being synthesized.

**repressor** A protein that inhibits gene transcription. In prokaryotes, repressors bind to the DNA in or near the promoter. In eukaryotes, repressors may bind to control elements within enhancers, to activators, or to other proteins in a way that blocks activators from binding to DNA.

**reproductive isolation** The existence of biological factors (barriers) that impede members of two species from producing viable, fertile offspring.

**reproductive table** An age-specific summary of the reproductive rates in a population.

**reptile** A member of the clade of amniotes that includes tuataras, lizards, snakes, turtles, crocodilians, and birds.

**residual volume** The amount of air that remains in the lungs after forceful exhalation.

**resource partitioning** The division of environmental resources by coexisting species such that the niche of each species differs by one or more significant factors from the niches of all coexisting species.

**respiratory pigment** A protein that transports oxygen in blood or hemolymph.

**response** (1) In cellular communication, the change in a specific cellular activity brought about by a transduced signal from outside the cell. (2) In feedback regulation, a physiological activity triggered by a change in a variable.

**resting potential** The membrane potential characteristic of a nonconducting excitable cell, with the inside of the cell more negative than the outside.

**restriction enzyme** An endonuclease (type of enzyme) that recognizes and cuts DNA molecules foreign to a bacterium (such as phage genomes). The enzyme cuts at specific nucleotide sequences (restriction sites).

**restriction fragment** A DNA segment that results from the cutting of DNA by a restriction enzyme.

**restriction site** A specific sequence on a DNA strand that is recognized and cut by a restriction enzyme.

**retina** (ret′-i-nuh) The innermost layer of the vertebrate eye, containing photoreceptor cells (rods and cones) and neurons; transmits images formed by the lens to the brain via the optic nerve.

**retinal** The light-absorbing pigment in rods and cones of the vertebrate eye.

**retrotransposon** (re′-trō-trans-pō′-zon) A transposable element that moves within a genome by means of an RNA intermediate, a transcript of the retrotransposon DNA.

**retrovirus** (re′-trō-vī′-rus) An RNA virus that replicates by transcribing its RNA into DNA and then inserting the DNA into a cellular chromosome; an important class of cancer-causing viruses.

**reverse transcriptase** (tran-skrip′-tās) An enzyme encoded by certain viruses (retroviruses) that uses RNA as a template for DNA synthesis.

**reverse transcriptase–polymerase chain reaction (RT-PCR)** A technique for determining expression of a particular gene. It uses reverse transcriptase and DNA polymerase to synthesize cDNA from all the mRNA in a sample and then subjects the cDNA to PCR amplification using primers specific for the gene of interest.

**Rhizaria** (rī-za′-rē-uh) One of the three major subgroups for which the "SAR" eukaryotic supergroup is named. Many species in this clade are amoebas characterized by threadlike pseudopodia.

**rhizobacterium** A soil bacterium whose population size is much enhanced in the rhizosphere, the soil region close to a plant's roots.

**rhizoid** (rī'-zoyd) A long, tubular single cell or filament of cells that anchors bryophytes to the ground. Unlike roots, rhizoids are not composed of tissues, lack specialized conducting cells, and do not play a primary role in water and mineral absorption.

**rhizosphere** The soil region close to plant roots and characterized by a high level of microbiological activity.

**rhodopsin** (rō-dop'-sin) A visual pigment consisting of retinal and opsin. Upon absorbing light, the retinal changes shape and dissociates from the opsin.

**ribonucleic acid (RNA)** (rī'-bō-nū-klā'-ik) A type of nucleic acid consisting of a polynucleotide made up of nucleotide monomers with a ribose sugar and the nitrogenous bases adenine (A), cytosine (C), guanine (G), and uracil (U); usually single-stranded; functions in protein synthesis, in gene regulation, and as the genome of some viruses.

**ribose** The sugar component of RNA nucleotides.

**ribosomal RNA (rRNA)** (rī'-buh-sō'-mul) RNA molecules that, together with proteins, make up ribosomes; the most abundant type of RNA.

**ribosome** (rī'-buh-sōm) A complex of rRNA and protein molecules that functions as a site of protein synthesis in the cytoplasm; consists of a large and a small subunit. In eukaryotic cells, each subunit is assembled in the nucleolus. *See also* nucleolus.

**ribozyme** (rī'-buh-zīm) An RNA molecule that functions as an enzyme, such as an intron that catalyzes its own removal during RNA splicing.

**RNA interference (RNAi)** A mechanism for silencing the expression of specific genes. In RNAi, double-stranded RNA molecules that match the sequence of a particular gene are processed into siRNAs that either block translation or trigger the degradation of the gene's messenger RNA. This happens naturally in some cells, and can be carried out in laboratory experiments as well.

**RNA polymerase** An enzyme that links ribonucleotides into a growing RNA chain during transcription, based on complementary binding to nucleotides on a DNA template strand.

**RNA processing** Modification of RNA primary transcripts, including splicing out of introns, joining together of exons, and alteration of the 5' and 3' ends.

**RNA splicing** After synthesis of a eukaryotic primary RNA transcript, the removal of portions of the transcript (introns) that will not be included in the mRNA and the joining together of the remaining portions (exons).

**rod** A rodlike cell in the retina of the vertebrate eye, sensitive to low light intensity.

**root** An organ in vascular plants that anchors the plant and enables it to absorb water and minerals from the soil.

**root cap** A cone of cells at the tip of a plant root that protects the apical meristem.

**root hair** A tiny extension of a root epidermal cell, growing just behind the root tip and increasing surface area for absorption of water and minerals.

**root pressure** Pressure exerted in the roots of plants as the result of osmosis, causing exudation from cut stems and guttation of water from leaves.

**root system** All of a plant's roots, which anchor it in the soil, absorb and transport minerals and water, and store food.

**rooted** Describing a phylogenetic tree that contains a branch point (often, the one farthest to the left) representing the most recent common ancestor of all taxa in the tree.

**rough ER** That portion of the endoplasmic reticulum with ribosomes attached.

**round window** In the mammalian ear, the point of contact where vibrations of the stapes create a traveling series of pressure waves in the fluid of the cochlea.

**R plasmid** A bacterial plasmid carrying genes that confer resistance to certain antibiotics.

**r-selection** Selection for life history traits that maximize reproductive success in uncrowded environments; also called density-independent selection.

**rubisco** (rū-bis'-kō) Ribulose bisphosphate (RuBP) carboxylase-oxygenase, the enzyme that normally catalyzes the first step of the Calvin cycle (the addition of $CO_2$ to RuBP). When excess $O_2$ is present or $CO_2$ levels are low, rubisco can bind oxygen, resulting in photorespiration.

**saccule** In the vertebrate ear, a chamber in the vestibule behind the oval window that participates in the sense of balance.

**salicylic acid** (sal'-i-sil'-ik) A signaling molecule in plants that may be partially responsible for activating systemic acquired resistance to pathogens.

**salivary gland** A gland associated with the oral cavity that secretes substances that lubricate food and begin the process of chemical digestion.

**salt** A compound resulting from the formation of an ionic bond; also called an ionic compound.

**saltatory conduction** (sol'-tuh-tōr'-ē) Rapid transmission of a nerve impulse along an axon, resulting from the action potential jumping from one node of Ranvier to another, skipping the myelin-sheathed regions of membrane.

**"SAR" clade** One of four supergroups of eukaryotes proposed in a current hypothesis of the evolutionary history of eukaryotes. This supergroup contains a large, extremely diverse collection of protists from three major subgroups: stramenopiles, alveolates, and rhizarians. *See also* Excavata, Archaeplastida, and Unikonta.

**sarcomere** (sar'-kō-mēr) The fundamental, repeating unit of striated muscle, delimited by the Z lines.

**sarcoplasmic reticulum (SR)** (sar'-kō-plaz'-mik ruh-tik'-yū-lum) A specialized endoplasmic reticulum that regulates the calcium concentration in the cytosol of muscle cells.

**saturated fatty acid** A fatty acid in which all carbons in the hydrocarbon tail are connected by single bonds, thus maximizing the number of hydrogen atoms that are attached to the carbon skeleton.

**savanna** A tropical grassland biome with scattered individual trees and large herbivores and maintained by occasional fires and drought.

**scaffolding protein** A type of large relay protein to which several other relay proteins are simultaneously attached, increasing the efficiency of signal transduction.

**scanning electron microscope (SEM)** A microscope that uses an electron beam to scan the surface of a sample, coated with metal atoms, to study details of its topography.

**scatter plot** A graph in which each piece of data is represented by a point. A scatter plot is used when the data for all variables are numerical and continuous.

**schizophrenia** (skit'-suh-frē'-nē-uh) A severe mental disturbance characterized by psychotic episodes in which patients have a distorted perception of reality.

**Schwann cell** A type of glial cell that forms insulating myelin sheaths around the axons of neurons in the peripheral nervous system.

**science** An approach to understanding the natural world.

**scion** (sī'-un) The twig grafted onto the stock when making a graft.

**sclereid** (sklār'-ē-id) A short, irregular sclerenchyma cell in nutshells and seed coats. Sclereids are scattered throughout the parenchyma of some plants.

**sclerenchyma cell** (skluh-ren'-kim-uh) A rigid, supportive plant cell type usually lacking a protoplast and possessing thick secondary walls strengthened by lignin at maturity.

**scrotum** A pouch of skin outside the abdomen that houses the testes; functions in maintaining the testes at the lower temperature required for spermatogenesis.

**second law of thermodynamics** The principle stating that every energy transfer or transformation increases the entropy of the universe. Usable forms of energy are at least partly converted to heat.

**second messenger** A small, nonprotein, water-soluble molecule or ion, such as a calcium ion ($Ca^{2+}$) or cyclic AMP, that relays a signal to a cell's interior in response to a signaling molecule bound by a signal receptor protein.

**secondary cell wall** In plant cells, a strong and durable matrix that is often deposited in several laminated layers around the plasma membrane and provides protection and support.

**secondary consumer** A carnivore that eats herbivores.

**secondary endosymbiosis** A process in eukaryotic evolution in which a heterotrophic eukaryotic cell engulfed a photosynthetic eukaryotic cell, which survived in a symbiotic relationship inside the heterotrophic cell.

**secondary growth** Growth produced by lateral meristems, thickening the roots and shoots of woody plants.

**secondary immune response** The adaptive immune response elicited on second or subsequent exposures to a particular antigen. The secondary immune response is more rapid, of greater magnitude, and of longer duration than the primary immune response.

**secondary oocyte** (ō´-uh-sīt) An oocyte that has completed meiosis I.

**secondary production** The amount of chemical energy in consumers' food that is converted to their own new biomass during a given time period.

**secondary structure** Regions of repetitive coiling or folding of the polypeptide backbone of a protein due to hydrogen bonding between constituents of the backbone (not the side chains).

**secondary succession** A type of succession that occurs where an existing community has been cleared by some disturbance that leaves the soil or substrate intact.

**secretion** (1) The discharge of molecules synthesized by a cell. (2) The active transport of wastes and certain other solutes from the body fluid into the filtrate in an excretory system.

**seed** An adaptation of some terrestrial plants consisting of an embryo packaged along with a store of food within a protective coat.

**seed coat** A tough outer covering of a seed, formed from the outer coat of an ovule. In a flowering plant, the seed coat encloses and protects the embryo and endosperm.

**seedless vascular plant** An informal name for a plant that has vascular tissue but lacks seeds. Seedless vascular plants form a paraphyletic group that includes the phyla Lycophyta (club mosses and their relatives) and Monilophyta (ferns and their relatives).

**selective permeability** A property of biological membranes that allows them to regulate the passage of substances across them.

**self-incompatibility** The ability of a seed plant to reject its own pollen and sometimes the pollen of closely related individuals.

**semelparity** (seh´-mel-pār´-i-tē) Reproduction in which an organism produces all of its offspring in a single event; also called big-bang reproduction.

**semen** (sē´-mun) The fluid that is ejaculated by the male during orgasm; contains sperm and secretions from several glands of the male reproductive tract.

**semicircular canals** A three-part chamber of the inner ear that functions in maintaining equilibrium.

**semiconservative model** Type of DNA replication in which the replicated double helix consists of one old strand, derived from the parental molecule, and one newly made strand.

**semilunar valve** A valve located at each exit of the heart, where the aorta leaves the left ventricle and the pulmonary artery leaves the right ventricle.

**seminal vesicle** (sem´-i-nul ves´-i-kul) A gland in males that secretes a fluid component of semen that lubricates and nourishes sperm.

**seminiferous tubule** (sem´-i-nif´-er-us) A highly coiled tube in the testis in which sperm are produced.

**senescence** (se-nes´-ens) The growth phase in a plant or plant part (as a leaf) from full maturity to death.

**sensitive period** A limited phase in an animal's development when learning of particular behaviors can take place; also called a critical period.

**sensor** In homeostasis, a receptor that detects a stimulus.

**sensory adaptation** The tendency of sensory neurons to become less sensitive when they are stimulated repeatedly.

**sensory neuron** A nerve cell that receives information from the internal or external environment and transmits signals to the central nervous system.

**sensory reception** The detection of a stimulus by sensory cells.

**sensory receptor** A specialized structure or cell that responds to a stimulus from an animal's internal or external environment.

**sensory transduction** The conversion of stimulus energy to a change in the membrane potential of a sensory receptor cell.

**sepal** (sē´-pul) A modified leaf in angiosperms that helps enclose and protect a flower bud before it opens.

**septum** (plural, **septa**) One of the cross-walls that divide a fungal hypha into cells. Septa generally have pores large enough to allow ribosomes, mitochondria, and even nuclei to flow from cell to cell.

**serial endosymbiosis** A hypothesis for the origin of eukaryotes consisting of a sequence of endosymbiotic events in which mitochondria, chloroplasts, and perhaps other cellular structures were derived from small prokaryotes that had been engulfed by larger cells.

**serotonin** (ser´-uh-tō´-nin) A neurotransmitter, synthesized from the amino acid tryptophan, that functions in the central nervous system.

**set point** In homeostasis in animals, a value maintained for a particular variable, such as body temperature or solute concentration.

**seta** (sē´-tuh) (plural, **setae**) The elongated stalk of a bryophyte sporophyte.

**sex chromosome** A chromosome responsible for determining the sex of an individual.

**sex-linked gene** A gene located on either sex chromosome. Most sex-linked genes are on the X chromosome and show distinctive patterns of inheritance; there are very few genes on the Y chromosome.

**sexual dimorphism** (dī-mōr´-fizm) Differences between the secondary sex characteristics of males and females of the same species.

**sexual reproduction** A type of reproduction in which two parents give rise to offspring that have unique combinations of genes inherited from both parents via the gametes.

**sexual selection** A form of natural selection in which individuals with certain inherited characteristics are more likely than other individuals to obtain mates.

**Shannon diversity** An index of community diversity symbolized by $H$ and represented by the equation $H = -(p_A \ln p_A + p_B \ln p_B + p_C \ln p_C + \ldots)$, where A, B, C . . . are species,

$p$ is the relative abundance of each species, and ln is the natural logarithm.

**shared ancestral character** A character, shared by members of a particular clade, that originated in an ancestor that is not a member of that clade.

**shared derived character** An evolutionary novelty that is unique to a particular clade.

**shoot system** The aerial portion of a plant body, consisting of stems, leaves, and (in angiosperms) flowers.

**short tandem repeat (STR)** Simple sequence DNA containing multiple tandemly repeated units of two to five nucleotides. Variations in STRs act as genetic markers in STR analysis, used to prepare genetic profiles.

**short-day plant** A plant that flowers (usually in late summer, fall, or winter) only when the light period is shorter than a critical length.

**short-term memory** The ability to hold information, anticipations, or goals for a time and then release them if they become irrelevant.

**sickle-cell disease** A recessively inherited human blood disorder in which a single nucleotide change in the β-globin gene causes hemoglobin to aggregate, changing red blood cell shape and causing multiple symptoms in afflicted individuals.

**sieve plate** An end wall in a sieve-tube element, which facilitates the flow of phloem sap in angiosperm sieve tubes.

**sieve-tube element** A living cell that conducts sugars and other organic nutrients in the phloem of angiosperms; also called a sieve-tube member. Connected end to end, they form sieve tubes.

**sign stimulus** An external sensory cue that triggers a fixed action pattern by an animal.

**signal** In animal behavior, transmission of a stimulus from one animal to another. The term is also used in the context of communication in other kinds of organisms and in cell-to-cell communication in all multicellular organisms.

**signal peptide** A sequence of about 20 amino acids at or near the leading (amino) end of a polypeptide that targets it to the endoplasmic reticulum or other organelles in a eukaryotic cell.

**signal-recognition particle (SRP)** A protein-RNA complex that recognizes a signal peptide as it emerges from a ribosome and helps direct the ribosome to the endoplasmic reticulum (ER) by binding to a receptor protein on the ER.

**signal transduction** The linkage of a mechanical, chemical, or electromagnetic stimulus to a specific cellular response.

**signal transduction pathway** A series of steps linking a mechanical, chemical, or electrical stimulus to a specific cellular response.

**silent mutation** A nucleotide-pair substitution that has no observable effect on the phenotype; for example, within a gene, a mutation that results in a codon that codes for the same amino acid.

**simple fruit** A fruit derived from a single carpel or several fused carpels.

**simple sequence DNA** A DNA sequence that contains many copies of tandemly repeated short sequences.

**single bond** A single covalent bond; the sharing of a pair of valence electrons by two atoms.

**single circulation** A circulatory system consisting of a single pump and circuit, in which blood passes from the sites of gas exchange to the rest of the body before returning to the heart.

**single-lens eye** The camera-like eye found in some jellies, polychaete worms, spiders, and many molluscs.

**single nucleotide polymorphism (SNP)** A single base-pair site in a genome where nucleotide variation is found in at least 1% of the population.

**single-strand binding protein** A protein that binds to the unpaired DNA strands during DNA replication, stabilizing them and holding them apart while they serve as templates for the synthesis of complementary strands of DNA.

**sinoatrial** (sī′-nō-ā′-trē-uhl) **(SA) node** A region in the right atrium of the heart that sets the rate and timing at which all cardiac muscle cells contract; the pacemaker.

**sister chromatids** Two copies of a duplicated chromosome attached to each other by proteins at the centromere and, sometimes, along the arms. While joined, two sister chromatids make up one chromosome. Chromatids are eventually separated during mitosis or meiosis II.

**sister taxa** Groups of organisms that share an immediate common ancestor and hence are each other's closest relatives.

**skeletal muscle** A type of striated muscle that is generally responsible for the voluntary movements of the body.

**sliding-filament model** The idea that muscle contraction is based on the movement of thin (actin) filaments along thick (myosin) filaments, shortening the sarcomere, the basic unit of muscle organization.

**slow block to polyspermy** The formation of the fertilization envelope and other changes in an egg's surface that prevent fusion of the egg with more than one sperm. The slow block begins about 1 minute after fertilization.

**slow-twitch fiber** A muscle fiber that can sustain long contractions.

**small interfering RNA (siRNA)** One of multiple small, single-stranded RNA molecules generated by cellular machinery from a long, linear, double-stranded RNA molecule. The siRNA associates with one or more proteins in a complex that can degrade or prevent translation of an mRNA with a complementary sequence.

**small intestine** The longest section of the alimentary canal, so named because of its small diameter compared with that of the large intestine; the principal site of the enzymatic hydrolysis of food macromolecules and the absorption of nutrients.

**smooth ER** That portion of the endoplasmic reticulum that is free of ribosomes.

**smooth muscle** A type of muscle lacking the striations of skeletal and cardiac muscle because of the uniform distribution of myosin filaments in the cells; responsible for involuntary body activities.

**social learning** Modification of behavior through the observation of other individuals.

**sociobiology** The study of social behavior based on evolutionary theory.

**sodium-potassium pump** A transport protein in the plasma membrane of animal cells that actively transports sodium out of the cell and potassium into the cell.

**soil horizon** A soil layer with physical characteristics that differ from those of the layers above or beneath.

**solute** (sol′-yūt) A substance that is dissolved in a solution.

**solute potential** $(\Psi_S)$ A component of water potential that is proportional to the molarity of a solution and that measures the effect of solutes on the direction of water movement; also called osmotic potential, it can be either zero or negative.

**solution** A liquid that is a homogeneous mixture of two or more substances.

**solvent** The dissolving agent of a solution. Water is the most versatile solvent known.

**somatic cell** (sō-mat′-ik) Any cell in a multicellular organism except a sperm or egg or their precursors.

**somite** One of a series of blocks of mesoderm that exist in pairs just lateral to the notochord in a vertebrate embryo.

**soredium** (suh-rē′-dē-um) (plural, **soredia**) In lichens, a small cluster of fungal hyphae with embedded algae.

**sorus** (plural, **sori**) A cluster of sporangia on a fern sporophyll. Sori may be arranged in various patterns, such as parallel lines or dots, which are useful in fern identification.

**spatial learning** The establishment of a memory that reflects the environment's spatial structure.

**spatial summation** A phenomenon of neural integration in which the membrane potential of the postsynaptic cell is determined by the combined effect of EPSPs or IPSPs produced nearly simultaneously by different synapses.

**speciation** (spē′-sē-ā′-shun) An evolutionary process in which one species splits into two or more species.

**species** (spē′-sēz) A population or group of populations whose members have the potential to interbreed in nature and produce viable, fertile offspring but do not produce viable, fertile offspring with members of other such groups.

**species-area curve** (spē′-sēz) The biodiversity pattern that shows that the larger the geographic area of a community is, the more species it has.

**species diversity** (spē′-sēz) The number and relative abundance of species in a biological community.

**species richness** (spē′-sēz) The number of species in a biological community.

**specific heat** The amount of heat that must be absorbed or lost for 1 g of a substance to change its temperature by 1°C.

**spectrophotometer** An instrument that measures the proportions of light of different wavelengths absorbed and transmitted by a pigment solution.

**sperm** The male gamete.

**spermatheca** (sper′-muh-thē′-kuh) (plural, **spermathecae**) In many insects, a sac in the female reproductive system where sperm are stored.

**spermatogenesis** (sper-ma′-tō-gen′-uh-sis) The continuous and prolific production of mature sperm in the testis.

**spermatogonium** (sper-ma′-tō-gō′-nē-um) (plural, **spermatogonia**) A cell that divides mitotically to form spermatocytes.

**S phase** The synthesis phase of the cell cycle; the portion of interphase during which DNA is replicated.

**sphincter** (sfink′-ter) A ringlike band of muscle fibers that controls the size of an opening in the body, such as the passage between the esophagus and the stomach.

**spiral cleavage** A type of embryonic development in protostomes in which the planes of cell division that transform the zygote into a ball of cells are diagonal to the vertical axis of the embryo. As a result, the cells of each tier sit in the grooves between cells of adjacent tiers.

**spliceosome** (splī′-sō-sōm) A large complex made up of proteins and RNA molecules that splices RNA by interacting with the ends of an RNA intron, releasing the intron and joining the two adjacent exons.

**spongocoel** (spon′-jō-sēl) The central cavity of a sponge.

**spontaneous process** A process that occurs without an overall input of energy; a process that is energetically favorable.

**sporangium** (spōr-an′-jē-um) (plural, **sporangia**) A multicellular organ in fungi and plants in which meiosis occurs and haploid cells develop.

**spore** (1) In the life cycle of a plant or alga undergoing alternation of generations, a haploid cell produced in the sporophyte by meiosis. A spore can divide by mitosis to develop into a multicellular haploid individual, the gametophyte, without fusing with another cell. (2) In fungi, a haploid cell, produced either sexually or asexually, that produces a mycelium after germination.

**sporophyll** (spō′-ruh-fil) A modified leaf that bears sporangia and hence is specialized for reproduction.

**sporophyte** (spō-ruh-fīt′) In organisms (plants and some algae) that have alternation of generations, the multicellular diploid form that results from the union of gametes. The sporophyte produces haploid spores by meiosis that develop into gametophytes.

**sporopollenin** (spōr-uh-pol′-eh-nin) A durable polymer that covers exposed zygotes of charophyte algae and forms the walls of plant spores, preventing them from drying out.

**stabilizing selection** Natural selection in which intermediate phenotypes survive or reproduce more successfully than do extreme phenotypes.

**stamen** (stā′-men) The pollen-producing reproductive organ of a flower, consisting of an anther and a filament.

**standard deviation** A measure of the variation found in a set of data points.

**standard metabolic rate (SMR)** Metabolic rate of a resting, fasting, and nonstressed ectotherm at a particular temperature.

**starch** A storage polysaccharide in plants, consisting entirely of glucose monomers joined by α glycosidic linkages.

**start point** In transcription, the nucleotide position on the promoter where RNA polymerase begins synthesis of RNA.

**statocyst** (stat′-uh-sist′) A type of mechanoreceptor that functions in equilibrium in invertebrates by use of statoliths, which stimulate hair cells in relation to gravity.

**statolith** (stat′-uh-lith′) (1) In plants, a specialized plastid that contains dense starch grains and may play a role in detecting gravity. (2) In invertebrates, a dense particle that settles in response to gravity and is found in sensory organs that function in equilibrium.

**stele** (stēl) The vascular tissue of a stem or root.

**stem** A vascular plant organ consisting of an alternating system of nodes and internodes that support the leaves and reproductive structures.

**stem cell** Any relatively unspecialized cell that can produce, during a single division, one identical daughter cell and one more specialized daughter cell that can undergo further differentiation.

**steroid** A type of lipid characterized by a carbon skeleton consisting of four fused rings with various chemical groups attached.

**sticky end** A single-stranded end of a double-stranded restriction fragment.

**stigma** (plural, **stigmata**) The sticky part of a flower's carpel, which receives pollen grains.

**stimulus** In feedback regulation, a fluctuation in a variable that triggers a response.

**stipe** A stemlike structure of a seaweed.

**stock** The plant that provides the root system when making a graft.

**stoma** (stō′-muh) (plural, **stomata**) A microscopic pore surrounded by guard cells in the epidermis of leaves and stems that allows gas exchange between the environment and the interior of the plant.

**stomach** An organ of the digestive system that stores food and performs preliminary steps of digestion.

**Stramenopila** (strah′-men-ō′-pē-lah) One of the three major subgroups for which the "SAR" eukaryotic supergroup is named. This clade arose by secondary endosymbiosis and includes diatoms and brown algae.

**stratum** (strah′-tum) (plural, **strata**) A rock layer formed when new layers of sediment cover older ones and compress them.

**strigolactone** Any of a class of plant hormones that inhibit shoot branching, trigger the germination of parasitic plant seeds, and stimulate the association of plant roots with mycorrhizal fungi.

**strobilus** (strō-bī′-lus) (plural, **strobili**) The technical term for a cluster of sporophylls known commonly as a cone, found in most gymnosperms and some seedless vascular plants.

**stroke** The death of nervous tissue in the brain, usually resulting from rupture or blockage of arteries in the head.

**stroke volume** The volume of blood pumped by a heart ventricle in a single contraction.

**stroma** (strō′-muh) The dense fluid within the chloroplast surrounding the thylakoid membrane and containing ribosomes and DNA; involved in the synthesis of organic molecules from carbon dioxide and water.

**stromatolite** Layered rock that results from the activities of prokaryotes that bind thin films of sediment together.

**structural isomer** One of several compounds that have the same molecular formula but differ in the covalent arrangements of their atoms.

**style** The stalk of a flower's carpel, with the ovary at the base and the stigma at the top.

**substrate** The reactant on which an enzyme works.

**substrate feeder** An animal that lives in or on its food source, eating its way through the food.

**substrate-level phosphorylation** The enzyme-catalyzed formation of ATP by direct transfer of a phosphate group to ADP from an intermediate substrate in catabolism.

**sugar sink** A plant organ that is a net consumer or storer of sugar. Growing roots, shoot tips, stems, and fruits are examples of sugar sinks supplied by phloem.

**sugar source** A plant organ in which sugar is being produced by either photosynthesis or the breakdown of starch. Mature leaves are the primary sugar sources of plants.

**sulfhydryl group** A chemical group consisting of a sulfur atom bonded to a hydrogen atom.

**suprachiasmatic nucleus (SCN)** (sūp′-ruh-kē′-as-ma-tik) A group of neurons in the hypothalamus of mammals that functions as a biological clock.

**surface tension** A measure of how difficult it is to stretch or break the surface of a liquid. Water has a high surface tension because of the hydrogen bonding of surface molecules.

**surfactant** A substance secreted by alveoli that decreases surface tension in the fluid that coats the alveoli.

**survivorship curve** A plot of the number of members of a cohort that are still alive at each age; one way to represent age-specific mortality.

**suspension feeder** An animal that feeds by removing suspended food particles from the surrounding medium by a capture, trapping, or filtration mechanism.

**sustainable agriculture** Long-term productive farming methods that are environmentally safe.

**sustainable development** Development that meets the needs of people today without limiting the ability of future generations to meet their needs.

**swim bladder** In aquatic osteichthyans, an air sac that enables the animal to control its buoyancy in the water.

**symbiont** (sim′-bē-ont) The smaller participant in a symbiotic relationship, living in or on the host.

**symbiosis** An ecological relationship between organisms of two different species that live together in direct and intimate contact.

**sympathetic division** One of three divisions of the autonomic nervous system; generally increases energy expenditure and prepares the body for action.

**sympatric speciation** (sim-pat′-rik) The formation of new species in populations that live in the same geographic area.

**symplast** In plants, the continuum of cytoplasm connected by plasmodesmata between cells.

**synapse** (sin′-aps) The junction where a neuron communicates with another cell across a narrow gap via a neurotransmitter or an electrical coupling.

**synapsid** (si-nap′-sid) A member of an amniote clade distinguished by a single hole on each side of the skull. Synapsids include the mammals.

**synapsis** (si-nap′-sis) The pairing and physical connection of duplicated homologous chromosomes during prophase I of meiosis.

**synaptonemal** (si-nap′-tuh-nē′-muhl) **complex** A zipper-like structure composed of proteins, which connects two homologous chromosomes tightly along their lengths.

**systematics** A scientific discipline focused on classifying organisms and determining their evolutionary relationships.

**systemic acquired resistance** A defensive response in infected plants that helps protect healthy tissue from pathogenic invasion.

**systemic circuit** The branch of the circulatory system that supplies oxygenated blood to and carries deoxygenated blood away from organs and tissues throughout the body.

**systems biology** An approach to studying biology that aims to model the dynamic behavior of whole biological systems based on a study of the interactions among the system's parts.

**systole** (sis′-tō-lē) The stage of the cardiac cycle in which a heart chamber contracts and pumps blood.

**systolic pressure** Blood pressure in the arteries during contraction of the ventricles.

**taproot** A main vertical root that develops from an embryonic root and gives rise to lateral (branch) roots.

**tastant** Any chemical that stimulates the sensory receptors in a taste bud.

**taste bud** A collection of modified epithelial cells on the tongue or in the mouth that are receptors for taste in mammals.

**TATA box** A DNA sequence in eukaryotic promoters crucial in forming the transcription initiation complex.

**taxis** (tak′-sis) An oriented movement toward or away from a stimulus.

**taxon** (plural, **taxa**) A named taxonomic unit at any given level of classification.

**taxonomy** (tak-son′-uh-mē) A scientific discipline concerned with naming and classifying the diverse forms of life.

**Tay-Sachs disease** A human genetic disease caused by a recessive allele for a dysfunctional enzyme, leading to accumulation of certain lipids in the brain. Seizures, blindness, and degeneration of motor and mental performance usually become manifest a few months after birth, followed by death within a few years.

**T cells** The class of lymphocytes that mature in the thymus; they include both effector cells for the cell-mediated immune response and helper cells required for both branches of adaptive immunity.

**technology** The application of scientific knowledge for a specific purpose, often involving industry or commerce but also including uses in basic research.

**telomere** (tel′-uh-mēr) The tandemly repetitive DNA at the end of a eukaryotic chromosome's DNA molecule. Telomeres protect the organism's genes from being eroded during successive rounds of replication. *See also* repetitive DNA.

**telophase** The fifth and final stage of mitosis, in which daughter nuclei are forming and cytokinesis has typically begun.

**temperate broadleaf forest** A biome located throughout midlatitude regions where there is sufficient moisture to support the growth of large, broadleaf deciduous trees.

**temperate grassland** A terrestrial biome that exists at midlatitude regions and is dominated by grasses and forbs.

**temperate phage** A phage that is capable of replicating by either a lytic or lysogenic cycle.

**temperature** A measure in degrees of the average kinetic energy (thermal energy) of the atoms and molecules in a body of matter.

**template strand** The DNA strand that provides the pattern, or template, for ordering, by complementary base pairing, the sequence of nucleotides in an RNA transcript.

**temporal summation** A phenomenon of neural integration in which the membrane potential of the postsynaptic cell in a chemical synapse is determined by the combined effect of EPSPs or IPSPs produced in rapid succession.

**tendon** A fibrous connective tissue that attaches muscle to bone.

**terminator** In bacteria, a sequence of nucleotides in DNA that marks the end of a gene and signals RNA polymerase to release the newly made RNA molecule and detach from the DNA.

**territoriality** A behavior in which an animal defends a bounded physical space against encroachment by other individuals, usually of its own species.

**tertiary consumer** (ter′-shē-ār′-ē) A carnivore that eats other carnivores.

**tertiary structure** (ter′-shē-ār′-ē) The overall shape of a protein molecule due to interactions of amino acid side chains, including hydrophobic interactions, ionic bonds, hydrogen bonds, and disulfide bridges.

**test** In foram protists, a porous shell that consists of a single piece of organic material hardened with calcium carbonate.

**testcross** Breeding an organism of unknown genotype with a homozygous recessive individual to determine the unknown genotype. The ratio of phenotypes in the offspring reveals the unknown genotype.

**testis** (plural, **testes**) The male reproductive organ, or gonad, in which sperm and reproductive hormones are produced.

**testosterone** A steroid hormone required for development of the male reproductive system, spermatogenesis, and male secondary sex characteristics; the major androgen in mammals.

**tetanus** (tet′-uh-nus) The maximal, sustained contraction of a skeletal muscle, caused by a very high frequency of action potentials elicited by continual stimulation.

**tetrapod** A vertebrate clade whose members have limbs with digits. Tetrapods include mammals, amphibians, and birds and other reptiles.

**thalamus** (thal′-uh-mus) An integrating center of the vertebrate forebrain. Neurons with cell bodies in the thalamus relay neural input to specific areas in the cerebral cortex and regulate what information goes to the cerebral cortex.

**theory** An explanation that is broader in scope than a hypothesis, generates new hypotheses, and is supported by a large body of evidence.

**thermal energy** Kinetic energy due to the random motion of atoms and molecules; energy in its most random form. *See also* heat.

**thermocline** A narrow stratum of abrupt temperature change in the ocean and in many temperate-zone lakes.

**thermodynamics** (ther′-mō-dī-nam′-iks) The study of energy transformations that occur in a collection of matter. *See also* first law of thermodynamics and second law of thermodynamics.

**thermophile** *See* extreme thermophile.

**thermoreceptor** A receptor stimulated by either heat or cold.

**thermoregulation** The maintenance of internal body temperature within a tolerable range.

**theropod** A member of a group of dinosaurs that were bipedal carnivores.

**thick filament** A filament composed of staggered arrays of myosin molecules; a component of myofibrils in muscle fibers.

**thigmomorphogenesis** (thig′-mō-mor′-phō-gen′-uh-sis) A response in plants to chronic mechanical stimulation, resulting from increased ethylene production. An example is thickening stems in response to strong winds.

**thigmotropism** (thig-mō′-truh-pizm) A directional growth of a plant in response to touch.

**thin filament** A filament consisting of two strands of actin and two strands of regulatory protein coiled around one another; a component of myofibrils in muscle fibers.

**threatened species** A species that is considered likely to become endangered in the foreseeable future.

**threshold** The potential that an excitable cell membrane must reach for an action potential to be initiated.

**thrombus** A fibrin-containing clot that forms in a blood vessel and blocks the flow of blood.

**thylakoid** (thī′-luh-koyd) A flattened, membranous sac inside a chloroplast. Thylakoids often exist in stacks called grana that are interconnected; their membranes contain molecular "machinery" used to convert light energy to chemical energy.

**thymus** (thī′-mus) A small organ in the thoracic cavity of vertebrates where maturation of T cells is completed.

**thyroid gland** An endocrine gland, located on the ventral surface of the trachea, that secretes two iodine-containing hormones, triiodothyronine ($T_3$) and thyroxine ($T_4$), as well as calcitonin.

**thyroid hormone** Either of two iodine-containing hormones (triiodothyronine and thyroxine) that are secreted by the thyroid gland and that help regulate metabolism, development, and maturation in vertebrates.

**thyroxine ($T_4$)** One of two iodine-containing hormones that are secreted by the thyroid gland and that help regulate metabolism, development, and maturation in vertebrates.

**tidal volume** The volume of air a mammal inhales and exhales with each breath.

**tight junction** A type of intercellular junction between animal cells that prevents the leakage of material through the space between cells.

**tissue** An integrated group of cells with a common structure, function, or both.

**tissue system** One or more tissues organized into a functional unit connecting the organs of a plant.

**Toll-like receptor (TLR)** A membrane receptor on a phagocytic white blood cell that recognizes fragments of molecules common to a set of pathogens.

**tonicity** The ability of a solution surrounding a cell to cause that cell to gain or lose water.

**top-down model** A model of community organization in which predation influences community organization by controlling herbivore numbers, which in turn control plant or phytoplankton numbers, which in turn control nutrient levels; also called the trophic cascade model.

**topoisomerase** A protein that breaks, swivels, and rejoins DNA strands. During DNA replication, topoisomerase helps to relieve strain in the double helix ahead of the replication fork.

**topsoil** A mixture of particles derived from rock, living organisms, and decaying organic material (humus).

**torpor** A physiological state in which activity is low and metabolism decreases.

**totipotent** (tō′-tuh-pōt′-ent) Describing a cell that can give rise to all parts of the embryo and adult, as well as extraembryonic membranes in species that have them.

**trace element** An element indispensable for life but required in extremely minute amounts.

**trachea** (trā′-kē-uh) The portion of the respiratory tract that passes from the larynx to the bronchi; also called the windpipe.

**tracheal system** In insects, a system of branched, air-filled tubes that extends throughout the body and carries oxygen directly to cells.

**tracheid** (trā′-kē-id) A long, tapered water-conducting cell found in the xylem of nearly all vascular plants. Functioning tracheids are no longer living.

**trait** One of two or more detectable variants in a genetic character.

**trans fat** An unsaturated fat, formed artificially during hydrogenation of oils, containing one or more *trans* double bonds.

**transcription** The synthesis of RNA using a DNA template.

**transcription factor** A regulatory protein that binds to DNA and affects transcription of specific genes.

**transcription initiation complex** The completed assembly of transcription factors and RNA polymerase bound to a promoter.

**transcription unit** A region of DNA that is transcribed into an RNA molecule.

**transduction** (1) A process in which phages (viruses) carry bacterial DNA from one bacterial cell to another. When these two cells are members of different species, transduction results in horizontal gene transfer. (2) In cellular communication, the conversion of a signal from outside the cell to a form that can bring about a specific cellular response; also called signal transduction.

**transfer RNA (tRNA)** An RNA molecule that functions as a translator between nucleic acid and protein languages by carrying specific amino acids to the ribosome, where they recognize the appropriate codons in the mRNA.

**transformation** (1) The conversion of a normal cell into a cell that is able to divide indefinitely in culture, thus behaving like a cancer cell. (Malignant transformation may also describe the series of changes in a normal cell in an organism that change it into a malignant (cancerous) cell.) (2) A change in genotype and phenotype due to the assimilation of external DNA by a cell. When the external DNA is from a member of a different species, transformation results in horizontal gene transfer.

**transgenic** Pertaining to an organism whose genome contains a gene introduced from another organism of the same or a different species.

**translation** The synthesis of a polypeptide using the genetic information encoded in an mRNA molecule. There is a change of "language" from nucleotides to amino acids.

**translocation** (1) An aberration in chromosome structure resulting from attachment of a chromosomal fragment to a nonhomologous chromosome. (2) During protein synthesis, the third stage in the elongation cycle, when the RNA carrying the growing polypeptide moves from the A site to the P site on the ribosome. (3) The transport of organic nutrients in the phloem of vascular plants.

**transmission** The passage of a nerve impulse along axons.

**transmission electron microscope (TEM)** A microscope that passes an electron beam through very thin sections stained with metal atoms and is primarily used to study the internal ultrastructure of cells.

**transpiration** The evaporative loss of water from a plant.

**transport epithelium** One or more layers of specialized epithelial cells that carry out and regulate solute movement.

**transport protein** A transmembrane protein that helps a certain substance or class of closely related substances to cross the membrane.

**transport vesicle** A small membranous sac in a eukaryotic cell's cytoplasm carrying molecules produced by the cell.

**transposable element** A segment of DNA that can move within the genome of a cell by means of a DNA or RNA intermediate; also called a transposable genetic element.

**transposon** A transposable element that moves within a genome by means of a DNA intermediate.

**transverse (T) tubule** An infolding of the plasma membrane of skeletal muscle cells.

**triacylglycerol** (trī-as′-ul-glis′-uh-rol) A lipid consisting of three fatty acids linked to one glycerol molecule; also called a fat or triglyceride.

**triple response** A plant growth maneuver in response to mechanical stress, involving slowing of stem elongation, thickening of the stem, and a curvature that causes the stem to start growing horizontally.

**triplet code** A genetic information system in which sets of three-nucleotide-long words specify the amino acids for polypeptide chains.

**triploblastic** Possessing three germ layers: the endoderm, mesoderm, and ectoderm. All bilaterian animals are triploblastic.

**trisomic** Referring to a diploid cell that has three copies of a particular chromosome instead of the normal two.

**trochophore larva** (trō′-kuh-fōr) Distinctive larval stage observed in some lophotrochozoan animals, including some annelids and molluscs.

**trophic efficiency** The percentage of production transferred from one trophic level to the next higher trophic level.

**trophic structure** The different feeding relationships in an ecosystem, which determine the route of energy flow and the pattern of chemical cycling.

**trophoblast** The outer epithelium of a mammalian blastocyst. It forms the fetal part of the placenta, supporting embryonic development but not forming part of the embryo proper.

**tropic hormone** A hormone that has an endocrine gland or endocrine cells as a target.

**tropical dry forest** A terrestrial biome characterized by relatively high temperatures and precipitation overall but with a pronounced dry season.

**tropical rain forest** A terrestrial biome characterized by relatively high precipitation and temperatures year-round.

**tropics** Latitudes between 23.5° north and south.

**tropism** A growth response that results in the curvature of whole plant organs toward or away from stimuli due to differential rates of cell elongation.

**tropomyosin** The regulatory protein that blocks the myosin-binding sites on actin molecules.

**troponin complex** The regulatory proteins that control the position of tropomyosin on the thin filament.

**true-breeding** Referring to organisms that produce offspring of the same variety over many generations of self-pollination.

**tubal ligation** A means of sterilization in which a woman's two oviducts (fallopian tubes) are tied closed and a segment of each is removed to prevent eggs from reaching the uterus.

**tube foot** One of numerous extensions of an echinoderm's water vascular system. Tube feet function in locomotion and feeding.

**tumor-suppressor gene** A gene whose protein product inhibits cell division, thereby preventing the uncontrolled cell growth that contributes to cancer.

**tundra** A terrestrial biome at the extreme limits of plant growth. At the northernmost limits, it is called arctic tundra, and at high altitudes, where plant forms are limited to low shrubby or matlike vegetation, it is called alpine tundra.

**tunicate** A member of the clade Urochordata, sessile marine chordates that lack a backbone.

**turgid** (ter′-jid) Swollen or distended, as in plant cells. (A walled cell becomes turgid if it has a lower water potential than its surroundings, resulting in entry of water.)

**turgor pressure** The force directed against a plant cell wall after the influx of water and swelling of the cell due to osmosis.

**turnover** The mixing of waters as a result of changing water-temperature profiles in a lake.

**turnover time** The time required to replace the standing crop of a population or group of populations (for example, of phytoplankton), calculated as the ratio of standing crop to production.

**twin study** A behavioral study in which researchers compare the behavior of identical twins raised apart with that of identical twins raised in the same household.

**tympanic membrane** Another name for the eardrum, the membrane between the outer and middle ear.

**Unikonta** (yū′-ni-kon′-tuh) One of four supergroups of eukaryotes proposed in a current hypothesis of the evolutionary history of eukaryotes. This clade, which is supported by studies of myosin proteins and DNA, consists of amoebozoans and opisthokonts. *See also* Excavata, "SAR" clade, and Archaeplastida.

**unsaturated fatty acid** A fatty acid that has one or more double bonds between carbons in the hydrocarbon tail. Such bonding reduces the number of hydrogen atoms attached to the carbon skeleton.

**urban ecology** The study of organisms and their environment in urban and suburban settings.

**urea** A soluble nitrogenous waste produced in the liver by a metabolic cycle that combines ammonia with carbon dioxide.

**ureter** (yū-rē′-ter) A duct leading from the kidney to the urinary bladder.

**urethra** (yū-rē′-thruh) A tube that releases urine from the mammalian body near the vagina in females and through the penis in males; also serves in males as the exit tube for the reproductive system.

**uric acid** A product of protein and purine metabolism and the major nitrogenous waste product of insects, land snails, and many reptiles. Uric acid is relatively nontoxic and largely insoluble in water.

**urinary bladder** The pouch where urine is stored prior to elimination.

**uterine cycle** In humans and certain other primates, a type of reproductive cycle in which the nonpregnant endometrium is shed through the cervix into the vagina; also called the menstrual cycle.

**uterus** A female organ where eggs are fertilized and/or development of the young occurs.

**utricle** (yū′-trih-kuhl) In the vertebrate ear, a chamber in the vestibule behind the oval window that opens into the three semicircular canals.

**vaccine** A harmless variant or derivative of a pathogen that stimulates a host's immune system to mount defenses against the pathogen.

**vacuole** (vak′-yū-ōl′) A membrane-bounded vesicle whose specialized function varies in different kinds of cells.

**vagina** Part of the female reproductive system between the uterus and the outside opening; the birth canal in mammals. During copulation, the vagina accommodates the male's penis and receives sperm.

**valence** The bonding capacity of a given atom; usually equals the number of unpaired electrons required to complete the atom's outermost (valence) shell.

**valence electron** An electron in the outermost electron shell.

**valence shell** The outermost energy shell of an atom, containing the valence electrons involved in the chemical reactions of that atom.

**van der Waals interactions** Weak attractions between molecules or parts of molecules that result from transient local partial charges.

**variable** A factor that varies in an experiment or other test.

**variation** Differences between members of the same species.

**vas deferens** In mammals, the tube in the male reproductive system in which sperm travel from the epididymis to the urethra.

**vasa recta** The capillary system in the kidney that serves the loop of Henle.

**vascular cambium** A cylinder of meristematic tissue in woody plants that adds layers of secondary vascular tissue called secondary xylem (wood) and secondary phloem.

**vascular plant** A plant with vascular tissue. Vascular plants include all living plant species except liverworts, mosses, and hornworts.

**vascular tissue** Plant tissue consisting of cells joined into tubes that transport water and nutrients throughout the plant body.

**vascular tissue system** A transport system formed by xylem and phloem throughout a vascular plant. Xylem transports water and minerals; phloem transports sugars, the products of photosynthesis.

**vasectomy** The cutting and sealing of each vas deferens to prevent sperm from entering the urethra.

**vasoconstriction** A decrease in the diameter of blood vessels caused by contraction of smooth muscles in the vessel walls.

**vasodilation** An increase in the diameter of blood vessels caused by relaxation of smooth muscles in the vessel walls.

**vector** An organism that transmits pathogens from one host to another.

**vegetal pole** The point at the end of an egg in the hemisphere where most yolk is concentrated; opposite of animal pole.

**vegetative propagation** Asexual reproduction in plants that is facilitated or induced by humans.

**vegetative reproduction** Asexual reproduction in plants.

**vein** (1) In animals, a vessel that carries blood toward the heart. (2) In plants, a vascular bundle in a leaf.

**ventilation** The flow of air or water over a respiratory surface.

**ventral** Pertaining to the underside, or bottom, of an animal with radial or bilateral symmetry.

**ventricle** (ven′-tri-kul) (1) A heart chamber that pumps blood out of the heart. (2) A space in the vertebrate brain, filled with cerebrospinal fluid.

**venule** (ven′-yūl) A vessel that conveys blood between a capillary bed and a vein.

**vernalization** The use of cold treatment to induce a plant to flower.

**vertebrate** A chordate animal with vertebrae, the series of bones that make up the backbone.

**vesicle** (ves′-i-kul) A membranous sac in the cytoplasm of a eukaryotic cell.

**vessel** A continuous water-conducting micropipe found in most angiosperms and a few nonflowering vascular plants.

**vessel element** A short, wide water-conducting cell found in the xylem of most angiosperms and a few nonflowering vascular plants. Dead at maturity, vessel elements are aligned end to end to form micropipes called vessels.

**vestigial structure** A feature of an organism that is a historical remnant of a structure that served a function in the organism's ancestors.

**villus** (plural, **villi**) (1) A finger-like projection of the inner surface of the small intestine. (2) A finger-like projection of the chorion of the mammalian placenta. Large numbers of villi increase the surface areas of these organs.

**viral envelope** A membrane, derived from membranes of the host cell, that cloaks the capsid, which in turn encloses a viral genome.

**viroid** (vī′-royd) A plant pathogen consisting of a molecule of naked, circular RNA a few hundred nucleotides long.

**virulent phage** A phage that replicates only by a lytic cycle.

**virus** An infectious particle incapable of replicating outside of a cell, consisting of an RNA or DNA genome surrounded by a protein coat (capsid) and, for some viruses, a membranous envelope.

**visceral mass** One of the three main parts of a mollusc; the part containing most of the internal organs. *See also* foot and mantle.

**visible light** That portion of the electromagnetic spectrum that can be detected as various colors by the human eye, ranging in wavelength from about 380 nm to about 750 nm.

**vital capacity** The maximum volume of air that a mammal can inhale and exhale with each breath.

**vitamin** An organic molecule required in the diet in very small amounts. Many vitamins serve as coenzymes or parts of coenzymes.

**viviparous** (vī-vip′-uh-rus) Referring to a type of development in which the young are born alive after having been nourished in the uterus by blood from the placenta.

**voltage-gated ion channel** A specialized ion channel that opens or closes in response to changes in membrane potential.

**vulva** Collective term for the female external genitalia.

**water potential (Ψ)** The physical property predicting the direction in which water will flow, governed by solute concentration and applied pressure.

**water vascular system** A network of hydraulic canals unique to echinoderms that branches into extensions called tube feet, which function in locomotion and feeding.

**wavelength** The distance between crests of waves, such as those of the electromagnetic spectrum.

**wetland** A habitat that is inundated by water at least some of the time and that supports plants adapted to water-saturated soil.

**white matter** Tracts of axons within the CNS.

**whole-genome shotgun approach** Procedure for genome sequencing in which the genome is randomly cut into many overlapping short segments that are sequenced; computer software then assembles the complete sequence.

**wild type** The phenotype most commonly observed in natural populations; also refers to the individual with that phenotype.

**wilting** The drooping of leaves and stems as a result of plant cells becoming flaccid.

**wobble** Flexibility in the base-pairing rules in which the nucleotide at the 5′ end of a tRNA anticodon can form hydrogen bonds with more than one kind of base in the third position (3′ end) of a codon.

**xerophyte** (zir′-ō-fīt′) A plant adapted to an arid climate.

**X-linked gene** A gene located on the X chromosome; such genes show a distinctive pattern of inheritance.

**X-ray crystallography** A technique used to study the three-dimensional structure of molecules. It depends on the diffraction of an X-ray beam by the individual atoms of a crystallized molecule.

**xylem** (zī'-lum) Vascular plant tissue consisting mainly of tubular dead cells that conduct most of the water and minerals upward from the roots to the rest of the plant.

**xylem sap** (zī'-lum) The dilute solution of water and minerals carried through vessels and tracheids.

**yeast** Single-celled fungus. Yeasts reproduce asexually by binary fission or by the pinching of small buds off a parent cell. Many fungal species can grow both as yeasts and as a network of filaments; relatively few species grow only as yeasts.

**yolk** Nutrients stored in an egg.

**zero population growth (ZPG)** A period of stability in population size, when additions to the population through births and immigration are balanced by subtractions through deaths and emigration.

**zona pellucida** The extracellular matrix surrounding a mammalian egg.

**zoned reserve** An extensive region that includes areas relatively undisturbed by humans surrounded by areas that have been changed by human activity and are used for economic gain.

**zone of polarizing activity (ZPA)** A block of mesoderm located just under the ectoderm where the posterior side of a limb bud is attached to the body; required for proper pattern formation along the anterior-posterior axis of the limb.

**zoonotic pathogen** A disease-causing agent that is transmitted to humans from other animals.

**zoospore** Flagellated spore found in chytrid fungi and some protists.

**zygomycete** (zī'-guh-mī'-sēt) A member of the fungal phylum Zygomycota, characterized by the formation of a sturdy structure called a zygosporangium during sexual reproduction.

**zygosporangium** (zī'-guh-spōr-an'-jē-um) (plural, **zygosporangia**) In zygomycete fungi, a sturdy multinucleate structure in which karyogamy and meiosis occur.

**zygote** (zī'-gōt) The diploid cell produced by the union of haploid gametes during fertilization; a fertilized egg.